THERMODYNAMICS
FOR
ENGINEERS

PRENTICE-HALL INTERNATIONAL SERIES
IN ENGINEERING OF THE PHYSICAL SCIENCES

PRENTICE-HALL, INC.
PRENTICE-HALL INTERNATIONAL, INC., UNITED KINGDOM AND EIRE
PRENTICE-HALL OF CANADA, LTD., CANADA

PRENTICE-HALL SERIES IN
ENGINEERING OF THE PHYSICAL SCIENCES

James B. Reswick and Warren M. Rohsenow, *editors*

Michel A. Saad

Professor of Mechanical Engineering
University of Santa Clara

THERMODYNAMICS
FOR
ENGINEERS

Prentice-Hall, Inc., Englewood Cliffs, New Jersey

Library of Congress Catalog Card Number 66-16548
Printed in the United States of America
C-91491

PRENTICE-HALL INTERNATIONAL, INC.,	*London*
PRENTICE-HALL OF AUSTRALIA, PTY. LTD.,	*Sydney*
PRENTICE-HALL OF CANADA, LTD.,	*Toronto*
PRENTICE-HALL OF INDIA (PRIVATE) LTD.,	*New Delhi*
PRENTICE-HALL OF JAPAN, INC.,	*Tokyo*

PREFACE

Preface
By means of laws centered about energy and the interaction of various forms of energy, thermodynamics attempts to describe the behavior of matter. Traditionally, the behavior of matter is considered in thermodynamic studies from the macroscopic point of view, without regard for molecular structure. But statistical thermodynamics has been able to provide significant interpretations of the behavior of matter through use of statistical techniques applied to particles of atomic dimensions. Consequently, both classical thermodynamics and statistical thermodynamics are equally important in the study of this subject; in complementing each other they provide more insight to this fundamental science. The engineering student must be able to apply classical thermodynamics, but he should also have capabilities in the area of statistical thermodynamics.

Although the attempt is made in this book to integrate the two approaches, the first chapters deal entirely with classical thermodynamics. Justification comes from the fact that the classical treatment is somewhat more direct than the statistical approach. Furthermore, the student is more familiar with physical macroscopic aspects than with microscopic particularities, and can therefore sense the physical systems more readily. In fact, throughout the book, concepts are introduced, whenever possible, through discussions of specific phenomena that are already familiar to the student, before the generalized concept is presented. However, this technique is intended only as a teaching aid; the book still aims to provide a firm foundation in thermodynamics, emphasizing the basic concepts rather than particular applications.

The first six chapters deal with concepts related to classical thermodynamics. The first law of thermodynamics is developed carefully, because this law serves as a genesis for general energy relationships useful in describing closed systems, open systems, and steady-flow systems. The second law of thermodynamics leads to concepts related to the absolute temperature scale, the entropy function, and thermodynamic reversibility. Restrictions imposed by the second law are presented through the discussions of thermodynamic potentials and of availability of energy. The second law also leads to development of the concept of thermodynamic equilibrium.

In Chapters 7, 8, and 9, both kinetic theory of gases and statistical concepts are introduced, offering to the student parallel routes for development of thermodynamic concepts. The material presents important aspects of thermodynamics, but in addition it introduces the student to the statistical methods used in predicting the thermodynamic behavior of matter.

The application of thermodynamic relations is illustrated in Chapters 10, 11, and 12, which deal with reactive and nonreactive gas mixtures and thermodynamic cycles. In these subjects, the attempt is made to relate classically developed functions with molecular structure. Chapter 13 is an introduction to irreversible thermodynamics.

Mathematics beyond the level of differential and integral calculus is needed only in the portions of the text dealing with statistical problems. It was felt necessary to include some information about statistical methods, and this information is therefore outlined in appendices of the appropriate chapters.

No book is the result of the effort of a single individual. My students for the past several years have contributed indirectly to this book through questions they have raised and through class discussions. Further invaluable assistance came from my colleagues who kindly consented to read the manuscript. Peter Szego and Samuel Goldwasser made numerous suggestions which greatly improved the presentation of the material. I wish to express my appreciation to Anmarie Roache for reading and assisting in preparation of the manuscript. I extend my gratitude to the secretarial staff of the Engineering School at the University of Santa Clara for typing the manuscript.

MICHEL A. SAAD

TABLE OF
CONTENTS

1 Fundamental Concepts and Definitions   1

2 Energy and Conservation Laws   41

3 The First Law of Thermodynamics   87

4 *The Second Law of Thermodynamics* 139

5 *Availability, Thermodynamic Potentials, and Criteria of Equilibrium* 193

6 *One-Component System and Equations of State* 233

7 *Kinetic Theory of Gases* 293

THERMODYNAMICS
FOR
ENGINEERS

NOMENCLATURE

A	Area	p	Pressure
a	Acceleration	q	Heat per unit mass
a, b	Constants	R	Gas constant
E	Bulk modulus of elasticity	$\mathscr{R}$	Universal gas constant
F	Force	r	Radius
g	Acceleration due to gravity	T	Absolute temperature
g_c	Constant of proportionality in Newton's second law	t	Temperature
		V	Volume or velocity
h	Height	v	Specific volume or velocity
K	Coefficient of compressibility	w	Weight
k	Boltzmann's constant	X	Thermometric property
L	Length	x, y, z	Cartesian coordinates
M	Molecular weight or mass	γ	Specific weight
m	Mass	β	Coefficient of volumetric expansion
N	Number of molecules		
N_0	Avogadro's number	ρ	Density
n	Number of moles	τ	Time
P	Property	θ	Angle

1

FUNDAMENTAL
CONCEPTS AND
DEFINITIONS

1-1
Introduction

Thermodynamics is an axiomatic science concerned with energy interactions between material systems. It describes states and changes in state of physical systems and in doing so, it becomes concerned with certain physical variables and their interrelationships. Thermodynamics was formalized in the past century mainly by Carnot, Joule, Kelvin, and Clausius. In 1876, J. W. Gibbs developed classical thermodynamics into a science of such a broad scope that it can be applied to almost all physical and chemical phenomena.

The principles of thermodynamics may be summarized as four laws or axioms known as the zeroth, first, second, and third laws of thermodynamics. Although the formulation of these laws is simple, their implications are remarkably extensive. The zeroth law deals with thermal equilibrium and establishes the concept of temperature. The first law introduces the concept of internal energy. The second law indicates the limits of converting heat into work and introduces the principle of increase of entropy.* Finally, the third law defines the absolute zero of entropy. These laws were deduced from experimental observations, and there is no mathematical proof for them but, like all physical laws, thermodynamic laws are based on logical reasoning; evidence which justifies their continued use is obtained from experiments which verify their consequences.

The first six chapters of this text are based on the classical, which is the macroscopic, view of matter. In this approach, matter is considered as a continuum without any concern to its atomistic structure. Chapters 7 to 9 outline the statistical approach of thermodynamics. The remainder of the text presents thermodynamics from the standpoint of both the classical and the statistical approaches.

When matter is considered from the microscopic viewpoint, the subject is called *statistical thermodynamics*, which may be regarded as a branch of statistical mechanics. The microscopic approach focuses on the statistical behavior of a mass consisting of numerous individual molecules, and correlates macroscopic properties of matter with molecular configuration and with intermolecular forces. In this sense, the thermodynamic behavior of a system represents its time-average behavior. The difference between the two approaches may be illustrated by considering the pressure exerted by a gas confined in a container. The gas is composed of a large number of molecules, each molecule having at a given instant certain characteristics such as velocity, momentum, and position. Statistical and quantum mechanics describe the behavior of the gas by first describing the behavior of the individual molecules and then by averaging their individual properties. From a microscopic point of view, the pressure exerted by the gas at a given point

---

*The terms *internal energy* and *entropy* are defined in Chapters 3 and 4.

and at a certain instant depends on the momentary behavior of the molecules in the neighborhood of that particular point. It is clear that pressure does fluctuate with time owing to the random motion of the molecules. Statistical methods employ the concept of probability, which predicts that the average behavior of the molecules remains uniform although the behavior of the individual molecules does not. In this sense, pressure has a meaning only when averaging over a large number of molecules. On the other hand, the macroscopic point of view concerns itself with the over-all force per unit area, regardless of the atomic or microscopic origins of the force.

Classical thermodynamics, because of its generality, does not explain certain phenomena adequately. These phenomena include, for example the kinetics involved in the approach to equilibrium states, the specific heats of certain molecules, and entropy from the physical, rather than the mathematical, standpoint. The desire to gain understanding of these problems led to the development of the microscopic approach, which provides a deeper insight into the principles involved. This approach employs simplified models of matter and interprets macroscopic behavior in terms of molecular properties. The microscopic treatment of matter is particularly helpful when dealing with systems in which the mean free path of the molecules is large compared with the dimensions of the system. Although in most physical applications the mean free path is small, gases under high vacuum have relatively long free paths and, the more rarified the gas, the longer is the mean free path.

Classical and statistical thermodynamics tend to complement each other, so that the two disciplines provide more insight into the behavior of matter than either of them alone can offer. If, however, both approaches are integrated, classical thermodynamics becomes dependent on the laws and assumptions governing the behavior of individual particles and, therefore, loses its primary quality of generality. Evidently if a problem can be solved by the two approaches, the final result should be the same. This fact allows classical thermodynamics to be used as a check on molecular theories.

**1-2
Dimensions
and Units**

A *dimension* defines qualitatively a physical entity which can be measured or observed; a *unit* expresses magnitude of the dimension. For example, the units of time might be seconds, minutes or hours, but they all have the dimension of time.

The dimensions of physical entities may be expressed uniquely by the choice and the number of a set of *primary* dimensions, such as force, mass, length, time, temperature, etc. In general, there are several choices of sets of primary dimensions, some of which, together with their common units, follow:

Dimension		Unit	
Force	[F]*	pound force	lbf†
Mass	[M]	pound mass	lbm
Length	[L]	foot	ft
Time	[τ]	second	sec
Temperature	[T]	degree Fahrenheit	°F

Once the primary dimensions are chosen, *secondary* dimensions can be derived to express related entities. For example, the dimensions of an area can be conceived as length square and those of velocity as length divided by time.

Newton's second law of motion may be expressed in terms of four physical quantities with completely independent primary dimensions: mass, length, force, and time. Newton's law states that the net force acting on a particle of mass m is proportional to the product of the mass m and the acceleration a. With $1/g_c$ as a proportionality factor, Newton's law is written

$$F = \frac{1}{g_c} ma, \tag{1.1}$$

where g_c is an experimentally determined dimensional constant. In the FMLτ system, where force [F], mass [M], length [L], and time [τ] are chosen as primary dimensions, the dimension of g_c is [ML/Fτ²]. The magnitude of g_c depends on the chosen units of force, mass, length, and time. Note that the dimensions of the acceleration due to gravity g are [Lτ⁻²] and are quite different from those of g_c. Any value may be assigned to g_c; however, the size of the unit of one of the remaining quantities F, m, or a must be specified according to Eq. (1.1).

Several systems of dimensions are currently used. In the FMLτ system of dimensions, the unit of force is the pound force; the unit of mass is the pound mass; the unit of length is the foot; and the unit of time is the second. The *pound force* is defined as that force necessary to accelerate 1 lbm at the rate of 32.174 ft/sec². Substituting in Eq. (1.1) gives

$$1 \text{ lbf} = \frac{1 \text{ lbm} \times 32.174 \text{ ft/sec}^2}{g_c},$$

from which

$$g_c = 32.174 \frac{\text{lbm-ft}}{\text{lbf-sec}^2}.$$

*The brackets designate "dimensions of."

†Since the word "pound" in common usage designates either mass or force, they are differentiated in this text by calling them *lbm* and *lbf* respectively. Note that the mass of a body is a measure of its inertial property, whereas the weight of a body is the force with which it is attracted to the earth.

Therefore,

$$\text{force in lbf} = \frac{1}{32.174} \text{ (mass in lbm) (acceleration in ft/sec}^2).$$

In the MLτ system, only three primary dimensions are used, and the fourth dimension is derived. The primary dimensions, based on Newton's law in the form $F = ma$, are mass, length, and time with unity chosen as the value of g_c. In this system, called the *English absolute system*, the force F has the dimension of

$$[F] = [ML\tau^{-2}].$$

If the unit of mass is the pound mass, the unit of length is the foot, and the unit of time is the second, a unit force called the *poundal* is defined as the force necessary to accelerate a mass of 1 lbm at the rate of 1 ft/sec², or

$$1 \text{ poundal} = (1 \text{ lbm)} (1 \text{ ft/sec}^2).$$

Therefore,

$$\text{force in poundals} = \text{(mass in lbm) (acceleration in ft/sec}^2),$$

and

$$1 \text{ poundal} = \frac{1}{32.174} \text{ lbf.}$$

In the FLτ system of dimensions, the dimension of mass is derived from the primary dimensions of force, length, and time. According to Newton's law ($F = ma$), the derived dimension of mass is $[FL^{-1}\tau^2]$. In this system, the unit of force is the pound force, the unit of length is the foot, and the unit of time is the second. The unit of mass, called the *slug*, is

$$1 \text{ slug} = \frac{1 \text{ lbf}}{1 \text{ ft/sec}^2}.$$

The *slug* is defined as that mass which accelerates at the rate of 1 ft/sec² when a force of 1 lbf is applied to it. Therefore,

$$\text{force in lbf} = \text{(mass in slugs) (acceleration in ft/sec}^2).$$

The slug and the pound mass are units of mass of different magnitudes; in fact,

1 slug = 32.174 lbm.

The common metric system of units is the CGS (centimeter-gram-second) system. The unit of mass is the gram, the unit of length is the centimeter, and the unit of time is the second. The unit of force is the *dyne* defined as that force which imparts an acceleration of 1 cm/sec² when applied to a mass of 1 gram. Thus, the unit of force is

$$1 \text{ dyne} = 1\frac{\text{gm-cm}}{\text{sec}^2},$$

and

force in dynes = (mass in grams) (acceleration in cm/sec²).

Another metric system which uses larger units is the MKS (meter-kilogram-second) system. The unit of force is the *newton* (kg-meter/sec²), which is the force that imparts an acceleration of 1 meter/sec² when applied to a mass of 1 kg.

Table 1.1 presents some values of g_c in consistent systems of units for several systems of dimensions and units.

TABLE 1.1 SUMMARY OF UNITS

Mass	Length	Time	Force	g_c FMLτ system	g_c FLτ or MLτ systems
lbm	ft	sec	lbf	$32.174 \frac{\text{lbm-ft}}{\text{lbf-sec}^2}$	—
slug	ft	sec	lbf	$1.0 \frac{\text{slug-ft}}{\text{lbf-sec}^2}$	1.0
lbm	ft	sec	poundal	$1.0 \frac{\text{lbm-ft}}{\text{poundal-sec}^2}$	1.0
gm	cm	sec	dyne	$1.0 \frac{\text{gm-cm}}{\text{dyne-sec}^2}$	1.0
kg	meter	sec	newton	$1.0 \frac{\text{kg-meter}}{\text{newton-sec}^2}$	1.0

The energy unit in the English system is usually the lbf-ft; in the CGS system it is the *erg*,

1 erg = 1 dyne-cm,

and in the MKS system it is the newton-meter (which is also called the *joule*),

1 newton-meter = 1 joule = 10^7 ergs.

The *watt*, which is equal to 1 joule/sec, is the unit of power.

EXAMPLE 1.1:   A mass of 2 slugs is attracted to the earth at a location where the gravitational acceleration is 31 ft/sec². What is its weight in pounds force? What is its mass in pounds mass?

Solution: The force exerted on the mass to hold it in equilibrium against the action of the field of gravity is equal to its weight. Therefore,

$$w = F = m \frac{g}{g_c} = 2 \text{ slugs} \frac{31 \text{ ft/sec}^2}{1 \text{ (slug-ft/lbf-sec}^2)} = 62 \text{ lbf},$$

and the mass is

$$m = 2 \text{ slugs} \frac{32.174 \text{ lbm}}{\text{slug}} = 64.348 \text{ lbm}.$$

1-3
Thermodynamic
Systems

A *system* is a prescribed region of space or a finite quantity of matter. It is surrounded by an envelope called the *boundary*, which may be a real physical surface, such as the walls of a vessel, or it may be an imaginary surface enclosing some matter. The boundary may be fixed or it may move, as when a system containing a gas is compressed or expanded.

Two types of systems of particular importance are the *closed* and the *open* systems. If the boundary of the system is impervious to the flow of matter, it is called a *closed system*. On the other hand, if matter flows into or out of a system, the system is considered to be an *open system*. Consider the system consisting of the gas confined between the cylinder and the piston, as shown in Fig. 1.1. Although heat and work* may cross the boundary, and the volume of the system may change owing to the motion of the piston, the system is a closed system since no mass crosses

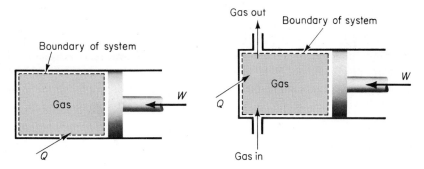

Fig. 1.1.   *Closed system, mass does not cross the boundary of the system.*

Fig. 1.2.   *Open system, mass crosses the boundary of the system.*

*The terms *heat* and *work* are defined in Chapter 2.

its boundary. Other examples of closed systems include a free body and a point mass as used in mechanics.

In the open system shown in Fig. 1.2, heat, work, and matter may cross the boundary of the system, and the net amount of mass within the system may vary with time. In the closed system, the analysis is focussed on a fixed mass of matter, whereas in the open system the analysis centers about a region in space through which matter flows. It is frequently useful to think of a fixed region in space, called a *control volume*, through which mass, momentum, and energy may flow. The surface of the control volume is called the *control surface*. The control volume may be either stationary or moving at a constant velocity. If the control volume changes both in size and in position, the control volume is equivalent to an open system. If no mass transfer occurs across the control surface, the control volume becomes identical with the closed system. The control volume is a useful concept whenever fluid flow is involved.

The region outside the boundaries of a system and contiguous to it is called the *environment* or the *surroundings*. The combined system and environment are usually referred to as the *universe*. A system which exchanges neither energy nor matter with any other system or with the environment is called an *isolated system*.

Thermodynamic analyses employ systems, referred to as *thermodynamic systems*, which are idealized versions of the complex real systems. Regardless of the type of system considered in a thermodynamic analysis, the boundaries of the system and environment must be well defined as a first and important step in solving thermodynamic problems.

Classical thermodynamics is concerned with systems in *thermodynamic equilibrium*. A system is said to have attained a *state of thermodynamic equilibrium* when a spontaneous change of its state is impossible. Intensive properties of a system, which will be discussed in the next section, are significant, ordinarily, only when a system is in thermodynamic equilibrium, since they apply to the system as a whole. Any change of state of the system, however, leads to a nonequilibrium condition which results in difficulty in specifying the interior state of the system. The name *thermodynamics* is therefore a misnomer. The word *dynamic* implies nonequilibrium, but thermodynamic laws apply only to equilibrium states, and therefore the name *thermophysics* or *thermostatics* would be preferable.

1-4
Properties of
Systems

The equilibrium state of a thermodynamic system at a particular time is defined by observable characteristics called state functions, thermodynamic coordinates, state parameters, or simply *properties*. Properties are functions of the state of the system only; hence they do not depend on the history of the system or the process by which the state was attained. The change in the value of a property is thus fixed only by the end states of the system.

Properties may be divided into two categories: *intensive* and *extensive*. Intensive properties such as temperature, pressure, and density do not depend on the mass of the system. An *intensive* property may be defined at a point since it has a finite value when the size of the system surrounding the point approaches zero. Intensive properties define the *intensive state* of a system. Properties which depend on the size of the system, such as length, volume, mass, and energy, are extensive properties. Any extensive property of the whole system is equal to the sum of the respective partial properties of the components of the system. A property indicative of the extent or mass of the system, in addition to intensive properties, is needed to define the extensive state of system. Three properties,* one of which may be mass, are required to determine uniquely an extensive property of a single-component, single-phase substance. For example, the volume of such a substance can be determined by its mass, temperature, and pressure. Also, the ratio of two extensive properties of a homogeneous system is an intensive property. Mass per unit volume, for example, is an intensive property.

The number of properties necessary to define a system depends on the complexity of the system. In a simple system, the intensive state has two degrees of freedom. If such a system is in equilibrium, the intensive state is specified by two independent intensive properties. Systems which contain more than one component or one phase substances require more than two independent properties to specify their state.

Those properties which define the state of a system are called *independent* properties. Those properties which become fixed when the state of the system is defined by the independent properties are called *dependent* properties.

It must be realized that macroscopic properties are manifestations of the microscopic behavior of the particles of a system. The microscopic property continuously fluctuates about a time-average value, so that the macroscopic property represents the time-average of microscopic properties. The microscopic property of a system at a certain instant is thus a characteristic of the system at that instant. The instantaneous state of each particle is necessary to define the microscopic state of the system.

Properties may be expressed in a functional relationship known as the *equation of state* of the system. As an example, consider an equation of state relating three properties of a system such as x, y, z,

$$f(x, y, z) = 0. \tag{1.2}$$

*This requires the absence of kinetic, electrical, surface, magnetic, gravitational effects with no changes in the components of the system.

Suppose it is possible to solve Eq. (1.2) explicitly for each of the variables x, y, z, as

$$x = x(y, z),$$
$$y = y(z, x), \tag{1.3}$$
$$z = z(x, y).$$

In the last expression, for example, z is the dependent variable while x and y are the independent variables. The differential of the dependent property can be written in terms of its partial derivatives and the differentials of the independent properties:

$$dz = \left(\frac{\partial z}{\partial x}\right)_y dx + \left(\frac{\partial z}{\partial y}\right)_x dy.$$

If

$$M = \left(\frac{\partial z}{\partial x}\right)_y \quad \text{and} \quad N = \left(\frac{\partial z}{\partial y}\right)_x,$$

then

$$dz = M\,dx + N\,dy. \tag{1.4}$$

The subscripts on the partial derivatives indicate the independent variables. If Eq. (1.4) has a solution, then dz is called an *exact* or *perfect differential* and Eq. (1.4) is integrable. Otherwise it is an *inexact differential* and is written as dz.

If variable z is to be adequately defined by the thermodynamic coordinates x, y, its value must be the same regardless of the order taken in approaching it. In evaluating dz, it should be possible to make the changes dx and dy in either sequence, without changing the result. If the function $z = z(x, y)$ and its partial derivatives are continuous, then the second derivative of z, with respect to x and y, is independent of the order of the successive differentiation. Thus

$$\frac{\partial}{\partial y}\left(\frac{\partial z}{\partial x}\right) = \frac{\partial}{\partial x}\left(\frac{\partial z}{\partial y}\right) \tag{1.5}$$

or

$$\frac{\partial M}{\partial y} = \frac{\partial N}{\partial x}. \tag{1.6}$$

Equation (1.6) is a necessary condition for the existence of a function of x and y satisfying Eq. (1.4). Equation (1.6) is also a sufficient condition, for when Eq. (1.6) is integrated twice, the expression of z is obtained. A function which satisfies Eq. (1.6) is called a *point function* or a *property* of the system.

It may also be shown that the sum, or the difference, of two point functions is also a point function, provided that the functions and their derivatives are continuous. Similarly, the product of two point functions is a point function; on the other hand, the product of a point function and an inexact differential is an inexact differential. Proofs of these statements are left for the reader as exercises.

EXAMPLE 1.2:   The heat interaction with a system is given in terms of two independent functions T and v by the equation

$$dq = f(T)\,dT + \frac{RT}{v}\,dv,$$

where R is a constant and T and v are the temperature and the specific volume of the system. Is dq an exact differential?

Solution: The test for exactness requires the equality of

$$\frac{\partial f(T)}{\partial v} = 0,$$

and of

$$\frac{\partial (RT/v)}{\partial T} = \frac{R}{v}.$$

Since $0 \neq R/v$, dq is not an exact differential, hence no state function exists that has a differential equal to dq.

1-5
Mathematical
Relations

The differentials of the functions x and y as expressed by Eq. (1.3) can be written as

$$dx = \left(\frac{\partial x}{\partial y}\right)_z dy + \left(\frac{\partial x}{\partial z}\right)_y dz, \tag{1.7}$$

$$dy = \left(\frac{\partial y}{\partial x}\right)_z dx + \left(\frac{\partial y}{\partial z}\right)_x dz. \tag{1.8}$$

Eliminating dy between the foregoing equations gives

$$dx = \left(\frac{\partial x}{\partial y}\right)_z \left[\left(\frac{\partial y}{\partial x}\right)_z dx + \left(\frac{\partial y}{\partial z}\right)_x dz\right] + \left(\frac{\partial x}{\partial z}\right)_y dz,$$

or

$$\left[1 - \left(\frac{\partial x}{\partial y}\right)_z \left(\frac{\partial y}{\partial x}\right)_z\right] dx = \left[\left(\frac{\partial x}{\partial y}\right)_z \left(\frac{\partial y}{\partial z}\right)_x + \left(\frac{\partial x}{\partial z}\right)_y\right] dz,$$

where x and z may be regarded as independent variables. If $dz = 0$ and $dx \neq 0$, then

$$\left(\frac{\partial x}{\partial y}\right)_z \left(\frac{\partial y}{\partial x}\right)_z = 1. \tag{1.9}$$

Similarly, if $dx = 0$ and $dz \neq 0$, then

$$\left(\frac{\partial x}{\partial y}\right)_z \left(\frac{\partial y}{\partial z}\right)_x + \left(\frac{\partial x}{\partial z}\right)_y = 0,$$

or in an alternate form,

$$\left(\frac{\partial x}{\partial y}\right)_z \left(\frac{\partial y}{\partial z}\right)_x \left(\frac{\partial z}{\partial x}\right)_y = -1. \tag{1.10}$$

Now let a property P be a single-valued continuous function of two independent variables. First, P may be expressed as a function of x and y; then P may be expressed as a function of z and y:

$$dP = \left(\frac{\partial P}{\partial x}\right)_y dx + \left(\frac{\partial P}{\partial y}\right)_x dy, \tag{1.11}$$

and

$$dP = \left(\frac{\partial P}{\partial z}\right)_y dz + \left(\frac{\partial P}{\partial y}\right)_z dy. \tag{1.12}$$

The integral of dP between state 1 and state 2 depends only on the value of P at these two states and is independent of the path followed between the two states. After substituting for dx from Eq. (1.7), Eq. (1.11) becomes

$$dP = \left[\left(\frac{\partial P}{\partial x}\right)_y \left(\frac{\partial x}{\partial z}\right)_y\right] dz + \left[\left(\frac{\partial P}{\partial x}\right)_y \left(\frac{\partial x}{\partial y}\right)_z + \left(\frac{\partial P}{\partial y}\right)_x\right] dy.$$

When this equation is compared with Eq. (1.12), it becomes evident that the coefficients of dz and dy can be equated, since z and y are independent variables, giving:

$$\left(\frac{\partial P}{\partial z}\right)_y = \left(\frac{\partial P}{\partial x}\right)_y \left(\frac{\partial x}{\partial z}\right)_y \quad \text{or} \quad \left(\frac{\partial P}{\partial x}\right)_y \left(\frac{\partial x}{\partial z}\right)_y \left(\frac{\partial z}{\partial P}\right)_y = 1, \tag{1.13}$$

and

$$\left(\frac{\partial P}{\partial y}\right)_z = \left(\frac{\partial P}{\partial x}\right)_y \left(\frac{\partial x}{\partial y}\right)_z + \left(\frac{\partial P}{\partial y}\right)_x. \tag{1.14}$$

Equation (1.13) applies to systems with three independent variables, and is an extension of Eq. (1.9) which applies to systems with only two variables.

Equations (1.9), (1.10), (1.13), and (1.14) are useful in relating properties of systems as will be shown in subsequent chapters. The following sections deal with some of the continuum properties.

1-6 Density, Specific Weight, Specific Volume, Specific Gravity

The *average density* of a system is its total mass divided by its total volume. In determining the density of a continuum at a point, a small volume ΔV is chosen so as to include the point. The corresponding mass is Δm, and the density is therefore,

$$\rho = \lim_{\Delta V \to 0} \frac{\Delta m}{\Delta V}.$$

The volume ΔV must contain a large number of molecules and yet it must be small compared to the dimensions of the system, so that the volume ΔV is the smallest volume capable of maintaining the continuum model. In aerodynamics, density is usually expressed in units of slugs per cubic foot (slugs/ft³); in mechanical engineering it often is expressed in lbm/ft³.

Specific weight, which is also known as weight density, is weight per unit volume. It may be expressed in units of lbf/ft³ and depends on both the density of the substance and the value of the gravitational acceleration g. Let w represent the weight corresponding to a certain mass m; then,

$$w = \frac{1}{g_c} mg.$$

If both sides of this equation are divided by the volume, then

$$\gamma = \rho \frac{g}{g_c}, \tag{1.15}$$

where γ is weight density and ρ is mass density. For example, if the density of water at 68°F is 62.3 lbm/ft³, its specific weight is

$$\gamma = \frac{62.3g}{g_c}.$$

Specific weight is the same numerically as density only if the local acceleration g is numerically equal to the dimensional constant g_c. Note, however, that γ is force per unit volume, whereas ρ is mass per unit volume.

The *specific volume* v is defined as volume per unit mass and may be expressed in ft³/lbm. It is the reciprocal of the density,

$$v = \frac{1}{\rho}. \tag{1.16}$$

The *specific gravity* of a substance is the ratio of the density of the substance to the density of a reference substance. Specific gravity can also be expressed as the ratio of specific weights, rather than densities, provided that the specific weights are evaluated in regions having the same gravitational acceleration. For liquids and solids, the reference substance is pure water at atmospheric pressure; for gases, the reference substance is air. Common reference temperatures for liquids and solids are 4°C (39.2°F), 15°C (59.0°F), or 20°C (68°F). At these temperatures the density of water is respectively, 62.43, 62.37, and 62.32 lbm/ft³. In the case of a gas, specific gravity is the ratio of the density of the gas to the density of air, at the same temperature and pressure.

1-7
Pressure

The *pressure* exerted by a system is the force exerted normal to a unit area of the boundary. When a fluid is contained within a vessel, the pressure exerted on the vessel is equal to the mean change of momentum of the molecules exerted perpendicular to the confining boundary per unit area and per unit time. Pressure of fluids is analogous to normal stress in solids.

For a pressure continuum model, the pressure at a point is defined as the force per unit area in the limit when the area tends to zero. If ΔF_n is the force normal to the area ΔA, then

$$p = \lim_{\Delta A \to 0} \frac{\Delta F_n}{\Delta A}.$$

The area ΔA is the smallest possible area capable of maintaining the continuum model.

A *fluid* is defined as a substance in which the shear stresses are zero whenever it is at rest relative to its container. When a fluid is at rest, only normal stresses exist; when a fluid is in motion, shear or tangential stresses exist in addition to the compressive stresses. When a fluid is in equilibrium, the pressure becomes a scalar point function (independent of direction) and is called *static pressure*. When a fluid is not in equilibrium, the pressure may vary according to direction. One exception is the ideal or inviscid fluid.

In an *ideal* fluid, shear stresses are absent even if there is relative motion within the fluid. Pressure, in this case, is independent of direction whether the ideal fluid is in motion or at rest.

Consider a homogeneous fluid of density ρ in static equilibrium. A pressure difference exists between two points that are separated by distance h in the vertical direction. The weight of a cylinder of fluid can be equated to the difference between forces due to pressure at the two ends of the cylinder, so that the fundamental hydrostatic relationship is

$$\Delta pA = \gamma hA,$$

or

$$\Delta p = \gamma h = \frac{\rho gh}{g_c}. \tag{1.17}$$

The hydrostatic pressure is the same at all points in a horizontal plane, and varies only with depth.

The standard atmospheric pressure is defined as the pressure produced by a column of mercury 760 mm high, the mercury density being 13.5951 gm/cm^3 and the acceleration due to gravity being its standard value of 980.665 cm/sec^2. The standard atmospheric pressure is 14.6959 psia, 29.92 in. Hg abs or 1.01325×10^6 dynes/cm^2.

Thermodynamic investigations are more concerned with values of absolute pressure, rather than with gauge pressure. Conversion from gauge pressure to absolute pressure is accomplished according to the relation:

$$p_{abs} = p_{gauge} + p_{atm}. \tag{1.18}$$

Figure 1.3 shows this relationship. Note that the datum of absolute pressure is perfect vacuum; whereas the datum of the gauge scale is atmospheric pressure. Table 1.2 gives some conversion factors for pressure.

In dealing with fluid flow problems, various types of pressure are commonly used. *Static* pressure is the pressure sensed by a measuring device if it were moving with the same velocity as the fluid stream. *Impact* pressure is the force per unit area perpendicular to the direction of flow when the

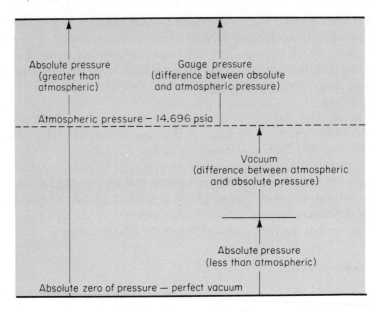

Fig. 1.3. *Pressure relationships.*

fluid is brought reversibly* to rest. For a constant density fluid, the impact pressure is given by

TABLE 1.2 CONVERSION FACTORS FOR PRESSURE

		lbf/in^2	$dyne/cm^2$	kgf/cm^2	in. Hg (at 70°F)	mm Hg (at 70°F)	in. H_2O (at 70°F)	atm
1 lbf/in^2	=	1	689.473 $\times 10^2$	0.07031	2.0360	51.715	27.71	0.06805
1 $dyne/cm^2$	=	145.0383 $\times 10^{-7}$	1	101.972 $\times 10^{-8}$	295.299 $\times 10^{-7}$	750.062 $\times 10^{-6}$	4.0188 $\times 10^{-4}$	986.923 $\times 10^{-9}$
1 kgf/cm^2	=	14.2234	980.665 $\times 10^3$	1	28.959	735.559	394.0918	967.841 $\times 10^{-3}$
1 in. Hg(70°F)	=	0.4912	338.64 $\times 10^2$	0.03453	1	25.40	13.608	0.03342
1 mm Hg(70°F)	=	0.01934	1333.223	1.359 $\times 10^{-3}$	0.03937	1	0.5358	1.315 $\times 10^{-3}$
1 in. H_2O(70°F)	=	0.03609	24.883 $\times 10^2$	2.537 $\times 10^{-3}$	0.0735	1.8665	1	2.458 $\times 10^{-3}$
1 atm	=	14.6959	101.325 $\times 10^4$	1.03323	29.9212	760.	460.80	1

*See Section 1.15 for a definition of reversibility.

$$p_{impact} = \frac{\rho V^2}{2g_c} + p_{static},$$ (1.19)

where ρ is the fluid density, V is the velocity. The difference between the impact pressure and the static pressure is due to the velocity. This difference, $\rho V^2/2g_c$, is called *velocity pressure*. Figure 1.4 shows the different types of pressures.

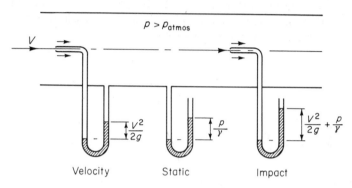

Fig. 1.4. *Types of pressures.*

In fluid flow through a duct, static conditions prevail at the walls of the duct. The velocity at the wall is zero and therefore the pressure measured at the wall is the static pressure. If the fluid particles move parallel to the center line of the duct, the static pressure is uniform across any section of the duct.

To measure pressures slightly different from atmospheric, a manometer is normally used, and the pressure is determined according to the hydrostatic formula given by Eq. (1.17). The manometer liquid may be mercury, water,

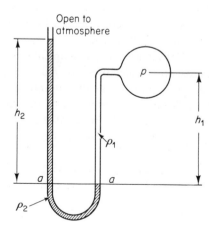

Fig. 1.5. *Measuring pressure by the means of a manometer.*

alcohol, etc. A typical manometer is shown in Fig. 1.5. Since the manometer fluid is in equilibrium, the pressure along a horizontal line *aa* is the same for either branch of the manometer. Then,

$$p + \rho_1 h_1 \frac{g}{g_c} = p_a + \rho_2 h_2 \frac{g}{g_c},$$ (1.20)

where p is the absolute pressure in the bulb, p_a is the atmospheric pressure exerted on the liquid-free surface, and ρ_1, ρ_2 are the densities of the fluid in the bulb and the manometer, respectively.
If

$$\rho_1 \ll \rho_2,$$

then

$$p - p_a = \rho_2 h_2 \frac{g}{g_c}.$$ (1.21)

**1-8
Molecular
Interpretation
of Pressure**

When a perfect gas* is examined from a macroscopic viewpoint, the gas appears as though it were a homogeneous system, and it is described with such parameters as pressure, volume, and temperature. However, when the gas is considered from the microscopic viewpoint, it consists of a multitude of small particles which are separated from each other by considerable space and which are in constant random motion. The properties of a gas that we observe on the macroscopic scale are determined by the behavior of the particles on a microscopic scale. It will be shown that such properties of molecules as mass and velocity are related to the macroscopic properties of pressure and temperature. Furthermore, information deduced about a system from observations made on one scale should be consistent with information deduced from observations made on the other scale.

Consider the macroscopically measured parameter of pressure. On the microscopic scale, pressure may be considered as the result of the force exerted by particles as they bombard a surface. The magnitude of the force depends on the momentum of the particles and the frequency with which they collide with the walls of the system. An expression for the pressure of a perfect gas can be derived by employing a model that arises from the kinetic theory of gases.

Consider a gas occupying a spherical volume as shown in Fig. 1.6. Molecules of the gas move continuously in all directions at velocities that

*See Section 1-16 for a definition of a perfect gas.

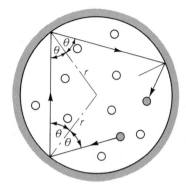

Fig. 1.6.   *Molecules in a spherical vessel.*

encompass a wide range of values. The size of molecules is assumed to be small compared with the distance between molecules. The pressure exerted by the gas arises from the collisions of the molecules with the walls of the vessel. Assume that there are N molecules of masses $m_1, m_2, m_3, \ldots$ and velocities $v_1, v_2, v_3, \ldots$; also assume, for the present, that the molecules do not collide with each other. When a particle of mass m_i collides with the wall of the vessel, it rebounds at an angle equal to the angle of incidence. The radial components of momentum of the particle before and after collision are $-m_i v_i \cos \theta_i$ and $+m_i v_i \cos \theta_i$. The rate of change of momentum in the radial direction is

$$\frac{m_i v_i \cos \theta_i - (-m_i v_i \cos \theta_i)}{\Delta \tau_i} = \frac{2m_i v_i \cos \theta_i}{\Delta \tau_i},$$

where $\Delta \tau_i$ is the mean time of impact with the wall. The total rate of change of momentum of all the molecules is the sum of the rate of change of momenta of the individual molecules:

$$\sum_{i=1}^{i=N} \frac{2m_i v_i \cos \theta_i}{\Delta \tau_i},$$

where N is the number of molecules. The pressure on the wall of the vessel is equal to the total rate of change of momentum of the molecules per unit area or

$$p = \frac{1}{4\pi r^2} \sum_{i=1}^{i=N} \frac{2m_i v_i \cos \theta_i}{\Delta \tau_i}.$$

Since the distance between collisions with the wall is $2r \cos \theta$, the time between collisions is

$$\frac{2r \cos \theta_i}{v_i}.$$

The number of collisions per unit time is, therefore,

$$\frac{v_i}{2r \cos \theta_i}.$$

But the average time of impact is equal to the average time between collisions with the walls of the vessel. Hence

$$\frac{1}{\Delta \tau_i} = \frac{v_i}{2r \cos \theta_i}.$$

Substituting for $\Delta \tau_i$, the expression for pressure becomes

$$p = \frac{1}{4\pi r^3} \sum_{i=1}^{i=N} m_i v_i^2.$$

But the volume of the sphere is $V = \frac{4}{3}\pi r^3$, so that

$$pV = \frac{1}{3} \sum_{i=1}^{i=N} m_i v_i^2. \qquad (1.22)$$

Effective velocity, or rms velocity (i.e., *root-mean-square*) is defined by

$$v_{\text{rms}}^2 = \frac{\sum\limits_{i} m_i v_i^2}{\sum\limits_{i} m_i}. \qquad (1.23)$$

When only one chemical species is present, the rms velocity is defined by

$$v_{\text{rms}}^2 = \frac{\sum\limits_{i} v_i^2}{N}.$$

In a single-component system, Eq. (1.22) becomes

$$pV = \frac{1}{3} Nm v_{\text{rms}}^2, \qquad (1.24)$$

where m is the mass of one molecule. This equation shows the relationship between the macroscopic properties pressure and volume with the microscopic properties molecular mass and molecular velocity. Note that the root-mean-square velocity is different from the *average* velocity of the molecule. Since a molecule shows equal probability of moving in each direction, the average velocity of a molecule is zero.

In the derivation of Eq. (1.24), collisions between the molecules were not considered. Such collisions can occur when the molecules rebound between the walls of the vessel. However, intermolecular collisions tend to be elastic. Momentum is therefore conserved despite the collisions, and so Eq. (1.24) is still valid. Pressure does not depend upon orientation of the area on which it acts, and this can be attributed to the random motion of the particles.

Although the derivation of the expression of pressure was based on a spherical volume, it can be shown that Eq. (1.24) is valid irrespective of the shape of the volume.

1-9 Temperature and the Zeroth Law of Thermodynamics

In the macroscopic treatment, temperature is considered a primary concept like length and mass. However, it will be shown in Chapter 6 that temperature can be derived from mechanical properties and therefore need not be considered a primary concept.

A satisfactory definition of temperature cannot be stated at this point. In fact, absolute temperature cannot be rigorously defined unless the second law of thermodynamics is applied, employing a temperature unit that does not depend on the properties of a particular substance. In this section, some important characteristics of temperature based on experimental observation are discussed.

The concept of temperature arises from the sensory perception of *hotness* or *coldness*. It is evident, however, that such a physiological sensation is insufficient for precise evaluation of temperature. Maxwell defined the temperature of a body as "its thermal state considered with reference to its ability to communicate heat to other bodies."

To establish a method of defining and measuring temperature, consider a body A that is brought into thermal contact with a body B, both bodies being isolated from their environment. Energy in the form of heat will be transferred from the body at the higher temperature to the body at the lower temperature. If sufficient time is allowed, bodies A and B approach a state at which no further change is observed, so that the two bodies are in a state of *thermal equilibrium*. When this state is reached, the two bodies are said to be at the *same temperature*.* As a corollary to this observation it may be noted that *if two systems are each in thermal equilibrium with a third system, they are also in thermal equilibrium with each other.* This statement is known as the *zeroth law of thermodynamics*. The zeroth law is the basis of the con-

*The word "temperature" comes from the Latin word "temperatura" meaning proper mixing or tempering, implying attainment of thermal equilibrium.

cept of temperature and enables us to compare temperatures of two bodies A and B with the help of a third body C, and say that the temperature of A is the same as the temperature of B without actually bringing A and B in contact with each other. The test body C is called a *thermometer*. It must be noted that thermal equilibrium does not describe temperature in a physical sense. It merely defines *equality of temperature*. In other words, equality or inequality of temperature of two systems is the property of being or not being in thermal equilibrium when the two systems are brought into contact. It is important to realize that the thermometer C indicates its own temperature which is the same as the temperature of a system in thermal equilibrium with the thermometer. Note that the concept of temperature as just described applies to equilibrium states only.

From the microscopic point of view, temperature is a manifestation of the activity of the molecules. An increase in temperature is accompanied by a simultaneous increase in the kinetic energy of the molecules. When two systems are in thermal equilibrium, the average kinetic energy of the molecules is the same for the two systems.

Temperature can be measured only by indirect methods. Generally heat is transferred to an instrument such as body C, and the change due to temperature in some property or response of C is measured. A property which changes in value as a function of temperature is called a *thermometric property*. Examples of thermometric properties include the length of the column of liquid in a capillary connected to a bulb, the pressure of a fixed mass of gas kept at constant volume, the volume of a fixed mass of gas kept at constant pressure, the electrical resistance of a metallic wire at atmospheric pressure, and the emf of a thermocouple.

In establishing a temperature scale, an arbitrary number is assigned to represent the temperature of one *fixed point*, and other temperatures are specified with this fixed point as a reference. In 1854, Kelvin pointed out that a single fixed point, such as the triple point of water (solid, liquid, and vapor coexisting in equilibrium), is sufficient to define the datum of an absolute temperature scale. This fixed point was adopted in 1954 by the Tenth International Conference on Weights and Measures due to the great accuracy with which it can be determined, and its value was set at $273.16°K$. Previously, the two fixed points which defined the temperature scale were the ice point, which is the temperature at which ice melts under atmospheric pressure and is $0.01°C$ below the triple point, and the steam point, which is the temperature at which water boils at atmospheric pressure.

1-10
Comparison of Thermometric Substances

In establishing a temperature scale it is necessary to clarify the relationship between temperature and the thermometric property in order to make interpolation and extrapolation possible.

Consider the thermometric property X, such that the temperature t is a linear function of this property:

$$t = a + bX,$$
(1.25)

where a and b are arbitrary constants. Note that equal temperature intervals are defined as those which produce equal changes in the property X. To determine the constants a and b, first assign numerical values to any two temperatures; for example, to the steam point and the ice point of water. Let X_i represent the value of the thermometric property of a substance in thermal equilibrium with ice melting under atmospheric pressure, and let X_s represent the value of the thermometric property of this substance in thermal equilibrium with steam at atmospheric pressure. The numerical change in the thermometric property accompanying the change in temperature over this standard interval is $X_s - X_i$, which is called the *standard property change*.

The *Celsius* scale, for example, assigns 0 to the *ice point*, and 100 to the *steam point*. Then $X_s - X_i$ is 100 degrees or intervals. By substituting these values for t, Eq. (1.25) gives

$$a = -\frac{100 X_i}{X_s - X_i}, \quad b = \frac{100}{X_s - X_i}.$$

Thus the temperature t is given by

$$t = -\frac{100 X_i}{X_s - X_i} + \frac{100}{X_s - X_i} X = 100 \frac{X - X_i}{X_s - X_i}.$$
(1.26)

The *Fahrenheit* scale, on the other hand, assigns the number 32 to the ice point temperature and the number 212 to the steam point temperature. There are then $212 - 32 = 180$ intervals involved, and after the constants a and b are evaluated, Eq. (1.25) becomes

$$t = 180 \frac{X - X_i}{X_s - X_i} + 32.$$
(1.27)

Several types of thermometers, each measuring a different thermometric property, are used to measure temperature. The scale used in these thermometers depends on the manner in which the thermometric property changes with temperature. To cover a wide range of temperature, a series of thermometers, each having different thermometric properties, may be used. Discontinuities in the rate of change of temperature with the thermometric property occur at the transition points.

**1-11
Perfect-Gas
Thermometer**
In a perfect-gas thermometer, the expansion and contraction of a gas as function of temperature serves as the thermometric property. Consider a fixed mass of a perfect gas that undergoes a change of temperature. The ratio of pressures associated with the end states, if the volume is maintained

constant, is the same as the ratio of volumes associated with the end states if the pressure is maintained constant:

$$\left(\frac{p_1}{p_2}\right)_V = \left(\frac{V_1}{V_2}\right)_p. \tag{1.28}$$

A perfect gas shows this property.

A temperature scale may therefore be established in which the ratio between any two temperatures, T_1 and T_2, is indicated by the pressure ratio or volume ratio of the enclosed perfect gas:

$$\frac{T_1}{T_2} = \left(\frac{p_1}{p_2}\right)_V = \left(\frac{V_1}{V_2}\right)_p. \tag{2.19}$$

In this thermometer, the gas may undergo changes in two successive steps. As a constant-volume process, following path 1-a in Fig. 1.7, the temperature changes from T_1 to T_a:

$$\frac{T_a}{T_1} = \frac{p_a}{p_1} = \frac{p_2}{p_1}; \tag{1.30}$$

then as a constant-pressure process, along with a-2, the temperature changes from T_a to T_2:

$$\frac{T_2}{T_a} = \frac{V_2}{V_a} = \frac{V_2}{V_1}. \tag{1.31}$$

When T_a is eliminated, this becomes

$$\frac{T_2}{T_1} = \frac{p_2 V_2}{p_1 V_1}, \tag{1.32}$$

or pV/T is a constant (perfect gas relation). At each temperature, the product (pV) is a constant, so that when pressure-volume relationships at constant temperature are plotted on a p-V diagram, as shown in Fig. 1.8, families of curves result. It is important to note that the products $(pV)_{T_1}$, $(pV)_{T_2}$, etc. are functions of temperature only and can therefore be used as a thermometric property to measure temperature.

The *constant-volume* and the *constant-pressure* gas thermometers operate according to the foregoing principle. In the constant-volume (or constant-density) thermometer shown in Fig. 1.9, a real gas in bulb A must exist at a specified pressure, which is characteristic of the gas, if the bulb is maintained at the triple point. The volume of the gas in the calibrated bulb is

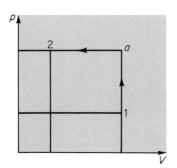

Fig. 1.7. *Change of state from 1 to 2 along 1-a and a-2.*

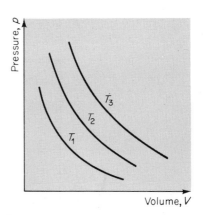

Fig. 1.8. *Constant-temperature curves on a p-V diagram.*

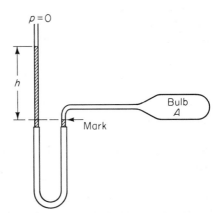

Fig. 1.9. *Constant-volume gas thermometer.*

kept constant by raising or lowering the mercury column until the mercury level is at the mark indicated in the figure. Thus the height $h_{t.p.}$ of the mercury column indicates the gauge pressure of the gas in the bulb when the gas is at its triple point. Similarly, the mercury will be at some other level, height h, when the gas is maintained at a different temperature. Note that this thermometer is an idealized model, for it assumes that a uniform temperature can be easily maintained, and that the bulb's volume does not change with temperature. Now suppose that discrete portions of the gas are removed from the bulb, so that the pressure of the gas in the bulb decreases from initial value at the triple point. The height of the mercury then indicates gas pressure; at the same time, the resultant temperature of the gas, at each pressure, is measured. As shown in Fig. 1.10, when the temperature ratio

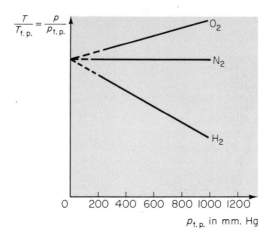

Fig. 1.10. *At zero pressure, different constant-volume gas thermometers indicate the same ratio of $T/T_{t.p.}$ or $p/p_{t.p.}$.*

$T/T_{t.p.}$ is plotted against pressure, several curves result. If these curves are extrapolated to zero pressure, it is found that they all meet at one point. A thermodynamic temperature T can then be defined as

$$\frac{T}{T_{t.p.}} = \lim_{p \to 0} \frac{p}{p_{t.p.}}. \tag{1.33}$$

The temperature T is called the *absolute temperature*.

Two absolute scales exist, the *Kelvin* and the *Rankine* scales. In the Kelvin scale a value of 273.16 is assigned to the triple point of water. The Kelvin scale has the same numerical intervals as the Celsius scale, but its value at the ice point corresponds to 0.01°C, rather than to zero, on the Celsius scale. Conversions between the Kelvin and Celsius temperature scales are accomplished through the following relationship:

$$T[°K] = t[°C] + 273.15. \tag{1.34}$$

In the Rankine scale, the triple point of water is at 491.69°R, whereas the ice point is 491.67°R. Since the Rankine scale, like the Kelvin scale, is an absolute scale, the numerical value of a temperature on the Rankine scale is related to the value on the Kelvin scale by the following ratio:

$$\frac{T[°R]}{T[°K]} = \frac{491.69}{273.16} = \frac{180}{100} = \frac{9}{5}.$$

The Rankine scale has the same unit temperature intervals as the Fahrenheit scale, but its zero value is 459.67°F below the zero of the Fahrenheit scale. The two scales are related by the following equation:

$$T[°R] = t[°F] + 459.67. \qquad (1.35)$$

Table 1.3 and Fig. 1.11 compare the several temperature scales.

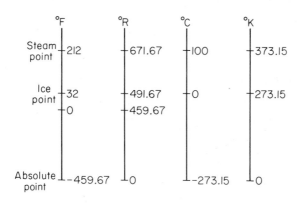

Fig. 1.11. *Relation between Fahrenheit, Rankine, Celsius, and Kelvin scales.*

TABLE 1.3   COMPARISON OF TEMPERATURE SCALES AT SOME
STANDARD AND FIXED POINTS

Fixed point	Celsius	Fahrenheit	Kelvin	Rankine
Absolute zero	−273.15	−459.67	0.00	0.00
Ice point	0.00	32.00	273.15	491.67
Triple point of water	0.0100	32.02	273.16	491.69
Steam point	100.00	212.00	373.15	671.67

**1-12
Thermo-
dynamic
Temperature
Scale**

If temperatures are measured with several thermometers, and if each thermometer employs a different thermometric substance, the readings of the various thermometers are likely to be identical only at the fixed point. This is due to the fact that in calibrating a thermometer it is assumed that the thermometric property varies with temperature in a linear fashion. Such a linear relation is valid only as a first approximation; furthermore, the thermometric property of each substance varies with temperature in its own characteristic and complex manner. For this reason, the temperature measured by the different thermometers cannot be expected to coincide except at the fixed point. All thermometers attempt, with varying degrees of success, to indicate the *thermodynamic temperature* (or the absolute temperature), which is a temperature independent of the properties of a particular system and which is based on the second law of thermodynamics. The thermodynamic temperature is always positive in value, and these values increase as a function of the *degree of hotness*. The thermodynamic or absolute temperature scale is the most fundamental scale. A perfect-gas thermometer indicates temperatures which coincide with thermodynamic temperatures. A further discussion of this temperature scale will be given in Chapter 4 when the second law of thermodynamics is presented.

1-13
The
International
Temperature
Scale
The International Committee of Weights and Measures in 1927 and 1948 specified the procedure to be followed in measuring temperature in order to yield values which are reproducible and universally comparable over the range of $-182.97°C$ to $4300°C$. The International Temperature Scale, which was established by this committee, is identical to the Celsius scale and is therefore called the *International Celsius Scale*. In establishing the International Scale, the committee specified: (a) temperature values at certain selected fixed points; (b) the fixed points at which instruments (thermocouple, resistance thermometer, and optical pyrometer) are to be calibrated; (c) the forms of equations for calculating temperatures at points other than the fixed points; (d) the experimental procedure for calibration and measurements.

The fixed points are given in Table 1.4 at a pressure of one standard

TABLE 1.4 BASIC FIXED POINTS*

(a) Temperature of equilibrium between liquid and gaseous oxygen (oxygen point) $-182.97°C$
$$t_p = t_{760} + 0.0126(p - 760) - 0.0000065(p - 760)^2$$

(b) Temperature of equilibrium between ice and air-saturated water (ice point) $0.000°C$

(c) Temperature of equilibrium between liquid water and its vapor (steam point) $100.00°C$
$$t_p = t_{760} + 0.0367(p - 760) - 0.000023(p - 760)^2$$

(d) Temperature of equilibrium between liquid sulfur and its vapor (sulfur point) $444.60°C$
$$t_p = t_{760} + 0.0909(p - 760) - 0.000048(p - 760)^2$$

(e) Temperature of equilibrium between solid silver and liquid silver (silver point) $960.8°C$

(f) Temperature of equilibrium between solid gold and liquid gold (gold point) $1063.0°C$

---

*For a pressure of 1.01325×10^6 dynes/cm², which corresponds to a barometric height of 760 mm at 0°C, for $g = 980.665$ cm/sec²).

atmosphere. In addition, formulas are given for calculating temperature when the pressure of the substance used for calibration is maintained at any point between 680 mm to 780 mm of mercury.

For temperature interpolation, the International scale is divided into four regions. Each region uses an interpolation equation chosen to give the best agreement with gas thermometer measurements. From $-182.97°C$ to $0°C$, the temperature is measured by a platinum thermometer; from $0°C$ to $630.5°C$, a platinum thermometer is also used but the temperature is defined by a different formula; from $630.5°C$ to $1063°C$, a platinum/platinum-rhodium thermometer is used; above $1063°C$, an optical pyrometer is used.

1-14 Thermo-dynamic Processes and Cycles

A *process* is a transition in which a system changes from an initial state to a final state. It is described by the thermodynamic path taken by the system as it undergoes the changes of state. An ideal or *quasi-static* process is one in which the state of the system deviates from an equilibrium state by only infinitesimal amounts throughout the entire process. Consider the pressure p_1 of a gas on one face of a frictionless piston and a pressure p_2 on the opposite face. If the two pressures are equal, the piston is in equilibrium. If p_1 is infinitesimally larger than p_2, the gas on side p_1 will undergo a small expansion as the piston moves; at the same time, the gas on both sides still remains essentially in equilibrium. This is called a *quasi-static expansion.*

During the course of a process, energy transfer may take place at a system's boundary, and changes in properties of the system may occur. Those properties or phenomena that do not change during a process serve in describing the process. For example, an *isochoric* process describes a process in which the volume of a system remains constant. Similarly, an *isobaric* process is one in which the pressure remains constant, whereas an *isothermal* process is one in which the temperature remains constant. A process which involves no work interaction is called a *no-work* process, whereas one which involves no heat interaction is called an *adiabatic* process.

When a system undergoes a series of processes and then returns to its original state, so that the properties of the system at the end of the cycle are the same as at its beginning, the system has completed a thermodynamic *cycle.*

1-15 Reversible and Irreversible Processes

If a process can occur in a reverse order, and if the initial state and all energies transferred or transformed during the process can be completely restored in both system and environment, then the process is called *reversible*. If a process is really reversible, then no aftereffects or changes are evident in the system or in the environment when the process occurs in the forward and then in the reverse direction. An *irreversible* process is a process that is not reversible. A quasi-static process implies an infinitely slow process since all potential differences acting on the system are infinitesimally small. Such a process may be thought of as an infinite succession of equilibrium states. It may be stopped at any time and made to proceed in the opposite direction, thereby reversing the original process in every detail and restoring the system (and environment) to its original state. On the other hand if a process is non-quasi-static, it cannot be reversed along its original path without causing a change in the environment. Therefore, quasi-static conditions are necessary if a process is to be reversible. Conversely, if a process occurs at a finite rate, it is an irreversible process.

In reversible processes, any energy transferred, such as mechanical, thermal, and chemical, would have to be transferred reversibly. Thus processes involving dissipative effects, such as fluid flow, in which friction losses occur, and convective heat transfer, in which there is turbulent flow, cannot be reversible. For heat transfer to occur, there must be a temperature difference. If heat is transferred from system A to system B during a process, then system A must be at a higher temperature than system B. In order for the reverse process to occur, heat would have to flow in the opposite direction, from system B to system A. This is impossible, since system B is at a lower temperature than system A and heat never flows in that direction without creating another change in the universe. Thus it can be stated that actual processes involving heat interaction are irreversible. For a heat transfer process to be reversible, the changes of temperature must be infinitesimal in magnitude and the time allowed to reach equilibrium must be infinite in length.

Another factor which causes irreversiblity is friction. When a piston moves in a cylinder as a gas expands to lower pressure, some work energy is expended in overcoming the friction between the piston and the cylinder. This friction produces heat. If the gas is compressed to its original volume, more heat is produced, but the work energy expended in overcoming friction is not recovered. Therefore the flow of real fluids is irreversible since it involves inherently irreversible effects.

All real or natural processes are irreversible, since they take place with finite differences of potential between parts of the system or between the system and its environment. Nevertheless, processes can be made almost reversible. Friction can be reduced, processes can be performed slowly, and temperature differences can be made small, so that conditions can be made virtually reversible. All these conditions imply that reversible processes are carried out with an infinitesimal departure from equilibrium. The concept of reversibility is, therefore, useful because it indicates the limits of possible change in a real system and, as will be shown in chapter 4, is a consequence of the second law of thermodynamics.

1-16
Equation of
State of a
Perfect Gas

Thermodynamic properties of simple systems are established by any two independent properties. A relationship between properties x, y, and z of a system, such as

$$f(x, y, z) = 0, \tag{1.36}$$

is called an *equation of state*. If values of any two of the properties are known, then the value of the third property is established. In the case of a perfect gas, the equation of state relating pressure, volume and temperature is

$$pv = RT \quad \text{or} \quad p = \rho RT, \tag{1.37}$$

where p = absolute pressure,
v = specific volume,
R = gas constant,
T = absolute temperature,
ρ = density.

Extensive properties may be expressed on a mole basis (that is, per gram-mole or pound-mole). A *pound-mole* is defined as the quantity of a substance whose mass in pounds is numerically equal to the molecular weight M of the substance. The equation of state for a perfect gas, on a mole basis, can thus be written,

$$pV = mRT = n\mathscr{R}T, \tag{1.38}$$

where V = volume of m lbm or n moles,
$\mathscr{R} = MR$ = universal gas constant approximately independent of the nature of the gas and equals 1545.33 ft-lbf/lb-mole°R.

Noting that $n = m/M$ and $v = V/m = V/nM$, it is clear that Eq. (1.37) and (1.38) are equivalent.

A number of real gases, such as hydrogen, nitrogen, oxygen, and helium, follow the perfect gas law at room temperatures so closely that they can be treated as perfect gases. Equations of state for perfect and real gases will be discussed in more detail in Chapter 6.

EXAMPLE 1.3:   Air is at 200°F and 14.7 psia. If the gas constant $R = 53.34$ ft-lbf/lbm°R, find the specific volume and the molecular weight of this gas, assuming it behaves as a perfect gas.

Solution: $pv = RT$

$(14.7 \times 144)v = 53.34\ (200 + 459.67)$

$\qquad v = 16.63\ \text{ft}^3/\text{lbm}.$

$$M = \frac{1545.33}{R} = \frac{1545.33}{53.34} = 28.97\ \text{lbm/lb-mole}.$$

1-17
Avogadro's
Number and
Boltzmann's
Constant

According to Avogadro's law, equal volumes of gas at the same temperature and pressure contain an equal number of molecules, if they are perfect gases. Experimental measurements indicate that the number of molecules in 1 gm-mole of a perfect gas is equal to $(6.0248 \pm 0.0003) \times 10^{23}$ (Avogadro's number N_0). Note that regardless of temperature and pressure 1 gm-mole of a gas always contains this number of molecules.

One lb-mole of any perfect gas at standard atmospheric pressure and at 32°F occupies a volume of 359 cu ft. The specific volume of a gas (the volume occupied by a unit mass of gas) is equal to its molal volume (the volume occupied by 1 mole) divided by the molecular weight of the gas. From this it follows that the density of a gas at standard conditions of temperature and pressure is proportional to its molecular weight.

The ratio of the universal gas constant $\mathscr{R}$ to Avogadro's number N_0 is called *Boltzmann's constant*. It is denoted by k and may be regarded as the universal gas constant per molecule. The value of k is $(1.38041 \pm 0.00007) \times 10^{-16}$ ergs/molecule°K. The equation of state of a perfect gas in terms of Boltzmann's constant takes the form

$$pV = nN_0kT = NkT, \tag{1.39}$$

where N is the number of molecules in the volume V.

1-18
Coefficients of
Volumetric
Expansion and
Compressi-
bility

In a single-component, single-phase system, changes in volume may occur due to changes in pressure or temperature, and can be expressed as

$$dV = \left(\frac{\partial V}{\partial T}\right)_p dT + \left(\frac{\partial V}{\partial p}\right)_T dp. \tag{1.40}$$

Dividing by V, this becomes

$$\frac{dV}{V} = \frac{1}{V}\left(\frac{\partial V}{\partial T}\right)_p dT + \frac{1}{V}\left(\frac{\partial V}{\partial p}\right)_T dp.$$

The expression $1/V\,(\partial V/\partial T)_p$ is called the *coefficient of volumetric expansion,* β, and the expression $-1/V\,(\partial V/\partial p)_T$ is called the *coefficient of isothermal compressibility, K.* Both β and K are intensive properties independent of the volume of the system.

Volume change can therefore be expressed in terms of β and K:

$$\frac{dV}{V} = \beta\,dT - K\,dp. \tag{1.41}$$

Density change can be expressed in a similar way:

$$\frac{d\rho}{\rho} = K\,dp - \beta\,dT. \tag{1.42}$$

The coefficient of volumetric expansion, β, is defined as the fractional change in volume at constant pressure, per unit change of temperature when the change in temperature and the corresponding change in volume become infinitesimal.

$$\beta \equiv \frac{1}{v}\left(\frac{\partial v}{\partial T}\right)_p = -\frac{1}{\rho}\left(\frac{\partial \rho}{\partial T}\right)_p. \tag{1.43}$$

In the case of a perfect gas, the coefficient of volumetric expansion is

$$\beta = \frac{1}{v}\left(\frac{\partial v}{\partial T}\right)_p = \frac{p}{RT}\left(\frac{R}{p}\right) = \frac{1}{T}. \tag{1.44}$$

Thus, the coefficient of volumetric expansion of a perfect gas varies inversely with absolute temperature and is independent of both pressure and volume. The coefficient of volume expansion of a real gas, however, depends on both pressure and temperature.

The coefficient of compressibility, K, is defined as the fractional change in volume at constant temperature per unit change of pressure when the change in pressure and the corresponding change in volume become infinitesimal.

$$K \equiv -\frac{1}{v}\left(\frac{\partial v}{\partial p}\right)_T = \frac{1}{\rho}\left(\frac{\partial \rho}{\partial p}\right)_T. \tag{1.45}$$

The negative sign is included in the preceding equation because an increase in pressure generally results in a decrease in volume. When the system consists of a perfect gas, the coefficient of compressibility becomes

$$K = -\frac{1}{v}\left(\frac{\partial v}{\partial p}\right)_T = -\frac{1}{v}\left(-\frac{RT}{p^2}\right) = \frac{1}{p}. \tag{1.46}$$

The compressibility of a substance is measured by its change of volume when the external pressure changes. Let the pressure on a certain substance of volume V be increased by dp. As a result, the volume is diminished by dV. The *bulk modulus of elasticity*, E, is given by

$$E = -\frac{dp}{dV/V} = -V\frac{dp}{dV}, \tag{1.47}$$

where dV/V is the volumetric strain. Note that E is not a property since the derivative dp/dV depends on the process. From Eq. (1.41), the bulk modulus can be expressed as

$$E = \frac{1}{K - \beta\, dT/dp}. \tag{1.48}$$

In the case of solids and liquids, changes in pressure produce negligible changes in temperature, so that the term dT/dp is essentially zero. Thus the reciprocal of the coefficient of compressibility of solids and liquids is the bulk modulus of elasticity. In the case of gases, the term dT/dp cannot be neglected and therefore the bulk modulus of elasticity, E, is not a property.

A substance is not inherently compressible or incompressible. The process in which a substance is involved determines whether it behaves in a compressible or incompressible way. The volume change, ΔV, due to pressure change, of a liquid such as water ($E = 20,000$ kgf/cm^2) is small, but at large pressures its compressibility becomes evident. On the other hand, the volume change of a flowing gas as the pressure changes is ordinarily quite large. But in a process where there are negligible velocity changes at constant temperature, a gas behaves as though it were incompressible.

EXAMPLE 1.4: The isothermal coefficient of compressibility of water at 50°F and atmospheric pressure is 50×10^{-6} atm^{-1}. What absolute pressure must be exerted on a certain mass of water to decrease its volume 5 per cent at the same temperature?

Solution: $\quad 50 \times 10^{-6} = -\frac{1}{v}\left(\frac{\partial v}{\partial p}\right)_T.$

By integration:

$$\int_{p=1\text{ atm}}^{p} dp = -2 \times 10^4 \int_{v}^{0.95v} \frac{dv}{v} = -2 \times 10^4 \ln 0.95 = 1024.$$

Therefore

$$p = 1024 + 1 = 1025 \text{ atm.}$$

REFERENCES

1.1 American Institute of Physics, *Temperature, Its Measurements and Control*, vol. I, II, 1954.

1.2 Cambel, A. B., and B. H. Jennings, *Gas Dynamics*. New York: McGraw-Hill Book Company, 1958, chap. 1.

1.3 Keenan, J. H., *Thermodynamics*. New York: John Wiley & Sons, Inc., 1952, chap. 1.

1.4 Kiefer, P. J., G. F. Kinney, and M. C. Stuart, *Principles of Engineering Thermodynamics*. New York: John Wiley & Sons, Inc., 1954, chap. 4.

1.5 Lee, J. F., and F. W. Sears, *Thermodynamics*. Reading, Mass.: Addison-Wesley Publishing Company, Inc., 1963, 2nd Edition, chap. 1, 2.

1.6 Van Wylen, G. J., *Thermodynamics*. New York: John Wiley & Sons, Inc., 1958, chap. 2.

1.7 Shapiro, A. H., *Compressible Fluid Flow*. Ronald Press Company, 1953, chap. 1.

1.8 Sheehan, W. F., *Physical Chemistry*. Boston, Mass.: Allyn and Bacon, Inc., 1961, chap. 1.

1.9 Wilson, A. H., *Thermodynamics and Statistical Mechanics*. Cambridge: Cambridge University Press, 1957, chap. 1.

1.10 Zemansky, M. W., *Heat and Thermodynamics*. New York: McGraw-Hill Book Company, 1951, chap. 1, 2.

PROBLEMS

1.1 Calculate the force exerted on a mass of 5 lbm moving at an acceleration of 5 ft/sec^2 in (a) lbf; (b) dynes; (c) poundals; (d) newtons.

1.2 The weight of 1 cu ft of air at 70°F is 0.0751 lbf at a location where $g = 32.174$ ft/sec^2. What is the density of air in lbm/ft^3 and in slugs/ft^3?

1.3 A force of 60 lbf is applied on a mass of 2 slugs along an incline at a location where $g = 30.5$ ft/sec^2. If the force and the incline make a 30° angle with the vertical, determine the acceleration of the mass if the force is acting (a) upwards; (b) downwards.

1.4 Prove that the weight of a body at an elevation z above sea level is given by

$$w = \frac{mg}{g_c}\left(\frac{r}{r+z}\right)^2,$$

where r is the radius of the earth at the equator.

1.5 If U is a function of three properties x, y, and z such that

$$dU = M\,dx + N\,dy + P\,dz,$$

where M, N, and P are functions of the properties x, y, and z. Prove that the following conditions are necessary in order for U to be an exact differential

$$\frac{\partial P}{\partial y} = \frac{\partial N}{\partial z}, \quad \frac{\partial M}{\partial z} = \frac{\partial P}{\partial x}, \quad \frac{\partial N}{\partial x} = \frac{\partial M}{\partial y}.$$

1.6 Ascertain the exactness of the following differential

$$df = (x^2 + y^2)\,dx + 2xy\,dy,$$

and find an expression for the function $f(x, y)$.

1.7 Complete the following table if atmospheric pressure is 14.7 lbf/in².

psia	psig	psfa	in. Hg abs
	5		
			10
20			
		2000	

1.8 A pressure gauge reads 20 psig and the barometer reads 29.9 in. Hg. Find the absolute pressure in inches of Hg and in psia.

1.9 Calculate the height of a column of water equivalent to atmospheric pressure of 14.7 lbf/in.² if the water is at 60°F. What is the height if the water is replaced by mercury?

1.10 If all atmospheric air is liquified, what will be the equivalent height of this liquid air in inches of water at 60°F?

1.11 Find the weight of air in lbf of the atmosphere surrounding the earth if the pressure is 14.7 psia everywhere on the surface. Assume that the earth is a sphere of diameter 7926 miles.

1.12 The pressure in the bulb A of Fig. 1.12 is 20 in. Hg vacuum. What is the height h of the mercury in the tube? (S.G. of Hg = 13.58 and barometric pressure = 29.92 in. Hg.)

1.13 For the conditions shown in Fig. 1.13, determine $p_a - p_b$ in lbf/in.²

1.14 Complete the following table:

°F	°R	°C	°K
60			
	600		
		−5	
			400

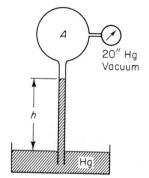

Fig. 1.12. Problem 1.12.

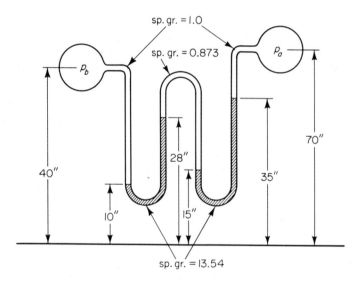

Fig. 1.13. Problem 1.13.

1.15 A Celsius and a Fahrenheit thermometer are immersed in a fluid. If the reading of the Fahrenheit thermometer is numerically twice that of the Celsius thermometer, what is the temperature of the fluid in °R and °K?

1.16 If a temperature scale is graduated according to the equation $t = 100 + 3t_c$, where t is the temperature reading on the scale and t_c is the Celsius temperature: (a) Find the freezing and boiling points of the thermometric substance. (b) What is the absolute temperature corresponding to 20° temperature reading on this scale?

1.17 A thermometric property X (length of a mercury column in a mercury-in-glass thermometer) is equal to 3 in. and 21 in. when the thermometer is at the ice and steam points. The temperature t varies linearly with X. Now assume that a temperature t^* on a certain Fahrenheit scale is defined by the equation

$t^* = a + bX^2$, where $t^* = 32°$ and $212°$ at the ice and steam points, and a and b are constants. Find the temperature t^* on this scale when the temperature t is $100°F$.

1.18 The temperature scale of a thermometer is given by

$$t^* = ae^X + b,$$

where a and b are constants and X is the same thermometric property as defined in Problem 1.17. If 32 and 212 denote the ice and steam points on the new scale, plot a graph of t versus t^* and find the temperature reading corresponding to $100°F$ on this scale. Assume a linear variation of t with X.

1.19 A balloon containing a perfect gas has a volume of 2 ft³. The temperature and pressure of the gas are $60°F$ and 14.7 psia. If the gas is heated to $150°F$, what must the applied pressure be in order that the volume remains constant?

1.20 Find the mass of air enclosed in a cylindrical tank 6 in. in diameter and 3 ft long (inside dimensions). The temperature of the air is $70°F$ and the pressure is 90 psia. If a valve mounted on the tank is opened till the cylinder pressure becomes atmospheric, find the mass of air that escaped from the tank if the final temperature is $70°F$.

1.21 Prove that

$$\left(\frac{\partial \beta}{\partial p}\right)_T = -\left(\frac{\partial K}{\partial T}\right)_p.$$

1.22 The coefficient of volumetric expansion and the compressibility are defined as

$$\beta = \frac{1}{v}\left(\frac{\partial V}{\partial T}\right)_p, \qquad K = -\frac{1}{V}\left(\frac{\partial V}{\partial p}\right)_T.$$

Calculate $(\partial p/\partial T)_r$ for a perfect gas in terms of β and K.

1.23 Compute the coefficient of volumetric expansion β and the compressibility K for a gas obeying the Clausius equation of state

$$p(v - b) = RT.$$

1.24 The equation of state for 1 mole of a "Van der Waal" gas is

$$\left(p + \frac{a}{v^2}\right)(v - b) = RT,$$

where a and b are constants, prove that

$$\beta = \frac{Rv^2(v - b)}{RTv^3 - 2a(v - b)^2}, \quad \text{and} \quad K = \frac{v^2(v - b)^2}{RTv^3 - 2a(v - b)^2}.$$

1.25 The differential of the pressure of a certain gas is given by one of the following equations:

$$dp = \frac{2RT}{(v-b)^2}\, dv + \frac{R}{v-b}\, dT$$

or

$$dp = -\frac{RT}{(v-b)^2}\, dv + \frac{R}{v-b}\, dT.$$

Identify the correct equation and find the equation of state of that gas.

NOMENCLATURE

A	Area	Q	Heat
a	Acceleration	q	Heat per unit mass
C	Charge, quantity of electricity or a constant	R	Gas constant
		$\mathscr{R}$	Universal gas constant
c	Velocity of light or specific heat	r	Distance
E	Total internal energy or electric intensity	T	Absolute temperature or torque
		t	Temperature
F	Force	U	Internal energy
g	Acceleration due to gravity	V	Volume or velocity
g_c	Constant of proportionality in Newton's second law	v	Specific volume
H	Total head or magnetic intensity	X	Generalized intensive property
I	Magnetization	x, y, z	Cartesian coordinates
i	Electric current	W	Weight or work
K	Proportionality constant in Coulomb's law	α	Angle
		$\mathscr{E}$	Electric potential
L	Length	γ	Specific weight
M	Moment or molecular weight	ω	Angular velocity
m	Mass	ρ	Density
n	Exponent	σ	Surface tension
P	Power or electric polarization	τ	Time
p	Pressure	θ	Angle

2

ENERGY AND CONSERVATION LAWS

2-1
Introduction
Physical laws are relationships which describe patterns of behavior in physical systems. Conservation laws comprise a particular class of physical laws and are characterized by their simplicity, generality, and utility. They describe the behavior of a system when certain physical quantities are maintained constant.

This chapter discusses the following conservation laws:* the law of conservation of (a) mass; (b) energy; (c) electrical charge; (d) linear momentum; (e) moment of momentum. The laws of conservation of mass, energy, and charge are utilized in dealing with energy relationships; the laws of conservation of linear momentum, moment of momentum, and mass will be introduced with emphasis on fluid flow.

2-2
Conservation
of Mass
The law of conservation of mass states that the total mass of a closed system cannot change. This law is valid when the system is moving at a velocity much smaller than the velocity of light. The system then obeys Newtonian mechanics and is called a *Newtonian system*. This constancy of mass does not prevail in high-velocity systems, which are known as *relativistic systems*. In relativistic systems, the *rest-mass*, which is the mass measured at rest with repect to an observer, is denoted by m_o; the *relativistic mass*, which is the mass when it moves at a velocity V relative to the same observer, is denoted by m. The rest-mass m_o is a constant, but the relativistic mass of an isolated system moving at a velocity V is larger, according to the theory of relativity, than its rest-mass; the relationship being

$$m = \frac{m_o}{\sqrt{1 - (V^2/c^2)}}, \tag{2.1}$$

where c, the velocity of light in vacuum is 3×10^{10} cm/sec. As seen from Eq. (2.1), when $V \ll c$ then $m = m_o$. At high velocities, however, the value of m is larger than m_o, and $m \longrightarrow \infty$ as $V \longrightarrow c$. For example, when $V = 0.1c$, the relativistic mass is $1.005\,m_o$; on the other hand, when $V = 0.98c$ the relativistic mass is $5\,m_o$. In most applications of thermodynamics the significant velocities are much smaller than the velocity of light, so that the masses are essentially independent of velocities.

2-3
Energy
The concept of energy was first introduced in mechanics by Newton when he hypothesized about kinetic and potential energies. Energy is a *scalar* quantity that cannot be observed directly but can be recorded and evaluated by indirect measurements.

*An additional law is the law of conservation of chemical species, discussed in Chapter 11.

The sun is the major source of the earth's energy. It emits a spectrum of energy which travels across space as electromagnetic radiation. Light and heat are its most important forms. Energy is also associated with the structure of matter and can be released by chemical and atomic reactions. Man has discovered new energy sources in the universe and he strives to manipulate them in the most effective ways.

Energy exists in different forms which are either internal or transient and any one form of energy can be converted to any other form. The extent of conversion, however, may be complete or partial. Mechanical, electrical, chemical, or other forms of energy can be converted completely to heat. The conversion of heat to mechanical energy (in cyclic operation), on the other hand, is only partial.

Energy may be classified as:

(1) *Energy in transition due to a potential difference:* Gradients of force, temperature and electrical potential result in the transfer of mechanical work, heat and electrical energy.

There are numerous modes of energy transmission. One form of mechanical energy consists of sound waves, where the energy is transmitted by adjacent masses of air that alternately expand and contract. Although the energy is transmitted by local movement of the molecules of the medium, as an over-all effect, the medium remains at one general location. Another mode of energy transmission is electromagnetic radiation. Visible light, X rays, gamma rays, radio waves, and radiant heat are examples of energy transmitted by this means. Electromagnetic waves are emitted by vibrating molecules, and the waves may be transmitted to other molecules with or without the aid of an intervening medium.

(2) *Internal energy:* Examples of this type are potential, kinetic, chemical, and atomic energy. Internal energy is present in a system by virture of its orientation in a force field, its motion, its chemical composition, or its atomic structure.

From the microscopic point of view, particles or molecules of a system that move translationally possess kinetic translational energy; polyatomic molecules that rotate about their centers of mass possess rotational energy; and molecules that vibrate along their centers of mass possess vibrational energy. The magnitude of the translational, rotational, and vibrational energies is a function of temperature. Translational and rotational energies comprise most of the molecular kinetic energy at room temperature. High temperatures, however, are required before vibrational energy becomes significant. Additional energies attributed to the molecular structure are bonding, electronic, ionic, nuclear, etc.

Thermodynamics is concerned with changes in energy, rather than with absolute energies. In most cases, there are no means of measuring absolute energies; and since only knowledge of changes of energy is needed for solving most problems, the zero level of energy may be set at an arbitrary state.

2-4
Conservation
of Energy

The law of conservation of energy* states that the energy of an isolated system is conserved. In an isolated system neither matter nor energy crosses the boundaries. Consequently, no change in the total energy occurs. This does not exclude the possibility of the redistribution of energy within the isolated system. The molecules of a gas in a container, for example, are continuously exchanging energies owing to collisions with the walls and collisions among themselves. Nevertheless, the total energy of the system is conserved under isolated conditions.

2-5
Conservation
of Electrical
Charge

Electrical charges produce electric fields analogous in many respects to gravitational fields. Charged particles, such as electrons, may be accelerated by electric and magnetic fields just as a mass of matter may be accelerated in a gravity field.

The attractive or repulsive force between two stationary charges is proportional to the product of the charges and inversely proportional to the square of the distance separating them. This phenomenon is expressed by Coulomb's law as

$$F = K\frac{C_1 C_2}{r^2}, \tag{2.2}$$

where C_1 and C_2 are the electrical charges, r is the distance between them, and K is a dimensional constant whose value depends on material and the system of units chosen. For example, if F is in dynes, the charge is in the absolute CGS electrostatic system of units so that C is in coulombs $(gm^{1/2}\ cm^{3/2}\ sec^{-1})$, and r is in cm, then K has the value unity.

Coulomb forces play an important part in the structural configuration of atoms and molecules. The orbiting of electrons around the nucleus is a result of the attractive forces between these negative electrons and the positive protons in the nucleus. For a system of a fixed charge, when the charge of an atom increases, owing to a loss of an electron (electronic charge $= -1.602 \times 10^{-19}$ coulombs), an equal decrease in charge must take place to conserve the total charge of the system. The law of conservation of electrical charge states that the electrical charge of an isolated system is conserved.

In the following sections some forms of energy are discussed in detail.

*As will be shown in Chapter 3, the first law of thermodynamics provides a definition of the term "energy," and therefore the law of conservation of energy becomes dependent on the first law; in fact, it is a special case of the first law.

2-6
Work
Work is a form of energy interaction between two systems. It is identified at the interaction boundary *if the sole effect external to each system can be reduced to the change in level of a weight.* This definition does not say that a weight is actually raised or lowered; rather, it indicates that the sole effect external to each system could have been the rise or the fall of a weight.* Work done on the system by the environment is considered positive; work done by the system on the environment, negative.†

Consider mechanical work as defined in mechanics. Mechanical work is the product of an external force acting at the boundaries of a system and the distance through which the force moves along its line of action. Considering motion in only one dimension, the work done is

$$W_{1\text{-}2} = \int_{x_1}^{x_2} F_x \, dx, \tag{2.3}$$

where F_x is the component of force in the direction of the displacement dx. But from the standpoint of thermodynamics, work can also arise from other effects, not only from mechanical motion.

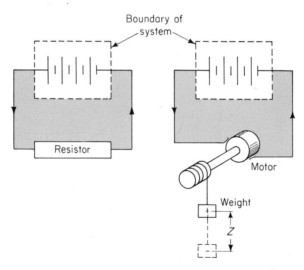

Fig. 2.1. *Equivalence of electrical energy to work.*

*This definition assumes a knowledge of the second law of thermodynamics, since heat cannot be converted completely and continuously into work.

†This sign convention differs from that in many texts, but it is less confusing to consider energies entering the system as positive and those leaving the system as negative. This convention is in accordance with mechanics which the student has usually studied before thermodynamics.

Work that is not of a mechanical nature and cannot be expressed by Eq. (2.3) can still be recognized as work by the following criterion: Imagine a device which utilizes this nonmechanical energy to produce mechanical work, resulting then in the change of level of a weight. If this is feasible, then this nonmechanical energy is work, provided that no other effects are produced. As an example, electrical energy from a storage battery may cross the boundaries of a system, as shown in Fig. 2.1. Does work cross the boundaries? This question is answered by imagining that the electrical energy drives an ideal motor, which rotates a frictionless pulley, which, in turn, raises a weight. Assuming that the net number of electrons carried by the electric wiring is zero, there is no net flow of mass across the system and electrical energy is work.

Now consider the frictionless piston-cylinder arrangement shown in Fig. 2.2. Let the system be the fluid enclosed between the piston and the cylinder. The system exerts a pressure p on the piston face of area A. If the piston is allowed to move a distance dx, the force F acting on the piston may vary but at any instant is given by

$$F = pA,$$

where p is the absolute pressure exerted by the system on the inside face of the piston at a particular instant. Note that p is the pressure of the system at the moving boundaries.

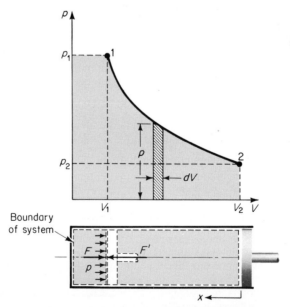

Fig. 2.2. Work done on a system is $-\int p\,dV$.

To maintain the piston in equilibrium, let the inner face of the piston exert a force F' on the system. F' is equal and opposite to F. Suppose the piston moves to the left a distance dx in the direction of the force F'. The work done is $dW = F'\,dx$ and the environment has done work on the system. If, on the other hand, the piston moves to the right, work is done by the system on the environment, which is the same, algebraically, as saying that negative work is done on the system.

When the piston moves to the left a small distance dx, an amount of work dW is done, which may be expressed in terms of the fluid pressure p. The work done on the system is

$$dW = F'\,dx.$$

But since

$$F' = pA,$$

therefore,

$$dW = pA\,dx.$$

Let V be the initial volume of the system, $V + dV$ the final volume after the motion of the piston. Since compression is involved, dV is a negative quantity and equal to $-A\,dx$. Therefore the work done on the system is

$$dW = -p\,dV. \tag{2.4}$$

In the opposite case, when the piston moves to the right so that expansion occurs, dV is positive. Work is done by the system (or negative work is done on the system), and therefore $dW = -p\,dV$. Hence, Eq. (2.4) indicates the work done *on* the system when either expansion or compression occurs. In a finite process in which the volume changes from V_1 to V_2, the total work interaction is obtained by integrating Eq. (2.4):

$$W_{1\text{-}2} = \int_1^2 dW = -\int_{V_1}^{V_2} p_{\text{inside}}\,dV. \tag{2.5}$$

To integrate this equation, the relationship between p and V must be known. For the particular case where the pressure remains constant during a process, the work is given by

$$W_{1\text{-}2} = -p\int_{V_1}^{V_2} dV = p(V_1 - V_2).$$

Equation (2.5) applies to any process as long as p is the pressure at the face of the piston (or at the boundaries of the system that move); the pressure at other points in the system need not be the same. The pressure on the face of the moving piston is the same as the pressure throughout the system only if the process goes slowly, proceeding through a series of equilibrium states (which may require infinite time), that is, a quasi-static process. A process involving rapid expansion or compression is usually accompanied by fluid friction or mechanical friction, and in such non-quasi-static processes, the fluid pressure at the boundary differs from that in the interior of the system. It is then difficult to determine actual pressures, and consequently the work done is uncertain. Note that the work done on the system, whether the compression is quasi-static or not, is the work of the exterior force F'. The value of the force F' as a function of the position of the piston is then required in order to calculate work interaction.

When the exterior face of the piston is exposed to a constant pressure p_o, such as atmospheric pressure, the work done by the force exerted by the atmospheric pressure must be taken into consideration. In the case of compression, for example, the work done by an external force in moving the piston is equal to the work received by the fluid $-\int_{V_1}^{V_2} p\, dV$ minus the work done by the atmosphere $p_o(V_1 - V_2)$. It may be remarked that in a complete cycle, the total work done by the atmosphere is zero, since $V_1 = V_2$. This means that the work done by the atmosphere during the outward motion of the piston is equal and opposite to that during the inward motion of the piston.

Work interaction in a quasi-static process can be represented graphically on a p-V diagram, appearing as the area under the curve 1–2 of Fig. 2.2.

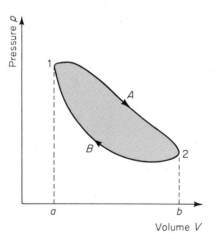

Fig. 2.3.   Work done in a cycle $-\oint p\, dV$.

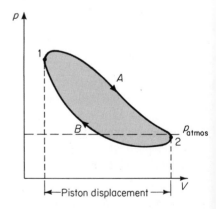

Fig. 2.4.   Indicator diagram.

In an expansion process, in which the system changes from state 1 to state 2, the work interaction is negative since the volume increases. In this case, work is done by the system on the environment. Conversely, if the process proceeds from state 2 to state 1, as in compression, the work interaction is positive and work is done on the system by the environment.

A cyclic process can be represented on a p-V diagram by the closed curve 1-A-2-B-1 of Fig. 2.3. The work done on the system during the expansion process 1-A-2 is

$$-\int_{1(A)}^{2} p \, dV = \text{area } a\text{-}1\text{-}A\text{-}2\text{-}b\text{-}a,$$

and the work done on the system during the compression process 2-B-1 is

$$-\int_{2(B)}^{1} p \, dV = \text{area } b\text{-}2\text{-}B\text{-}1\text{-}a\text{-}b.$$

Hence the net work done is

$$W = -\int_{1(A)}^{2} p \, dV - \int_{2(B)}^{1} p \, dV = -\oint p \, dV = -(\text{area } 1\text{-}A\text{-}2\text{-}B\text{-}1),$$

where the symbol $\oint$ denotes a cyclic integral. Note that the work interaction is negative. If the cycle of Fig. 2.3 were performed in the opposite direction 1-B-2-A-1, the area of the closed curve would represent work done on the system.

In representing work done in a cycle by means of a p-V diagram, the following rule can be applied to distinguish positive work from negative work: If an observer is moving along the boundary of the $\int p \, dV$ area in the direction of the process, and if the area lies to the right of the observer, then work is done by the system and the work interaction is negative.

Indicator diagrams or cards traced by engine indicators provide a plot of gauge pressure versus piston travel as shown in Fig. 2.4. The area of an indicator diagram may be used to determine actual work done on the piston during a complete cycle. The area can be determined by counting squares on graph paper, by measuring directly with a planimeter, or by using a numerical integration method (such as Simpson's rule). The work done is given by

$$W/\text{cycle} = -\oint p \, dV = -\oint pA \, dL = -p_m \, AL,$$

where A = area of the piston face
$\quad L$ = stroke
$\quad p_m$ = indicated mean effective pressure

$$= \frac{-\oint p\,dV}{V_2 - V_1} = \frac{\text{area } 1\text{-}A\text{-}2\text{-}B\text{-}1}{V_2 - V_1}$$

$V_2 - V_1$ = volume swept by the piston (the piston displacement).

EXAMPLE 2.1: Find the work done per cycle by a 4-in. bore, 5-in. stroke engine if the area of the indicator card is 1.5 in.², the card length is 2.1 in., and the indicator spring constant is 80 psi for every inch of card displacement.

Solution: Piston area $A = \frac{\pi}{4}(4^2) = 12.56$ in.²

$$\text{Stroke} = \frac{5}{12} = 0.4167 \text{ ft.}$$

$$W/\text{cycle} = -p_m AL = -\left(\frac{1.5}{2.1} \times 80\right) \times 12.56 \times 0.4167 = -299.5 \text{ ft-lbf.}$$

2-7
Work as a
Path Function

Several reversible processes leading from state 1 to state 2 are shown in Fig. 2.5. The work interaction in each case is represented by the area underneath the corresponding path. The work done is obviously different in each case because the path depends on the nature of the process. This means that work is not a property or a state function; rather, it is a *path function* and an infinitesimal increment of work is an inexact differential. Therefore, a system does not possess work; instead, work is a mode of transfer of energy. This transfer occurs only at the boundaries of the

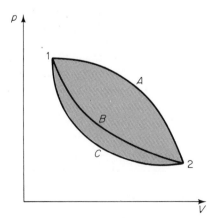

Fig. 2.5. *Work depends on the path.*

system as the system undergoes a change of state. For this reason, work is expressed by

$$\int_1^2 dW = W_{1\text{-}2}, \quad \text{and not by} \quad W_2 - W_1.$$

Hereafter, the symbols d and $\overline{d}$ will be used to distinguish between quantities, such as pressure, which are fixed by the end states of the system, and quantities, such as work, which are functions of the path.

2-8   Work is a scalar quantity having the dimen-
Units of Work   sions of energy. The basic unit of work in the
English engineering system is the *foot-pound force*, which is equivalent to a force of 1 lbf acting through a distance of 1 ft in the direction of the displacement. In the CGS system, the unit of work is the *erg*, defined as the amount of work done by a force of 1 dyne when it acts through a distance of 1 cm in the direction of the displacement. The *joule* or watt-sec ($kg\text{-}m^2/sec^2$) is the energy associated with an electromotive force of 1 volt and the passage of 1 coulomb of electricity. The joule is also a unit of work and is equal to 10^7 ergs.

Power is the time rate of doing work. The common units of power are

1 hp (horsepower) = 550 ft-lbf/sec = 33000 ft-lbf/min
1 kw (kilowatt) = 44240 ft-lbf/min

Also   1 hp-hr = 2545 Btu*
1 kw-hr = 3413 Btu.

EXAMPLE 2.2:   A reversible cycle of a work-producing machine is represented by a circle of 2-in. diameter on a *p-V* diagram, as shown in Fig. 2.6. The pressure and specific volume scales are

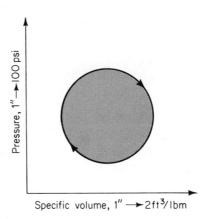

Fig. 2.6.   Example 2.2.   Specific volume, $1'' \longrightarrow 2\,ft^3/lbm$

Pressure, $1'' \longrightarrow 100$ psi

*The British thermal unit (Btu) is defined later in this chapter.

p-scale: 1 in. = 100 lbf/in^2,
v-scale: 1 in. = 2 ft^3/lbm.
Compute the work done on 1 lbm of fluid.

Solution: $\quad W = -\oint p\,dv$

$$= -(\text{area of circle shown in Fig. 2.6})$$

$$= -\frac{\pi}{4}(2^2)(100 \times 144)(2) = -90{,}500 \text{ ft-lbf/lbm.}$$

EXAMPLE 2.3: Helium contained in a cylinder fitted with a piston expands reversibly according to the relation $pV^{1.5} = \text{constant}$. The initial volume is 2 ft^3, the initial pressure is 70 psia, and the initial temperature is 400°R. After expansion, the pressure is 30 psia. Calculate the work done during the expansion process.

Solution:

$$pV^n = C$$

$$W = -\int_{V_1}^{V_2} p\,dV = -\int_{V_1}^{V_2} \frac{C}{V^n}\,dV = C\left[\frac{V^{-n+1}}{n-1}\right]_{V_1}^{V_2} = \left[\frac{C}{n-1}\frac{V}{V^n}\right]_{V_1}^{V_2}$$

$$= \left[\frac{pV}{n-1}\right]_{V_1}^{V_2} = \frac{p_2 V_2 - p_1 V_1}{n-1}.$$

To determine V_2:

$$p_1 V_1^n = p_2 V_2^n = C$$

or

$$\frac{V_2}{V_1} = \left(\frac{p_1}{p_2}\right)^{1/n}, \qquad V_2 = 2\left(\frac{70}{30}\right)^{0.667} = 3.52 \text{ ft}^3.$$

Then

$$W = \frac{(30 \times 144) \times 3.52 - (70 \times 144) \times 2}{0.5} = \frac{15{,}200 - 20{,}150}{0.5}$$

$$= -\frac{4950}{0.5} = -9900 \text{ ft-lbf.}$$

Another way of solving this problem is to introduce the perfect-gas law ($pV = mRT$); thus the expression for the work interaction becomes

$$W = \frac{mRT_2 - mRT_1}{n-1}.$$

To determine m:

$$p_1 V_1 = mRT_1$$

where $R = \mathscr{R}/M = 1545/4$ ft-lbf/lbm°R. Therefore,

$$m = \frac{70 \times 144 \times 2}{(1545/4) \times 400} = 0.1305 \text{ lbm.}$$

To determine T_2:

$$\frac{p_2 V_2}{p_1 V_1} = \frac{T_2}{T_1}.$$

But

$$\frac{V_2}{V_1} = \left(\frac{p_1}{p_2}\right)^{1/n},$$

which, when substituted in the previous equation, gives

$$\frac{p_2}{p_1}\left(\frac{p_1}{p_2}\right)^{1/n} = \frac{T_2}{T_1} \quad \text{or} \quad \frac{T_2}{T_1} = \left(\frac{p_2}{p_1}\right)^{(n-1)/n}.$$

Hence,

$$T_2 = 400\left(\frac{30}{70}\right)^{0.333} = 400 \times 0.754 = 302°\text{R,}$$

and

$$W = 0.1305\left(\frac{1545}{4}\right)\left(\frac{302 - 400}{0.5}\right) = -9900 \text{ ft-lbf.}$$

EXAMPLE 2.4:   Calculate the work done on 2 lbm of air when they expand reversibly and isothermally at 60°F from a volume of 30 ft³ to a volume of 90 ft³.

Solution: $W = -\displaystyle\int_{V_1}^{V_2} p\, dV$

and, considering air as a perfect gas,

$$p = \frac{mRT}{V}.$$

Then,

$$W = -mRT\int_{V_1}^{V_2}\frac{dV}{V} = mRT\ln\frac{V_1}{V_2}$$

$$= 2 \times 53.34 \times 520 \ln\frac{30}{90} = 61,000 \text{ ft-lbf.}$$

The work done in the preceding example may be calculated in terms of pressures instead of volumes since, for an isothermal process,

$$p_1 V_1 = p_2 V_2 = mRT = \text{constant}, \quad \text{or} \quad \frac{V_2}{V_1} = \frac{p_1}{p_2},$$

and

$$W = -mRT \ln \frac{V_2}{V_1} = -mRT \ln \frac{p_1}{p_2}.$$

2-9
Flow Energy
Flow energy is associated with flow phenomena and represents the work necessary to advance a fluid against the existing pressure. Consider an element of a fluid in a duct of mass dm and volume dV. As shown in Fig. 2.7(a), the mass dm is at the threshold of a system, and at this point the pressure is p. It is required to calculate the amount of energy exerted by matter behind this element of fluid in pushing it into the system. Let an imaginary piston be placed behind dm, as shown in Fig. 2.7(b), and calculate the amount of work done by the piston in moving dm past line a-a.

$$\text{Flow energy per unit mass} = \frac{(pA)\,dx}{dm} = \frac{pA\,(dV/A)}{dm} = p\,\frac{dV}{dm} = pv.$$

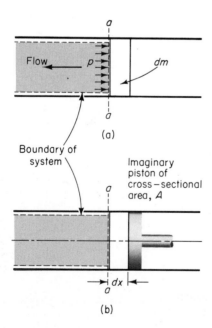

(a)

(b)

Fig. 2.7. *Flow energy* $= pv$.

Thus the flow energy per unit mass is simply the product of the absolute pressure and the specific volume of the fluid. It is sometimes called *flow work* since it represents the amount of work that must be done on a system to introduce a unit mass of material into it. When mass leaves the boundary of a system, flow energy must be expended on the environment.

2-10
Expressions of
Work for Some
Thermo-
dynamic
Systems

Most engineering thermodynamics involves systems whose equilibrium states are described by the coordinates p, V, and T. For such systems, the work during a quasi-static process is equal to $-\int p\, dV$. In determining work for other types of systems, an analogy may be made between such systems and the p-V-T system. Some examples are now cited:

(a) *Electrical work:* Energy transfer due to an electric potential is called *electrical work*. The potential difference between two points is the work that must be done by an electric field in moving a unit charge against this potential. If a quantity of electricity or a charge dC of a condenser is flowing across an electric potential $\mathscr{E}$, then the electrical work done on the condenser (system) is given by

$$dW_e = \mathscr{E}\, dC.$$

The current is the time rate of change of the electrical charge, or

$$i = \frac{dC}{d\tau}.$$

Then,

$$W_e = \int_{\tau_1}^{\tau_2} \mathscr{E} i\, d\tau$$

and power

$$P = \frac{dW_e}{d\tau} = \mathscr{E} i,$$

where W_e = electrical work done on the system (joules)
   C = quantity of electricity flowing (coulombs)
   $\mathscr{E}$ = electrical potential (volts)
   i = rate of flow of electricity or current (amperes)
   τ = time (seconds).

The usual units of electrical work are joules.

1 joule = 1 volt $\times$ 1 coulomb   (1 coulomb = 1 ampere-sec),

also

$$1 \text{ joule} = 0.7376 \text{ ft-lbf} = 1 \text{ watt-sec.}$$

The watt is the unit of electric power defined as the energy transferred at the rate of 1 joule per second or the power developed by a current of 1 ampere flowing through a potential of 1 volt.

EXAMPLE 2.5: A current of 0.3 amp is flowing through an electric resistance. If the voltage across the resistance is 110 volts, find the power consumption.

Solution: $P = \mathscr{E}i = 110 \times 0.3 = 33$ watts.

(b) *Work done in stretching a wire:* The work done in stretching a wire from a length L to $L + dL$ under a force F is

$$\dbar W = F \, dL.$$

The integral is therefore:

$$W_{1\text{-}2} = \int_{L}^{L+\Delta L} F \, dL.$$

The work in this case is positive since work must be done on the system (the wire) in order to increase the length of the wire.

(c) *Work done in changing the area of a surface film:* The work done on a homogeneous liquid film in changing its surface area by an infinitesimal amount dA is

$$\dbar W = \sigma \, dA$$

and

$$W_{1\text{-}2} = \int_{A_1}^{A_2} \sigma \, dA,$$

where σ is the interfacial tension per unit length.

(d) *Magnetization of a paramagnetic solid:* The work done per unit volume on a magnetic material through which the magnetic and magnetization fields are uniform is

$$\dbar W = H \, dI$$

and

$$W_{1\text{-}2} = \int_{I_1}^{I_2} H \, dI,$$

where H is the field strength and I is the component of the magnetization field in the direction of the field. Work must be done by the system to increase the magnetization (positive dI).

(e) *Polarization of a dielectric:* The work done per unit volume on a dielectric material through which the electric and polarization fields are uniform is

$$dW = E\, dP$$

and

$$W_{1\text{-}2} = \int_{P_1}^{P_2} E\, dP,$$

where E is the electric intensity within the dielectric, and P is the component of the polarization field in the direction of the electric field.

The foregoing equations for work indicate that work can be expressed as a function of an intensive property and an extensive property. If X is an intensive property and dx is a differential of an extensive property, then the general expression for work can be written as

$$dW = X\, dx. \tag{2.6}$$

If the intensive property is plotted against the extensive property, the area underneath the curve is a measure of work.

**2-11
Work Done in
Two Irrevers-
ible Processes**
It was previously mentioned that work is equal to $-\int p\, dV$ only if the process is quasi-static. Two examples will be considered in which the processes are non-quasi-static. The first is the free expansion process.

Consider an insulated vessel divided by a diaphragm into two compartments, as shown in Fig. 2.8. One compartment contains gas in an equilibrium state while the other compartment is evacuated. If the diaphragm is removed, the gas will expand freely into the evacuated compartment. No work or heat interaction takes place between the system and its environment. This process is called *free expansion.* According to the conditions of reversibility, the initial state of the system and environment cannot be restored unless some energy is supplied from an external source. Therefore, the free expansion process is irreversible. During the expansion process, one portion of the system is doing work on the other, but this is an internal effect and, for the system defined in Fig. 2.8, no work is done at the boundaries.

The second irreversible process involves a system in which a paddle wheel stirs a fixed mass of fluid, as shown in Fig. 2.9. If there is no heat

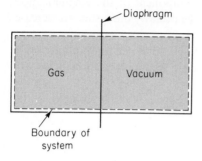

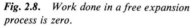

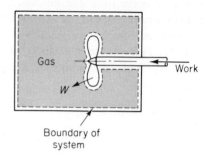

Fig. 2.8. *Work done in a free expansion process is zero.*

Fig. 2.9. *Work done on a system at constant volume.*

interaction, the work done increases the energy of the system. The turbulence in the fluid due to the stirring action is the cause of the irreversibility of the process, and hence the amount of work done is not equal to $-\int p\, dV$. Note that work is done in this case while the system is maintained at a constant volume. This is in contrast to the free expansion process in which no work is done, but there is a change in the volume of the system. During both processes the pressure and specific volume are not uniform throughout the system and therefore the state of the system cannot be adequately described. For this reason, and because of irreversibility, work interaction cannot be described by $-\int p\, dV$.

**2-12
Potential
Energy**

The energy which a system possesses by virtue of its position in a force field is called *potential energy*. For example, gravitational potential energy is associated with the gravitational force field. The amount of work done on a system of mass m when it is lifted with negligible acceleration through a distance dz in a gravitational field is equal to the product of its weight, mg/g_c, and the height dz. Since the force required to lift the system is equal and opposite to its weight, then

$$dW = \frac{m}{g_c} g\, dz.$$

The increase in potential energy is equal to work done on a system (in the absence of friction) in changing its position. Therefore, the change in potential energy of a system that has been moved through a uniform gravitational field is

$$\Delta \text{ (Pot E)} = \int_{z_1}^{z_2} F_z\, dz = \int_{z_1}^{z_2} \frac{m}{g_c} g\, dz$$

$$= \frac{mg}{g_c}(z_2 - z_1). \tag{2.7}$$

Similar expressions can be obtained for the potential energy in any conservative force field, such as magnetic or electric fields. Note that the potential energy is an extensive scalar property and depends on the initial and final states of the system. It is not possible to ascribe an absolute value to potential energy. Only changes in potential energies are indicated.

2-13   The energy a system possesses owing to its motion is *kinetic energy*. According to Newton's **Kinetic Energy** second law of motion, the force F, acting on a particle, is equal to the product of its mass m and its acceleration a, or

$$F = \frac{m}{g_c} a.$$

Acceleration along the x direction can be expressed as

$$a = \frac{dV}{d\tau} = \frac{dV}{dx}\frac{dx}{d\tau} = V\frac{dV}{dx}.$$

Therefore,

$$F_x = \frac{m}{g_c} V\frac{dV}{dx}.$$

The infinitesimal amount of work done on the particle in moving it a distance dx is

$$dW = F_x\, dx.$$

This work is equal to the change in kinetic energy of the system (in the absence of friction). Therefore,

$$\Delta(KE) = \int_{x_1}^{x_2} F_x\, dx = \frac{m}{g_c} \int_{V_1}^{V_2} V\, dV$$
$$= \frac{1}{g_c} \frac{m(V_2^2 - V_1^2)}{2}. \tag{2.8}$$

When rotational motion about a fixed axis occurs, the change in the kinetic energy of a rigid body is given by

$$\Delta(KE) = \frac{1}{g_c} \frac{mr^2(\omega_2^2 - \omega_1^2)}{2}, \tag{2.9}$$

where r is the radius of gyration and ω is the angular velocity of the system.

Kinetic energy, like potential energy, is a scalar extensive property of a system.

The combined potential and kinetic energies of a system constitute the *mechanical energy* of the system. Any work done on a system appears as an increase in the mechanical energy of the system if no friction occurs and if only mechanical energy is involved. If the work is positive, the total mechanical energy of the system increases. Similarly, a decrease in the mechanical energy of a system occurs when work is done by the system. Since the change in mechanical energy of a system is entirely defined by its end states,* any work done is also a function of the end states. Two cases arise in which the mechanical energy of a system remains constant: The first occurs when the system has identical initial and final states. The second case is that of an isolated system in which no energy crosses its boundary. In both cases no work is done. Consequently, if there is an increase in kinetic energy, there is an equal decrease in potential energy. This leads to the concept of conservation of energy, which was first applied to freely falling bodies. As an example, consider a pendulum as an isolated system. Referring to Fig. 2.10, the vertical distance z represents the height of the center of mass of the pendulum at position M above its middle position B. The total mechanical energy of the system is given by

$$\frac{mg}{g_c}z + \frac{1}{2}\frac{m}{g_c}V^2 = \text{constant,}$$

where m is the mass of the pendulum and V is its velocity at position M. The mechanical energy remains constant as the pendulum swings between the extreme positions A and C. At points A and C, the potential energy is maximum and the kinetic energy is zero. As the pendulum moves from point

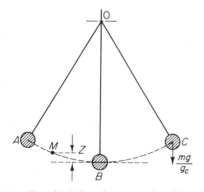

Fig. 2.10. *Conservation of mechanical energy.*

*Provided that the system is subjected to conservative forces only.

A to point *B*, potential energy is transformed into kinetic energy; as the pendulum moves from point *B* to point *C*, kinetic energy is transferred back to potential energy.

2-14

Internal Energy

The internal energy, *U*, of a substance is energy associated with the configuration and motion of its molecules, atoms, and subatomic particles relative to its center of mass. Internal energy *U* is a property consisting of the combined molecular kinetic energy and molecular potential energy, and is determined by intensive properties, such as pressure and temperature. It is part of the total internal energy *E*, which comprises all forms of internal energy, such as kinetic energy, potential energy, etc.:

$$E = (U + \cdots, \text{etc.}) + \text{KE} + \text{Pot E.} \tag{2.10}$$

The internal energy per unit mass (specific energy) at a point is defined by the equation:

$$e = \lim_{\Delta m \to 0} \frac{\Delta E}{\Delta m}, \tag{2.11}$$

where Δm is an elementary mass surrounding the point. Note that the ratio $\Delta E / \Delta m$ is the average energy per unit mass. The total energy *E* in terms of the specific energy *e* is

$$E = \int e \, dm. \tag{2.12}$$

A more detailed discussion of internal energy will be given in Chapter 3.

2-15

Heat

In the eighteenth century the accepted theory of the nature of heat was the caloric theory. It assumed that heat was a fluid-like substance without mass that was evolved from a body owing to the propulsion of its caloric particles. It was further assumed that the amount of caloric particles in a system is a property of the system and their number increases as the temperature is raised. The caloric theory was replaced in the latter part of the eighteenth century by the dynamic theory of heat, now generally accepted, which considers heat as a mode of energy transfer.

In previous sections it was shown that adiabatic work interaction between the environment and a closed system changes the energy of the system. The same energy change may also be obtained by heat interaction.

Since heat and work can produce the same energy changes, heat and work are quantitatively equivalent.

Let two closed systems at different temperatures be brought into contact with each other so that they have a common boundary. Energy in the form of heat is transferred between the two systems owing to the temperature difference, the high-temperature system losing a certain amount of energy and the low-temperature system gaining that same amount. This process continues until thermal equilibrium is attained. Note that heat is not observed; instead heat transfer is inferred through temperature changes or through other similar effects. The heat transfer may be regarded as energy interaction between two closed systems in which there is no work interaction. Hence heat may be defined as *the net energy* (*independent of mass transfer*) *in transit between a system and its environment due to temperature difference.* Regardless of the mechanism of heat transfer, a temperature difference is necessary for effecting heat interaction. Heat transferred to a system is considered positive, and heat transferred from a system is negative.

Heat may be transferred from one system to another by one or more of the following mechanisms: *conduction* and *radiation.* Heat is transferred by conduction when two systems at different temperatures are brought into direct or close contact with each other. In conduction heat flow, energy is transmitted by direct molecular collisions without appreciable macroscopic displacement of the molecules. Heat is transferred by thermal radiation as a result of the propagation of energy waves. These waves, assuming nonrelativistic conditions and no diffraction, travel in straight lines in homogeneous media or vacuum until they are reflected or absorbed. The velocity of propagation of these waves in vacuum is equal to the velocity of light. The mechanism of heat transfer by radiation is basically the same as that of light radiation.

Convection is a process which involves both mass transport and heat transfer in which the heat is transferred by both conduction and radiation. Convection is generally classified as *natural* or *forced*, depending on the forces acting on the fluid. When heat is transferred from a solid to a fluid, a density field is created in the fluid, and this nonuniform density field results in fluid motion. This process is called *natural* convection or *free* convection. If the fluid is circulated by means of a mechanical device, such as a pump, the process is called *forced* convection.

Heat is a path function and therefore, like work, is an inexact differential. Heat is generally associated with a process and may be identified at the boundaries of a system when there is a change of state, but it is not really possessed by the system. When energy enters a closed system, a change in properties occurs, and it then becomes impossible to identify the source energy as work or heat. Only by investigating phenomena occurring at the boundaries of a system during the interaction can energy due to heat be distinguished from energy due to work.

An *adiabatic* process is defined as one which involves no heat inter-action. Adiabatic conditions exist if the system is surrounded by an enclosure impermeable to heat or if the system is subjected to very rapid compression or expansion. In the latter case the rate of heat interaction is relatively slow, and therefore only a negligible amount of heat is transferred during the short duration of compression or expansion.

2-16
Units of Heat
In the English system, the *British thermal unit* (Btu) is the unit of heat. The quantity of heat required to raise the temperature of a 1 lbm of water from 59.5°F to 60.5°F under atmospheric pressure is called the 60°F Btu. Similarly, in the CGS system, the quantity of heat required to increase the temperature of 1 gram of water from 14.5°C to 15.5°C under atmospheric pressure is called the 15°C *calorie*. In measuring quantities of heat, it is impractical to choose that quantity of water which will confine the temperature rise between 59.5°F and 60.5°F. It is therefore common to use water at the ambient temperature and to measure the temperature change of a certain mass of water in order to determine the heat involved. Experience indicates that the heat transferred is equal numerically to the product of the mass of water and the temperature change. This is a fairly good approximation; however, the quantity of heat necessary to raise the temperature of 1 lbm of water 1°F is actually not constant but instead depends upon temperature. The correction is less than 0.1 per cent in the range between 60 to 70°F, and about 1 per cent at 32°F.

After the first law of thermodynamics was established, it was realized that heat and work, even though quantitatively equivalent, were expressed in different units. In order to make it possible to express heat in units of work, electrical measurements were made which established a unit of heat. In 1929 the International Steam Table Conference adopted the *International Calorie* (IT) as

$$1 \text{ IT calorie} = 4.1868 \text{ kg-m}^2/\text{sec}^2 = 4.1868 \text{ joules.}$$

The British thermal unit of heat then could be expressed in terms of the IT calorie:

$$1 \text{ Btu} = 251.996 \text{ IT calories.}$$

Note also that 1 Btu/lbm°F = 1 cal/gm°C.

2-17
Specific Heat*
When heat is transferred between a closed system and its environment, the energy interaction causes a change in the internal energy of the system. Two methods are used to calculate the change of internal energy. In one method, the temperature of

---

*The names *specific heat* and *heat capacity* arose from the caloric theory which considered heat as a fluid-like substance. These names are unfortunate as they erroneously imply that heat can be stored in a system.

the system changes, but the physical and chemical states are unaffected by the energy transfer. In the second method, the physical or chemical states change, but the temperature remains constant. This section deals with the first case.

The *specific heat* of a substance is equal to the amount of heat required to raise the temperature of a unit mass of the substance 1 degree. The *average* specific heat is equal to the amount of heat transferred per unit mass divided by the accompanying increase of its temperature or

$$c_{\text{avg}} = \frac{Q}{m\,\Delta T} = \frac{q}{\Delta T}, \tag{2.13}$$

where c_{avg} = average specific heat (Btu/lbm°F)
Q = heat interaction (Btu)
ΔT = temperature difference (°F or °R)
m = mass (lbm)
q = heat per unit mass (Btu/lbm).

When q and ΔT are very small, then the ratio $q/\Delta T$ tends to a limit which indicates the instantaneous specific heat at a temperature T. Thus,

$$c = \lim_{\Delta T \to 0} \frac{q}{\Delta T} = \frac{dq}{dT}. \tag{2.14}$$

To obtain a mean value of specific heat over a wide temperature range, the specific heat is integrated, by direct, numerical, or graphical methods, according to the equation:

$$c_{\text{avg}} = \frac{\int_{T_1}^{T_2} c\,dT}{\int_{T_1}^{T_2} dT} = \frac{\int_{T_1}^{T_2} c\,dT}{T_2 - T_1}. \tag{2.15}$$

In evaluating this integral graphically, values of specific heat c are first plotted against temperature, as shown in Fig. 2.11. The average value of specific heat divides the figure into two portions, shown as hatched areas, that are equal.

The specific heat of solids and liquids depends upon temperature, but, unlike gases, is not sensitive to the type of process involved during heat interaction. The law of Dulong and Petit indicates that the atomic specific heat (that is, heat transferred per unit mass per degree) of an element in the solid state at room temperature is equal to approximately 6.4 cal/gm-atom°C. If a substance undergoes a change of phase when heated, its specific heat appears to be infinitely large, since heating produces no change in temper-

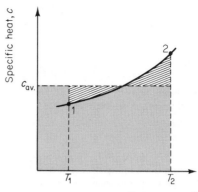

Fig. 2.11. *Average specific heat.*

ature. The specific heat of a gas depends on whether the gas is at constant pressure or at constant volume when the heat interaction takes place:

$$c_p = \left(\frac{dq}{dT}\right)_p, \tag{2.16}$$

$$c_v = \left(\frac{dq}{dT}\right)_v, \tag{2.17}$$

where c_p is the constant pressure specific heat and c_v is the constant volume specific heat. Both c_p and c_v are properties of the substance. Molal specific heat is given by

$$\bar{c}_p = \frac{mc_p}{n}, \tag{2.18}$$

$$\bar{c}_v = \frac{mc_v}{n}, \tag{2.19}$$

where $\bar{c}_p$ and $\bar{c}_v$ are in Btu/lb-mole, m is mass in lbm, and n is number of moles.

The specific heat of a gas changes with temperature in a complex manner, and various equations have been developed which indicate values over wide temperature ranges (see Table 3 in the Appendix).

The units of specific heat, c, are Btu/lbm°F in the English system and cal/gm°C in the CGS system. The numerical value of the specific heat is the same when expressed in either system.

2-18
Latent Heat
The amount of heat necessary to change the physical structure of a unit mass of a substance, without changing the temperature and without doing work other than flow energy pv, is called the *latent heat*. Latent heat that is associated with the

melting and solidification of a solid is called *heat of fusion*; that related to the vaporization and condensation of a liquid is called *heat of vaporization*, and that related to the sublimation of a solid is called the *heat of sublimation*.

Latent heats are expressed in terms of particular temperature and pressure conditions. The latent heats of solids are essentially constant over wide ranges in temperature; the latent heats of gases vary markedly with pressure.

EXAMPLE 2.6: Find the amount of heat required for each change of phase during the heating of 2 lbm of ice initially at 20°F till it becomes superheated steam at 300°F. The pressure is atmospheric.

Assume c of ice $= 0.5$ Btu/lbm°F
c of water $= 1.0$ Btu/lbm°F
c_p of steam $= 0.441$ Btu/lbm°F
Latent heat of fusion of ice $= 143.3$ Btu/lbm
Latent heat of vaporization of water $= 970$ Btu/lbm

Solution:

Heating of ice:	$Q = 2 \times 0.5(32 - 20)$	$= 12.0$
Melting of ice:	$Q = 2 \times 143.3$	$= 286.6$
Heating of water:	$Q = 2 \times 1 \times (212 - 32)$	$= 360.0$
Vaporization of water:	$Q = 2 \times 970$	$= 1940.0$
Heating of steam:	$Q = 2 \times 0.441 \times (300 - 212) =$	77.6
	Total Q	$= 2676.2$ Btu

EXAMPLE 2.7: A 5-lbm system undergoes a process wherein its temperature changes from 50°F to 150°F. Determine the heat interaction if the specific heat of the system for the process in question is given by

$$c = \left(0.2 + \frac{15}{t + 126}\right) \text{ Btu/lbm°F}.$$

What is the average specific heat?

Solution:

$$Q = 5 \int_{t=50}^{t=150} c \, dt$$

$$= 5 \int_{t=50}^{t=150} \left(0.2 + \frac{15}{t + 126}\right) dt$$

$$= 5 \left[0.2t + 15 \ln (t + 126)\right]_{50}^{150}$$

$$= 5 \left[0.2(150 - 50) + 15 \ln \frac{276}{176}\right]$$

$$= 133.75 \text{ Btu.}$$

The average specific is

$$c_{\text{avg}} = \frac{Q}{m\,\Delta t} = \frac{133.75}{5 \times 100} = 0.268 \text{ Btu/lbm}^\circ\text{F}.$$

**2-19
Summary** The various forms of energy may be described in terms of the product of an intensive property (intensity factor) and the differential of an extensive property (capacity factor). Some examples of energy described in this manner are listed in Table 2.1.

TABLE 2.1 CLASSIFICATION OF ENERGY

Form of energy	Intensive property	Extensive property
Mechanical (linear) (ft-lbf)	Force (lbf)	Distance (ft)
Mechanical (rotational) (ft-lbf)	Torque (lbf-ft)	Angle (radians)
Expansion or compression (ft-lbf)	Pressure (lbf/ft^2)	Volume (ft^3)
Electrical (watt-sec or joules)	Electrical potential difference (volts)	Charge (coulombs or amp-sec)
Electric polarization per unit volume (gm/cm-sec^2)	Electric field strength (gauss or gm$^{1/2}$/cm$^{1/2}$-sec)	Polarization (gm$^{1/2}$/cm$^{1/2}$-sec)
Flow (ft-lbf)	Pressure (lbf/ft^2)	Volume (ft^3)
Magnetic per unit volume (gm/cm-sec^2)	Field strength (gm$^{1/2}$/cm$^{1/2}$-sec)	Magnetization (gm$^{1/2}$/cm$^{1/2}$- sec)
Heat (Btu)	Temperature ($^\circ$R)	Entropy (Btu/$^\circ$R)*
Potential (ft-lbf)	Elevation $\times$ acceleration (ft/sec)^2	Mass (lbm)
Kinetic (ft-lbf)	Square of velocity (ft/sec)^2	1/2 mass (lbm)
Surface (ft-lbf)	Surface tension (lbf/ft)	Area (ft^2)

*The term *entropy* is defined in Chapter 4.

**2-20
Law of
Conservation
of Mass for a
Control Volume** In order to interpret the phenomena which occur in flow systems, the principles of conservation of mass, momentum, and moment of momentum† are applied. A general form of the law of conservation of mass for a control volume will be developed in this section.

Consider a control volume fixed in space in a fluid flow field. At an

†The procedure used in the derivation of the principles of conservation of mass and momentum follows closely that outlined in reference 2.4.

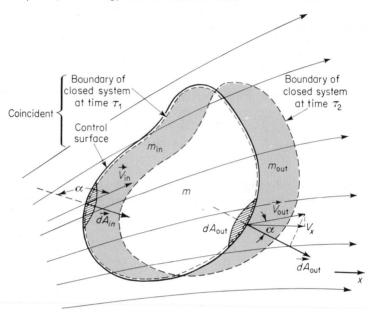

Fig. 2.12. *Notation for conservation of mass and momentum principles.*

initial time τ_1, let a closed system coincide with the control volume and, therefore, the mass in the closed system coincides with that of the control volume. Figure 2.12 shows the positions of the control volume and the closed system at time τ_1 and also at subsequent time τ_2 after an infinitesimally small time interval. In the interval $(\tau_2 - \tau_1)$, some matter from the closed system leaves the control volume while new matter enters the control volume. The solid boundary represents the control surface at any time, and the dotted boundaries represent the closed system at times τ_1 and τ_2. Let primes denote values associated with the control volume. Since the mass of the closed system is equal to the mass within the control surface at time τ_1, then

$$m_{\tau_1} = m'_{\tau_1}.$$

At time τ_2, the mass of the closed system is equal to the mass within the control surface plus the net mass leaving the control volume, or,

$$m_{\tau_2} = m'_{\tau_2} + m_{\text{out}} - m_{\text{in}}.$$

Subtracting the two preceding equations gives

$$m_{\tau_2} - m_{\tau_1} = m'_{\tau_2} - m'_{\tau_1} + m_{\text{out}} - m_{\text{in}}. \tag{2.20}$$

But the mass within the closed system is conserved ($m_{\tau_2} = m_{\tau_1}$), therefore,

$$m'_{\tau_2} - m'_{\tau_1} = m_{in} - m_{out}.$$

When $d\tau$ approaches 0, the foregoing equation becomes

$$dm' = \int_{cs} dm_{in} - \int_{cs} dm_{out}, \tag{2.21}$$

where $\int_{cs}$ designates the integration over the surface area of the control volume. Equation (2.21) may then be written as a rate equation:

$$\frac{dm'}{d\tau} = \int_{cs} \frac{dm_{in}}{d\tau} - \int_{cs} \frac{dm_{out}}{d\tau},$$

which states that the rate of change of mass within the control volume is equal to the net rate of mass entering the control surface. Expressing the mass flow rate in terms of density, velocity and area, the preceding equation becomes

$$\int_{cv} \frac{dm'}{d\tau} = \int_{cs} \rho_{in} V_{in} \cos \alpha_{in} \, dA_{in} - \int_{cs} \rho_{out} V_{out} \cos \alpha_{out} \, dA_{out}, \tag{2.22}$$

where α is the angle between the velocity vector $\vec{V}$ and the area vector $d\vec{A}$ as shown in Fig. 2.12. In general,

$$\int_{cv} d\dot{m}' = \int_{across\ cs} d\dot{m}. \tag{2.23}$$

Note that the velocities in Eq. (2.22) are velocities relative to the control surface.

Under steady-state conditions there is no change of mass within the control surface so that the mass rates entering and leaving the control volume are equal. Hence

$$\int_{cs} \rho_{in} V_{in} \cos \alpha_{in} \, dA_{in} = \int_{cs} \rho_{out} V_{out} \cos \alpha_{out} \, dA_{out}. \tag{2.24}$$

When one-dimensional flow occurs (fluid properties are uniform at any cross section), integration of the preceding equation gives the mass rate of flow $\dot{m}$ as

$$\dot{m} = \rho \, AV = \text{constant}, \tag{2.25}$$

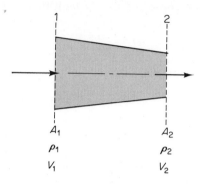

Fig. 2.13. *Flow in one dimension.*

where A is the area of flow perpendicular to the velocity V. Taking the logarithm and differentiating Eq. (2.25) leads, under steady-state conditions, to the following:

$$d(\ln \rho) + d(\ln A) + d(\ln V) = 0,$$

or

$$\frac{d\rho}{\rho} + \frac{dA}{A} + \frac{dV}{V} = 0. \tag{2.26}$$

Under steady-state conditions, the mass rate of flow across any two sections of areas A_1 and A_2, as shown in Fig. 2.13, is

$$\dot{m} = \rho_1 A_1 V_1 = \rho_2 A_2 V_2,$$

or

$$\frac{A_1 V_1}{v_1} = \frac{A_2 V_2}{v_2},$$

where v_1 and v_2 are the specific volumes at sections 1 and 2. It must be pointed out that the preceding equation is applicable at sections 1 and 2 as long as the flow is uniform at these two sections, even though the flow may not be uniform between the two sections.

2-21 Momentum Principle

If no net external force acts on a system, the linear momentum along three mutually perpendicular directions is conserved both in magnitude and direction. A familiar example from mechanics is the collision of two spheres. Conservation of momentum occurs whether the collision is elastic or not, such that the sums of the momenta of the two spheres before and after collision are equal in magnitude and direction.

When a net external force acts on a system, the linear momentum is no longer conserved. Under this condition the phenomenon is described by a principle that is more general than the momentum principle, namely, Newton's second law.

According to Newton's second law of motion, the sum of the forces acting in a certain direction on a particle at rest or in motion is equal to the time rate of change of its momentum in the same direction. The motion of the particle must be described relative to an inertial coordinate system, that is, a coordinate system moving at constant velocity in one direction. Considering the x direction, for example, Newton's law for a particle yields

$$\sum F_x = \frac{1}{g_c} \frac{d}{d\tau} (mV_x), \tag{2.27}$$

where $\sum F_x$ is the net force acting on the particle in the x direction. The net force includes body forces (such as gravitational, magnetic, and electrical forces which act on the mass of the particle) and surface forces (such as pressure, shear, and surface tension forces which act on the surface of the particle).

In a system in which there are many particles each of a different acceleration, internal forces between particles balance according to Newton's third law. Hence Newton's second law can be applied to a closed system containing numerous particles by considering the momentum of the system to be the vectorial sum of momenta of the particles in the system.

Referring to Fig. 2.12, the rate of change of the x momentum of a closed system is equal to the rate of change of the x momentum of the control volume plus the net rate of change of momentum leaving the control volume in the same direction, or

$$\frac{\Delta(mV_x)}{\Delta\tau} = \frac{(mV_x)'_{\tau_2} + (mV_x)_{\text{out}} - (mV_x)'_{\tau_1} - (mV_x)_{\text{in}}}{\Delta\tau}$$

$$= \frac{\Delta(mV_x)'}{\Delta\tau} + \frac{(mV_x)_{\text{out}} - (mV_x)_{\text{in}}}{\Delta\tau}, \tag{2.28}$$

where $(mV_x)_{\text{in}}$ and $(mV_x)_{\text{out}}$ are the momenta of the fluid entering and leaving the control volume in time $\Delta\tau$.

The first term on the right-hand side of Eq. (2.28) represents the time rate of change of the x momentum of the fluid within the control volume. The second term represents the net x momentum flux leaving the control volume. When very small time intervals are considered, Newton's second law can be written as

$$\sum F_x = \frac{1}{g_c} \frac{d}{d\tau} (mV_x) = \frac{1}{g_c} \frac{d}{d\tau} (mV_x)' + \frac{1}{g_c} \int_{\text{out}} V_x \, d\dot{m} - \frac{1}{g_c} \int_{\text{in}} V_x \, d\dot{m}$$

or

$$\Sigma F_x + \frac{1}{g_c} \int_{\text{net in}} V_x \, d\dot{m} = \frac{1}{g_c} \frac{d}{d\tau} (mV_x)', \tag{2.29}$$

where $\dot{m}$ is the mass rate of flow. Equation (2.29) is the momentum equation applied to a control volume in the x direction. It states that the sum of the external forces acting on the fluid within a control volume in a certain direction plus the net inflow of momentum flux across the control surface in that direction is equal to the time rate of change of momentum within the control volume in the same direction. By expressing mass flow in terms of density, velocity, and area, Eq. (2.29) becomes:

$$\Sigma F_x + \frac{1}{g_c} \int_{\text{net in}} \rho V \cos \alpha \, V_x \, dA = \frac{1}{g_c} \frac{d}{d\tau} (mV_x)', \tag{2.30}$$

where α is the angle between the velocity vector $\vec{V}$ and the area vector $\vec{dA}$. Equations similar to Eq. (2.30) can be derived for the y and z directions.

Under steady-state conditions, the rate of change of momentum within the control surface is zero and Eq. (2.30) reduces to

$$\Sigma F_x + \frac{1}{g_c} \int_{\text{net in}} \rho V \cos \alpha \, V_x \, dA = 0 \tag{2.31}$$

or, in general,

$$\Sigma \vec{F} + \frac{1}{g_c} \int_{\text{net entering cs}} \vec{V} \, d\dot{m} = 0. \tag{2.32}$$

A positive value of the second term of Eq. (2.32) means an increase of momentum of the control volume.

Even if there are frictional forces or nonequilibrium regions within the control surface, the momentum equation still applies. The momentum principle has wide applications in the field of propulsion and is used, in particular, in evaluating the propulsive forces imposed on a system.

In solving momentum problems, the following procedure is recommended: (a) select a control volume and define a positive direction; (b) identify the body forces and the surface forces; (c) investigate the control volume to determine whether the flow is steady, one-dimensional, incompressible, etc.; (d) investigate the control surface to determine the momentum flux terms. Note that all velocities must be expressed in the same coordinate system as the control surface.

EXAMPLE 2.8:   What is the propulsive force on a jet engine propelling an airplane at a constant speed of 450 ft/sec.? The combustion products are discharged at 3000 ft/sec relative to the airplane and the engine exhausts 25 lbm/sec. (Neglect the mass and momentum of the fuel and assume horizontal flight.)

Solution: Considering the jet engine as a control volume, the air enters the engine with a velocity of 450 ft/sec. Assuming the inlet and exit pressures are atmospheric, the force F opposite to the direction of motion of the airplane is given by the momentum equation as

$$F = \frac{25}{32.174}(3000 - 450) = 1980 \text{ lbf thrust.}$$

EXAMPLE 2.9: Water flows in a 2-in. inside diameter pipe at 100°F. The water flows through a 90° bend in the pipe and then discharges through a convergent nozzle to the atmosphere (14.7 psia) as shown in Fig. 2.14. At the entrance to the bend the fluid pressure is 100 psia and the flow velocity is 1800 ft/min. At the nozzle discharge the velocity is 7200 ft/min. Calculate the magnitude and direction of the net force that the bend exerts on the remaining pipe. Neglect the weight of the bend.

Solution: Let R_x and R_y be the forces acting on the system from the remaining pipe. Assume steady state and one-dimensional analysis.

$$\dot{m} = \rho A V$$

$$= 62.4 \frac{\pi}{4}\left(\frac{2}{12}\right)^2 \times \frac{1800}{60} = 40.8 \text{ lbm/sec.}$$

Assuming that atmospheric pressure surrounds the pipe, gauge pressures are considered in the momentum equation. For the x direction:

$$F_x = (p_1 A_1)_x + R_x = \frac{\dot{m}}{g_c}(V_2 - V_1)_x;$$

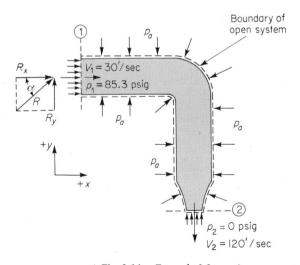

Fig. 2.14. Example 2.9.

therefore,

$$R_x = \frac{40.8}{32.174}\left(0 - \frac{1800}{60}\right) - 85.3\,\frac{\pi}{4}\,(2^2)$$

$$= -306.1 \text{ lbf.}$$

Noting that $p_2 = 0$ psig, the momentum equation for the y direction is

$$F_y = (p_2 A_2)_y + R_y = \frac{\dot{m}}{g_c}(V_2 - V_1)_y;$$

therefore,

$$R_y = \frac{40.8}{32.174}\left(-\frac{7200}{60} - 0\right) - 0 = -152.4 \text{ lbf.}$$

The negative signs mean that R_x and R_y are in opposite directions from those shown in the figure. The total reaction $R = \sqrt{R_x^2 + R_y^2} = 341$ lbf at an angle $\alpha = \tan^{-1} 152.4/306.1 = 26.5°$ with the horizontal.

EXAMPLE 2.10: A 2-in. diameter water jet of constant area has a velocity of 80 ft/sec. It strikes a blade as shown in Fig. 2.15. If the deflection angle of the jet is 150°, calculate the x and y components of the force exerted by the jet on the blade for the following cases:

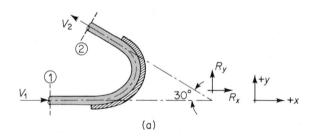

(a)

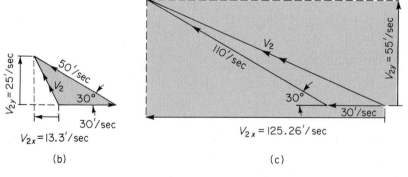

(b)

(c)

Fig. 2.15. Example 2.10.

(a) The blade is stationary.

(b) The blade is moving in the same direction as the entering jet at 30 ft/sec.

(c) The blade is moving in the opposite direction from the entering jet at 30 ft/sec.

Assume there is no friction and neglect gravitational effects.

Solution: (a) $\dot{m} = \rho A V = 62.4 \, \frac{\pi}{4} \left(\frac{2}{12}\right)^2 \times 80 = 109 \, \text{lbm/sec}.$

Applying the momentum principle in the x and y directions gives

$$R_x = \frac{\dot{m}}{g_c} (V_{2x} - V_{1x})$$

$$= \frac{\dot{m}}{g_c} (-V_2 \cos 30 - V_1)$$

$$= \frac{109}{32.174} (-80 \cos 30 - 80) = -504 \, \text{lbf}$$

and

$$R_y = \frac{\dot{m}}{g_c} (V_{2y} - V_{1y})$$

$$= \frac{\dot{m}}{g_c} (V_2 \sin 30 - 0)$$

$$= \frac{109}{32.174} \times 40 = 135.2 \, \text{lbf}.$$

(b) When the blade moves to the right, less mass strikes the blade per unit time and therefore less mass has its momentum changed. The relative velocity at section $1 = 80 - 30 = 50$ ft/sec. The mass striking the blade per unit time is

$$\dot{m} = \left(\frac{62.4}{32.174}\right) \frac{\pi}{4} \left(\frac{2}{12}\right)^2 \times 50 = 68 \, \text{lbm/sec}.$$

The absolute velocity of water at section 2 is the vectorial sum of the blade velocity and the relative velocity of the jet with respect to the blade. From Fig. 2.15,

$$V_{2x} = 13.3 \, \text{ft/sec to the left,} \qquad V_{2y} = 25 \, \text{ft/sec upwards}$$

$$R_x = \frac{\dot{m}}{g_c} (V_{2x} - V_{1x})$$

$$= \frac{68}{32.174} (-13.3 - 80) = -197 \, \text{lbf}$$

and

$$R_y = \frac{\dot{m}}{g_c} (V_{2y} - V_{1y})$$

$$= \frac{68}{32.174} (25 - 0) = 52.7 \, \text{lbf}.$$

(c) When the blade moves to the left, then, relative velocity at section 1 = 80 + 30 = 110 ft/sec and the mass striking the blade per unit time is

$$\dot{m} = 62.4 \, \frac{\pi}{4} \left(\frac{2}{12}\right)^2 \times 110 = 149.8 \text{ lbm/sec.}$$

From Fig. 2.15(c),

$$V_{2x} = 125.26 \text{ ft/sec to the left,} \quad V_{2y} = 55 \text{ ft/sec upwards.}$$

$$R_x = \frac{149.8}{32.174}(-125.26 - 80) = -954 \text{ lbf.}$$

$$R_y = \frac{149.8}{32.174}(55 - 0) = 256 \text{ lbf.}$$

This example can also be solved using relative velocities rather than absolute velocities.

In cases when a series of blades is involved, as in a turbine wheel, the impinging fluid strikes one or more blades as the turbine rotates, and in this case the rate of mass striking the blades is constant.

2-22
Principle of
Moment of
Momentum
The law of conservation of moment of momentum, which is also known as the law of conservation of angular momentum, states that the total angular momentum of a system is conserved if no net external torque acts on the system.

According to the principle of the moment of momentum, the sum of the moments of external forces acting on a system about an axis in inertial space is equal to the time rate of change of the moment of momentum. This relationship can be derived from Newton's second law of motion. Following the same procedure that was used in deriving the momentum principle, summation of moments about the z axis yields

$$\sum M_z + \int_{\text{net in}} \frac{\rho}{g_c} rV \cos \alpha \, V_t \, dA = \frac{1}{g_c} \int_{\text{cv}} \frac{d}{d\tau}(rV_t) \, dm, \qquad (2.33)$$

where r is the distance from the z axis to the particle, V_t is the velocity component normal to r projected onto the xy plane and α is the angle between the velocity and area vectors. A diagram showing this system appears in Fig. 2.16. The moment, or torque, acting on a control volume, together with the net inflow of the rate of moment of momentum, are equal to the rate of change of the moment of momentum of the control volume.

Under steady-state conditions, Eq. (2.33) becomes

$$\sum M_z + \int_{\text{net in}} \frac{\rho}{g_c} rV \cos \alpha \, V_t \, dA = 0, \qquad (2.34)$$

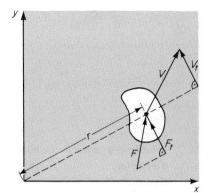

Fig. 2.16. *Principle of moment of momentum.*

which can be expressed in a more general way as

$$\sum \vec{M} + \frac{1}{g_c} \int_{\substack{\text{net entering cs}}} (\vec{V} \times \vec{r})d\dot{m} = 0. \tag{2.35}$$

EXAMPLE 2.11:   The water sprinkler shown in Fig. 2.17 is rotating at 25 rpm. Find the torque and power produced by the water issuing from the nozzles.

Solution: The mass flow rate $\dot{m}$ is given by

$$\dot{m} = \rho A_1 V_1 = 62.4 \frac{\pi}{4} \left(\frac{2}{12}\right)^2 \times 3 = 4.08 \text{ lbm/sec.}$$

$$V_{2 \text{ rel}} = \frac{\dot{m}/2}{\rho A_2} \text{ or } = \frac{A_1 V_1}{2 A_2}$$

$$= \frac{1}{2}\left(\frac{2}{0.5}\right)^2 \times 3 = 24 \text{ ft/sec.}$$

$$V_{\text{abs}} = V_{\text{rel}} + V_{\text{nozzle}} = 24 - \omega r$$

$$= 24 - \frac{2\pi \times 25}{60}\left(\frac{8}{12}\right) = 24 - 1.74 = 22.26 \text{ ft/sec.}$$

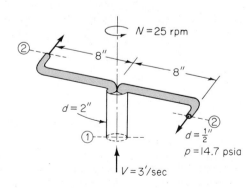

Fig. 2.17. *Example 2.11.*

Applying the moment of momentum equation yields

$$T = \frac{4.08}{32.174}\left(22.26 \times \frac{8}{12}\right) = 1.883 \text{ ft-lbf,}$$

and

$$P = T\omega = 1.883\left(\frac{2\pi \times 25}{60}\right) = 4.93 \text{ ft-lbf/sec.}$$

**2-23
Dynamic
Analysis and
Euler's
Equation**
Euler's equation is one of the basic equations in fluid dynamics and can be derived from Newton's second law of motion. The product of the mass and the acceleration of a fluid particle can be equated vectorially, with the external forces acting on the particle. Consider the frictionless steady flow of a fluid in a streamtube* of infinitesimal length. As shown in Fig. 2.18, the center streamline is inclined at an angle θ with the vertical, and ds is the distance along the center between two adjacent sections. The cross-sectional areas at the two sections are A and $A + dA$, while the properties at the two sections differ from each other by infinitesimal quantities.

The external forces acting on the fluid element are the pressure forces and the weight of the fluid element in the streamtube. The weight is equal to the volume multiplied by the specific weight of the fluid or

$$\gamma\left(A + \frac{dA}{2}\right) ds,$$

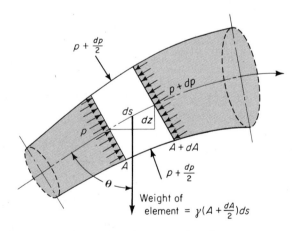

Fig. 2.18. *Flow in a streamtube.*

*A streamline is a line whose tangent at each instant and at any point gives the direction of the velocity of the fluid at that point. A streamtube is formed by a family of streamlines passing through each point of a closed curve. The mass flow across each section of the streamtube is constant in steady flow.

where $[A + (dA/2)]$ is the average cross-sectional area between the two sections. The component of weight in the s direction is

$$-\gamma\left(A + \frac{dA}{2}\right) ds \cos\theta = -\gamma\left(A + \frac{dA}{2}\right) ds\, \frac{dz}{ds} = -\gamma\left(A + \frac{dA}{2}\right) dz,$$

where $\cos\theta = dz/ds$.

Applying the momentum equation in the s direction gives

$$pA + \left(p + \frac{dp}{2}\right) dA - (p + dp)(A + dA) - \gamma\left(A + \frac{dA}{2}\right) dz = \frac{\rho A V}{g_c}\, dV.$$

The second term in the foregoing equation is the component of the force due to pressure that is exerted on the sides of the fluid element in the direction of motion. By expanding terms and by neglecting second-order differentials, this equation becomes

$$A\, dp + \gamma A\, dz + \frac{\rho A V}{g_c}\, dV = 0.$$

Substituting $\rho g/g_c$ for γ and dividing by $A\rho$ yields

$$\frac{dp}{\rho} + \frac{V\, dV}{g_c} + \frac{g}{g_c}\, dz = 0. \tag{2.37}$$

Equation (2.37) is Euler's equation for one-dimensional flow. Note that the fluid was assumed frictionless and that gravity was assumed to be the only field force. Euler's equation applies to both compressible and incompressible flows.

In treating one-dimensional incompressible flow, since density is constant, Euler's equation can be integrated directly to give

$$\frac{1}{\rho}(p_2 - p_1) + \frac{V_2^2 - V_1^2}{2g_c} + \frac{g}{g_c}(z_2 - z_1) = 0$$

or

$$\frac{p_1}{\rho} + \frac{V_1^2}{2g_c} + \frac{gz_1}{g_c} = \frac{p_2}{\rho} + \frac{V_2^2}{2g_c} + \frac{gz_2}{g_c}, \tag{2.38}$$

which can also be expressed as

$$\frac{p_1}{\gamma} + \frac{V_1^2}{2g} + z_1 = \frac{p_2}{\gamma} + \frac{V_2^2}{2g} + z_2 = H. \tag{2.39}$$

Each term now has the dimensions of length. In Eq. (2.39), which is *Bernoulli's equation*, H is called the *total head* and is equal to the sum of the *pressure head* p/γ, the *velocity head* $V^2/2g$, and the *potential head* z. According to Bernoulli's equation, the total head H, which represents the sum of the pressure, velocity, and potential heads, is a constant along a streamline if the flow is steady and the fluid is frictionless and incompressible.

EXAMPLE 2.12: Water flows through the reducer shown in Fig. 2.19. If the velocity at section 2 is 4 ft/sec, what is the pressure at that section?

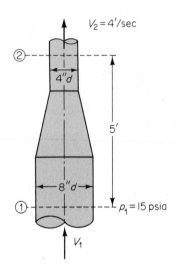

Fig. 2.19. *Example 2.12.*

Solution: The velocity at section 1 is

$$V_1 = \left(\frac{A_2}{A_1}\right)V_2 = \frac{16}{64} \times 4 = 1 \text{ ft/sec.}$$

Applying Bernoulli's equation between sections 1 and 2 gives

$$5 + \frac{p_2 \times 144}{62.4} + \frac{4^2}{2 \times 32.174} = 0 + \frac{15 \times 144}{62.4} + \frac{1^2}{2 \times 32.174},$$

from which $p_2 = 12.7$ psia.

REFERENCES

2.1 P. J. Kiefer, G. F. Kinney, and M. C. Stuart, *Principles of Engineering Thermodynamics.* New York: John Wiley & Sons, Inc., 1954, chap. 1, 2.

2.2 J. F. Lee and F. W. Sears, *Thermodynamics.* Reading, Mass.: Addison-Wesley Publishing Company, Inc., 1955, chap. 3.

2.3 D. A. Mooney, *Mechanical Engineering Thermodynamics.* Englewood Cliffs, N.J.: Prentice-Hall, Inc., 1958, chap. 2, 3.

2.4 A. S. Shapiro, *The Dynamics and Thermodynamics of Compressible Fluid Flow*, Vol. I. New York: Ronald Press Co., 1953, chap. 1.

2.5 S. L. Soo, *Thermodynamics of Engineering Science.* Englewood Cliffs, N.J.: Prentice-Hall, Inc., 1958, chap. 1.

2.6 R. T. Weidner, R. L. Sells, *Elementary Modern Physics.* New York: Allyn & Bacon, Inc., 1963, chap. 1.

2.7 M. W. Zemansky, *Heat and Thermodynamics.* New York: McGraw-Hill Book Company, Inc., 1951, chap. 4.

PROBLEMS

2.1 A spherical balloon has a diameter of 10 in. and contains air at a pressure of 20 psia. The diameter of the balloon increases to 12 in. because of heating, and during this process the pressure is proportional to the diameter. Calculate the work done on the gas assuming reversible work interaction.

2.2 If the initial state of a perfect gas is 14.7 psia and 5 ft³/lbm, calculate the reversible work interaction per lbm for the following processes:
(a) Constant pressure process if the final volume is 20 ft³/lbm.
(b) Isothermal process according to $pV = $ constant and the final volume 7 ft³/lbm.
(c) Constant volume process till the final pressure is 60 psia. Sketch the p-V diagram for each case.

2.3 A mass of 10 lbm of air is compressed reversibly from an initial pressure of 14.7 psia to 100 psia according to the relation $pV = C$. If the initial density of the air is 0.075 lbm/ft³, find the work necessary for compression.

2.4 One lbm of hydrogen at 80°F expands reversibly till it doubles its volume according to the relation $pV^n = C$. Determine the value of n if the final temperature is 0°F. What is the work done?

2.5 Find the maximum work done per lbm of air in a cycle according to the following processes:
(a) Isothermal expansion from state 1 to state 2.
(b) Constant volume compression from state 2 to state 3.
(c) Constant pressure compression from state 3 to the initial state 1.
Data: $p_1 = 50$ psia
$v_1 = 15$ ft³/lbm
$t_3 = 3000$°F
Represent the work on a p-V diagram.

2.6 The relation between the pressure and volume of a system during an expansion process is

$$p = 300 \, V + 1500,$$

where p is in lbf/ft² and V in ft³. Find the maximum work done by the system in expanding from an initial volume of 6 ft³ to a final volume of 12 ft³.

2.7 A perfect gas changes from an initial state 1 to a final state 3 first at a constant temperature following the path 1–2 and then at constant pressure following the path 2–3 as shown in Fig. 2.20. Find the work interactions during each of the processes 1–2 and 2–3. All processes are reversible.

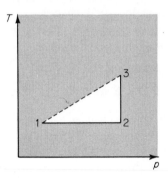

Fig. 2.20. Problem 2.7.

2.8 An indicator card of a 4-in. bore, 5-in. stroke cylinder has an area of 2.7 in.² and is 3 in. long. The indicator spring constant is 100 psi per inch displacement.
(a) Find the mean effective pressure.
(b) If the cycle is repeated 80 times per minute, what is the indicated horsepower?

2.9 The indicator card of a 3-in. bore, 4-in. stroke water pump is in the shape of a rectangle of dimension 1×4 in. The indicator spring constant is 80 psi/in.
(a) Find the mean effective pressure.
(b) If the cycle is repeated once every second, what is the power rating in horsepower required by the pump?

2.10 If the differential of the pressure p in terms of volume and temperature is given by

$$dp = \left(\frac{\partial p}{\partial v}\right)_t dv + \left(\frac{\partial p}{\partial t}\right)_v dt.$$

Prove that dW is an inexact differential.

2.11 If 5000 ft-lbf units of work are available to charge a 6-volt storage battery at 5 amp with 100 per cent efficiency, how long would the charging continue?

2.12 An internal combustion engine uses fuel of calorific value 19,000 Btu/lbm and consumes 50 lbm/hour when developing 100 hp. What is the ratio of work output to energy supplied?

2.13 The molal specific heat of a perfect gas (molecular weight 16) at constant pressure is given by

$$\bar{c}_p = 4.52 + 7.37 \times 10^{-4}T \quad \text{Btu/lb-mole°R.}$$

Find the heat transfer per lbm during a constant pressure expansion from an initial volume of 7 ft³/lbm to a final volume of 50 ft³/lbm at a constant pressure of 20 psia.

2.14 Two lbm of ice at 32°F are placed in a container with 3 lbm of water at 150°F. The container is in an atmosphere which remains at 60°F. There is free exchange of energy between all items so that a final temperature of 60°F is reached. Calculate the amount of heat transferred to (a) the original 2 lbm of ice; (b) the water; (c) the atmosphere. Indicate the direction of heat interaction in each case.

2.15 Water is delivered at a velocity of 70 ft/sec from a nozzle in a vertical direction. For 1 lbm of water, compute the relative potential, kinetic and mechanical energies at elevations zero, 30, and 60 ft. What is the maximum elevation the water will reach? Neglect friction of the air.

2.16 A stone is directed vertically upward from ground level at a velocity of 100 ft/sec. If 15 per cent of the initial kinetic energy is converted to frictional effects on ascent and 15 per cent of the maximum potential energy is converted on descent, (a) determine the peak elevation, (b) determine the final velocity just before the stone strikes the ground.

2.17 A conical diverging tube is attached at the end of a pipeline as shown in Fig. 2.21. If the water discharges into the air at atmospheric pressure, find the magnitude and sense of the force exerted by the conical tube on the pipe line. Assume no frictional losses in the system.

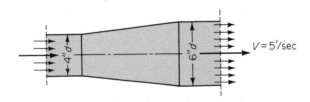

Fig. 2.21. Problem 2.17.

2.18 Determine the magnitude and sense of the *x* and the *y* components of the force necessary to support the water hose shown in Fig. 2.22. The wall of the hose at section 1 cannot transmit any force. Neglect the weight of the hose and assume no losses.

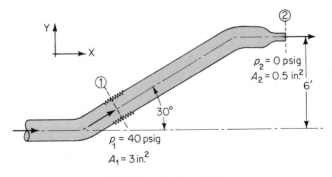

Fig. 2.22. Problem 2.18.

2.19   A 2-in. diameter horizontal jet of water strikes a vertical plate. If the horizontal force needed to support the plate is 80 lbf, what is the velocity of the jet?

2.20   Water flows in a 6-in. diameter horizontal pipe. The pipe reduces to 4 in. diameter by means of a reducer. If the pressure and velocity in the pipeline are 40 psig and 20 ft/sec, find the force exerted by the water on the reducer.

2.21   The deflector shown in Fig. 2.23 divides the flow of the impinging jet 1 ft wide such that two-thirds of the flow is directed upwards and one-third downwards. If the velocity of the water jet is 10 ft/sec, find the magnitude and sense of the horizontal and vertical components of the force necessary to keep the deflector in equilibrium. (Neglect friction and gravitational effects.)

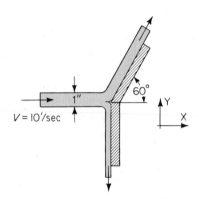

Fig. 2.23.   Problem 2.21.

2.22   Solve the previous problem if the deflector is moving upstream at a velocity of 3 ft/sec.

2.23   Find the torque T_z that must be exerted about pivot z to keep the bend shown in Fig. 2.24 in equilibrium. Neglect friction and gravitational effects. Assume that the walls of the pipe cannot transmit any force at sections 1 and 2.

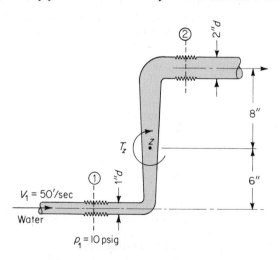

Fig. 2.24.   Problem 2.23.

NOMENCLATURE

A	Area	q	Heat per unit mass
c	Specific heat	T	Absolute temperature
E	Total internal energy	t	Temperature
e	Total internal energy per unit mass	U	Internal energy
g	Acceleration due to gravity	ΔU°	Internal energy of reaction at the standard state
g_c	Constant of proportionality in Newton's second law	u	Internal energy per unit mass
H	Enthalpy	V	Volume or velocity
ΔH°	Enthalpy of reaction at the standard state	v	Specific volume
H_t	Head loss	R	Gas constant
h	Enthalpy per unit mass	$\mathscr{R}$	Universal gas constant
J	Mechanical equivalent of heat	z	Cartesian coordinate
m	Mass	W	Work or weight
n	Number of moles	w	Work per unit mass
p	Pressure	γ	Ratio of specific heats $= c_p/c_v$
Q	Heat	μ_h	Joule-Thomson coefficient
		τ	Time

3

THE FIRST LAW OF THERMODYNAMICS

**3-1
Joule's
Experiments**
Between 1843 and 1848, Joule conducted experiments which were the first steps in the quantitative analysis of thermodynamic systems, and which led to the first law of thermodynamics. Joule's experiments were conducted with equipment similar to that shown in Fig. 3.1(a). In the system that he studied, work was done on a fluid by means of a paddle wheel. This work caused a rise in the temperature of the fluid. The amount of work done was measured by the change in potential energy as the weight W fell through distance z. The system was then placed in contact with a water bath so that heat was transferred from the fluid until the original state of the fluid was reestablished, as indicated by temperature and pressure. The system had, in this way, gone through a complete cycle. The amount of heat rejected by the fluid was equal to the increase of energy of the water bath and therefore could easily be determined by measuring the rise in temperature of the water bath. Joule carried out many similar experiments involving different work interactions in a variety of systems. For example, Joule used work in the form of electrical energy and, after measuring the heat transferred by a heating coil, completed the cycle by restoring the system to its initial state. By repeating the cycle for different amounts of work interaction and measuring the heat transfer to the bath in every case, Joule found that the net work input W was always proportional to the net heat Q transferred from the system, regardless of the kind of work done, the rate at which the work was done, and the scheme used for transforming it into heat. Since the system at the end of a cycle experiences no \net change, the algebraic

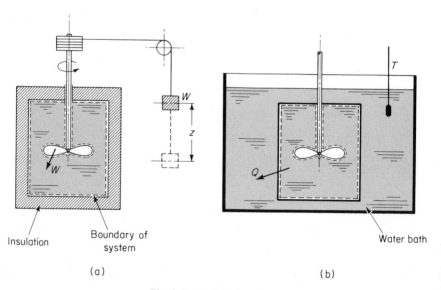

(a)   (b)

Fig. 3.1. Joule's experiment.

88

sum of heat and work during the cycle is zero. Symbolically this may be written as

$$\oint dQ + \oint dW = 0, \tag{3.1}$$

where dQ and dW are infinitesimal amounts of heat and work and the symbol $\oint$ denotes integration along a closed path (cyclic integral). The symbol d has been used to indicate that both heat and work are inexact differentials depending on the path of the cycle. Equation (3.1) implies that the same units are used for both heat and work. If different units are used, a proportionality factor relating work and heat, called the *mechanical equivalent of heat* (symbol J) is required. It is equal to the ratio of the work done to the heat transferred from a system during a cycle or number of cycles. The value of J is 778.26 ft-lbf/Btu, but the approximate value 778 ft-lbf/Btu (427 kgf-m/kcal) is usually adequate for engineering calculations.

Equation (3.1) is a mathematical statement of the first law of thermodynamics involving a closed system undergoing one or more cycles. According to the first law, when heat and work interactions take place between a closed system and its environment, the algebraic sum of the work and heat interactions during a complete cycle is zero. Thus there is an equivalence between heat and work which represent two forms of the same concept— energy. Heat and work can be expressed in the same units; that is, heat can be expressed in foot-pounds force or dynes-centimeter, whereas work can be expressed in Btu or calories. This, however, does not mean that heat and work are equivalent forms of energy, nor does it mean that their basic definitions no longer apply.

The first law of thermodynamics cannot be proved analytically, but experimental evidence has repeatedly confirmed its validity, and since no phenomenon has been shown to contradict it, the first law is accepted as a law of nature. It may be remarked that no restriction was imposed which limited the first law to reversible energy transformations. Hence, the first law applies to reversible as well as to irreversible transformations.

For noncyclic processes, a more general formulation of the first law is required. A new concept which involves a term called *internal energy* fulfills this need.

3-2
Total Internal
Energy

One important consequence of the first law of thermodynamics is that the energy of a system is a property. To prove this, consider a cyclic change of a system whose states are specified by two thermodynamic variables, such as p and V. As shown in Fig. 3.2, the system may proceed from state 1 to state 2 along path A, and then back to the original state 1 along path

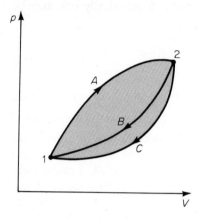

Fig. 3.2. *The* $\int_{1}^{2}(dQ + dW)$ *is a function of states 1 and 2.*

B. If the system operates over the cycle 1-*A*-2-*B*-1, the following changes of energy occur, according to Eq. (3.1):

$$\left(\int_{1(A)}^{2} dQ + \int_{2(B)}^{1} dQ\right) + \left(\int_{1(A)}^{2} dW + \int_{2(B)}^{1} dW\right) = 0.$$

If the system proceeds along path *C*, rather than path *B*, so that the cycle is 1-*A*-2-*C*-1, the energy relationship is

$$\left(\int_{1(A)}^{2} dQ + \int_{2(C)}^{1} dQ\right) + \left(\int_{1(A)}^{2} dW + \int_{2(C)}^{1} dW\right) = 0.$$

Subtracting and rearranging,

$$\int_{2(B)}^{1} dQ + \int_{2(B)}^{1} dW = \int_{2(C)}^{1} dQ + \int_{2(C)}^{1} dW,$$

or

$$\int_{2(B)}^{1} (dQ + dW) = \int_{2(C)}^{1} (dQ + dW). \tag{3.2}$$

This means that when a system operates between state 1 and state 2, the quantity $\int_{1}^{2}(dQ + dW)$ is a constant whether the system proceeds along path *B* or path *C*. Thus, $\int_{1}^{2}(dQ + dW)$ is a function of the initial and final states of the system and does not depend on the path of the process.

Energy is transferred to or from a closed system when heat, or work, is transferred across the boundaries of the system. Although the system absorbs or supplies energy across its boundaries in the form of heat or work, the system does not maintain this energy as work or heat. Energy which includes all forms of energy of a system is called the *total internal energy* of the system and is given the symbol E. The total internal energy of a closed system may change as a result of interaction, involving heat or work with the environment, and the change of E during a process equals the algebraic sum of the heat interaction and the work interaction. Thus the first law applied to a closed system undergoing a process is

$$\Delta E = Q + W. \tag{3.3}$$

In the processes shown in Fig. 3.2, it was found that the energy change was the same, whether path B or path C was chosen, and therefore:

$$\Delta E_B = \Delta E_C. \tag{3.4}$$

Hence, the change of internal energy is the same for any path between the states 1 and 2. Since ΔE approaches dE in the limit, Eq. (3.3) becomes

$$đQ + đW = dE, \tag{3.5}$$

where $đQ$ is the net heat transfer to the system, $đW$ is the net work done on the system, and dE is the excess of the final over the initial energy of the system. According to the sign convention established in Chapter 2, heat or work supplied to a system is positive, whereas heat or work rejected from a system is negative. The work done on a system, $đW$, consists of the work of expansion or compression of the system in addition to types of work, such as mechanical, electrical, magnetic, potential work, so that if $đW'$ is work other than p-V work, then

$$đW = -p\,dV + đW'. \tag{3.6}$$

On a unit mass basis, Eq. (3.5) becomes

$$đq + đw = de. \tag{3.7}$$

When Eq. (3.5) is expressed as a time rate equation,

$$\frac{đQ}{d\tau} + \frac{đW}{d\tau} = \frac{dE}{d\tau}, \tag{3.8}$$

where τ represents time.

Although $đQ$ and $đW$ are not properties, their algebraic sum is a property. This means that an infinite number of combinations of $đQ$ and $đW$ can accomplish a certain change of state dE; their sum, however, must be exactly equal to dE.

In an isolated system, $Q = 0$ and $W = 0$, and therefore, from Eq. (3.5), $E_1 = E_2$. It is therefore evident that the energy of the isolated system remains constant, which is a statement of the principle of conservation of energy. Note that the general definition of energy was introduced through the first law* and, therefore, the law of conservation of energy may be considered as a consequence of the first law.

Any change in the total internal energy of a system is reflected in changes in the various forms of energy that comprise the total internal energy:

$$dE = (dU + \ldots, \text{etc.}) + d(KE) + d(\text{Pot } E),$$

where U is internal energy due to the molecular kinetic and potential energies, and is independent of macroscopic motion, gravity, electricity, magnetism, and surface tension.

The integrated form of Eq. (3.5) is

$$Q_{1-2} + W_{1-2} = (E_2 - E_1).$$

When the total internal energy consists only of internal energy U, kinetic energy, and potential energy, this equation becomes

$$Q_{1-2} + W_{1-2} = (U_2 - U_1) + \frac{m(V_2^2 - V_1^2)}{2g_c} + \frac{mg}{g_c}(z_2 - z_1). \tag{3.9}$$

A device which creates energy or continuously produces work without any other interaction with the environment is called a *perpetual motion machine of the first kind*. Such a machine violates the first law of thermodynamics. All attempts to achieve perpetual motion have failed, thus providing experimental proof (by contradiction) of the validity of the first law.

EXAMPLE 3.1: Utilizing Joule's experiments as a guide and assuming that energy can be measured only when it is in the form of work, evaluate the heat interaction between a closed system and its surroundings when the system changes its state from 1 to 2 along path B as shown in Fig. 3.3. Assume that the states of the system are defined by p and V and that state 2 can be reached by an adiabatic path (1-A-2).

Solution: The work in the actual process 1-B-2 is given per unit mass by

$$w_{1-2 \text{ actual}} = \Delta e - q_{1-2}.$$

Measure the work done in the actual process 1-B-2 and in the adiabatic process 1-A-2. Since the internal energy change in process 1-B-2 is the same as that in process 1-A-2, the first law gives

$$w_{1-2 \text{ adia}} = \Delta e.$$

*Although the preceding form, Eq. (3.5), of the first law applies only to closed systems, other forms, as will be shown later in this chapter, are applicable to open systems.

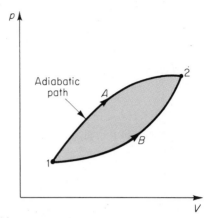

Fig. 3.3. Example 3.1.

Subtraction of these two equations yields

$$q_{1-2} = w_{1-2\ \text{adia}} - w_{1-2\ \text{actual}}.$$

This result indicates that the heat interaction with a closed system is equal to the difference between the work done if the process proceeded adiabatically and the work actually done.

The following section presents some properties of the internal energy U.

3-3
Internal
Energy

The internal energy, U, is an extensive property. It is a function of the state of the system, and its integral around a complete cycle is therefore zero. The cyclic integral of the function U is then *conserved*,*

$$\oint dU = 0. \tag{3.10}$$

If the kinetic and potential energies do not change, heat or work provides the only means by which the internal energy of a closed system can change, according to Eq. (3.9). Note also that the internal energy of an isolated system is constant. Internal energy is expressed in the same dimensions as heat or work, the units usually being Btu, whereas specific internal energy is expressed in Btu/lbm. If the state of a system is determined by any two of the properties p, t, and v, and if electrical, magnetic, surface tension effects are negligible, then the work done per unit mass in a quasi-static process is

$$dw = -p\ dv.$$

---

*A function X is said to be *conserved* if its integral around a cycle is zero or $\oint dX = 0$.

If only internal energy u changes, then Eq. (3.7) becomes

$$đq - p\,dv = du. \tag{3.11}$$

When u is expressed in terms of t and v, then

$$u = u(t, v),$$

and the change of u is given by

$$du = \left(\frac{\partial u}{\partial t}\right)_v dt + \left(\frac{\partial u}{\partial v}\right)_t dv. \tag{3.12}$$

Combining Eq. (3.11) with Eq. (3.12) yields

$$đq - p\,dv = \left(\frac{\partial u}{\partial t}\right)_v dt + \left(\frac{\partial u}{\partial v}\right)_t dv.$$

This may be rearranged as

$$đq = \left(\frac{\partial u}{\partial t}\right)_v dt + \left[p + \left(\frac{\partial u}{\partial v}\right)_t\right] dv. \tag{3.13}$$

In a constant-volume process, no volume change occurs, so that

$$đq = \left(\frac{\partial u}{\partial t}\right)_v dt.$$

But at constant volume, $đq = c_v\,dt$. Therefore c_v may be defined as

$$c_v \equiv \left(\frac{\partial u}{\partial t}\right)_v. \tag{3.14}$$

Note that a change of temperature does not necessarily result from heat transfer since work can also cause a change of temperature. Thus the name *specific heat* is a misnomer since it implies that c_v is associated with a heat quantity when it is really associated with a property. This means that c_v may replace $(\partial u/\partial t)_v$ in any process, quasi-static or not, even when the process does not take place at constant volume. Note also that c_v is equal to $(đq/dt)_v$ only in a constant-volume process which involves no work interaction.

3-4
Internal Energy
of a Perfect
Gas

In experiments performed by Gay-Lussac and by Joule, the free expansion of gases was studied, in order to determine whether the internal energy of real gases depends on other factors besides temperature. The apparatus used is essentially that shown in Fig. 3.4. Chamber A contains a gas in thermodynamic equilibrium, while chamber B is evacuated. The two chambers constitute a closed system and are immersed in a water bath. Initially the system is in thermal equilibrium with its environment at a uniform temperature t_1. When the stopcock between chambers

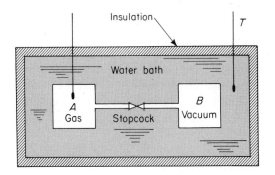

Fig. 3.4. *Experiment to show that the internal energy of a perfect gas is a function of temperature only.*

A and B is opened, the gas in A expands freely into B, occupying both chambers. During the expansion process, the temperature of the gas in A decreases below its initial value while the temperature in B increases. These temperature changes develop temperature gradients so that heat flows from the water bath to chamber A and from chamber B to the water bath. This causes an additional flow of gas from A to B. After sufficient time has passed, the system and environment reach thermodynamic equilibrium. The heat transferred to the system from the environment as a result of this process is

$$Q_{sys} = -Q_{envir} = mc(t_2 - t_1),^*$$

where m and c are the mass and average specific heat of the environment and $(t_2 - t_1)$ is the temperature change in the environment (it is also the temperature change of the system). Since the boundaries of the system do not move, no external work is done during the free expansion of the gas. When the first law of thermodynamics is applied to this system, it becomes

*The subscripts "sys" and "envir" refer to interaction with system or environment.

$$\Delta U = Q_{sys}.$$

By substituting for Q_{sys}, this becomes

$$\Delta U = mc(t_2 - t_1)$$

or

$$U_2 - U_1 = mc(t_2 - t_1).$$

The specific heat and the temperatures t_1 and t_2 can be measured readily. Measurements show that the temperature of the water bath remains practically constant. This means that chamber A loses as much energy as chamber B gains, so that there is no net heat interaction between the system and the environment. The absence of both heat interaction and work interaction indicates that the internal energy of this system remains constant, even though work involving a volume change was done between parts of the system. Therefore, in gases that tend to behave like perfect gases, the internal energy is independent of volume and depends only on temperature. This statement is called *Joule's law* and is expressed as

$$\left(\frac{\partial u}{\partial v}\right)_t = 0. \tag{3.15}$$

In Joule's experiment, any temperature changes that might have occurred were very small, because they were obscured as a result of the large thermal capacity of chamber A, chamber B, and the water bath compared with the thermal capacity of the gas. In the Joule-Thomson experiment, explained later in this chapter, results of greater accuracy were obtained.

The change in internal energy of a perfect gas per unit mass as the gas changes from state 1 to state 2, is

$$\int_1^2 du = \int_{t_1}^{t_2} c_v \, dt. \tag{3.16}$$

If c_v is a constant, then

$$u_2 - u_1 = c_v(t_2 - t_1).$$

3-5
Enthalpy

Equation (3.5) can be rewritten as

$$dQ - p \, dV + dW' = dE, \tag{3.17}$$

where dW' represents all work done on the system other than p-V work, such as shaft, electrical, magnetic, etc. When $d(pV)$ is added to both sides, Eq. (3.17) becomes

$$dQ + V \, dp + dW' = d(E + pV).$$

If E comprises only internal energy, the foregoing equation becomes

$$\bar{d}Q + V\,dp + \bar{d}W' = d(U + pV). \tag{3.18}$$

The combination $(U + pV)$ often plays an important role in calculations where matter crosses the boundaries of a system. For this reason it is convenient to combine $(U + pV)$ under the name of a new property called *enthalpy* H. As will be seen in the following section, enthalpy is directly associated with the flux of energy in flow processes. Enthalpy is defined by

$$H \equiv U + pV, \tag{3.19}$$

and specific enthalpy by

$$h \equiv u + pv. \tag{3.20}$$

The unit of H is Btu and that of h is Btu/lbm. Since enthalpy is a combination of functions of state (u, p, and v), it, too, is a function of state. Also, enthalpy is an internal, extensive property. Note that the difference between the enthalpy h and the internal energy u is the product pv. The term pv accounts for the work done on a fluid as it flows across the boundaries of an open system. Thus enthalpy has a physical meaning only in flow situations and is the characteristic thermodynamic property of flow through open systems. Note that, although one can calculate the enthalpy of a closed system, the characteristic energy of a closed system is the internal energy u. If a closed system undergoes a constant-pressure process, and if the only work involved is p-V work, then according to the first law

$$q_{1-2} - p(v_2 - v_1) = u_2 - u_1,$$

or

$$q_{1-2} = h_2 - h_1. \tag{3.21}$$

The heat transfer to a closed system is thus equal to the change of enthalpy under the two constraints just mentioned.

When enthalpy is substituted into Eq. (3.18), it becomes, for a unit mass,

$$\bar{d}q = dh - v\,dp - \bar{d}w'. \tag{3.22}$$

Since $\bar{d}q = c_p\,dt$, under conditions of constant pressure and when p-V work is the only work, then c_p may be defined as

$$c_p \equiv \left(\frac{\partial h}{\partial t}\right)_p. \tag{3.23}$$

The constant pressure specific heat, c_p, or $(\partial h/\partial t)_p$ is an extensive property depending on the state of the system. This means that c_p may replace $(\partial h/\partial t)_p$ in any process, quasi-static or not, even when the process is not at constant pressure. The constant-pressure specific heat, is equal to $(đq/dt)_p$ only in a constant-pressure process in which $đw' = 0$. As stated in the case of c_v, c_p must be thought of as a change of property with respect to temperature.

If enthalpy is a function of two independent parameters, such as t and p, then the change in enthalpy in any process is

$$dh = \left(\frac{\partial h}{\partial t}\right)_p dt + \left(\frac{\partial h}{\partial p}\right)_t dp$$

$$= c_p\, dt + \left(\frac{\partial h}{\partial p}\right)_t dp. \tag{3.24}$$

In the case of a perfect gas, Eq. (3.20) becomes

$$dh = du + d(pv)$$

$$= c_v\, dt + R\, dt = (c_v + R)\, dt.$$

In this case, enthalpy depends only on temperature, so that $(\partial h/\partial p)_t = 0$. Therefore, Eq. (3.24) becomes, for a perfect gas,

$$dh = c_p\, dt.$$

Hence, $c_p\, dt = (c_v + R)\, dt,$

or

$$c_p = c_v + R. \tag{3.25}$$

In the following sections, the first law of thermodynamics will be applied first to closed systems and then to control volumes.

3-6 Application of the First Law to a Closed System (Nonflow Processes)

The first law of thermodynamics accounts for all energy interactions between a system and its environment. A change in the energy of a system is accompanied by an equal but opposite change in the energy of its surroundings. According to the first law, any heat or work that crosses the boundaries of a closed system represents energy which is equal in magnitude to the change in internal energy of the system. Remember the sign convention adopted for the transition energies: Energy entering the system is considered positive and energy leaving the system is negative.

When applying the first law to typical processes, a sketch which shows energy flow across well-defined boundaries of a system will prove particularly helpful.

(a) *The constant-volume (isochoric) process:* Consider the transfer of heat to a system consisting of a fluid in a rigid vessel, as shown in Fig. 3.5.

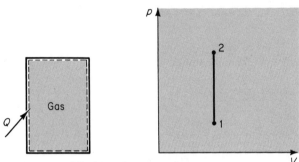

Fig. 3.5.   *Constant-volume process.*

The process is represented by a vertical line on the p-V diagram. Since $dV = 0$, the displacement work is zero. Assuming that only internal energy comprises e, the first law for this system, based on a unit mass becomes

$$đq = du.$$

Thus, the heat transfer to the system is utilized entirely in increasing the internal energy of the system. Similarly, any heat transfer from the system represents equivalent reduction in the internal energy of the system.

When a solid or liquid is heated, the resultant change in volume of the solid or liquid is relatively small. Heat transfer to solids and liquids may therefore be considered to take place at constant volume, and the energy supplied is essentially equal to the increase in internal energy of the system.

Quasi-static work, $-\int p\, dV$, is represented by the area, in the p-V plane, below the process path. In the constant-volume process, this area is clearly zero, so that it is impossible to have quasi-static work done in a constant volume process. Work, however, still can be done on a constant-volume system, if the process is irreversible, as demonstrated by Joule's paddle-wheel experiments.

EXAMPLE 3.2:   One lbm of air (assumed perfect gas, $R = 53.34$ ft-lbf/lbm°R) is confined to a constant-volume vessel. The volume and the initial pressure of the air are 5 ft³ and 50 psia respectively. If 20 Btu of heat are supplied to the gas, the temperature increases to 332°F. Find (a) the work done; (b) the change of internal energy; (c) the specific heat of the gas at constant volume.

Solution: (a) The displacement work is zero since there is no change in volume.

(b) First law: $q = \Delta u = 20$ Btu/lbm

$$= 20 \times 778 = 15{,}560 \text{ ft-lbf/lbm}.$$

(c) The initial temperature may be determined from the perfect gas equation of state,

$$pv = RT,$$

from which

$$T = \frac{50 \times 144 \times 5}{53.34} = 675°R = 215°F.$$

Therefore

$$\Delta t = 332 - 215 = 117°R.$$

The average specific heat at constant volume is

$$c_v = \left(\frac{\Delta u}{\Delta t}\right)_v = \frac{20 \text{ Btu/lbm}}{117°R} = 0.171 \text{ Btu/lbm}°R.$$

(b) *The constant-pressure (isobaric) process:* A fluid maintained at constant pressure by means of a piston and a cylinder is shown in Fig. 3.6. In a system of unit mass, work $w_{1-2} = -\int_{v_1}^{v_2} p \, dv = -p\,(v_2 - v_1)$ and is represented by the hatched area in Fig. 3.6. The first law, as indicated by Eq. (3.11), becomes, after integration,

$$q_{1-2} - p(v_2 - v_1) = u_2 - u_1$$
$$= (u_2 + pv_2) - (u_1 + pv_1)$$
$$= h_2 - h_1,$$

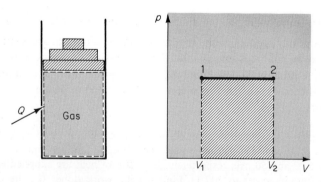

Fig. 3.6. *Constant-pressure process.*

which is the same as Eq. (3.21). This relationship is valid for constant-pressure systems if only p-V work is done. Note that the heat interaction in this case depends only on the end states of the system.

EXAMPLE 3.3:   Twenty lbm of a certain gas are compressed at a constant pressure of 200 psia from a volume of 50 ft³ to a volume 10 ft³. If the internal energy increase is 1.75×10^6 ft-lbf and the temperature changes from 70°F to 350°F find (a) the work done during the reversible compression; (b) the heat transferred; (c) the change of enthalpy; (d) the average specific heat at constant pressure.

Solution: (a) Referring to Fig. 3.6,

$$W_{1-2} = -p(V_2 - V_1) = -200 \times 144(10 - 50)$$
$$= 1.152 \times 10^6 \text{ ft-lbf.}$$

(b) $Q_{1-2} + W_{1-2} = (U_2 - U_1)$.

Hence, $Q_{1-2} = -1.152 \times 10^6 + 1.75 \times 10^6 = 0.598 \times 10^6$ ft-lbf $= 770$ Btu.

(c) Since the process is at constant pressure, and $đW' = 0$, then

$$H_2 - H_1 = Q_{1-2} = 770 \text{ Btu.}$$

(d) $c_p = \left(\dfrac{\Delta h}{\Delta t}\right)_p = \dfrac{1}{20}\dfrac{770}{(350 - 70)} = 0.1373$ Btu/lbm°F.

(c) *Process at constant internal energy:* When the internal energy of a system remains constant, the first law becomes

$$đq + đw = 0.$$

If a closed system undergoes a process in which the internal energy does not change, the heat interaction and the work interaction must be equal to each other in magnitude but of opposite sign. This means that the heat transfer to the system produces an equivalent amount of work.

If two dissimilar metals are joined, and if two such junctions are held at different temperatures, an electric potential is developed between the junctions. When the circuit is closed, an electric current flows through the metals. The thermoelectric generator utilizes this phenomnon to convert heat into electric energy. In many applications solar energy serves as the heat source, but the efficiency of conversion is low. The components of a thermoelectric generator, as shown in Fig. 3.7, consist of a series of semiconductors, A and B, connected to the hot and cold conductors, C and D. The electrical terminals connected to the conductors D carry the output electrical energy to the load G.

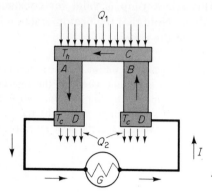

Fig. 3.7.   *Thermoelectric generator.*

EXAMPLE 3.4:   It is required to make a first law analysis of a thermoelectric device under the following conditions:

rate of heat transfer $= 20$ watts
emf generated $\quad= 2.5$ volts
current flow $\qquad= 0.6$ amp

Assume steady state and steady flow.

Solution: Since the current flow through the device is constant, the electric power output is equal to the voltage drop multiplied by the current, or

$$\dot{W} = P = VI = 2.5 \times 0.6 = 1.5 \text{ watts.}$$

The first law applied to the system shown is

$$P + \dot{Q} = \Delta \dot{E}.$$

At steady state there is no change in internal energy of the system, so that $\Delta \dot{E} = 0$. Hence,

$$-1.5 + (20 - \dot{Q}_2) = 0 \quad \text{or} \quad \dot{Q}_2 = 18.5 \text{ watts.}$$

The efficiency of the energy conversion is

$$\eta = \frac{\text{electric power output}}{\text{rate of heat input}} = \frac{1.5}{20} = 7.5 \text{ per cent.}$$

(d) *The constant temperature (isothermal) process:*   During this process, the temperature of a system is maintained constant. If a perfect gas is subjected to an isothermal process, Eq. (3.11) becomes, since its internal energy is a function of temperature alone,

$$đq + đw = 0.$$

Thus, in an isothermal compression or expansion process that involves only a perfect gas, the sum of the heat and work input is zero, just as in a constant-internal-energy process. Fig 3.8 shows a p-V diagram for an isothermal process of a perfect gas.

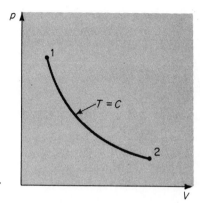

Fig. 3.8. *Isothermal process.*

EXAMPLE 3.5:   A perfect gas occupying a volume of 4 ft³ at a pressure of 250 psia, expands isothermally in a nonflow process, to a volume of 10 ft³. Find the final pressure, W, Q, and ΔU.

Solution: $p_1 V_1 = mRT,$ $p_2 V_2 = mRT.$

Then,

$$p_2 = p_1 \left(\frac{V_1}{V_2}\right) = 250\left(\frac{4}{10}\right) = 100 \text{ psia},$$

since the temperature remains constant $\Delta U = 0$, and the first law gives

$$Q_{1-2} = -W_{1-2}.$$

But

$$W_{1-2} = \int_1^2 dW = -\int_{V_1}^{V_2} p\, dV = -\int_{V_1}^{V_2} \frac{mRT}{V}\, dV = -mRT \ln \frac{V_2}{V_1}$$

$$= -p_1 V_1 \ln \frac{V_2}{V_1}$$

$$= -(250 \times 144) \times 4 \ln 2.5$$

$$= -128,200 \text{ ft-lbf.}$$

(e) *The adiabatic process:* In an adiabatic process, no heat interaction occurs between the system and the environment. The first law then becomes

$$dW = dU,$$

which when integrated, is

$$W_{1-2} = U_2 - U_1.$$

Therefore the work done on the system is equal to the change in the system's internal energy. In the case of a unit mass of a perfect gas subjected to a reversible adiabatic process, the preceding equation can be written as

$$c_v \, dT = -p \, dv = -\frac{RT}{v} dv$$

or

$$c_v \frac{dT}{T} = -R \frac{dv}{v},$$

which may be integrated to give

$$\ln \frac{T_2}{T_1} = \frac{R}{c_v} \ln \frac{v_1}{v_2},$$

or

$$\frac{T_2}{T_1} = \left(\frac{v_1}{v_2} \right)^{R/c_v}. \tag{3.26}$$

The temperature ratio may also be expressed in terms of the pressure ratio. From the perfect gas equation, the volume ratio can be replaced, so that

$$\frac{T_2}{T_1} = \left(\frac{p_2 T_1}{p_1 T_2} \right)^{R/c_v} = \left(\frac{p_2}{p_1} \right)^{R/(R+c_v)}. \tag{3.27}$$

In the case of a perfect gas, $c_p = c_v + R$. Combining Eq. (3.26) and (3.27), the pressure-volume relationship in an adiabatic process is

$$\frac{v_2}{v_1} = \left(\frac{p_1}{p_2} \right)^{c_v/c_p}, \tag{3.28}$$

or

$$p_2 v_2^\gamma = p_1 v_1^\gamma = \text{constant}, \tag{3.29}$$

where γ is the ratio of specific heats:

$$\gamma = \frac{c_p}{c_v}. \tag{3.30}$$

(f) *The polytropic process:* The pressure-volume relationship $pv^\gamma = C$ which describes the reversible adiabatic process may be extended to describe a reversible process in which heat transfer does occur. This is called a *polytropic process*. The equation takes the form

$$pv^n = C, \tag{3.31}$$

where n is the "*index*" of the process and may have any value from $-\infty$ to $+\infty$. In a constant-pressure process, $n = 0$; in an isothermal process (for a perfect gas), $n = 1$; and in a constant-volume process, $n \rightarrow \infty$.

Pressure-volume relationships of several reversible processes corresponding to different values of n are plotted in Fig. 3.9. Starting at point a, expansion and compression processes are curves located in the lower right and upper left quadrants. Processes that exhibit negative values of n are not commonly encountered in practice. Although these processes are

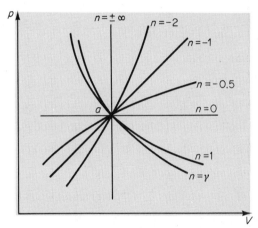

Fig. 3.9. *Polytropic processes.*

possible, they imply a simultaneous decrease in volume accompanying a decrease in pressure. Areas underneath the curves shown in Fig. 3.9 represent reversible work. The work done on a system, as outlined in Chapter 2, is

$$W_{1-2} = \frac{p_2 V_2 - p_1 V_1}{n - 1}. \tag{3.32}$$

Note that Eq. (3.32) does not apply if $n = 1$. A summary of process relations of a perfect gas with constant specific heat is presented in Table 3.1.

EXAMPLE 3.6: One lbm of a perfect gas expands in a polytropic process according to the law $pV^n = C$ (where $n = 1.3$). The initial pressure and volume are 95 psia and 0.5 ft³. The final volume is 3.8 ft³. Find (a) the final temperature; (b) the

TABLE 3.1 PROCESS-RELATIONS FOR PERFECT GAS

Process	Q	$-\int_1^2 p\,dV$	$\int_1^2 V\,dp$	ΔU	p-V-T Relations	Exponent in $pV^n = C$
Constant volume	$mc_v(T_2 - T_1)$	0	$V(p_2 - p_1)$	$mc_v(T_2 - T_1)$	$\dfrac{T_2}{T_1} = \dfrac{p_2}{p_1}$	$n = \infty$
Constant pressure	$mc_p(T_2 - T_1)$	$p(V_1 - V_2)$	0	$mc_v(T_2 - T_1)$	$\dfrac{T_2}{T_1} = \dfrac{V_2}{V_1}$	$n = 0$
Constant temperature	$p_1 V_1 \ln \dfrac{V_2}{V_1}$	$p_1 V_1 \ln \dfrac{V_1}{V_2}$	$p_1 V_1 \ln \dfrac{V_1}{V_2}$	0	$p_1 V_1 = p_2 V_2$	$n = 1$
Reversible adiabatic	0	$\dfrac{p_2 V_2 - p_1 V_1}{\gamma - 1}$	$\dfrac{\gamma}{\gamma - 1}(p_2 V_2 - p_1 V_1)$	$mc_v(T_2 - T_1)$	$p_1 V_1^\gamma = p_2 V_2^\gamma,$ $\dfrac{T_2}{T_1} = \left(\dfrac{V_1}{V_2}\right)^{\gamma - 1} = \left(\dfrac{p_2}{p_1}\right)^{(\gamma - 1)/\gamma}$	$n = \gamma$
Polytropic	$mc_v\left(\dfrac{\gamma - n}{1 - n}\right)(T_2 - T_1)$	$\dfrac{p_2 V_2 - p_1 V_1}{n - 1}$	$\dfrac{n}{n - 1}(p_2 V_2 - p_1 V_1)$	$mc_v(T_2 - T_1)$	$p_1 V_1^n = p_2 V_2^n,$ $\dfrac{T_2}{T_1} = \left(\dfrac{V_1}{V_2}\right)^{n - 1} = \left(\dfrac{p_2}{p_1}\right)^{(n - 1)/n}$	$n = n$

work done; (c) the change of internal energy; (d) the heat interaction. (R for the gas is 24.1 ft-lbf/lbm°R, and $c_v = 0.122$ Btu/lbm°R.)

Solution: (a) $p_1 v_1^{1.3} = p_2 v_2^{1.3}$,

then

$$p_2 = 95 \left(\frac{0.5}{3.8}\right)^{1.3} = 6.8 \text{ psia.}$$

The temperatures T_1 and T_2 are determined from the perfect-gas law as

$$T_1 = \frac{p_1 v_1}{R} = \frac{95 \times 144 \times 0.5}{24.1} = 284°R$$

and

$$T_2 = \frac{p_2 v_2}{R} = \frac{6.8 \times 144 \times 3.8}{24.1} = 154.5°R.$$

(b) $w_{1-2} = -\int_{v_1}^{v_2} p \, dv = \frac{p_2 v_2 - p_1 v_1}{n - 1}$

$$= \frac{6.8 \times 144 \times 3.8 - 95 \times 144 \times 0.5}{1.3 - 1}$$

$$= -10,400 \text{ ft-lbf/lbm} = -13.36 \text{ Btu/lbm.}$$

(c) $\Delta u = c_v(T_2 - T_1) = 0.122 (154.5 - 284) = -15.8$ Btu/lbm.

(d) $q_{1-2} = \Delta u - w_{1-2} = -15.8 + 13.36 = -2.44$ Btu/lbm.

3-7
Application of
the First Law
to a Control
Volume (Flow
Processes)

Energy may be conveyed across the boundaries of a control volume not only by heat and work but also by the matter that crosses the boundaries. Matter may convey internal, kinetic, potential, chemical, and magnetic energies across boundaries. The following analysis is limited to the first three forms of energy, but the same procedure applies to systems in which any form of internal energy is involved. The first law indicates that

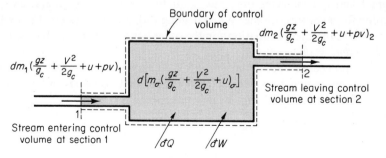

Fig. 3.10.   *The first law of thermodynamics applied to a control volume.*

an energy balance exists between a system and its environment. When heat, work, or internal energy enters a system, the decrease in energy of the environment is equal to the increase in the internal energy of the system. As shown in Fig. 3.10, matter enters a control volume at section 1 and leaves at section 2. Also heat and work are exchanged between the control volume and environment. According to the first law of thermodynamics, the energy entering the control volume must be equal to the energy leaving the control volume plus any accumulation of energy within the control volume:

energy entering the control volume at section 1 $+$ heat and work interaction

$=$ energy leaving the control volume through section 2 $+$ accumulation of energy within the control volume.

Expressed mathematically, this becomes

$$dm_1 \left(u + pv + \frac{V^2}{2g_c} + \frac{gz}{g_c} \right)_1 + dQ + dW$$

$$= dm_2 \left(u + pv + \frac{V^2}{2g_c} + \frac{gz}{g_c} \right)_2 + d\left[m_\sigma \left(u + \frac{V^2}{2g_c} + \frac{gz}{g_c} \right)_\sigma \right]. \quad (3.33a)$$

A more general form of this statement is

$$W + Q + \sum_{net=in-out} m \left(h + \frac{V^2}{2g_c} + \frac{gz}{g_c} \right) = \Delta E_\sigma. \quad (3.33b)$$

As a rate equation, this becomes

$$\dot{Q} + P + \sum_{net=in-out} \dot{m} \left(h + \frac{V^2}{2g_c} + \frac{gz}{g_c} \right) = \frac{dE_\sigma}{d\tau}, \quad (3.34)$$

where dm_1 is the mass entering at section 1 and dm_2 is the mass leaving at section 2 during the short time interval $d\tau$; dW is work other than flow work; subscripts 1, 2, and σ refer to section 1, section 2, and the control volume; and ($\cdot$) indicates time rate. Equation (3.33) is the general energy equation for a control volume. When dealing with a closed system, Eq. (3.33) still serves as the energy equation; on the other hand, some of the terms drop out since $dm_1 = dm_2 = 0$.

The procedure outlined in Section 2–20 may also be applied and leads to the preceding equations. In a closed system that coincides initially with the control volume, the change of internal energy is

$$dE = dE_\sigma + dE_{out} - dE_{in},$$

where E_σ is the internal energy of the control volume, E_{out} is the internal energy of the fluid leaving the control volume, and E_{in} is the internal energy of the fluid entering the control volume. The first law, applied to the closed system, is

$$\delta Q_{sys} + \delta W_{sys} = dE_\sigma + dE_{out} - dE_{in}.$$

The energies δQ_{sys} and δW_{sys} are associated with the closed system. But the flow of heat δQ_{sys} into (or out of) the closed system is independent of the flow of fluid into (and out of) the control volume. Therefore, the flow of heat is the same for the control volume as for the closed system. On the other hand, the amount of work δW_{sys} done on the closed system is not necessarily the same as that done on the control volume. Some flow work* is necessary to introduce mass into, and to remove it from, the control volume. The foregoing equation then becomes

$$\delta Q + \delta W + d(pV) = dE_\sigma - dE_{net\ in},$$

where δW in the preceding equation represents work done on the control volume other than flow work. If the properties are uniform at the points where matter enters (and leaves) the control volume, then flow work and internal energy can be grouped together:

$$\delta Q + \delta W + \sum (e + pv)\, dm = dE_\sigma. \tag{3.35}$$

Summing up for all the masses, this equation becomes

$$Q + W + \sum (e + pv)m = \Delta E_\sigma.$$

When this equation is expressed on a rate basis,

$$\dot{Q} + P + \sum (e + pv)\dot{m} = \frac{dE_\sigma}{d\tau}, \tag{3.36}$$

it becomes the same as Eq. (3.34).

Two cases will now be considered. First is the steady flow process and second is the unsteady or transient flow process.

**3-8
The Steady
Flow Process**
In a steady flow process, the following conditions exist:

1. The mass entering a system flows at a constant rate, and at any time, the mass flow at the entrance is the same as the mass flow at the exit. This implies that the mass within the system neither increases nor diminishes at any time.

2. The state and energy of the fluid at the entrance, at the exit, and at every point in the system do not change.

---

*Neglecting shear work on the fluid at the boundaries as well as magnetic, electric, and capillary effects.

3. The rate at which any energy, in the form of heat or work, crosses the boundaries of the system is constant.

When steady flow exists, the following conditions are added to those of Eq. (3.33a):

$$\Sigma \, dm = 0$$

and

$$dE_\sigma = d \left[m_\sigma \left(u + \frac{V^2}{2g_c} + \frac{gz}{g_c} \right)_\sigma \right] = 0.$$

Thus Eq. (3.33b) becomes, under steady-state conditions,

$$dQ + dW + \Sigma \, dm \left(h + \frac{V^2}{2g_c} + \frac{gz}{g_c} \right) = 0,$$

where h is the enthalpy function. Integration leads to

$$Q + W + \Sigma \, m \left(h + \frac{V^2}{2g_c} + \frac{gz}{g_c} \right) = 0. \tag{3.37}$$

On a unit mass basis, this is

$$q + w + \Sigma \left(h + \frac{V^2}{2g_c} + \frac{gz}{g_c} \right) = 0. \tag{3.38}$$

On a rate basis, the energy equation for steady flow is

$$\frac{dQ}{d\tau} + \frac{dW}{d\tau} + \Sigma \frac{dm}{d\tau} \left(h + \frac{V^2}{2g_c} + \frac{gz}{g_c} \right) = 0, \tag{3.39}$$

or

$$\dot{m}q + \dot{m}w + \Sigma \, \dot{m} \left(h + \frac{V^2}{2g_c} + \frac{gz}{g_c} \right) = 0,$$

where $\dot{m}$ is the mass flow per unit time.

When more than one fluid enters and leaves the system in steady flow, as shown in Fig. 3.11, the continuity equation becomes

$$m_a + m_b + \ldots = m_c + m_d + \ldots,$$

where m_a, m_b, m_c, and m_d represent masses of the different constituents entering and leaving the system in a given time interval. The steady flow energy equation is

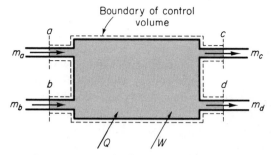

Fig. 3.11. *Control volume with multiple streams.*

$$Q + W + m_a \left(h + \frac{V^2}{2g_c} + \frac{gz}{g_c} \right)_a + m_b \left(h + \frac{V^2}{2g_c} + \frac{gz}{g_c} \right)_b + \cdots$$

$$= m_c \left(h + \frac{V^2}{2g_c} + \frac{gz}{g_c} \right)_c + m_d \left(h + \frac{V^2}{2g_c} + \frac{gz}{g_c} \right)_d + \cdots,$$

where subscripts a, b, etc., refer to flows entering, and c, d, etc., refer to flows leaving the system.

EXAMPLE 3.7:   Saturated water at 200 psia ($u = 354.68$ Btu/lbm, $h = 355.36$ Btu/lbm) is injected into saturated steam at a pressure of 200 psia ($u = 1113.7$ Btu/lbm, $h = 1198.4$ Btu/lbm). If the mixing process is accomplished at constant pressure and the mixing ratio of water to steam is 1:10 by mass, find the enthalpy of the mixture. (Assume steady-state and adiabatic mixing.)

Solution: Neglecting changes in kinetic and potential energies and assuming that there is no work except flow work, the first law may be written

$$\sum m(h) = 0$$

or

$$m_s h_s + m_w h_w = m_{\text{mixt}} h_{\text{mixt}}.$$

But

$$m_{\text{mixt}} = m_s + m_w;$$

therefore,

$$m_s h_s + m_w h_w = (m_s + m_w) h_{\text{mixt}}.$$

Dividing by m_s and rearranging gives

$$h_{\text{mixt}} = \frac{h_s + (m_w/m_s) h_w}{1 + (m_w/m_s)}.$$

Substituting values,

$$h_{\text{mixt}} = \frac{1198.4 + 0.1 \times 355.36}{1 + 0.1} = 1122 \text{ Btu/lbm.}$$

3-9
Work
Interaction in
A Reversible
Steady Flow
Process

In an open system, the work interaction between the system and its environment is expressed, under steady-state conditions, by

$$đw = dh + \frac{V\,dV}{g_c} + \frac{g}{g_c}\,dz - đq. \qquad (3.40)$$

In a closed system, the reversible heat interaction $đq$ is described by

$$đq = du + p\,dv = dh - v\,dp.$$

This equation also indicates the heat interaction for an open system or a control volume. Therefore, when $đq$ is replaced in Eq. (3.40), the work interaction for an open system is

$$w_{\text{rev}} = \int_1^2 v\,dp + \frac{V_2^2 - V_1^2}{2g_c} + \frac{g}{g_c}(z_2 - z_1). \qquad (3.41)$$

On the other hand, Euler's equation states

$$0 = \int_1^2 v\,dp + \frac{V_2^2 - V_1^2}{2g_c} + \frac{g}{g_c}(z_2 - z_1). \qquad (3.42)$$

Comparison of Eq. (3.41) with Eq. (3.42) indicates that Euler's equation applies only if no work is done. Furthermore, if reversible work is done, then unsteady-state conditions must exist within the system, although steady-state conditions may prevail at the inlet and exit of the system.

Equation (3.41) expresses energy relationships in terms of properties of the fluid at the boundaries of the system, without regard for properties within the system. Euler's equation, on the other hand, expresses the relationship of the fluid flow during the entire course of the process.

In a system undergoing a steady-state process, the reversible work is $\int v\,dp$. This assumes that the kinetic energy and the potential energy of the system are not changing. In a closed system the reversible work is equal to $-\int p\,dv$. These are represented on a p-v diagram in Fig. 3.12, where points 1 and 2 are the end points of a reversible process. Area 1–2-a-b represents the work $-\int p\,dv$ and area 1-2-c-d represents the work $\int v\,dp$. The difference between these two is the flow work resulting from the force of the fluid exerted against existing pressures at the entrance and exit. This relation can be seen from the following:

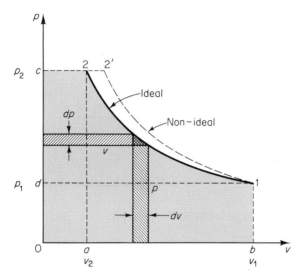

Fig. 3.12. $\int v\,dp$ and $-\int p\,dv$.

$$\int_1^2 d(pv) = \int_1^2 p\,dv + \int_1^2 v\,dp.$$

Therefore,

$$p_2 v_2 - p_1 v_1 = \int_1^2 p\,dv + \int_1^2 v\,dp. \tag{3.43}$$

The terms in the preceding equation are represented respectively by the areas $c2ao$, $d1bo$, $21ba$ and $c21d$ of Fig. 3.12. It is also evident from the figure that $c2ao - d1bo = -21ba + c21d$ in accordance with the previous equation. In the case of an irreversible compression, the path followed is described in Fig. 3.12 by process 1–2′. In such cases, the work required is more than in the reversible process because of such factors as friction and turbulence.

EXAMPLE 3.8: Air is compressed reversibly and adiabatically from 14.7 psia and 70°F to 80 psia according to the relation $pv^{1.5} = C$. Neglecting changes in kinetic and potential energies, compute the work done in compression for the following cases: (c) nonflow process; (b) steady flow process. Show that the flow work accounts for the difference between (a) and (b). Also, compute the work done if the compression were accomplished isothermally at 70°F.

Solution: (a) $v_1 = \dfrac{RT_1}{p_1} = \dfrac{53.34 \times 530}{14.7 \times 144} = 13.36 \text{ ft}^3/\text{lbm.}$

$$\frac{v_2}{v_1} = \left(\frac{p_1}{p_2}\right)^{1/1.5}$$

or

$$v_2 = 13.36 \left(\frac{14.7}{80}\right)^{1/1.5} = 4.31 \text{ ft}^3/\text{lbm}.$$

$$p_1 v_1^{1.5} = (14.7 \times 144) \times 13.36^{1.5} = 10.27 \times 10^4$$

$$-\int_1^2 p\, dv = -\int_1^2 \frac{10.27 \times 10^4}{v^{1.5}}\, dv = -20.54 \times 10^4 \left[1/v^{0.5}\right]_{v_1}^{v_2}$$

$$= -20.54 \times 10^4 \left[\frac{1}{\sqrt{4.31}} - \frac{1}{\sqrt{13.36}}\right] = 4.27 \times 10^4 \text{ ft-lbf/lbm}.$$

(b) $\displaystyle \int_1^2 v\, dp = \int_1^2 \left(\frac{10.27 \times 10^4}{p}\right)^{1/1.5} dp = 2200 \left[\frac{p^{1/3}}{1/3}\right]_{p_1}^{p_2}$

$$= 6600 \left(\sqrt[3]{80 \times 144} - \sqrt[3]{14.7 \times 144}\right) = 64{,}200 \text{ ft-lbf/lbm}.$$

Check: $p_2 v_2 = \quad 4.97 \times 10^4$ ft-lbf/lbm

$\qquad\qquad -p_1 v_1 = -2.82 \times 10^4$

$$-\int_1^2 p\, dv = \quad 4.27 \times 10^4$$

adding $\qquad\qquad 6.42 \times 10^4 = \displaystyle\int_1^2 v\, dp.$

If compression is isothermal, the following work is done:

$$W_{1-2} = -\int_1^2 p\, dv = \int_1^2 v\, dp = RT \ln \frac{p_2}{p_1}$$

$$= 53.34 \times 530 \ln \frac{80}{14.7} = 47{,}800 \text{ ft-lbf/lbm}.$$

3-10
Applications of
the Steady
Flow Energy
Equation

In applying the steady flow energy equation to an open system or a control volume, it is important to know which forms of energy play dominant roles. Those energies that have only negligible effects can then be ignored, as is illustrated in the following applications:

(a) *Heating or cooling in a steady flow process:* In the steam generator shown in Fig. 3.13, chemical energy in the fuel is released by the combustion process. Most of this energy is transferred through the boiler heating surface to water, converting the water to steam. Finally, the gaseous combustion products leave through the stack. Although the water at the entrance and the steam at the exit differ markedly in enthalpy, the difference in both their kinetic energy and their potential energy is small compared to enthalpy changes. The piping system is ordinarily designed, in this type of equipment, for a low velocity flow, in order to minimize frictional losses. Therefore,

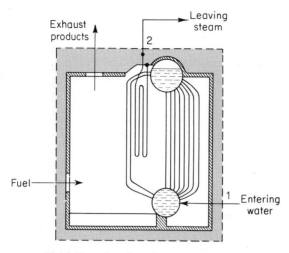

Fig. 3.13.   *Flow through a steam generator.*

these two types of energy can usually be neglected. Finally, since no work is done on the steam generator, application of the first law leads to

$$q_{1-2} + \sum h = 0 \quad \text{or} \quad q_{1-2} = h_2 - h_1,$$

where q_{1-2} is the net heat transferred to the system per unit mass between points 1 and 2.

(b) *Adiabatic steady flow process in a turbine (or a compressor)*: A turbine converts the enthalpy of a fluid into work. In the system shown in Fig. 3.14 some of the energy of the fluid exists as kinetic energy and potential energy. Only minor differences in these forms of energy occur as the fluid passes from section 1 to section 2. Since the heat interaction in a turbine is

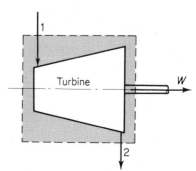

Fig. 3.14.   *Flow through a turbine.*

relatively small, expansion may be assumed adiabatic, so that the first law reduces to

$$w_{1-2} + \Sigma\, h = 0 \quad \text{or} \quad w_{1-2} = (h_2 - h_1).$$

EXAMPLE 3.9:   Steam at the rate of 1700 lbm/hr enters a turbine with an enthalpy of $h_1 = 1340$ Btu/lbm and leaves with an enthalpy of $h_2 = 1000$ Btu/lbm. The velocity of the steam at entrance is $V_1 = 300$ ft/sec and at exit is $V_2 = 400$ ft/sec. If section 1 is at an elevation 7 ft higher than section 2, and the heat transfer from the turbine casing to the environment is 600 Btu/hr, find the horsepower developed by the turbine. Assume steady flow conditions.

Solution: Substituting the values given in the problem into the first law gives

$$-\frac{600}{1700} + \frac{P_{1-2}}{1700} + \left(1340 + \frac{(300)^2}{2 \times 32.174 \times 778} + \frac{32.2 \times 7}{32.174 \times 778}\right)$$

$$-\left(1000 + \frac{(400)^2}{2 \times 32.174 \times 778} + \frac{0}{778}\right) = 0,$$

$$-0.353 + \frac{P_{1-2}}{1700} + (1340 + 1.8 + 0.009) - (1000 + 3.19 + 0) = 0,$$

from which

$$P_{1-2} = -575,000 \text{ Btu/hr}$$

$$= -226 \text{ hp}.$$

If the potential, kinetic, and heat energies were neglected in these calculations, the horsepower calculated in this example would amount to -227 hp.

EXAMPLE 3.10:   A pump raises the pressure of water in a line by 40 psi. The pump exit is 20 ft above the inlet. Neglecting the changes in internal and kinetic energies between inlet and exit, compute the shaft work needed to drive the pump. (The density of water is 62.4 lbm/ft³.)

Solution: The first law applied to this example is

$$w_{1-2} + \Sigma\left(pv + \frac{gz}{g_c}\right) = 0,$$

$$w_{1-2} - \frac{40 \times 144}{62.4} - 20 = 0,$$

from which

$$w_{1-2} = 112.1 \text{ ft-lbf/lbm}.$$

This is the amount of shaft work supplied if the system were 100 per cent efficient.

(c) *Steady flow through a nozzle, orifice or venturi meter:* In a nozzle, the flow of the fluid is accelerated while the enthalpy of the fluid is diminished accordingly. At the same time, the pressure drops. In the system shown in Fig. 3.15, there is no work interaction, the heat interaction is negligible, and

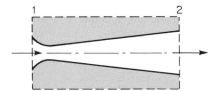

Fig. 3.15.   *Flow through a convergent-divergent nozzle.*

there is no change in potential energy. Hence, the enthalpy drop, according to the first law, is equal to the increase in kinetic energy:

$$\Sigma \left(h + \frac{V^2}{2g_c} \right) = 0 \quad \text{or} \quad \left(h_1 + \frac{V_1^2}{2g_c} \right) - \left(h_2 + \frac{V_2^2}{2g_c} \right) = 0.$$

When V_1 is small, then

$$V_2 = \sqrt{2g_c(h_1 - h_2)} = 223.8 \sqrt{h_1 - h_2} \text{ ft/sec,}$$

where the enthalpy is in Btu/lbm.

EXAMPLE 3.11:   Steam enters a nozzle at a pressure of 400 psia and a temperature of 600°F ($h_1 = 1306.9$ Btu/lbm) and leaves at a pressure of 250 psia with a velocity of 1567 ft/sec. The rate of flow of steam through the nozzle is 3000 lbm/hr. Neglecting the inlet velocity of the steam and considering the flow to be adiabatic, find (a) the enthalpy h_2, (b) the nozzle exit area if $v_2 = 2.122$ ft³/lbm.

Solution: Assuming one-dimensional flow, properties are uniform across the sections at inlet and outlet of the nozzle. Since the change in potential energy between entrance and exit is small compared with the changes in enthalpy and kinetic energy, therefore

(a) $h_1 = h_2 + \dfrac{V_2^2}{2g_c}$,

$$h_2 = 1306.9 - \frac{(1567)^2}{2 \times 32.174 \times 778} = 1257.9 \text{ Btu/lbm.}$$

(b) From the continuity equation,

$$A_2 = \frac{\dot{m}v_2}{V_2} = \frac{(3000/3600) \times 2.122}{1567} = 0.00118 \text{ ft}^2 = 0.17 \text{ in.}^2$$

(d) *Throttling process: Throttling* is an irreversible process in which a fluid, flowing across a restriction, undergoes a drop in total pressure. Such a process occurs in the flow through a porous plug, a partially closed valve, or a small orifice. Joule and Thomson performed the basic throttling experiments in the period 1852–62, and their experiments clarified the process and led to use of throttling as a method for determining certain properties of gaseous substances.

The apparatus used in the Joule-Thomson experiment is shown in Fig. 3.16. A steady stream of gas flows through a porous plug contained in

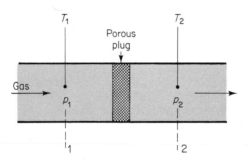

Fig. 3.16. *Throttling process, the Joule-Thomson porous-plug experiment.*

a horizontal tube. This system is open, is thermally insulated ($q_{1-2} = 0$), and does not exchange work with its environment ($w_{1-2} = 0$). At sections 1 and 2, both the temperature and the pressure are measured. If the kinetic energy does not change significantly as the fluid passes through the porous plug, the steady flow energy equation reduces to

$$h_1 = h_2. \tag{3.44}$$

Hence, in an adiabatic throttling process the enthalpy remains constant. When a series of Joule-Thomson experiments is performed at the same initial temperature t_1 and pressure p_1 but with a different downstream pressure, it is found that the temperature t_2 changes. Results from these experiments can be plotted as a constant-enthalpy curve on a T-p plane. If several different rates of flow are established at each condition of t_1 and p_1, a series of isenthalpic (constant enthalpy) curves is obtained. These are shown in Fig. 3.17. The maximum point on each curve is called the *inversion point* and the locus of the inversion points is called the *inversion curve*. The slope of an isenthalpic curve is called the *Joule-Thomson coefficient* μ_h and is expressed by

$$\mu_h = \left(\frac{\partial T}{\partial p}\right)_h. \tag{3.45}$$

At the left side of an inversion point, μ_h is positive; at the right side of an inversion point, μ_h is negative; at the inversion point, μ_h is zero. Since there

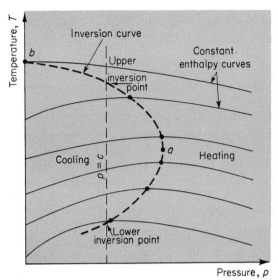

Fig. 3.17. *Inversion and constant-enthalpy curves of a real gas.*

is always a pressure drop in a throttling process, Δp is always negative. Therefore when μ_h is positive, the temperature change is negative, and throttling produces cooling. Similarly, when μ_h is negative, the temperature change is positive, and throttling produces a rise in temperature, even though the process itself is adiabatic. At any particular pressure, μ_h is positive only within a certain temperature range. These temperatures are called the *upper* and *lower* inversion points, and are indicated in Fig. 3.17. Between these two temperatures, throttling causes a drop in the temperature of the gas; outside of this temperature range, throttling results in a temperature rise. Above a certain pressure, throttling can cause only a heating effect. This is point a in Fig. 3.17. Similarly, above a certain temperature throttling can cause only a heating effect. This is point b in Fig. 3.17. In the case of a perfect gas, enthalpy is a function of temperature alone, and therefore the temperature of the gas remains constant in a throttling process so that $\mu_h = 0$. In the case of a real gas the temperature generally does change with pressure, and μ_h is a function of both temperature and pressure.

The Joule-Thomson experiments can be used to determine the specific heat of a gas. Let h be expressed in terms of p and t so that

$$dh = \left(\frac{\partial h}{\partial p}\right)_t dp + \left(\frac{\partial h}{\partial t}\right)_p dt.$$

But for an adiabatic throttling process, $dh = 0$, so that

$$0 = \left(\frac{\partial h}{\partial p}\right)_t \left(\frac{\partial p}{\partial t}\right)_h + \left(\frac{\partial h}{\partial t}\right)_p,$$

or

$$c_p = \left(\frac{\partial h}{\partial t}\right)_p = -\left(\frac{\partial h}{\partial p}\right)_t \left(\frac{\partial p}{\partial t}\right)_h = -\frac{1}{\mu_h}\left(\frac{\partial h}{\partial p}\right)_t. \tag{3.46}$$

The property $(\partial h/\partial p)_t$ is called the *constant temperature coefficient*. It can be determined by the Joule-Thomson experiment in which the fluid in the test section is maintained at a constant temperature but is subjected to different pressures. The test section is immersed in a constant-temperature bath, and as the pressure is changed, the energy (such as electrical energy) required to maintain the bath at a constant temperature is measured. In this case the enthalpy does not remain constant, and Δh is given by

$$\Delta h = h_2 - h_1 = q_{1-2},$$

where q_{1-2} is the heat interaction per unit mass between the system and the environment. As will be shown in Chapter 4, $(\partial h/\partial p)_t$ can be evaluated from measurable quantities. Equation (3.46) can then be used to calculate c_p and consequently other properties, such as internal energy, enthalpy, and specific volume.

**3-11
First Law
Applied to
Steady-state
Chemical
Processes**

Another application of the first law of thermodynamics lies in the analysis of chemical reactions, particularly where steady-state flow at constant pressure occurs. Consider reactants a and b undergoing a chemical process in which they are transformed into products c and d. According to the first law,

$$m_a h_a + m_b h_b + Q + W = m_c h_c + m_d h_d. \tag{3.47}$$

Note that changes in kinetic energy and potential energy are assumed to be negligible in this case and that the main changes occur in chemical energy which is included in the enthalpy terms. Because the chemical energies of the various substances must be expressed on a relative basis, all energies are based on an arbitrary reference standard state. Identifying the reference state by superscript ($°$), Eq. (3.47) becomes

$$m_a(h - h°)_a + m_b(h - h°)_b + Q + W = m_c(h - h°)_c + m_d(h - h°)_d$$
$$- [(m_a h_a° + m_b h_b°) - (m_c h_c° + m_d h_d°)], \tag{3.48}$$

where h represents sensible energy and $h°$ represents chemical energy at the reference state. The latter term of Eq. (3.48), representing the enthalpy of reaction at the reference state, can be determined by calorimetric measurements, and may be replaced by

$$(-\Delta H^\circ) = [(m_a h_a^\circ + m_b h_b^\circ) - (m_c h_c^\circ + m_d h_d^\circ)],$$

Equation (3.48) therefore becomes

$$m_a(h - h^\circ)_a + m_b(h - h^\circ)_b + Q + W + (-\Delta H^\circ)$$
$$= m_c(h - h^\circ)_c + m_d(h - h^\circ)_d , \qquad \textbf{(3.49)}$$

where ΔH° is the *enthalpy of reaction* or, in the case of combustion of a fuel, *enthalpy of combustion* at the standard state. The enthalpy of combustion represents the energy evolved in the complete oxidation of a fuel, provided that both reactants and products are at the standard state. The constant-pressure heating value of a fuel (defined in Chapter 11) and the enthalpy of combustion have the same magnitude but are of opposite sign.

When chemical reactions occur at constant volume, rather than at constant pressure, a similar analysis can be applied. From the first law of thermodynamics,

$$m_a(u - u^\circ)_a + m_b(u - u^\circ)_b + Q + W + (-\Delta U^\circ)$$
$$= m_c(u - u^\circ)_c + m_d(u - u^\circ)_d , \qquad \textbf{(3.50)}$$

where ΔU° is called the *internal energy of reaction*, or the *internal energy of combustion* at the standard state. The constant-volume heating value of a fuel (defined in Chapter 11) and the internal energy of combustion are of the same magnitude but of opposite sign.

The internal energy of reaction is related to the enthalpy of reaction as follows:

$$\Delta H = \Delta U + \Delta(pV)$$

and, at the reference state,

$$(\Delta H^\circ) = (\Delta U^\circ) + \Delta(pV)^\circ.$$

Using subscripts r and p to refer to reactants and products, this may be written as

$$(\Delta H^\circ)_{rp} = (\Delta U^\circ)_{rp} + [(pV)_p^\circ - (pV)_r^\circ]. \qquad \textbf{(3.51)}$$

Since the volume occupied by solids and liquids is negligible compared with gases, the last bracket in Eq. (3.51) would represent only the volumes of gaseous products and reactants when a combustion process is involved. If, furthermore, the gaseous reactants and products follow the perfect-gas laws,

$$(pV)_r^\circ = n_r \mathcal{R} T_o \, ,$$

$$(pV)_p^\circ = n_p \mathcal{R} T_o \, .$$

Equation (3.51), expressed on the basis of 1 mole of fuel, then becomes

$$(\Delta \bar{h}^\circ)_{rp} = (\Delta \bar{u}^\circ)_{rp} + (n_p - n_r) \mathcal{R} T_o \, , \qquad (3.52)$$

where $(\Delta \bar{h}^\circ)_{rp} =$ enthalpy of combustion per mole of fuel
$(\Delta \bar{u}^\circ)_{rp} =$ internal energy of combustion per mole of fuel
$n_p =$ number of moles of products per mole of fuel
$n_r =$ number of moles of reactants per mole of fuel.
Equation (3.52) can also be expressed on the basis of 1 lbm of fuel:

$$(\Delta h^\circ)_{rp} = (\Delta u^\circ)_{rp} + (n_p - n_r) \frac{\mathcal{R} T_o}{M_f} \, , \qquad (3.53)$$

where M_f is the molecular weight of the fuel. Chemical processes are discussed in more detail in Chapter 11.

EXAMPLE 3.12:   A fuel has an enthalpy of combustion ΔH° of $-19,000$ Btu/lbm at a reference temperature of 77°F (25°C). The fuel is supplied to a burner at 77°F with 30 lbm of air at 110°F per lbm of fuel. If the products of combustion leave at a temperature of 600°F, what is the amount of heat released per pound mass of fuel? Enthalpy values are as follows:

Temperature (°F)	Enthalpy of Air (Btu/lbm)	Enthalpy of Products (Btu/lbm)
77	128.34	130.5
110	136.26	138.7
600	255.96	263.5

Solution: Substituting in Eq. (3.48) yields

$$30(136.26 - 128.34) + 0 + Q + 0 + 19,000 = (30 + 1)(263.5 - 130.5),$$

from which,

$$Q = -18,274.6 \text{ Btu/lbm.}$$

EXAMPLE 3.13:   The energy of combustion of n-heptane (C_7H_{16}) at constant volume and 25°C is 1157 kcal/gm-mole. Find the enthalpy of combustion.

Solution: The chemical equation may be written as

$$C_7H_{16}(l) + 11\,O_2(g) \longrightarrow 7\,CO_2(g) + 8\,H_2O(l);$$

since $\Delta \bar{u}^\circ = -1157$ kcal/gm-mole, Eq. (3.52) gives

$$(\Delta \bar{h}^\circ)_{rp} = (\Delta \bar{u}^\circ)_{rp} + (n_p - n_r)\mathscr{R}T_0$$
$$= -1,157,000 + (7 - 11)\left(\frac{1545}{778}\right)(298) = -1,160,000 \text{ cal/gm-mole.}$$

3-12
Unsteady or
Transient Flow
Processes

In a transient flow process, both the mass and the state of the fluid within a system change continuously. Consider the flow of gas through a pipeline and into a vessel as shown in Fig. 3.18. Let subscripts 1 and 2 refer to the initial and final conditions in the vessel, respectively. While the gas is filling the vessel, conditions in the pipeline, denoted by subscript p, remain constant.

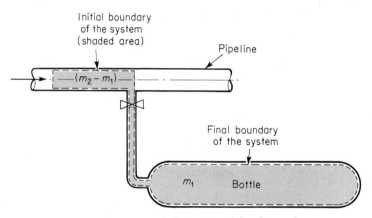

Fig. 3.18. *Unsteady flow process* (*closed system*).

We present two methods of solution: one a closed system analysis, the other, a control volume analysis.

First consider a closed system, so that no mass crosses the boundaries of the system. The system then includes not only the vessel but also that portion of the fluid in the pipeline which eventually will be introduced into the vessel. This system has variable boundaries, and in the final state, the boundaries are the same as those of the vessel. According to the first law of thermodynamics,

$$Q_{1-2} + W_{1-2} = (E_2 - E_1).$$

The initial energy of the system, E_1 consists of the energy of the mass initially in the vessel plus the energy of fluid which will eventually flow from the pipe into the vessel. Since changes in potential energies can be neglected, the change in internal energy is

$$\Delta E = E_2 - E_1 = m_2 u_2 - \left[m_1 u_1 + (m_2 - m_1) \left(\frac{V_p^2}{2g_c} + u_p \right) \right].$$

Work must be done on the system to introduce the mass $(m_2 - m_1)$ into the vessel, thus reducing the volume of the system to its final state, that is, the volume of the vessel. The mass in the pipeline, $m_2 - m_1$, is subjected to constant pressure, p_p, and therefore the work of compression is

$$W_{1-2} = -p_p \Delta V_p = p_p(m_2 - m_1)v_p,$$

where ΔV_p is the change in the volume of the system and v_p is the specific volume of the fluid in the pipeline. Substituting these expressions for ΔE and W_{1-2} in the first law, yields

$$Q_{1-2} + p_p(m_2 - m_1)v_p = m_2 u_2 - m_1 u_1 - (m_2 - m_1) \left(\frac{V_p^2}{2g_c} + u_p \right).$$

Since $h_p = u_p + p_p v_p$, therefore,

$$Q_{1-2} = m_2 u_2 - m_1 u_1 - (m_2 - m_1) \left(\frac{V_p^2}{2g_c} + h_p \right). \tag{3.54}$$

On the other hand, the system may be treated as a control volume, as shown in Fig. 3.19. The first law, according to Eq. (3.33b), takes the form,

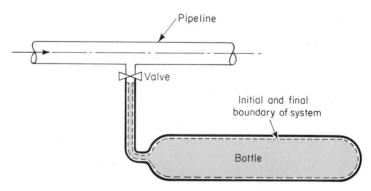

Fig. 3.19. *Unsteady flow process (open system).*

or expressed verbally:

transitional	net energy entering the	change of energy
energy	+ vessel and associated	= in the control
(W or Q)	with the entering matter	volume.

In this case, there is no work interaction, but the energy of the fluid in the pipeline represents enthalpy rather than internal energy. The first law therefore reduces to

$$Q_{1-2} + (m_2 - m_1)\left(h_p + \frac{V_p^2}{2g_c}\right) = m_2 u_2 - m_1 u_1.$$

Here, too, the potential energies have been considered negligible. Rearranging the preceding equation gives

$$Q_{1-2} = m_2 u_2 - m_1 u_1 - (m_2 - m_1)\left(\frac{V_p^2}{2g_c} + h_p\right),$$

which is the same result obtained previously.

EXAMPLE 3.14: An evacuated chamber is connected through a valve with a large pipeline containing steam at 50 psia and 400°F ($h = 1235.1$ Btu/lbm). The valve is opened and steam flows into the chamber until the pressure within the chamber is 50 psia. At the same time heat is transferred from the chamber at the rate of 300 Btu/lbm of steam introduced. Neglecting the kinetic and potential energies of the steam, determine the final specific internal energy of the steam in the chamber.

Solution: Treating this as a closed system or as a control volume, Eq. (3.54) gives

$$mq_{1-2} = mu_2 - 0 - m(0 + h_p).$$

Dividing by m,

$$q_{1-2} = u_2 - h_p.$$

Substituting values in the preceding equation gives

$$-300 = u_2 - 1235.1 \quad \text{or} \quad u_2 = 935.1 \text{ Btu/lbm.}$$

EXAMPLE 3.15: An insulated tank of volume V_1 (see Fig. 3.20), contains a perfect gas at temperature T_1 and pressure p_1. The tank is connected by a valve to an environment at a pressure p_2. If the valve is opened and the pressure in the tank drops to the environment pressure, find the ratio of the final to the initial temperature in the tank. Solve the problem by considering the system as a closed system, then as a control volume.

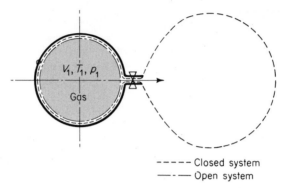

----- Closed system
---·--- Open system

Fig. 3.20. *Example 3.15.*

Solution: (a) Closed system: Since there is no heat interaction and since the work is associated with the expansion of the gas from p_1, V_1 to p_2, V_2, the first law can be written as

$$\bar{d}W = dU.$$

Noting that the surrounding pressure p_2 remains constant, then

$$-p_2(V_2 - V_1) = mc_v(T_2 - T_1).$$

Since

$$m = \frac{p_1 V_1}{R T_1} \quad \text{and} \quad c_v = \frac{R}{\gamma - 1},$$

therefore,

$$-p_2 V_1 \left(\frac{V_2}{V_1} - 1\right) = \frac{p_1 V_1}{R T_1} \frac{R}{\gamma - 1} (T_2 - T_1)$$

$$-\frac{p_2}{p_1}\left(\frac{p_1 T_2}{T_1 p_2} - 1\right) = \frac{1}{\gamma - 1}\left(\frac{T_2}{T_1} - 1\right)$$

$$-\frac{T_2}{T_1} + \frac{p_2}{p_1} = \frac{1}{\gamma - 1}\left(\frac{T_2}{T_1} - 1\right)$$

$$\frac{T_2}{T_1}\left(\frac{1}{\gamma - 1} + 1\right) = \frac{p_2}{p_1} + \frac{1}{\gamma - 1}$$

$$\frac{T_2}{T_1} = \frac{\gamma - 1}{\gamma}\left[\frac{p_2}{p_1} + \frac{1}{\gamma - 1}\right].$$

(b) Control volume: Considering the energy balance, the energy entering the control volume must be equal to the increase in energy of the control volume. The first law then becomes

$$-h(-dm) = dU.$$

Noting that $U = um$, then

$$h\,dm = m\,du + u\,dm.$$

But

$$h = u + pv = u + RT.$$

Therefore,

$$(u + RT) \, dm = m \, du + u \, dm$$

$$RT \, dm = m \, du$$

$$\frac{dm}{m} = \frac{c_v \, dT}{RT}.$$

Integrating,

$$\ln \frac{m_2}{m_1} = \frac{c_v}{R} \ln \frac{T_2}{T_1}.$$

But

$$m_1 = \frac{p_1 V}{R T_1} \quad \text{and} \quad m_2 = \frac{p_2 V}{R T_2},$$

and therefore,

$$\ln \frac{p_2 T_1}{T_2 p_1} = \frac{c_v}{R} \ln \frac{T_2}{T_1}$$

or

$$\frac{p_2 T_1}{p_1 T_2} = \left(\frac{T_2}{T_1} \right)^{c_v/R} = \left(\frac{T_2}{T_1} \right)^{(1/\gamma - 1)}$$

$$\frac{T_2}{T_1} = \left(\frac{p_2}{p_1} \right)^{(\gamma - 1)/\gamma} \qquad \text{(reversible adiabatic relation).}$$

Evidently, the results obtained in treating the problem as a closed system differ from those obtained by the control-volume approach. The closed system method is based on the assumption that equilibrium is maintained between the gas in the tank and the gas outside. This is nonrealistic because the process occurs very rapidly and because heat interaction between gas in the pipe and gas in the tank takes place through a pipe of small diameter so that the temperature of the gas in the tank is different from the temperature of the gas leaving the control volume. The two results are, however, not too dissimilar. For, if the reversible adiabatic relation, obtained by the control-volume procedure, is expanded by the binomial series, we obtain

$$\frac{T_2}{T_1} = \left(\frac{p_2}{p_1} \right)^{(\gamma - 1)/\gamma} = \left(1 - \frac{p_1 - p_2}{p_1} \right)^{(\gamma - 1)/\gamma}$$

$$= \left[1 - \frac{\gamma - 1}{\gamma} \left(\frac{p_1 - p_2}{p_1} \right) - \frac{\gamma - 1}{2! \gamma^2} \left(\frac{p_1 - p_2}{p_1} \right)^2 - \cdots \right]$$

$$= \frac{\gamma - 1}{\gamma} \left[\frac{1}{\gamma - 1} + \frac{p_2}{p_1} - \frac{1}{2! \gamma} \left(\frac{p_1 - p_2}{p_1} \right)^2 - \cdots \right].$$

The first two terms in this expansion are the same as the result obtained by the closed system technique.

3-13 Comparison of the Steady-state Energy Equation for an Open System with the Equations of Motion of Fluid Mechanics

The steady-state energy equation derived in this chapter is a general equation. But Euler's equation and Bernoulli's equation, which were derived in Chapter 2, apply only under restricted conditions. Euler's equation was derived by applying the momentum principle to a fluid particle along a streamline, and is

$$v \, dp + \frac{V \, dV}{g_c} + \frac{g}{g_c} dz = 0. \qquad (3.55)$$

This equation applies to flow under steady-state conditions, in which there is no shaft work, no friction, and no electrical, magnetic, or capillary forces.

Bernoulli's equation is

$$p_1 v + \frac{V_1^2}{2g_c} + \frac{g}{g_c} z_1 = p_2 v + \frac{V_2^2}{2g_c} + \frac{g}{g_c} z_2. \qquad (3.56)$$

The same restrictions that apply to Euler's equation also apply to Bernoulli's equation; however, in addition, this equation applies only to an incompressible fluid. Bernoulli's equation holds true along a streamline.

The steady-state energy equation for an open system or a control volume is

$$q_{1-2} + w_{1-2} + \left(p_1 v_1 + u_1 + \frac{V_1^2}{2g_c} + \frac{g z_1}{g_c} \right) = \left(p_2 v_2 + u_2 + \frac{V_2^2}{2g_c} + \frac{g z_2}{g_c} \right). \qquad (3.57)$$

Although all the terms in Bernoulli's equation (3.56) appear in the steady-state equation (3.57), Bernoulli's equation is not a special case of the steady-state energy equation. Bernoulli's equation, which applies to reversible incompressible flow is based on Newton's second law of motion and is independent of the first law of thermodynamics.

The differential form of the steady-state energy equation is

$$đq + đw = p \, dv + v \, dp + du + \frac{V \, dV}{g_c} + \frac{g \, dz}{g_c}. \qquad (3.58)$$

The steady-state equation may be applied to a system in which the restrictions specified by Euler's equation exist. Then when Eq. (3.55) is subtracted from

Eq. (3.58) and when $đw$ is set equal to zero, since Euler's equation requires that no shaft work be done, the following is obtained

$$đq = p \, dv + du.$$

This is the first law of thermodynamics applied to a closed system consisting of a one-component substance in which electrical, magnetic, and capillary effects are absent. The only work is the reversible $-p \, dv$ work.

Bernoulli's equation may be extended to include cases where frictional effects occur, taking the form:

$$\left(p_1 v + \frac{V_1^2}{2g_c} + \frac{gz_1}{g_c} \right) = \left(p_2 v + \frac{V_2^2}{2g_c} + \frac{gz_2}{g_c} \right) + \frac{gH_{l_{1-2}}}{g_c}, \tag{3.59}$$

where $H_{l_{1-2}}$ represents the total head loss due to dissipative effects between sections 1 and 2. If the foregoing equation is subtracted from the steady-state equation (3.57), then, in the absence of q and w, the following is obtained

$$\frac{gH_{l_{1-2}}}{g_c} = u_2 - u_1. \tag{3.60}$$

In the steady adiabatic flow of an incompressible fluid, energy dissipation due to friction, turbulence, etc., results in an increase in the internal energy of the fluid.

REFERENCES

3.1 Kiefer, P. J., G. F. Kinney, and M. C. Stuart, *Principles of Engineering Thermodynamics*. New York: John Wiley & Sons, Inc., 1954.

3.2 Lee, J. F., and F. W. Sears, *Thermodynamics*. Reading, Mass.: Addison-Wesley Publishing Company, Inc., 1955.

3.3 Mooney, D. A., *Mechanical Engineering Thermodynamics*. Englewood Cliffs, N.J.: Prentice-Hall, Inc., 1958.

3.4 Soo, S. L., *Thermodynamics of Engineering Science*. Englewood Cliffs, N.J.: Prentice-Hall, Inc., 1958.

3.5 Spalding, D. B., and E. H. Cole, *Engineering Thermodynamics*. New York: McGraw-Hill Book Company, 1959.

PROBLEMS

3.1 In a closed system, Fig. 3.21, a paddle wheel supplies work at the rate of 1 hp to the system. During a certain period of 1 min the system expands in volume from 1 ft³ to 3 ft³ while the pressure remains constant at 69.4 psia. Find the net work interaction during this 1-min period.

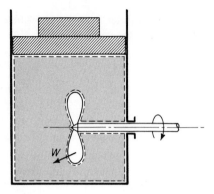

Fig. 3.21. Problem 3.1.

3.2 Ten lbm of a perfect gas are heated by supplying 170 Btu. During the process the volume is held constant at 131 ft³ but the pressure increases from 15 psia to 17.8 psia. Compute (a) maximum work done; (b) internal energy change of the gas; (c) density of the gas before and after the process.

3.3 The pressure of a gas in a piston-cylinder arrangement is given by the expression,

$p = 9V^2$; p = pressure in lbf/ft² and V = total volume in ft³.

(a) Find the work interaction if the volume increases from 5 ft³ to 10 ft³ in a reversible manner.

(b) If 6 Btu are transferred to the gas in the cylinder, what is the change of internal energy?

3.4 In a reversible steady flow process, a gas expands from an initial volume of 6 ft³ to a final volume of 12 ft³. The inlet line is located 12 ft below the outlet line, and the fluid enters with a negligible velocity. If the internal energy of the system decreases 30 Btu during the process, find the heat transferred. The relation between pressure and volume during the process is

$p = 300V + 1500$

(p is in lbf/ft², V in ft³).

3.5 The latent heat of vaporization of water at 40 psia is 933.7 Btu/lbm and the volume changes from 0.01715 ft³/lbm to 10.498 ft³/lbm. What is the change in internal energy due to evaporation?

3.6 The specific heat at constant volume, c_v, is given by the expression

$c_v = A + BT$,

where A and B are constants. Suppose that in general c_v is a function of both temperature and pressure. Determine whether the foregoing expression is a path or a point function by means of the properties of an exact differential.

3.7 A cylinder with a vertical axis has a frictionless piston in its upper end. The piston weight is such as to exert a pressure of 50 psia on the 1 lbm of gas enclosed. When the gas is cooled, its volume decreases from 3 to 1 ft³ and its internal energy increases from 50 to 20 Btu/lbm. Compute (a) work interaction; (b) heat interaction.

3.8 A perfect gas with $c_p = 0.241$ Btu/lbm°F and molecular weight $= 28.9$ lbm/lb-mole undergoes a reversible steady flow compression from 14.7 psia and 70°F to 73.5 psia. The relationship $pV^{1.25} = C$ describes the compression process.
(a) Derive a relationship to evaluate the work input necessary per lbm of gas.
(b) Find the horsepower necessary to drive the compressor for a flow rate of 2.5 lbm/min.
(c) Determine the cooling rate for the compressor in Btu/min.

3.9 Helium contained in a cylinder fitted with a piston expands reversibly according to the relation $pV^{1.5} = $ constant. The initial volume of the helium is 2 ft³, the initial pressure is 70 psia, and the initial temperature is 400°R. After expansion the pressure is 30 psia. Calculate (a) the work done during expansion and (b) the heat transfer during expansion.
For helium the following values apply:
   molecular weight $= 4.00$
   $c_p = 1.24$ Btu/lbm°F
   $\gamma = 1.66$.

3.10 Two lbm of a perfect gas with $c_p = 0.254$ Btu/lbm°F and $c_v = 0.155$ Btu/lbm°F, initially at a pressure of 50 psia and occupying a volume of 12 ft³, undergo a change of state during which the pressure and volume are both doubled. Find the change in internal energy.

3.11 The internal energy per lbm for a certain gas is given by

$$u = 0.17T + C,$$

where u is in Btu/lbm, T is °R, and C is a constant. If the gas is heated in a rigid container from a temperature of 100°F to 600°F, compute the work and the heat interactions per lbm?

3.12 Air initially at 100°F and 14.7 psia is compressed reversibly and isothermally in a nonflow process to a final pressure of 100 psia. Find
(a) Final temperature
(b) Work required per lbm of air
(c) Heat transferred per lbm of air.

3.13 The p-v-u relation for a certain gas is given by the equation:

$$u = 831 + 0.617pv,$$

where u is in Btu/lbm, p is in psia, and v is in ft³/lbm. Find the work done and the heat transferred to 1 lbm of this gas in the following reversible, nonflow processes:

Process	From		To	
	p (psia)	v (ft³/lbm)	p (psia)	v (ft³/lbm)
(a) Constant-pressure	124	4	124	8
(b) Constant internal energy	200	2	100	—

Find the work done in any nonflow process between the same end states as in process (b) if the heat transfer is 10 Btu/lbm.

3.14 A vessel with a volume of 2 ft³ contains air at 50 psia and 500°F. The vessel is connected to a cylinder in which the pressure is maintained at 15 psia by means of a movable piston. If the initial volume of the cylinder was zero and the process is reversible adiabatic, find
(a) The final temperature of the air occupying the vessel and the cylinder
(b) The work done.

3.15 An uninsulated frictionless piston is initially constrained in a rigid insulated cylinder. As shown in Fig. 3.22, air (assumed perfect gas) is trapped on

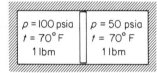

Fig. 3.22. Problem 3.15.

both sides of the piston. The piston is freed and equilibrium is reestablished.
(a) What is the final pressure?
(b) During the process, if a system boundary is imagined to pass through the piston, will heat be transferred? Explain.

3.16 Show that the increase in kinetic energy per unit decrease in pressure in a reversible adiabatic steady flow of a fluid is equal to the specific volume. Neglect changes in elevation.

3.17 Which of the following energies is always present in steady flow processes but never present in nonflow processes: (a) internal energy; (b) flow energy; (c) shaft work; (d) potential energy?

3.18 In a reversible nonflow process in which the pressure is maintained constant, the heat interaction is equal to (check the correct answer):
(a) Δu; (b) Δh; (c) W; (d) $p \Delta V$.

3.19 Which combination of the following energies may be encountered in a nonflow process:
(a) Kinetic energy, shaft work, and heat
(b) Flow work, heat, and internal energy
(c) Potential energy, flow work, and internal energy
(d) Internal energy, heat, and shaft work.

3.20 In a reversible steady flow compressor (neglecting kinetic, potential, and heat energies) the work supplied is equal to (check the correct answer):
(a) The drop in enthalpy
(b) The increase in internal energy
(c) The increase in flow work
(d) The increase in enthalpy.

3.21 An air preheater raises the temperature of the air supplied to a furnace from 60°F to 400°F, the pressure remaining constant. Considering $c_p = 0.241$ Btu/lbm°F and $c_v = 0.173$ Btu/lbm°F for air to be constant, find (a) the change in internal energy of each lbm of air; (b) the heat interaction per lbm of air.

3.22 The following values for steam are given for specific volume (ft³/lbm) and enthalpy (Btu/lbm).

	v	h
Water at 600 psia and 400°F	0.0186	375.4
Dry steam at 600 psia and 486.2°F	0.7698	1203.2

Compute the amount of energy supplied to a boiler per lbm of dry steam delivered at 600 psia if feedwater entered at 400°F. Separate this energy into the amount of increase in internal energy per lbm of the fluid, and the flow energy required to deliver the steam and that required for the entry of the water.

3.23 A nonflow process consists of an adiabatic expansion of 1 lbm of air in a cylinder. If the temperature of the air changes during the expansion from 70°F to 50°F, compute the work done on a frictionless piston during the process ($c_v = 0.173$ Btu/lbm°F).

3.24 Test-stand measurements indicate that the hot gases flowing through a rocket motor increase in velocity from effectively zero to 6100 ft/sec. What is the accompanying enthalpy change if the process is adiabatic, and what additional information is required to compute the accompanying temperature change?

3.25 In a test of a water-jacketed air compressor it was found that the shaft work required to drive the compressor was 60,000 ft lbf/lbm of air delivered, that the enthalpy of the air leaving was 30 Btu/lbm greater than that entering, and that the energy removed by the circulating water was 40.5 Btu/lbm of air. From these data compute the amount of energy which must have been dissipated as heat to the atmosphere from the bearings, cylinder walls, etc.

3.26 A stationary fluid system is subjected to a process in which the pressure and volume change according to the relation $pV^{1.4} = C$. The initial pressure and volume are respectively 100 psia and 3 ft³, and the final pressure is 20 psia. (a) Find the $-p\,dV$ work for this process. (b) Would this be the work for a real process? Why?

3.27 Steam expands reversibly through a steam turbine. The pressure of the steam at the entrance is 250 psia and is 14.7 psia at the exit. The relation between pressure and volume during the process is

$$p = 100 v + 1000$$

(p is in lbf/ft², v is in ft³/lbm).
Neglecting kinetic and potential energies, find
(a) The work interaction.
(b) If the turbine has a heat loss of 50 Btu/lbm during the process, what is the change of internal energy?

3.28 A centrifugal compressor handles 60 lbm/min of dry air. The inlet air temperature is 540°R and the delivery temperature is 660°R. What is the shaft work required per lbm of air, and what is the total horsepower required? Heat effects may be neglected.

T(°R)	h (Btu/lbm)	u (Btu/lbm)
540	129.06	92.04
660	157.92	112.67

3.29 A certain gas passes through a centrifugal compressor in a non-adiabatic manner. The following data apply to this process.

	p (psia)	v (ft³/lbm)	h (Btu/lbm)
Intake	10	15	130
Discharge	50	5	220

(a) Considering the compression to be reversible and $-\int p\,dv = 125$ Btu/lbm, find the work done. Neglect kinetic and potential energies.
(b) Find the heat interaction during the process.

3.30 Air enters a compressor at 14.7 psia, has a specific volume of 13.36 ft³/lbm, a velocity of 50 ft/sec and an internal energy of 90.34 Btu/lbm. During the compression 58.5 Btu/lbm of air were transferred from the air to a cooler, and the air was delivered at 73.5 psia, 2.67 ft³/lbm, 50 ft/sec, and an internal energy of 90.34 Btu/lbm. Determine the work ideally required to accomplish the compression.

3.31 Steam expands in a nozzle from an initial pressure of 400 psia to a final pressure of 3-in. Hg abs. If the initial and final enthalpies are 1250 Btu/lbm and 875 Btu/lbm respectively, calculate the final velocity in ft/sec if the initial velocity is negligible. Neglect potential energy changes and heat losses.

3.32 A nozzle is supplied with a fluid whose enthalpy is 1439 Btu/lbm and whose velocity is 800 ft/min. At exit the velocity is 2280 ft/sec. Neglecting potential energy changes and heat transfer, find the final enthalpy.

3.33 In a steady flow process, 100 lbm/min of water at 180°F enters a mixing tank where it mixes with 50 lbm/min of water at 60°F. If the enthalpy of water is given by $h = (1)\,(t - 32)$ Btu/lbm, what is the temperature of the exit mixture?

3.34 It is found for effectively dry air at atmospheric conditions that the change of enthalpy depends solely on change of temperature in conformity with the relation

$$\frac{\Delta h}{\Delta t} = 0.241 \text{ Btu/lbm}°\text{F}.$$

Using this information find the final temperature of air when it rises adiabatically from sea level to 10,000 ft altitude. The temperature of the air at sea level is 70°F. Change in velocity of the air is negligible. (*Hint:* Steady flow.)

3.35 Water flows adiabatically in a constant diameter pipe past a throttling valve that is partially open. Subscripts 1 and 2 refer to conditions before and after the valve.
(a) Is $(h_2 - h_1)$ positive, negative, or zero?
(b) Is $(p_2 - p_1)$ positive, negative, or zero?
(c) Is $(u_2 - u_1)$ positive, negative, or zero?
(d) Is $(t_2 - t_1)$ positive, negative, or zero?

3.36 Water is flowing in a 12-in. diameter, 500-ft long pipe at 10 ft per second. The friction drop per unit pipe length is given by

$$p_1 - p_2 = \frac{0.02 V^2}{2g_c} \frac{1}{v},$$

where p_1 = inlet pressure (lbf/ft²)
p_2 = outlet pressure (lbf/ft²)
V = water velocity (ft/sec)
v = specific volume (0.51 ft³/lbm)
(a) If the pipe is perfectly insulated, determine the change in internal energy of the fluid during its flow through the pipe (assume that water is incompressible).
(b) If the flow had been isothermal, determine the heat interaction.

3.37 Two air streams are mixed in a large chamber before passing through an air turbine as shown in Fig. 3.23. The exhaust of the turbine is discharged to

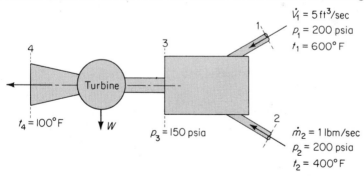

Fig. 3.23. *Problem 3.37.*

the atmosphere. Assuming steady adiabatic flow and neglecting changes in kinetic and potential energies determine:
(a) The temperature of the air at the turbine inlet
(b) The temperature at the discharge of the turbine if the rotor of the turbine is stalled, that is, not rotating

(c) The power developed by the turbine if the temperature at discharge is 100°F. (Assume air to be a perfect gas.)

$$c_p = 0.24 \text{ Btu/lbm°F}, \qquad c_v = 0.171 \text{ Btu/lbm°F}.$$

3.38 An air jet strikes a blade as shown in Fig. 3.24. Determine the magnitude and sense of R_x and R_y to hold the blade in place. Solve the problem for the following expansions in the nozzle: (a) adiabatic, (b) isothermal. (Assume air to be a perfect gas, and consider the system to be ideal.)

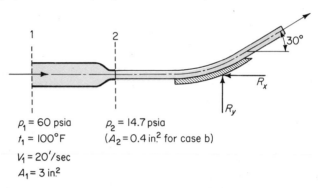

$p_1 = 60$ psia $p_2 = 14.7$ psia

$t_1 = 100°F$ $(A_2 = 0.4$ in.^{2} for case b)

$V_1 = 20'/\text{sec}$

$A_1 = 3$ in.^{2}

Fig. 3.24.   Problem 3.38.

3.39 Find the heat released when gaseous propane C_3H_8 (g) is burned in a constant-volume process at constant temperature of 77°F. Assume that the water vapor produced is in the vapor phase.

$$(\Delta H°)_{rp} = -19,929 \text{ Btu/lbm.}$$

3.40 Air $(c_p = 0.241$ Btu/lbm°F) at a pressure of 80 psia and 120°F flows through a pipeline. A tank which is connected to this line through a valve, initially contains air at a pressure of 14.7 psia and 70°F and has a volume of 6 ft³. Determine the mass of air which flows into the tank when the valve is opened if final pressure in the tank is 80 psia. (Assume an adiabatic process.)

NOMENCLATURE

c	Specific heat	s	Entropy per unit mass
c_p	Specific heat at constant pressure	T	Absolute temperature
c_v	Specific heat at constant volume	t	Temperature
E	Total internal energy	U	Internal energy
e	Total internal energy per unit mass	u	Internal energy per unit mass
		V	Volume
F, f	Function	v	Specific volume
I	Electric current	W	Work or probability
k	Boltzmann's constant	w	Work per unit mass
m	Mass of molecules	X, Y, Z	Functions of x, y, and z
N	Number of molecules	x, y, z	Cartesian coordinates
N_0	Avogadro's number	$\mathscr{E}$	Electric potential
p	Pressure		
Q	Heat	γ	Ratio of specific heats $= \dfrac{c_p}{c_v}$
q	Heat per unit mass	ψ, ϕ	Functions
R	Gas constant	ρ	Density
$\mathscr{R}$	Universal gas constant	λ	Integrating factor
S	Entropy		

4

THE SECOND LAW OF THERMODYNAMICS

4-1

Introduction

Physical processes proceeding toward equilibrium states occur spontaneously in nature. Water flows from higher to lower levels; heat flows from hot to cold bodies; and gases expand from higher pressures to lower pressures. Spontaneous processes can be reversed but they will not reverse themselves spontaneously; energy must be supplied to the system for a nonspontaneous process to occur. Energy from an external source is required to pump water from a lower to a higher level, or to compress a gas from a lower to a higher pressure, or to transfer heat from a cold body to a hot body.

A spontaneous process can proceed only in a particular direction. The first law of thermodynamics gives no information about direction; it states only that when one form of energy is converted into another, identical quantities of energy are involved regardless of the feasibility of the process. Thus the transfer of a certain quantity of heat from a low-temperature body to a high-temperature body, without the expenditure of work, would not violate the first law of thermodynamics. But experience indicates that this process is not possible. Similarly, many experiments demonstrated that when heat is transferred to a system only a portion of the heat can be converted into work. On the other hand, Joule's experiments showed that energy, when supplied to a system in the form of work, can be converted completely into heat. Evidently, heat and work are not completely interchangeable forms of energy. Furthermore, when energy is transferred from one form to another, there often is also a degradation of the supplied energy into a less "useful" form.

Consider the system shown in Fig. 4.1a. The engine receives a quantity of heat, Q_1 *, from a high-temperature reservoir at T_1 and performs an equal amount of work W_e, in accordance with the first law of thermodynamics. Also, a heat pump, operating between a low-temperature

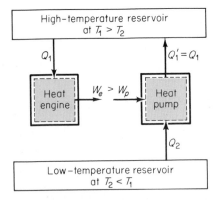

Fig. 4.1a. *Impossibility of converting heat completely into work in a cycle.*

*The subscript does *not* pertain to a state of a system but rather serves to identify a quantity of heat.

140

reservoir at T_2 and the high-temperature reservoir at T_1, extracts heat Q_2, delivers heat Q_1, and requires work W_p. If the pump could be adjusted so that the heat supplied by the pump and the heat transferred to the engine are identical, that is, $Q_1' = Q_1$, the high-temperature reservoir becomes super-fluous and can be eliminated without affecting the operation of either the engine or the pump. According to the first law, the energy required to perform work W_p would be less than the heat interaction Q_1. Therefore, as shown in Fig. 4.1b, the engine driving the pump would also be providing

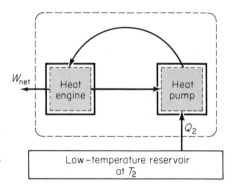

Fig. 4.1b. *Impossibility of converting heat completely into work in a cycle.*

net external work, such that $W_{net} = W_e - W_p$. In the system enclosed by the dotted boundaries, a quantity of heat, Q_2, would be transferred from the low temperature reservoir and an equal amount of work, W_{net}, would be delivered to the environment. If this were feasible, then it would be possible to convert the internal energy of low-temperature bodies in the universe, such as the earth or the ocean, into useful work. This has never been achieved and is not consistent with human experience. We must therefore conclude that our original assumption was invalid and that an engine extracting heat from a single thermal reservoir cannot convert all of the heat to work. On the other hand, there is no reason from the stand-point of thermodynamics why work cannot be completely converted into heat, and, in fact, this conversion is readily achieved.

The second law of thermodynamics provides a method of determining whether a process can take place, proceeding from one specified state to another specified state; it also explains why some processes can sponta-neously occur, whereas others cannot. Unlike the first law, the second law does not lead to an equation, but is instead expressed as an inequality. Like other physical laws of nature, the second law of thermodynamics has been confirmed by experimental evidence.

Following are some definitions which will be used in subsequent discussion of the second law.

Thermal reservoir: A thermal reservoir is a sufficiently large system in stable equilibrium to which and from which finite amounts of heat can be transferred without any change in its temperature. In dealing with heat-engine cycles, for example, a high-temperature reservoir, from which heat is transferred (heat source), and a low-temperature reservoir, to which heat is transferred (heat sink), will be considered.

Heat engine: A heat engine is a thermodynamic system operating in a cycle to which net heat is transferred and from which net work is delivered. The system or working fluid undergoes a series of processes which constitute the heat-engine cycle.

An index of performance of a work-producing machine or a heat engine is expressed by its *thermal efficiency*, defined as the ratio of the net work output to the heat input. Only a fraction of the heat input is converted into work and the rest is rejected. Referring to Fig. 4.2, let

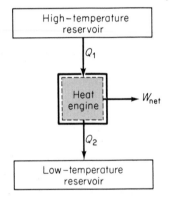

Fig. 4.2. *Principle of a heat engine.*

Q_1 = heat transferred to system,

Q_2 = heat transferred from system,

W_{net} = net work done by system.

Then the thermal efficiency is given by

$$\eta_{th} = \frac{W_{net}}{Q_1};$$

but the first law of thermodynamics applied to a cycle requires that,

$$\oint dQ + \oint dW = 0$$

or

$$Q_1 - Q_2 = W_{net}.$$

Therefore,

$$\eta_{\text{th}} = \frac{W_{\text{net}}}{Q_1} = \frac{Q_1 - Q_2}{Q_1} = 1 - \frac{Q_2}{Q_1}. \qquad (4.1)$$

Note that the efficiency of a heat engine operating between two thermal reservoirs is always less than unity.

A thermoelectric engine converts heat into electric energy. As shown in Fig. 4.3 it consists of two dissimilar electric conductors connected at two junctions. When the two junctions are maintained at different temperatures,

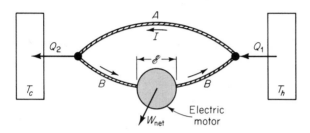

Fig. 4.3. *Thermoelectric heat engine.*

an electric current flows in the conductors. An electric motor placed in the circuit may be used to supply mechanical work. With the same notation used before, the efficiency of the thermoelectric device is

$$\eta = \frac{W_{\text{net}}}{Q_1} = \frac{\dot{W}_{\text{net}}}{\dot{Q}_1} = \frac{\mathscr{E} I}{\dot{Q}_1},$$

where $\mathscr{E}$ and I are the electric potential and current respectively.

Heat pump: A heat pump is a thermodynamic system operating in a cycle which removes heat from a low-temperature body and delivers heat to a high-temperature body. In accomplishing this, the heat pump receives

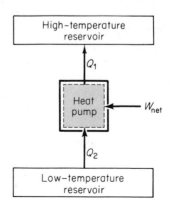

Fig. 4.4. *Principle of a heat pump.*

external energy in the form of work. The system or working substance undergoes a series of processes which constitute the heat pump cycle.

The heat pump may be used as a refrigerator where the primary function is the transfer of heat from a low-temperature system. In a heating system utilizing a heat pump, the primary function is the transfer of heat to a high-temperature system.

An index of performance of a heat pump is the coefficient of performance, COP. The definition of the COP depends on the primary interest, whether to operate the system as a heat pump or as a refrigerator. Referring to Fig. 4.4, let

Q_1 = heat rejected by system,

Q_2 = heat transferred to system,

W_{net} = net work required by system.

Applying the first law of thermodynamics to the cycle gives

$$\oint dQ + \oint dW = 0$$

or

$$Q_1 - Q_2 = W_{net}.$$

Therefore, the COP for a refrigerator is

$$COP_{ref} = \frac{Q_2}{W_{net}} = \frac{Q_2}{Q_1 - Q_2}, \qquad (4.2)$$

and for a heat pump,

$$COP_{\substack{heat \\ pump}} = \frac{Q_1}{W_{net}} = \frac{Q_1}{Q_1 - Q_2} = 1 + COP_{ref}. \qquad (4.3)$$

It is clear from Eq. (4.1), (4.2), and (4.3) that, in expressing the effectiveness of a heat engine in terms of efficiency or a heat pump in terms of coefficient of performance, the energy of primary interest is divided by the energy expended.

A thermoelectric heat pump transfers heat from a low- to a high-temperature thermal reservoir by supplying electric energy. As shown in Fig. 4.5, an amount of heat Q_2 is transferred from the low-temperature reservoir and an amount of heat Q_1 is transferred to the high-temperature reservoir. The COP of the thermoelectric heat pump is

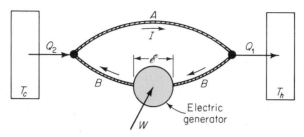

Fig. 4.5. *Thermoelectric heat pump.*

$$COP_{\text{heat pump}} = \frac{Q_1}{W} = \frac{\dot{Q}_1}{\mathscr{E}I},$$

and if the thermoelectric device is operated as a refrigerator then

$$COP_{\text{ref}} = \frac{Q_2}{W} = \frac{\dot{Q}_2}{\mathscr{E}I}.$$

4-2
The Second
Law of
Thermo-
dynamics

There are several statements of the second law of thermodynamics. This section deals with two of these: the *Kelvin-Planck* statement and the *Clausius* statement. Each statement is based on an irreversible process. The first considers the transformation of heat into work; the second considers the transfer of heat between two thermal reservoirs.

Kelvin-Planck statement: It is impossible to construct an engine that, operating continuously (in a cycle), will produce no effect other than the transfer of heat from a single thermal reservoir at a uniform temperature and the performance of an equal amount of work. This statement means that only part of the heat transferred to the working substance from a high-temperature reservoir is converted to work, the rest must be rejected to a low-temperature reservoir. Therefore, at least two thermal reservoirs of different temperature are necessary for a heat engine to operate. The statement further means that no heat engine can have a 100 per cent thermal efficiency. The word *continuous* in the Kelvin-Planck statement has an important implication. Consider the isothermal expansion of a perfect gas in a piston-cylinder arrangement as a result of heat interaction. Since the internal energy remains constant, the heat transfer, according to the first law, is completely converted into work. The motion of the piston results in an increase in the volume and a decrease in the pressures of the gas. The process continues till the end of the stroke at which no further work can be produced. This example indicates that continuous conversion of heat into work requires a *cyclic* process.

Clausius statement: It is impossible to construct a heat pump that, operating continuously, will produce no effect other than the transfer of heat from a lower-temperature body to a higher-temperature body. This statement means that energy (in the form of work) must be supplied to the heat pump in order to transfer heat from a cold body to a hot body. Therefore, the coefficient of performance can never be infinity.

Although the Kelvin-Planck and Clausius statements appear to be different, they are really equivalent in the sense that a violation of either statement implies the violation of the other. Assume that the heat engine shown in Fig. 4.6 is violating the Kelvin-Planck statement by absorbing heat from a single reservoir and producing an equal amount of work. The work

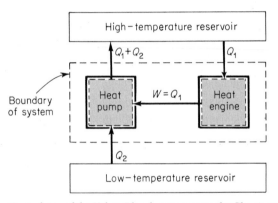

Fig. 4.6. *Equivalence of the Kelvin-Planck statement to the Clausius statement.*

output of the engine is used to drive a heat pump which transfers an amount of heat Q_2 from a low-temperature reservoir and an amount of heat $(Q_1 + Q_2)$ to a high-temperature reservoir. The combined system of the heat engine and heat pump then acts like a heat pump transferring an amount of heat Q_2 from the low-temperature to the high-temperature reservoir without any external work. This, of course, is a violation of the Clausius statement.

Similarly, to prove that a violation of the Clausius statement implies the violation of the Kelvin-Planck statement, consider a heat pump that is violating the Clausius statement. Figure 4.7 shows a heat pump which requires no work and transfers an amount of heat Q_2 from a low-temperature to a high-temperature reservoir. Let an amount of heat Q_1, greater than Q_2, be transferred from the high-temperature reservoir to a heat engine which develops a net work $W = Q_1 - Q_2$ and rejects Q_2 to the low-temperature

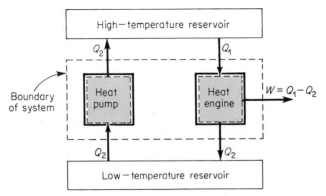

Fig. 4.7.   *Equivalence of the Clausius statement to the Kelvin-Planck statement.*

reservoir. Since there is no net heat interaction with the low-temperature reservoir, it can be eliminated. The combined system of the heat engine and heat pump acts then like a heat engine exchanging heat with a single reservoir, which is a violation of the Kelvin-Planck statement.

The foregoing analyses establish the equivalence of the Kelvin-Planck and Clausius statements of the second law of thermodynamics.

**4-3
Perpetual
Motion
Machine of the
Second Kind**
As shown in Section 3–2, a machine which violates the first law of thermodynamics was called a perpetual machine of the first kind. A *perpetual motion machine of the second kind* is one which operates in a cycle and delivers an amount of work equal to heat extracted from a single reservoir at a uniform temperature. Such a machine (efficiency 100 per cent) obviously violates the second law of thermodynamics and does not exist.

**4-4
The Carnot
Cycle**
French military engineer Nicolas Sadi Carnot (1769–1832), in his paper, "Réflections sur la puissance motrice du feu et les moyens propres à la développer,"* was among the first to study the principles of the second law of thermodynamics. Carnot was the first to introduce the concept of cyclic operation in which the working substance, after passing through a sequence of events, is brought back to its initial state. In his treatise, published in 1824, he devised a classical ideal cycle named after him. The Carnot cycle was based on the principles of the first law formulated later by Joule, and was the heuristic step in the evolution of the second law of thermodynamics 25 years later by Rudolf Clausius and William Thomson.

The Carnot cycle, as shown in Fig. 4.8, consists of an alternate series

*Reflections on the motive power of heat and the proper ways to develop it.

of two reversible isothermal processes and two reversible adiabatic processes. All processes are individually reversible and therefore the Carnot cycle as a whole is a reversible cycle. Let the system be an arbitrary but homogeneous working substance. Starting at an initial state 1 and referring to Fig. 4.8 the system undergoes a Carnot cycle in the following manner:

(a) During process 1-2 heat is transferred reversibly and isothermally to the working substance from a high-temperature reservoir at T_1. This process is accomplished reversibly by bringing the system in contact with a thermal reservoir whose temperature is equal to or infinitesimally higher than the working substance. During this process the system performs an amount of work equal to the area underneath path 1-2 of the p-V diagram.

(b) Process 2-3 is a reversible adiabatic expansion during which the system is thermally insulated and the temperature of the working substance decreases from the high temperature T_1 to the low temperature T_2. The work done in this process is represented by the area underneath path 2-3 of the p-V diagram.

(c) During process 3-4 the system is brought in contact with a low-temperature reservoir and heat is transferred reversibly and isothermally from the working substance to the low-temperature reservoir. This process requires that the temperature of the working substance be equal to or infinitesimally higher than the low-temperature reservoir. The work done on the system during this isothermal process is equal to the area underneath path 3-4 of the p-V diagram.

(d) The final process 4-1, which completes the cycle, is a reversible adiabatic process, and the working substance is returned to its original state at 1. During this process the temperature of the working substance is raised from the low temperature T_2 to the initial temperature T_1. The work done in this process is represented by the area underneath path 4-1 of the p-V diagram.

Since an amount of heat Q_1 is transferred to the working substance at the higher temperature, while Q_2 is transferred from the working substance at the lower temperature, the net heat transfer $Q_1 - Q_2$ is equal to the net work output of the cycle. This net work output is represented by the closed area 1-2-3-4 on the p-V diagram of Fig. 4.8 and is equal to $\oint p\,dV$.

The thermal efficiency of the cycle is given by,

$$\eta_{th} = \frac{W_{net}}{Q_1} = \frac{\oint p\,dV}{Q_1} = \frac{Q_1 - Q_2}{Q_1}. \tag{4.4}$$

If a Carnot cycle for a heat engine is carried out in a reversed sequence,

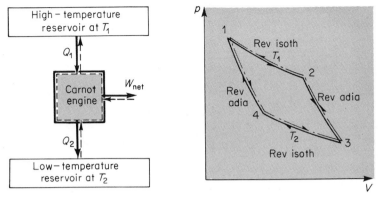

Fig. 4.8. The Carnot cycle. Solid and dotted lines apply to heat engine and heat pump respectively.

the result will be a Carnot cycle for a heat pump. Such a cycle is shown by dotted lines in Fig. 4.8. The individual reversible processes are performed in the following manner:

(a) Process 4-3 is a reversible isothermal process during which heat is transferred from the low-temperature reservoir to the working substance.

(b) Process 3-2 is a reversible adiabatic compression during which the temperature of the working substance is raised from the low temperature T_2 to the high temperature T_1.

(c) During process 2-1 heat is transferred reversibly and isothermally from the working substance to the high-temperature reservoir.

(d) To complete the cycle, the working substance is returned to its initial state 4 by the reversible adiabatic expansion 1-4. During this process the temperature of the working substance decreases from T_1 to T_2.

Similar to the heat engine cycle, the net work done on the system is represented by the area 1-2-3-4 of Fig. 4.8 and is equal to $-\oint p\,dV$. The coefficient of performance is

$$COP_{\text{ret}} = \frac{Q_2}{W_{\text{net}}} = \frac{Q_2}{-\oint p\,dV} = \frac{Q_2}{Q_1 - Q_2}. \tag{4.5}$$

Figures 4.9 and 4.10 show a heat engine and a heat pump operating on the Carnot cycle.

A final comment regarding the cycle is that any reversible cycle which operates between two constant but different temperature reservoirs and is composed of two reversible isothermals and two reversible adiabatics is a

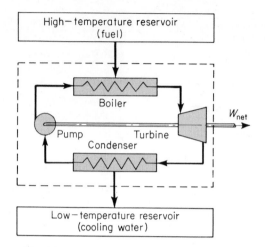

Fig. 4.9. *Carnot cycle for a heat engine.*

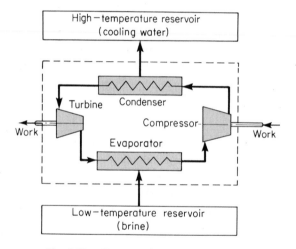

Fig. 4.10. *Carnot cycle for a heat pump.*

Carnot cycle. Reversible processes do not occur in nature and therefore the Carnot cycle is an ideal cycle. This however should not impair the concept of maximum work that could be obtained from ideal cycles. Ideal cycles are considered as a limit of optimum performance of real engines.

So far, in analyzing the Carnot cycle no specific characteristics were imposed regarding the working substance. As will be shown in the next section, the Carnot efficiency (and COP) is independent of the amount or the nature of the working substance.

4-5
The Carnot
Principle

The Carnot principle includes three propositions or corollaries which are of great use in comparing the performance of cycles. The method of proving Carnot propositions, is to assume first that the opposite of the proposition is true, and then to prove that the result leads to a violation of the second law of thermodynamics. The Carnot propositions are

(a) No heat engine operating in a cycle between two constant temperature reservoirs can be more efficient than a reversible engine operating between the same two reservoirs. As shown in Fig. 4.11, let any engine I and a reversible engine R operate between high- and low-temperature

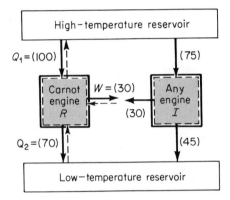

Fig. 4.11. The Carnot engine is the most efficient engine that could operate between two thermal reservoirs.

reservoirs. Engine R which operates on the Carnot cycle can be reversed to operate as a heat pump as shown by the dotted arrows in Fig. 4.11. For simplicity, assign numerical values to Q_1, Q_2, and W such as 100, 70, and 30. Operating as a heat engine, engine R will have an efficiency of 30 per cent; as a heat pump it will have a COP of $100/30 = 3.33$.

Assume that engine I is more efficient than engine R and has an efficiency of more than 30 per cent, say 40 per cent. Engine I then operates to develop 30 units of work so that it can be used to drive the Carnot heat pump. The heat input to engine I in this case should be $30/0.4 = 75$ units and the heat output is $75 - 30 = 45$ units.

If the foregoing is possible, then the combined system of the Carnot heat pump and engine I has the net effect of transferring 25 units of heat from the low- to the high-temperature reservoirs without any external work. This is obviously a violation of the Clausius statement of the second law of thermodynamics. Therefore the assumption that engine I has a higher efficiency than a reversible engine is invalid, and the reversible engine, operating on the Carnot cycle, is the most efficient engine that could operate between the two thermal reservoirs. Note that it was not proved explicitly that the efficiency of engine I is lower than that of a reversible engine, but rather no engine can be more efficient than a reversible one.

Another argument which leads to a violation of the Kelvin-Planck form of the second law and therefore leads to the same conclusion cited before, is

$$\eta_R = \frac{W_R}{Q_{1R}} = \frac{W_R}{W_R + Q_{2R}} = \frac{1}{1 + (Q_{2R}/W_R)}$$

and

$$\eta_I = \frac{W_I}{Q_{1I}} = \frac{W_I}{W_I + Q_{2I}} = \frac{1}{1 + (Q_{2I}/W_I)}.$$

Assume

$$\eta_I > \eta_R, \quad \text{then} \quad \frac{Q_{2R}}{W_R} > \frac{Q_{2I}}{W_I},$$

and for comparison, if

$$Q_{2R} = Q_{2I}, \quad \text{then} \quad W_I > W_R.$$

Now reversing the Carnot engine to operate as a heat pump, W_I can be used to supply W_R to the pump and a net work output $(W_I - W_R)$. Since $Q_{2R} = Q_{2I}$, the low-temperature reservoir can be eliminated and the net heat leaving the high-temperature reservoir is

$$Q_{1I} - Q_{1R} = (W_I + Q_{2I}) - (W_R + Q_{2R}) = W_I - W_R.$$

This means that heat is exchanged with a single reservoir and an equal amount of work is performed, which is contradictory to the Kelvin-Planck statement.

(b) The second corollary of Carnot states that all reversible engines operating between two constant temperature reservoirs, have the same efficiency irrespective of the working substance.

Let two reversible engines R and R' operate between the same constant-high and constant-low temperature reservoirs at temperature t_1 and t_2, respectively, and assume that engine R is more efficient than R'. Similar to the procedure outlined in proposition (a), if R is reversed to run as a heat pump using the output work of R', we come to the conclusion that the combined system of engine R and heat pump R' is removing heat continuously from the low- to the high-temperature reservoirs without any external work. This is contrary to the second law of thermodynamics. Therefore R cannot be more efficient than R'. Similarly if engine R' is assumed to be more efficient than R, it can be concluded that R' cannot be more efficient than R. Therefore, neither engine R nor R' can be more efficient than the other which means that they must have equal efficiencies, irrespective of the type of engine, so that

$$\eta_R = \eta_{R'}.$$

Hence

$$1 - \frac{Q_2}{Q_1} = 1 - \frac{Q_{2'}}{Q_{1'}},$$

where subscripts 1 and 2 refer to the higher and lower temperatures. The previous equation gives

$$\frac{Q_1}{Q_2} = \frac{Q_{1'}}{Q_{2'}}.$$

The ratio Q_1/Q_2 is therefore a constant for all reversible cycles operating between the two reservoirs and since no restrictions were imposed on the working substance, the efficiency of a reversible engine is independent of the nature of the working substance. This ratio is only a function of the two temperatures of the reservoirs, that is,

$$\frac{Q_1}{Q_2} = \phi(t_1, t_2) \tag{4.6}$$

and

$$\eta_R = 1 - \frac{Q_2}{Q_1} = 1 - \frac{1}{\phi(t_1, t_2)}. \tag{4.7}$$

The third corollary of Carnot, presented in Section 4.6, defines the nature of the function ϕ in Eq. (4.7).

**4-6
The Thermo-
dynamic
Temperature
Scale**
With the aid of the Carnot principle, Lord Kelvin (W. Thomson) in 1848 used energy as a thermometric property to define temperature and devised a temperature scale that is independent of the nature of the thermometric substance. It was shown in the previous section that the efficiency of a Carnot cycle operating between two thermal reservoirs is a function of the temperatures of the reservoirs. To determine the nature of the functions ϕ appearing in Eq. (4.6) and (4.7), consider three reversible engines operating between the pairs of temperature (t_1, t_2), (t_2, t_3), and (t_1, t_3) as shown in Fig. 4.12. Figure 4.13 shows the cycles on a p-V diagram where the three isotherms t_1, t_2, and t_3 $(t_1 > t_2 > t_3)$ intersect the two adiabatics a-f and b-e.

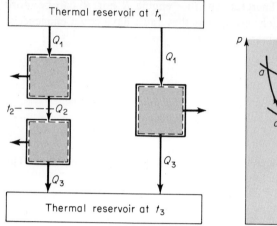

Fig. 4.12. *Definition of absolute temperature by means of Carnot engines.*

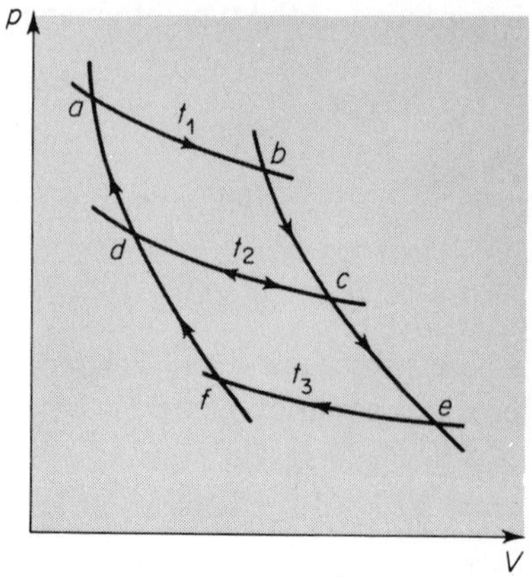

Fig. 4.13. *p-V diagram of Carnot engines.*

If Q_1, Q_2, and Q_3 represent the amounts of heat interaction at temperatures t_1, t_2, and t_3, then, for cycle *a-b-c-d*,

$$\frac{Q_1}{Q_2} = \phi(t_1, t_2),$$

for cycle *d-c-e-f*,

$$\frac{Q_2}{Q_3} = \phi(t_2, t_3),$$

and for cycle *a-b-e-f*,

$$\frac{Q_1}{Q_3} = \phi(t_1, t_3).$$

From the previous three equations then,

$$\frac{Q_1}{Q_2} = \frac{Q_1/Q_3}{Q_2/Q_3}$$

or

$$\phi(t_1, t_2) = \frac{\phi(t_1, t_3)}{\phi(t_2, t_3)}, \tag{4.8}$$

but since t_1, t_2, and t_3 are independent, and the efficiency of the engine operating between temperature t_1 and t_2 is unaffected by t_3, Eq. (4.8) is satisfied only when the function $\phi(t_1, t_2)$ is of the form* $\phi'(t_1)/\phi'(t_2)$, so that

$$\frac{Q_1}{Q_2} = \phi(t_1, t_2) = \frac{\phi'(t_1)}{\phi'(t_2)}.$$

If t_1 is higher than t_2, Q_1 is larger than Q_2 and therefore $\phi'(t_1)$ is larger than $\phi'(t_2)$. This means that the function $\phi'(t)$ increases with t and can be used for temperature measurement. If the arbitrary function $\phi'(t)$ is denoted by T, an absolute temperature scale may be defined to satisfy the relation,

$$\frac{Q_1}{Q_2} = \frac{T_1}{T_2}. \tag{4.9}$$

Equation (4.9) states that the ratio of any two temperatures on the absolute scale is equal to the ratio of the amounts of heat transferred to and from a reversible engine operating between reservoirs at these temperatures. Therefore, Eq. (4.9) may be used to measure the temperature of a system by imagining a Carnot engine to operate between the system and a thermal reservoir at a standard fixed point of temperature. By measuring the heat interaction between the engine and the system and between the engine and the reservoir, the temperature of the system can be determined in accord-

---

*Consider Eq. (4.8)

$$\phi(t_1, t_2)\phi(t_2, t_3) = \phi(t_1 t_3). \tag{4.8}$$

Differentiate with respect to t_3,

$$\phi(t_1, t_2) \frac{\partial}{\partial t_3} \phi(t_2, t_3) = \frac{\partial}{\partial t_3} \phi(t_1, t_3).$$

Substituting for $\phi(t_1, t_2)$ from Eq. (4.8), gives,

$$\frac{1}{\phi(t_2, t_3)} \frac{\partial}{\partial t_3} \phi(t_2, t_3) = \frac{1}{\phi(t_1, t_3)} \frac{\partial}{\partial t_3} \phi(t_1, t_3)$$

or

$$\frac{\partial \ln \phi(t_2, t_3)}{\partial t_3} = \frac{\partial \ln \phi(t_1, t_3)}{\partial t_3}.$$

Each of the two sides of the preceding equation is a function of t_3 because only t_3 appears on both sides. Therefore,

$$\frac{\partial \ln \phi(t_2, t_3)}{\partial t_3} = \frac{\partial \ln \phi(t_1, t_3)}{\partial t_3} = \psi(t_3).$$

Integrating

$$\ln \phi(t_2, t_3) = \psi_1(t_3) + \ln \phi'(t_2) \quad \text{or} \quad \phi(t_2, t_3) = \phi'(t_2)e^{\psi_1(t_3)}$$

and

$$\ln \phi(t_1, t_2) = \psi_1(t_3) + \ln \phi'(t_1) \quad \text{or} \quad \phi(t_1, t_2) = \phi'(t_1)e^{\psi_1(t_3)},$$

where $\ln \phi'(t_2)$ and $\ln \phi'(t_1)$ are constants of integration. Dividing the foregoing two equations gives

$$\frac{\phi(t_1, t_2)}{\phi(t_2, t_3)} = \frac{\phi'(t_1)}{\phi'(t_2)} = \phi(t_1, t_2).$$

ance with Eq. (4.9). Note that the absolute temperature scale is *independent of the thermometric substance* since it is defined in terms of heat quantities which do not depend on the working substance. It is called absolute since, as Q_1 approaches zero, the lowest possible temperature is approached. This may be explained by referring to Fig. 4.12. It is clear that Q_2 is smaller than Q_1, and Q_3 is smaller than Q_2, etc. Therefore, every successive Carnot engine serves to define a lower temperature at which an amount of heat is rejected. Thus it is conceivable that a lower limit of temperature is approached such that the heat rejected becomes zero in the limit. This temperature is called the *absolute zero.*

Consider a Carnot engine operating between two thermal reservoirs at temperatures T_1 and T_2. From the first law the work output is

$$W = Q_1 - Q_2,$$

but from Eq. (4.9),

$$Q_2 = Q_1 \frac{T_2}{T_1}.$$

Hence

$$W = Q_1 - Q_1 \frac{T_2}{T_1},$$

or

$$\frac{T_2}{T_1} = \left(1 - \frac{W}{Q_1}\right). \tag{4.10}$$

The second law of thermodynamics requires that the work W must be less than the heat input Q_1. Therefore, T_2/T_1 is always > 0, or the lowest value of T_2 is greater than zero. Thus the absolute zero is the lowest conceivable temperature, and absolute temperatures are positive numbers.

The next step is to determine the temperature interval on the absolute scale. Imagine a set of Carnot engines so arranged that each engine receives the heat rejected by the preceding one and each engine develops the same amount of work. The temperature intervals, in this case, are equal. For the first engine,

$$W = Q_1 - Q_2 = Q_1\left(1 - \frac{Q_2}{Q_1}\right) = Q_1\left(1 - \frac{T_2}{T_1}\right) = \frac{Q_1}{T_1}(T_1 - T_2).$$

Similarly for the second engine,

$$W = \frac{Q_2}{T_2}(T_2 - T_3),$$

and so on. Since each engine develops the same amount of work, then

$$\frac{Q_1}{T_1}(T_1 - T_2) = \frac{Q_2}{T_2}(T_2 - T_3) = \frac{Q_3}{T_3}(T_3 - T_4) = \ldots, \text{etc.}$$

But from Eq. (4.9),

$$\frac{Q_1}{T_1} = \frac{Q_2}{T_2} = \frac{Q_3}{T_3} = \ldots, \text{etc.}$$

Therefore,

$$T_1 - T_2 = T_2 - T_3 = T_3 - T_4 = \ldots, \text{etc.,}$$

which means that equal temperature intervals on the absolute scale are the temperature intervals between which Carnot engines operate in such a way that each engine absorbs the heat rejected by the preceding one and all engines develop the same amount of work.

The remaining item in the absolute scale is to assign a numerical value to one standard fixed point of temperature. In 1954 the value 273.16°K, the triple point of water was selected as the standard fixed point of temperature instead of the ice point (273.15°K). Kelvin had suggested that the absolute scale be based on this standard fixed point, instead of the previous procedure of fixing the size of the degree by means of two fixed points.

Assigning a numerical value of 273.16 to the triple point of water results in the absolute Celsius scale or Kelvin scale. Similarly, assigning a numerical value of 491.69 to the triple point of water results in the absolute Fahrenheit scale or the Rankine scale.

Equation (4.9) may be used to express the efficiency of a Carnot engine in terms of the absolute temperatures of the high and low thermal reservoirs as,

$$\eta_{th} = 1 - \frac{Q_2}{Q_1} = 1 - \frac{T_2}{T_1}. \tag{4.11}$$

Similarly, for a Carnot refrigerator,

$$COP_{ref} = \frac{1}{T_1/T_2 - 1} = \frac{T_2}{T_1 - T_2}, \tag{4.12}$$

and for a Carnot heat pump,

$$COP_{heat\ pump} = \frac{1}{1 - T_2/T_1} = \frac{T_1}{T_1 - T_2}. \tag{4.13}$$

**4-7
Equivalence
of the Absolute
and the
Perfect Gas
Scales**

The perfect gas scale was defined in Chapter 1. Figure 4.14 shows a p-V diagram of a Carnot cycle in which the working fluid is a perfect gas. Neglecting changes of potential and kinetic energies, the first law of thermodynamics is

$$đQ + đW = dU.$$

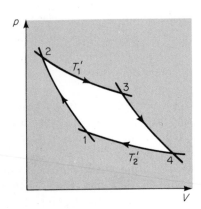

Fig. 4.14. *Equivalence of the absolute and the perfect-gas temperature scales.*

Since the working substance is a perfect gas and all the processes in the Carnot cycle are reversible, then

$$đQ - p\,dV = mc_v\,dT'$$

where c_v is the specific heat at constant volume, m is the mass of the gas, and T' is the temperature of the gas based on the perfect-gas scale. For the isothermal process 2-3, the heat transferred to the system is

$$Q_1 = \int_{V_2}^{V_3} p\,dV = mRT_1' \ln \frac{V_3}{V_2}.$$

Similarly for the isothermal process 4-1, the heat transferred from the system is

$$Q_2 = mRT_2' \ln \frac{V_4}{V_1}.$$

Therefore,

$$\frac{Q_1}{Q_2} = \frac{T_1' \ln (V_3/V_2)}{T_2' \ln (V_4/V_1)}.$$

Since processes 1-2 and 3-4 are reversible adiabatics, the temperature and volumes of the end states of each process are given by the following relations:

$$\left(\frac{V_1}{V_2}\right)^{\gamma-1} = \frac{T_1'}{T_2} = \left(\frac{V_4}{V_3}\right)^{\gamma-1},$$

from which

$$\frac{V_1}{V_2} = \frac{V_4}{V_3}.$$

The ratio of Q_1 to Q_2 then becomes

$$\frac{Q_1}{Q_2} = \frac{T_1'}{T_2'}.$$

But the absolute temperature scale is defined by

$$\frac{Q_1}{Q_2} = \frac{T_1}{T_2}.$$

Therefore,

$$\frac{T_1'}{T_2'} = \frac{T_1}{T_2},$$

and since the numerical value assigned to the fixed point (triple point) may be chosen to be the same on both scales, then $T' = T$, or the absolute thermodynamic temperature is *numerically equal* to the absolute temperature as measured by the perfect-gas thermometer.

Since the absolute thermodynamic temperature scale is independent of the thermometric substance it is the most fundamental temperature scale.

4-8
Clausius
Theorem

Consider a closed system undergoing a reversible process a-b, as shown on the p-V diagram of Fig. 4.15. The same change of states of both system and surroundings may be achieved if process a-b is replaced by an adiabatic process a-c, an isothermal process c-d, and an adiabatic process d-b, provided that the areas a-c-o and o-d-b are equal. The validity of this statement is established if both the heat and the work interactions during processes a-b and a-c-d-b are the same.

In the cycle a-c-d-b-a, since a-c and b-d are adiabatics, heat interaction

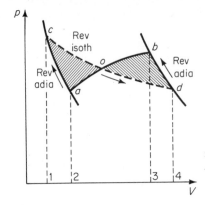

Fig. 4.15. *Replacement of a reversible process by two reversible adiabatics and a reversible isothermal.*

takes place during processes *a-b* and *c-d* only. Also the net work interaction in this cycle is zero since the areas *a-c-o* and *o-b-d* are equal. Therefore,

$$Q_{a-b} = Q_{c-d}.$$

But since processes *a-c* and *b-d* are adiabatics, then

$$Q_{a-b} = Q_{a-c-d-b}.$$

Substituting for Q_{a-b} and Q_{c-d} from the first law gives

$$E_b - E_a - W_{a-b} = E_b - E_a - W_{a-c-d-b}, \quad \text{or} \quad W_{a-b} = W_{a-c-d-b}.$$

The reversible process *a-b* can thus be replaced by a sequence of reversible processes consisting of an adiabatic, an isothermal, and an adiabatic such that the heat interaction during the isothermal process is equal to the heat interaction during the original process.

Consider a system specified by two independent variables undergoing a reversible cycle as represented on the *p-V* diagram of Fig. 4.16. The cycle is subdivided by a family of reversible adiabatics and every two adjacent adiabatics are connected by two reversible isothermals so that the heat transferred during all isothermal processes is equal to the heat transferred during the original cycle. Since no two adiabatics cross each other (Example 4.2), the cycle can be subdivided into a large number of Carnot cycles which provide the same amount of work as the original cycle. If magnitudes and directions of heat interactions are considered, Eq. (4.9) for the first Carnot cycle becomes

$$\frac{dQ_1}{T_1} = -\frac{dQ_2}{T_2}, \quad \text{or} \quad \frac{dQ_1}{T_1} + \frac{dQ_2}{T_2} = 0.$$

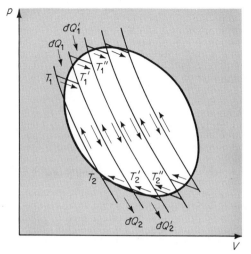

Fig. 4.16. *A reversible cycle can be subdivided into a large number of Carnot cycles.*

Similarly for the second cycle

$$\frac{dQ_1'}{T_1'} + \frac{dQ_2'}{T_2'} = 0, \text{ etc.}$$

Adding the preceding equations gives

$$\frac{dQ_1}{T_1} + \frac{dQ_2}{T_2} + \frac{dQ_1'}{T_1'} + \frac{dQ_2'}{T_2'} + \cdots = 0$$

or

$$\oint_R \frac{dQ}{T} = 0,$$

where the subscript R refers to a reversible cycle. The foregoing equation states that the algebraic sum of the quantity dQ/T vanishes around a reversible cycle which means that $(dQ/T)_{\text{rev}}$ is a *property* of the system. This property is called *entropy*.

In the case of an irreversible engine I, it was shown in Section 4.5 that $\eta_I < \eta_R$. Substituting for the efficiency in terms of heat quantities and absolute temperatures gives

$$1 - \frac{dQ_{2I}}{dQ_{1I}} < 1 - \frac{dQ_{2R}}{dQ_{1R}},$$

$$1 - \frac{dQ_{2I}}{dQ_{1I}} < 1 - \frac{T_2}{T_1},$$

or

$$\frac{dQ_{1I}}{T_1} - \frac{dQ_{2I}}{T_2} < 0.$$

Considering directions of heat interactions and noting that dQ_{2I} is heat rejection, then

$$\frac{dQ_{1I}}{T_1} + \frac{dQ_{2I}}{T_2} < 0,$$

and summing up all the formulas analogous to the preceding yields

$$\oint_I \frac{dQ}{T} < 0,$$

where the subscript I refers to an irreversible cycle and T is the temperature of the thermal reservoir.

From the foregoing analysis, we can write for any cycle,

$$\oint \frac{dQ}{T_{\text{reservoir}}} \leqslant 0. \tag{4.14}$$

Equation (4.14) is called the *inequality of Clausius* which states that when a system undergoes a complete cycle, the integral of dQ/T_{res} around the cycle is less than or equal to zero. The equality and inequality signs hold for reversible and irreversible cycles respectively. Note that the temperatures T in Clausius inequality pertain to reservoirs, not to systems.

EXAMPLE 4.1: Prove that the steam cycle shown in Fig. 4.17 is consistent with the Clausius theorem and state the condition if the cycle were to be reversible.
Data: heat transfer in boiler (at $t_1 = 381.79°F$) = 1137.3 Btu/lbm
heat rejected in condenser (at $t_2 = 101.14°F$) = 793 Btu/lbm

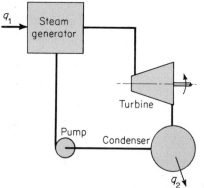

Fig. 4.17. Example 4.1.

Solution: Since heat is transferred only in the boiler and condenser and the temperature remains constant in both, then

$$\oint \frac{dq}{T} = \frac{1137.3}{841.79} - \frac{793}{561.14}$$

$$= 1.35 - 1.412 = -0.062 \text{ Btu/lbm}^\circ\text{R} < 0.$$

Since the result is negative, the cycle is irreversible according to the Clausius inequality (4.14). For this cycle to be reversible $\oint dq/T$ must be equal to zero.

EXAMPLE 4.2:   For a system of a perfect gas, prove that reversible adiabatic lines, plotted on any thermodynamic coordinates, do not intersect. Prove also that reversible adiabatic lines are steeper than reversible isothermal lines on a *p-V* plane.

Solution: To prove that reversible adiabatic lines do not intersect, assume that the opposite is true as shown on the *p-V* diagram of Fig. 4.18. Let an isotherm intersect both adiabatic lines and let the three lines form a cycle in which an amount of work equal to the enclosed area on the *p-V* diagram is produced. Since heat transfer to the system can take place during only one process of the cycle, namely the isothermal process, no other process is available for heat rejection. Therefore the system is exchanging heat with a single reservoir and yet performing work. This of course is impossible since the cycle forms a perpetual motion machine of the second kind. Therefore, two reversible adiabatic lines may not intersect.

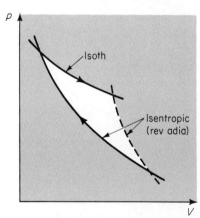

Fig. 4.18.   *Reversible adiabatic lines do not intersect.*

To prove that an adiabatic line is steeper than an isothermal line, consider a reversible adiabatic process of a perfect gas ($pV^\gamma = C$). The slope of an adiabatic line on the *p-V* diagram is

$$\frac{dp}{dV} = -\gamma \frac{p}{V},$$

and for an isothermal process ($pV = C$) the slope is

$$\frac{dp}{dV} = -\frac{p}{V}.$$

It is clear from the two preceding equations that the adiabatic line is steeper than the isothermal line on a p-V diagram since $\gamma > 1$. This further means that isothermal and adiabatic lines cannot touch without intersection.

4-9
Entropy

Except for Example 4.1, the second law of thermodynamics has been applied qualitatively. In 1854 Clausius attempted to make possible the application of the second law in a quantitative way. To do this, he introduced a mathematical function which he named *entropy*.* Entropy represents a consequence of the second law and provides a method, based on calculations, of explaining why certain energy transformations are impossible and of identifying the direction of any spontaneous process. For example, the maximum possible work that can be obtained from an engine may be determined from the second law. Kelvin proposed *the concept of the entropy of the universe*, which states that entropy continuously increases when spontaneous processes occur in nature. The definition of entropy will now be developed.

In Fig. 4.19, two equilibrium states, 1 and 2, are shown. They are

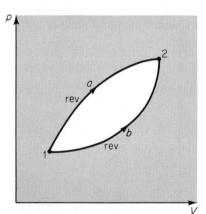

Fig. 4.19. *Entropy depends on the initial and final states of the system only.*

connected by two reversible paths a and b. If the direction of path b is reversed, then the reversible cycle 1-*a*-2-*b*-1 is formed. Applying the Clausius theorem to this cycle we have,

$$\oint_R \frac{dQ}{T} = 0.$$

*The word "entropy" comes from Greek meaning "transformability."

The cyclic integral can be expressed as the sum of two integrals, one along path a and the second along path b:

$$\oint_R \frac{dQ}{T} = \int_{1(a)}^2 \frac{dQ}{T} + \int_{2(b)}^1 \frac{dQ}{T} = 0.$$

From this it follows that

$$\int_{1(a)}^2 \frac{dQ}{T} = -\int_{2(b)}^1 \frac{dQ}{T}.$$

But since path b is reversible, the limits of the integral can be reversed and therefore

$$\int_{1(a)}^2 \frac{dQ}{T} = \int_{1(b)}^2 \frac{dQ}{T}.$$

No restriction was imposed on paths a and b, except that they must both be reversible. Consequently, the expression $\int_{\text{rev}} dQ/T$ is independent of the path and hence it represents a property. This property is called entropy, S, and is defined by the equation

$$dS \equiv \left(\frac{dQ}{T}\right)_{\text{rev}}. \tag{4.15}$$

This method of defining entropy is analogous to the method of defining total internal energy E in Eq. (3.5). Both equations express differences between two states of a system, but they do not provide a measure of absolute energy or absolute entropy. The amount of work interaction or heat interaction in a process connecting two fixed states depends on how the process is carried. On the other hand, the change in entropy and the change in total internal energy are invariant.

It should be noted that the change of entropy can be calculated from Eq. (4.15) only if the path connecting the end states of a system is reversible. The entropy change in an irreversible process can be calculated by devising a reversible process (or a series of reversible processes) between the initial and the final states of the system. Since the end states of both the reversible and irreversible processes are identical, the entropy change will be the same for the two processes.

Consider next a reversible process 1-2 along path a as shown in Fig. 4.20. Let the cycle be completed by an irreversible process 2-1 along path b, so that processes 1-a-2 and 2-b-1 together form an irreversible cycle.

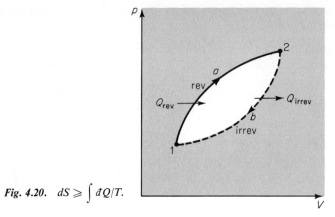

Fig. 4.20. $dS \geqslant \int dQ/T.$

The net change of entropy when the system changes from state 1 to state 2 and back to state 1 is zero or

$$\int_{1(a)}^{2} dS + \int_{2(b)}^{1} dS = 0.$$

Note that, if heat interaction during the reversible process results in an increase of entropy, heat must be rejected during the irreversible process to decrease the entropy such that the total change of entropy is zero according to the preceding equation. The Clausius inequality gives

$$\int_{1(a)}^{2} \frac{dQ}{T_{\text{envir}}} + \int_{2(b)}^{1} \frac{dQ}{T_{\text{envir}}} < 0,$$

but since path a is reversible, then

$$\int_{1(a)}^{2} dS = \int_{1(a)}^{2} \frac{dQ}{T_{\text{envir}}} = -\int_{2(b)}^{1} dS.$$

Therefore,

$$-\int_{2(b)}^{1} dS + \int_{2(b)}^{1} \frac{dQ}{T_{\text{envir}}} < 0$$

or

$$\int_{2(b)}^{1} dS > \int_{2(b)}^{1} \frac{dQ}{T_{\text{envir}}}.$$

If process b is reversible, an equality sign replaces the inequality sign in the foregoing equation. Therefore, a general differential form of that equation is

$$dS \geqslant \frac{dQ}{T}, \tag{4.16}$$

where the equality and inequality signs apply to reversible and irreversible processes respectively.

For an irreversible process,

$$dQ_{irr} < T_{envir} \; dS_{sys},$$

where dQ_{irr} is the heat interaction with the system and T_{envir} is the temperature of the environment. Although the entropy change between two states is the same for any path, reversible or not, the heat transfer to the system is less (more, if heat is transferred from the system) for the irreversible path than for the reversible one. This means that these two paths will not cause the same change of state in the environment.

For an isolated system which experiences no heat or work interaction with the environment, the total internal energy of all possible states remains constant. The second law, however, dictates that only those states for which the entropy increases or remains unchanged are possible. Thus, according to Eq. (4.16) and since $dQ = 0$,

$$dS_{isolated} \geqslant 0. \tag{4.17}$$

Therefore, for any irreversible process, there is a creation of entropy, and only those states resulting in entropy increase may be attained from the initial state of the system.

Equation (4.17) is called the *principle of increase of entropy* which may be considered another version of the second law. It states: The entropy of an isolated system either increases or, in the limit, remains constant.

Following the principle of increase of entropy, the entropy of the universe increases, owing to natural processes such that

$$\Delta S_{univ} = \Delta S_{sys} + \Delta S_{envir} > 0. \tag{4.18}$$

Note that for a reversible process,

$$\Delta S_{sys} = \left(\frac{Q}{T}\right)_{rev},$$

$$\Delta S_{envir} = -\left(\frac{Q}{T}\right)_{rev},$$

hence,

$$\Delta S_{univ} = 0 \quad \text{(reversible process)}.$$

To illustrate the previous relations, consider the free expansion of a perfect gas. For the system shown in Fig. 4.21, $\Delta U = 0$, $W = 0$, and by the first law, $Q = 0$. In order to calculate the entropy change, the irreversible process is replaced by a reversible process connecting the initial and final states of the system. Since the initial and final temperatures are the same, choose a reversible isothermal process during which the system is expanded

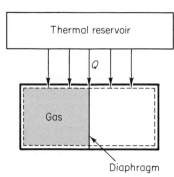

Diaphragm   **Fig. 4.21.**   *Free expansion of a perfect gas.*

in a controlled fashion. This may be accomplished by letting the system do work on a piston till the final state is reached. To maintain isothermal conditions, heat must be transferred to the system. Since the temperature remains constant, then

$$\Delta U = 0$$

and

$$Q_{\text{rev}} = -W_{\text{rev}} = \int_{V_1}^{V_2} p\, dV = RT \ln \frac{V_2}{V_1},$$

where subscripts 1 and 2 refer to the initial and final conditions. The entropy change for the reversible process is given by

$$\Delta S = \left(\frac{Q}{T} \right)_{\text{rev}} = R \ln \frac{V_2}{V_1},$$

which is the same for the irreversible process.

Entropy is an extensive property as can be easily seen from Eq. (4.15). If the heat transfer per unit mass is constant, the amount of heat transfer to a system is proportional to its mass and so is the entropy. In the case of irreversible processes, the particles of the system follow different paths between the initial and the final states. But since the mass of each particle in the system experiences the same change of entropy per unit mass between the end states, the total change of entropy is equal to the specific entropy change multiplied by the mass of the system or

$$\Delta S = \sum (dm \, \Delta s) = m \, \Delta s, \tag{4.19}$$

where m is the mass of the system.

The units of entropy in the English system are Btu/°R and for specific entropy are Btu/lbm°R. In the CGS system, they are cal/°K and, for the specific entropy, cal/gm°K.

4-10
Temperature-
Entropy
Diagram

The choice of T and S as two parameters to describe a thermodynamic system has a number of advantages. On a T-S diagram, isotherms and reversible adiabatics are horizontal and vertical lines. For a reversible process, the heat interaction is given by

$$d\!Q_{\rm rev} = T \, dS.$$

The amount of heat $d\!Q_{\rm rev}$ is represented by the shaded area of height T and width dS under the process path as shown in Fig. 4.22. The total amount of

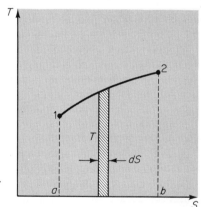

Fig. 4.22. *Temperature-entropy diagram.*

heat interaction during the reversible process 1-2 is equal to the integral of $T \, dS$ between states 1 and 2, or

$$Q_{\rm rev} = \int_1^2 T \, dS,$$

and is represented by area a-1-2-b on the T-S diagram. This is true only if the process 1-2 is reversible, and in this case the process is represented by a continuous curve on the T-S diagram. If the process were irreversible it is usually represented by a dotted line, and the area under an irreversible process path is greater than the amount of heat interaction. The dotted representation of irreversible processes serves also to indicate that, owing to the nonequilibrium conditions encountered in irreversible processes, a single continuous path is insufficient truly to describe the process.

Constant entropy processes are called *isentropic* processes and are presented by vertical lines on the T-S diagram. For a reversible adiabatic process, $dQ_{rev} = 0$, and since $dS = (dQ/T)_{rev}$, $dS = 0$. Thus, a reversible adiabatic process is an isentropic process. The opposite is not always true in the sense that an isentropic process does not necessarily mean a reversible adiabatic process. For example, fluid flow accompanied by friction results in an increase in entropy. If, at the same time, heat is transferred from the system at such a rate that the entropy of the system is maintained constant, then the process is isentropic. Such a process is obviously neither reversible nor adiabatic and is accompanied by an increase in entropy of the surroundings. The same conclusion may be reached by noting that since $dS = 0$ then $dQ/T \leqslant 0$; that is, $dQ \leqslant 0$. Thus an irreversible-isentropic process requires heat flow from the system.

The Carnot cycle is represented graphically on the T-S diagram of Fig. 4.23. Process 1-2 is a reversible isothermal process during which heat is

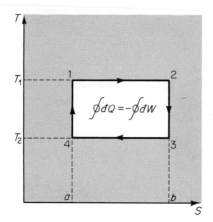

Fig. 4.23. Carnot cycle on a T-S diagram.

transferred to the system at constant temperature and the entropy change is given by

$$S_2 - S_1 = \int_1^2 \left(\frac{dQ}{T}\right)_{rev} = \frac{Q_{1-2}}{T_1}.$$

The heat transfer to the system, Q_{1-2}, is represented by the area 1-2-*b*-*a*. Process 2-3 is a reversible adiabatic process (isentropic) during which the entropy remains constant. Process 3-4 is a reversible isothermal compression during which heat is transferred from the system at constant temperature and the entropy change is given by

$$S_4 - S_3 = \int_3^4 \left(\frac{dQ}{T}\right)_{rev} = \frac{Q_{3-4}}{T_2}.$$

The heat rejection Q_{3-4} is represented by the area 3-4-*a*-*b*. Note that the increase of entropy of the system during process 1-2 is equal to the decrease in entropy during process 3-4. The final process 4-1 is an isentropic process which restores the system to its original state and thus completes the cycle.

The first law applied to the cycle gives

$$\oint dQ + \oint dW = 0,$$

or the net heat interaction during the cycle is equal to the net work output, and since the process is reversible, then

$$\oint T\, dS = \oint p\, dV.$$

Therefore, the heat or work interactions during the cycle may be represented by either the area 1-2-3-4 of Fig. 4.23 or the corresponding area on a *p-V* diagram.

**4-11
Entropy
Relation to
Other
Thermo-
dynamic
Properties**

Consider a closed system undergoing a reversible process during which there are heat and work interactions. The first law is

$$dQ + dW = dU.$$

Substituting $T\, dS$ and $-p\, dV$ for dQ and dW in the preceding equation and rearranging gives

$$T\, dS = p\, dV + dU. \tag{4.20}$$

But the differential of enthalpy is

$$dH = dU + p\, dV + V\, dp,$$

which when substituted in Eq. (4.20) gives

$$T\, dS = dH - V\, dp. \tag{4.21}$$

Equations (4.20) and (4.21) are fundamental thermodynamic relations combining the first and second laws into a single equation.

Although the foregoing equations have been derived for a reversible process, they are valid for any process because they express relationships between properties and therefore are independent of the path. Note that $đQ = T\,dS$ and $đW = -p\,dV$ are true only for a reversible process; hence for any irreversible process the difference between $T\,dS$ and $đQ$ is equal to the difference between $-p\,dV$ and $đW$.

Equations (4.20) and (4.21) can be written for a unit mass as

$$T\,ds = du + p\,dv \tag{4.22}$$

and

$$T\,ds = dh - v\,dp. \tag{4.23}$$

For a perfect gas $pv = RT$, $du = c_v\,dT$, and $dh = c_p\,dT$ which, when combined with Eqs. (4.22) and (4.23), give the following expressions for the differential of entropy per unit mass,

$$ds = c_v\frac{dT}{T} + \frac{p}{T}\,dv = c_v\frac{dT}{T} + R\frac{dv}{v}$$

and

$$ds = c_p\frac{dT}{T} - \frac{v}{T}\,dp = c_p\frac{dT}{T} - R\frac{dp}{p}.$$

Integrating the foregoing equations between states 1 and 2 gives

$$s_2 - s_1 = c_v\ln\frac{T_2}{T_1} + R\ln\frac{v_2}{v_1} \tag{4.24}$$

and

$$s_2 - s_1 = c_p\ln\frac{T_2}{T_1} - R\ln\frac{p_2}{p_1}. \tag{4.25}$$

Entropy, being a thermodynamic property, can be used as one of the parameters to define the state of a system. It can be expressed as a function of any two of the independent variables, such as pressure, volume, temperature, internal energy, etc. Therefore

$$\begin{aligned} s &= s(u, v) \\ &= s(T, p) \\ &= s(p, v),\ \text{etc.} \end{aligned} \tag{4.26}$$

If, for example, the first equation is considered, ds can be expressed as

$$ds = \left(\frac{\partial s}{\partial u}\right)_v du + \left(\frac{\partial s}{\partial v}\right)_u dv,$$

but

$$ds = \left(\frac{1}{T}\right) du + \frac{p}{T} \, dv.$$

Since u and v are independent variables, the coefficients of du and dv in the two preceding equations may be equated to give

$$\left(\frac{\partial s}{\partial u}\right)_v = \frac{1}{T} \tag{4.27}$$

and

$$\left(\frac{\partial s}{\partial v}\right)_u = \frac{p}{T}. \tag{4.28}$$

Since $(\partial s/\partial u)_v$ and $(\partial s/\partial v)_u$ are expressed in terms of properties, they themselves are also properties. Note that the slope of a constant volume line on an s-u diagram is equal to $1/T$ and the slope of a constant internal energy line on an s-v diagram is equal to p/T. Similarly, the second and third equations (4.26) provide useful property relations.

EXAMPLE 4.3:   Two lbm of water at 200°F are mixed with 3 lbm of water at 50°F in an isolated system. Calculate the change of entropy due to the mixing process.

Solution: Referring to the isolated system shown in Fig. 4.24, there is no

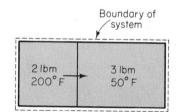

Boundary of
system

2 lbm
200° F

3 lbm
50° F

Fig. 4.24.   Example 4.2.

heat or work interaction with the surroundings. Therefore, from the first law of thermodynamics the change of the internal energy of the system is zero, or

$$m_1 c(t_f - t_1) + m_2 c(t_f - t_2) = 0,$$

where c is the specific heat of water. Substituting values gives

$$2 \times 1(t_f - 200) + 3 \times 1(t_f - 50) = 0$$

or

$$t_f = \frac{400 + 150}{5} = \frac{550}{5} = 110°\text{F}.$$

The total change of entropy of the system is the sum of the entropy changes of its components, or

$$\Delta S = \Delta S_1 + \Delta S_2$$
$$= m_1 c \ln \left(\frac{T_f}{T_i}\right)_1 + m_2 c \ln \left(\frac{T_f}{T_i}\right)_2.$$

Substituting values gives

$$\Delta S = 2 \times 1 \ln \left(\frac{110 + 460}{200 + 460}\right) + 3 \times 1 \times \ln \left(\frac{110 + 460}{50 + 460}\right)$$
$$= 2 \ln \frac{570}{660} + 3 \ln \frac{570}{510}$$
$$= -0.2914 + 0.3345 = 0.0431 \text{ Btu/}^\circ\text{R}.$$

Note that the entropy of the cold body has increased while the entropy of the hot body has decreased. There is, however, a net increase in entropy of the total system without heat transfer; a criterion of irreversible processes. Therefore, the mixing process is irreversible.

EXAMPLE 4.4:   Two lbm of water at 200°F are mixed with 5 lbm of ice at 32°F in an isolated system. Calculate (a) the change of entropy; (b) the change of entropy if 1 instead of 5 lbm of ice were present.

Solution: (a) The first step is to find the final temperature after the mixing process. Two cases arise: If the decrease in the internal energy of the water is less than the latent heat required to melt the ice, the final temperature will be 32°F and some ice will remain unmelted. If, on the other hand, the decrease in the internal energy of the water is more than the latent heat required to melt the ice, the final temperature of the mixture lies between 32 and 200°F. To find the final temperature, the energy balance gives

$$2 \times 1(200 - t_f) = 5 \times 144 + 5 \times (t_f - 32)$$

or

$$t_f = \frac{400 - 720 + 160}{7} = \frac{-440}{7} = -62.9^\circ\text{F}.$$

The preceding temperature indicates that the ice did not melt completely and the temperature of the mixture is therefore 32°F. To find the amount of ice that melted,

$$2(200 - 32) = x \times 144 \quad \text{or} \quad x = \frac{2 \times 168}{144} = 2.33 \text{ lbm of ice,}$$

$$\Delta S_{\text{water}} = 2 \ln \frac{492}{660} = -2 \times 0.2925 = -0.585 \text{ Btu/}^\circ\text{R,}$$

$$\Delta S_{\text{ice}} = \frac{2 \times 168}{492} = 0.683 \text{ Btu/}^\circ\text{R,}$$

$$\Delta S_{\text{total}} = -0.585 + 0.683 = 0.098 \text{ Btu/}^\circ\text{R.}$$

Since the process is adiabatic but involves an entropy change, the process must then be irreversible.

(b) If only 1 lbm of ice were present then

$$2 \times 1(200 - t_f) = 1 \times 144 + 1(t_f - 32),$$

$$t_f = \frac{400 - 144 + 32}{3} = \frac{288}{3} = 96°F,$$

$$\Delta S_{\text{water}} = 2 \ln \left(\frac{96 + 460}{200 + 460} \right) = -2 \times 0.1122 = -0.2244 \text{ Btu/}°R,$$

$$\Delta S_{\text{ice}} = \frac{144}{492} + 1 \ln \left(\frac{96 + 460}{32 + 460} \right) = 0.293 + 0.1221 = 0.4151 \text{ Btu/}°R,$$

$$\Delta S_{\text{total}} = 0.4151 - 0.2244 = 0.1907 \text{ Btu/}°R.$$

4-12
Isentropic
Relation for a
Perfect Gas

The relation describing an isentropic process of a perfect gas may be obtained by setting $s_2 - s_1 = 0$ in either Eq. (4.24) or Eq. (4.25). Using Eq. (4.24) then

$$c_v \ln \frac{T_2}{T_1} = -R \ln \frac{v_2}{v_1},$$

from which

$$\frac{T_2}{T_1} = \left(\frac{v_1}{v_2} \right)^{R/c_v},$$

but, for a perfect gas,

$$c_p = c_v + R \quad \text{or} \quad \frac{R}{c_v} = \gamma - 1.$$

Therefore,

$$\frac{T_2}{T_1} = \left(\frac{v_1}{v_2} \right)^{\gamma - 1}.$$

The preceding equation relates the temperatures and specific volumes of two states connected by an isentropic process. The relation between pressures and volumes may be obtained by substituting $p_2 v_2 / p_1 v_1$ for T_2/T_1 in the preceding equation. Hence

$$\frac{p_2 v_2}{p_1 v_1} = \left(\frac{v_1}{v_2} \right)^{\gamma - 1} \quad \text{or} \quad p_1 v_1^\gamma = p_2 v_2^\gamma.$$

Since any state along the isentropic path between states 1 and 2 satisfies the foregoing equation, the isentropic pressure volume relation is

$$pv^\gamma = C. \tag{4.29}$$

EXAMPLE 4.5:   During a certain process the volume of 1 lbm of air is doubled and its pressure is tripled. Find the change of entropy per lbm. Assume air to be a perfect gas, $c_p = 0.24$, and $c_v = 0.17$ Btu/lbm°F.

Solution: Using the equation of state of a perfect gas to eliminate the temperatures in Eq. (4.24),

$$s_2 - s_1 = c_v \ln \frac{p_2 v_2}{p_1 v_1} + R \ln \frac{v_2}{v_1}$$

$$= 0.17 \ln (3 \times 2) + \frac{53.34}{778} \ln 2$$

$$= 0.304 + 0.0475$$

$$= 0.3515 \text{ Btu/1bm°R.}$$

EXAMPLE 4.6:   Prove that the internal energy of a perfect gas is a function of temperature only.

Solution: Let the internal energy of a perfect gas be expressed in terms of two properties, such as T and v. If the dependence of u on v can be eliminated, then u becomes a function of T only.

$$u = u(T, v).$$

The differential of u is

$$du = \left(\frac{\partial u}{\partial T}\right)_v dT + \left(\frac{\partial u}{\partial v}\right)_T dv,$$

but

$$ds = \left(\frac{1}{T}\right) du + \frac{p}{T} dv$$

$$= \frac{1}{T}\left[\left(\frac{\partial u}{\partial T}\right)_v dT + \left(\frac{\partial u}{\partial v}\right)_T dv\right] + \frac{p}{T} dv.$$

From the perfect gas relation $p/T = R/v$, then

$$ds = \frac{1}{T}\left(\frac{\partial u}{\partial T}\right)_v dT + \left[\frac{1}{T}\left(\frac{\partial u}{\partial v}\right)_T + \frac{R}{v}\right] dv. \tag{a}$$

Entropy may be expressed in terms of T and v as

$$s = s(T, v).$$

The differential of entropy is

$$ds = \left(\frac{\partial s}{\partial T}\right)_v dT + \left(\frac{\partial s}{\partial v}\right)_T dv. \tag{b}$$

Comparing Eqs. (a) and (b) and noting that T and v are independent, the coefficients of dT and dv, in both equations, must be equal or

$$\left(\frac{\partial s}{\partial T}\right)_v = \frac{1}{T}\left(\frac{\partial u}{\partial T}\right)_v \tag{c}$$

and

$$\left(\frac{\partial s}{\partial v}\right)_T = \frac{1}{T}\left(\frac{\partial u}{\partial v}\right)_T + \frac{R}{v}. \tag{d}$$

Since entropy is a property, then

$$\frac{\partial^2 s}{\partial v\, \partial T} = \frac{\partial^2 s}{\partial T\, \partial v}.$$

Differentiating Eqs. (c) and (d) with respect to v and T respectively and equating gives

$$\frac{1}{T}\frac{\partial^2 u}{\partial v\, \partial T} = \frac{1}{T}\frac{\partial^2 u}{\partial T\, \partial v} + \left(\frac{\partial u}{\partial v}\right)_T\left(-\frac{1}{T^2}\right)$$

from which

$$\left(\frac{\partial u}{\partial v}\right)_T = 0.$$

4-13
Entropy
Changes for
a Control
Volume or
an Open
System

In the previous sections it was shown that the entropy of an isolated system can only increase or remain constant. For a closed system the change of entropy is due to internal irreversibilities and due to energy interactions in the form of heat with the environment. For a control volume or an open system, there is an additional change of entropy owing to the mass crossing the boundaries of the system. The net change of entropy of a system due to mass transport is equal to the difference between the product of the mass and its specific entropy at the inlet and at the exit from the system. Therefore the total change of entropy of the system during a small time interval is given by

$$dS \geqslant \frac{dQ}{T_{\text{envir}}} + \sum s_i\, dm_i - \sum s_e\, dm_e,$$

where T_{envir} is the temperature of the environment and subscripts i and e refer to inlet and exit conditions. In a compact form,

$$dS \geqslant \frac{dQ}{T_{\text{envir}}} + \sum s\, dm. \tag{4.30}$$

In Eq. (4.30) entropy flow into the system is considered positive and entropy outflow is considered negative. The equality sign applies to reversible processes in which the heat interaction, as well as the mass transport to and from the system, is accomplished reversibly. The inequality sign applies to irreversible processes. Equation (4.30), when divided by an interval of time $\Delta\tau$ that tends toward zero, becomes a rate equation,

$$\frac{dS}{d\tau} \geqslant \frac{1}{T_{\text{envir}}} \frac{dQ}{d\tau} + \sum \dot{m}\,s. \tag{4.31}$$

In the case of steady-state, steady-flow process, the time rate of change of entropy of the system is zero and the time rate of the mass entering is equal to that leaving the system. Under these conditions Eq. (4.31) becomes

$$\frac{1}{T_{\text{envir}}} \frac{dQ}{d\tau} + \sum \dot{m}\,s \leqslant 0, \tag{4.32}$$

and for an adiabatic steady flow process,

$$\sum \dot{m}\,s \leqslant 0. \tag{4.33}$$

If the process was further reversible, then

$$\sum \dot{m}\,s = 0. \tag{4.34}$$

EXAMPLE 4.7: In a desuperheater, water is sprayed into superheated steam in the proper amount to cause it to become saturated. Consider the process to be adiabatic, the system to be at steady state, and the following data to apply:
Steam flow 2000 lbm/hr
Steam entering at 400 psia and 600°F
 ($h = 1306.9$ Btu/lbm, $s = 1.5894$ Btu/lbm°R)
Water entering at 420 psia and 100°F
 ($h = 69.07$ Btu/lbm, $s = 0.12931$ Btu/lbm°R)
Steam leaving at 380 psia, 440.86°F dry and saturated
 ($h = 1204.3$ Btu/lbm, $s = 1.4891$ Btu/lbm°R)
Calculate the mass rate of flow of water necessary for desuperheating. What is the change of entropy of the system? Show that the process is irreversible.

Solution: The first law under the conditions of this problem reduces to

$$\dot{m}_w h_w + \dot{m}_{sh} h_{sh} - \dot{m}_s h_s = 0.$$

Substituting values gives

$$\dot{m}_w \times 69.07 + 2000 \times 1306.9 - (\dot{m}_w + 2000)1204.3 = 0,$$

from which $\dot{m}_w = 181$ lbm/hr.
 The change of entropy of the system is zero, since the process is executed under steady-state conditions.

From the Clausius inequality or Eq. (4.30),

$$\frac{dQ}{T} \leqslant 2181 \times 1.4891 - (2000 \times 1.5894 + 181 \times 0.12931),$$

$$\frac{dQ}{T} \leqslant 42.8 \ \text{Btu/hr°R}.$$

But since $dQ = 0$, the inequality sign applies and therefore the mixing process is irreversible. This further means that the entropy leaving the system is more than the entropy entering the system, so that the entropy of the system remains unchanged.

4-14 Mathematical Formulation of the Second Law

In Section 4-9, the concept of entropy and the second law of thermodynamics were introduced by the Carnot-Clausius use of cycles which is actually an application of the first law. This presentation, although simple and instructive, does not illustrate the broad scope of the second law. In an attempt to provide a basis for the concept of entropy and to formulate the second law by a formal mathematical procedure, Caratheodory, in 1909, used an integrating factor $(1/T)$ which renders dQ an exact differential. He postulated that, for reversible (physically impossible) processes between states in the vicinity of an arbitrary initial state of a system, there exists a function, S, and another, T, which satisfy the equation $dQ_{\text{rev}} = T \, dS$.

Before introducing Caratheodory's principle, an investigation of the condition for a linear differential equation to be integrable is in order.* Consider a linear differential equation of the form,

$$df = X \, dx + Y \, dy + Z \, dz, \tag{4.35}$$

where X, Y, and Z are continuous functions of the coordinates x, y, and z. The condition $df = 0$ defines a family of surfaces passing through a given point. If the foregoing equation has an integrating factor $\lambda(x, y, z)$ such that $\lambda \, df$ is a differential of a function and therefore is integrable, then the solutions of the differential equation $df = 0$ are functions of the form $\phi(x, y, z) = $ constant, called *solution curves*.

The condition for integrability, that is, the existence of unique solution curves, is as follows:

Considering the exact differential $d\phi$ as given by

$$d\phi = \lambda df = \lambda X \, dx + \lambda Y \, dy + \lambda Z \, dz,$$

*This procedure is an extension of the condition for an exact differential for two variables outlined in Section 1–5.

then,

$$\frac{\partial\phi}{\partial x} = \lambda X, \quad \frac{\partial\phi}{\partial y} = \lambda Y, \quad \frac{\partial\phi}{\partial z} = \lambda z.$$

Therefore

$$\frac{\partial(\lambda X)}{\partial y} = \frac{\partial^2\phi}{\partial y\,\partial x} = \frac{\partial(\lambda Y)}{\partial x}.$$

Performing the differentiation and arranging gives

$$\lambda\left(\frac{\partial X}{\partial y} - \frac{\partial Y}{\partial x}\right) = Y\frac{\partial\lambda}{\partial x} - X\frac{\partial\lambda}{\partial y}. \tag{4.36a}$$

Similarly,

$$\lambda\left(\frac{\partial Y}{\partial z} - \frac{\partial Z}{\partial y}\right) = Z\frac{\partial\lambda}{\partial y} - Y\frac{\partial\lambda}{\partial z}, \tag{4.36b}$$

and

$$\lambda\left(\frac{\partial Z}{\partial x} - \frac{\partial X}{\partial z}\right) = X\frac{\partial\lambda}{\partial z} - Z\frac{\partial\lambda}{\partial x}. \tag{4.36c}$$

Multiplying Eq. (4.36a) by Z, Eq. (4.36b) by X, and Eq. (4.36c) by Y and adding gives the condition for an integrating factor to exist as

$$X\left(\frac{\partial Z}{\partial y} - \frac{\partial Y}{\partial z}\right) + Y\left(\frac{\partial X}{\partial z} - \frac{\partial Z}{\partial x}\right) + Z\left(\frac{\partial Y}{\partial x} - \frac{\partial X}{\partial y}\right) = 0. \tag{4.37}$$

This means that, if an integrating factor exists, two neighboring points can be joined by one of the solution curves of the linear differential equation. Consider the equation,

$$X(x, y, z)\,dx + Y(x, y, z)\,dy + Z(x, y, z)\,dz = 0, \tag{4.38}$$

where x, y, and z are functions of two variables u and v so that

$$x = x(u, v), \quad y = y(u, v), \quad z = z(u, v).$$

Then

$$dx = \frac{\partial x}{\partial u}\,du + \frac{\partial x}{\partial v}\,dv,$$

$$dy = \frac{\partial y}{\partial u}\,du + \frac{\partial y}{\partial v}\,dv,$$

$$dz = \frac{\partial z}{\partial u}\,du + \frac{\partial z}{\partial v}\,dv.$$

Substituting in Eq. (4.38) and rearranging gives

$$\left(X\frac{\partial x}{\partial u} + Y\frac{\partial y}{\partial u} + Z\frac{\partial z}{\partial u} \right) du + \left(X\frac{\partial x}{\partial v} + Y\frac{\partial y}{\partial v} + Z\frac{\partial z}{\partial y} \right) dv = 0,$$

which is an equation in two variables u and v. It may be integrated to give a unique curve in the space (u, v) which satisfies Eq. (4.38) and passes through the initial point (u_0, v_0). Therefore points not lying on this curve cannot be reached from the initial point.

Caratheodory's principle states that in the neighborhood of any arbitrary initial state of a system there exist neighboring states which are not accessible from the initial state by means of a reversible adiabatic process. In other words they are not accessible along solution curves of Eq. (4.38), if and only if Eq. (4.38) is integrable, which requires the existence of a function $\lambda(x, y, z)$ and another $F(x, y, z)$ such that

$$X\,dx + Y\,dy + Z\,dz = \lambda\,dF, \tag{4.39}$$

where $dF = df/\lambda$. The irreversible adiabatic stirring of a fluid is a typical example of the inaccessibility of the original state. In this case, the reversal of the process cannot be achieved along an adiabatic path.

Therefore the second law of thermodynamics stated mathematically implies that the accessibility of neighboring states from a given initial state along a path is possible only if

$$đQ = X\,dx + Y\,dy + Z\,dz = T\,dS, \tag{4.40}$$

where $T(= \lambda)$ and $S(= F)$ are functions of the state.

Statistical mechanics as indicated in Chapter 8 shows that entropy is a measure of the distribution of internal energy of the system. This approach is also considered of broader scope in comparison to the definition deduced from the classical Carnot cycle.

4-15 Physical Interpretation of Entropy

It is not sufficient in discussing entropy to treat it only as a mathematical parameter. It is necessary to clarify the significance of entropy and of its continuous creation in irreversible processes. For this reason, the physical interpretations of entropy will be discussed.

When heat $đQ$ is transferred to a system operating in a cycle, only a portion of the heat is available for work. This portion is called the *available energy*. Consider a reversible engine operating between two thermal reservoirs, and let T_0 and T be the absolute temperatures of the cold and hot reservoirs respectively. The efficiency of the cycle is $(1 - T_0/T)$; the work done then is the efficiency multiplied by the heat input. Therefore the available energy is given by available energy $\leqslant dQ\left(1 - \dfrac{T_o}{T}\right)$.

In a reversible process, the equality applies; in an irreversible process, the inequality holds. When heat dQ is transferred reversibly to an engine, some of this energy is unavailable for work. This amounts to $dQ(T_o/T)$. But dQ/T represents the increase of entropy in a reversible process. Therefore

unavailable energy $= T_o \, dS$.

When irreversibilities occur in a process, the entropy of the system increases, and less energy is then available for work. This means that changes in entropy may be used to describe quantitatively any changes in the amount of available energy that may occur. Entropy is therefore associated with the degradation of energy into forms which are more difficult to utilize in the production of work.*

Consider the transfer of a quantity of heat from one reservoir at T_1 to another at a lower temperature T_2. The maximum available energy before the transfer of heat is $dQ \, (1 - T_o/T_1)$, where T_o is the temperature of the environment to which heat may be rejected. After the heat transfer process the maximum available energy is only $dQ(1 - T_o/T_2)$. The difference constitutes a degradation of energy into less useful forms for producing work.

Spontaneous processes can also be considered from the microscopic point of view. There is a tendency for all physical systems to proceed to states in which the particles become less ordered. This suggests that entropy can be regarded as a measure of the *disorder* of a system, or of the randomness of motion of the microscopic particles. Consider the transfer of heat to a homogeneous system. As the temperature rises, the molecules of the system move in a larger variety of ways in each of the various vibrational, rotational, translational, electronic, etc., modes. Conversely, the rejection of heat from a system decreases the disorder of the molecules, although an equivalent amount of disorder, or greater disorder results in the environment. The molecular disorder of the universe is therefore continuously increasing due to the irreversible processes of nature, so that the second law of thermodynamics is sometimes called the *law of increase of entropy*.

From the standpoint of probability, a system is less likely to be in an orderly state than in a disordered state. Spontaneous changes in nature proceed from the less probable to the more probable states. At thermodynamic equilibrium the degree of molecular disorder is maximum and the

---

*This statement, however, cannot be generalized since, in the case of isothermal expansion of a perfect gas, there is no degradation of energy, yet there is an increase of entropy.

state of the system is the state of highest probability.* Hence entropy, being a function of molecular disorder, may be used to measure the statistical probability of a macrostate of a system. In Section 4-9, it was shown that the entropy of an isolated system may increase or remain the same, but can never decrease:

$$dS_{\text{isolated}} \geqslant 0.$$

An isolated system tends to approach complete randomness. When an isolated system is in equilibrium, no changes in the properties of the system are observed, because the system is in a state corresponding to the macrostate of maximum probability. Through statistical thermodynamics, a relationship is developed between entropy and the number of microstates in the dominating macrostate of a system. A preliminary account is given in this section while a more detailed discussion will be presented in Chapter 8.

The meaning of thermodynamic probability can be clarified by means of an illustration. Consider the free expansion of a gas of volume V_a into an evacuated chamber. Let the total volume, after expansion, be V_b. If probability is represented by W, the probability that a certain molecule of the gas will be found in volume V_b is unity, or $W_b = 1$. The probability that it will be found in V_a is proportional to the ratio of the two volumes, so that $W_a = V_a/V_b$. When several independent events are considered, the probability that they will all occur simultaneously is the product of their individual probabilities. Hence, for N molecules, the probability that they all are located in V_a at any particular time is $(V_a/V_b)^N$. Therefore

$$\frac{W_a}{W_b} = \left(\frac{V_a}{V_b}\right)^N. \tag{4.41}$$

Boltzmann proposed the idea that a relationship exists between probability and entropy. From a probability point of view, the state of equilibrium is the most probable state; from the classical thermodynamic point of view, the state of equilibrium represents the state of maximum entropy. During an irreversible process, both the thermodynamic probability and the entropy of a system increase. Entropy is however an additive (i.e., extensive) property, whereas thermodynamic probability is a multiplicative property. Boltzmann, therefore, suggested that the relationship takes the form

$$S = k \ln W, \tag{4.42}$$

*The thermodynamic probability of a macrostate is equal to the number of microstates in a certain macrostate. It indicates the relative frequency with which a macrostate occurs. This is different from mathematical probability, which may be defined as the ratio of the number of favorable events to the total number of events. These two probabilities are proportional to each other.

where $k = \mathscr{R}/N_0$ is Boltzmann's constant and represents the gas constant based on one molecule. Consider a system made up of several parts, each of fixed energy, volume, and composition. The entropy of such a system is equal to the sum of the entropies of its components

$$S = S_1 + S_2 + \cdots.$$

The thermodynamic probability of a state of a system is equal to the product of the individual probabilities of the components of the system

$$W = W_1 W_2 \ldots.$$

The entropy of the system, according to Eq. (4.42) therefore is

$$S = S_1 + S_2 + \cdots = k \ln W_1 + k \ln W_2 + \cdots = k \ln W.$$

Let us now return to the example of a perfect gas undergoing free expansion. The change of entropy is

$$dS = mc_v \frac{dT}{T} + mR \frac{dV}{V}.$$

Since the temperature does not change, this equation, when integrated, becomes

$$S_b - S_a = mR \ln \frac{V_b}{V_a} = N \frac{\mathscr{R}}{N_0} \ln \frac{V_b}{V_a} = k \ln \frac{W_b}{W_a}. \tag{4.43}$$

According to this equation, the change of entropy is proportional to the logarithm of the ratio of the statistical probabilities of the end states of the system. Note that the final state of the process is of greater probability than is its initial state.

Mention should be made of the philosophical implications of entropy. According to the first and second laws of thermodynamics, the energy of the universe is constant but the entropy of the universe is increasing continuously. Can the entropy of the universe increase indefinitely? Or is there a maximum possible entropy for the universe? If such a limit exists, when will it be reached? Since all real processes are accompanied by an increase in entropy, the energy available for mankind is continuously decreasing. At some time in the future no more energy will be available for use. At that time, the entropy of the universe will be at its maximum and complete disorder and randomness will prevail. At that state of the universe all matter will be at the same temperature level, and the universe will reach, according to Clausius, the state of "thermal death." No energy will be available for use in raising local temperatures above that of the environment and performance of work will be impossible. Nevertheless, the total energy of the universe will be no different from its present value.

Another paradox that arises is centered about the theory of probability. According to this theory, all possible microstates of a macrostate are equally probable. That is to say, a system can exist in a particular microstate at any time so that no particular time for its existence is more probable than any other time. All possible events and states of the universe occur randomly. On the other hand, the second law of thermodynamics states that only those processes which result in an increase in the entropy of the universe can occur. Therefore, the second law may be interpreted as one of very high statistical probability but not one of absolute certainty. Perhaps the idea to keep in mind is that nature acts in a random way, but it also tends to act rationally.

REFERENCES

4.1 Buchdahl, H. A., "On the Principle of Caratheodory," *Amer. J. Physics*, January, 1949.

4.2 Denbigh, K. G., *The Principles of Chemical Equilibrium*. Cambridge: Cambridge University Press, 1957, chap. 1.

4.3 Kiefer, P. J., G. F. Kinney, and M. C. Stuart, *Principles of Engineering Thermodynamics*. New York: John Wiley & Sons, Inc., 1954, chap. 5, 6.

4.4 Lindsay, R. B., "Entropy Consumption and Values in Physical Science," *Amer. Scientist*, September, 1959.

4.5 Lee, J. F., and F. W. Sears, *Thermodynamics*. Reading, Mass.: Addison-Wesley Publishing Company, Inc., 1955, chap. 5.

4.6 Mooney, D. A., *Mechanical Engineering Thermodynamics*. Englewood Cliffs, N.J.: Prentice-Hall, Inc., 1958, chap. 7, 8.

4.7 Soo, S. L., *Thermodynamics of Engineering Science*. Englewood Cliffs, N.J.: Prentice-Hall, Inc., 1958, chap. 4, 5.

4.8 Van Wylen, G. J., *Thermodynamics*. New York: John Wiley & Sons, Inc., 1959, chap. 6, 7.

4.9 Zemansky, M. W., *Heat and Thermodynamics*. New York: McGraw-Hill Book Company, 1951, chap. 10.

PROBLEMS

4.1 A perfect gas initially at a pressure p_1 and a volume V_1 expands adiabatically and reversibly according to the law $pv^{1.5} = C$ until it doubles its initial volume. The gas is then compressed to its initial state by a sequence of constant-pressure and constant-volume processes. Compare the efficiency of the cycle to the maximum efficiency obtainable. Explain.

4.2 The thermal efficiency of a reversible engine is 50 per cent. Ambient temperature is 40°F.
(a) What is the temperature of the high-temperature source?
(b) If the engine consisted of a closed system and a 50°F temperature drop were necessary to cause heat flow, what would be the temperature of the source and receiver?
(c) What would be the maximum thermal efficiency of the irreversible engine mentioned in (b)?

4.3 Compare the thermal efficiencies of the cycles *a-b-d-e-a* and *a-b-c-e-a* of Fig. 4.25 by means of areas. Account for the difference in efficiencies. (All processes are reversible except for *b-c*.)

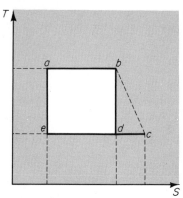

Fig. 4.25.   Problem 4.3.

4.4 A Carnot engine operating with a particular gas between temperatures of 400°F and 60°F receives 172 Btu of heat.
(a) Compute the change in entropy during the process in which the engine rejects heat to its receiver.
(b) Draw the Carnot cycle for this process on a temperature-entropy diagram.

4.5 A refrigerator driven by a 1-hp motor removes 200 Btu/min from a cold body. What is the coefficient of performance of this refrigerator? At what rate is heat rejected to the hot body?

4.6 A refrigeration system exhibits a coefficient of performance one-half of that of a Carnot cycle operating between the same temperature limits. It removes

600 Btu/min from a reservoir at $-100°F$ while the upper temperature is maintained at 260°F.

(a) How much energy is rejected to the high-temperature reservoir?

(b) If the refrigerator were reversed to operate as a power cycle (all data remaining the same) what horsepower would be developed?

4.7 A noncondensable gas is used in the cycle shown in Fig. 4.26. Is this possible? Sketch the T-S diagram.

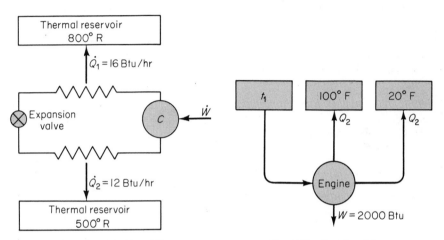

Fig. 4.26. Problem 4.7.   Fig. 4.27. Problem 4.8.

4.8 A reversible heat engine operates between three constant temperature reservoirs as shown in Fig. 4.27. If its thermal efficiency is 40 per cent and $W = 2000$ Btu, calculate the temperature t_1 and the heat quantity Q_2.

4.9 An inventor claims that his new heat engine will develop 0.25 hp when heat at the rate of 30 Btu/min is transferred to the engine. The cycle operates between a maximum temperature of 2000°F and a minimum temperature of 300°F. Would you invest money in this invention?

4.10 One lbm of ice at 32°F is contained initially in a beaker holding 2 lbm of water at 100°F. The beaker in turn is in a large air reservoir which remains substantially at 60°F. There is free exchange of heat between all the systems. The latent heat of fusion of water is 144 Btu/lbm. Determine the net change of entropy for all the systems involved in the foregoing process in going from the initial to a final state.

4.11 One lbm of ice at 32°F is melted by placing it into an insulated container with 2 lbm of water at 110°F.

(a) Determine the change in entropy of the mass that was originally ice.

(b) Determine the change in entropy of the mass that was originally water.

(c) Is the process reversible? Why? (*Note:* heat of fusion of ice is 144 Btu/lbm.)

4.12 In a certain reversible process the specific heat is constant and is

$$c = \frac{dq}{dt} = 0.5 \text{ Btu/lbm}°\text{F}.$$

(a) Find the increase in entropy of the system if its temperature rises from 500°R to 600°R.

(b) In a second process between the same end states, the temperature rise is accomplished by stirring accompanied by a heat transfer half as great as in (a). What is the increase in entropy in this case?

4.13 In Fig. 4.28 the circle represents a reversible engine. During a cycle of operation, the engine draws 1200 Btu from the 400°R reservoir and does 200 Btu of work.

(a) Find the amount and directions of heat interactions with the other two reservoirs.

(b) Evaluate the entropy change due to each of the heat interactions with the engine.

(c) How much "entropy growth" occurs during the cycle?

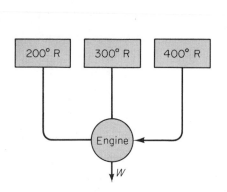

Fig. 4.28.   Problem 4.13.

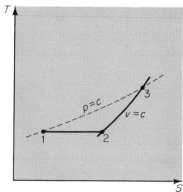

Fig. 4.29.   Problem 4.18.

4.14 A Carnot engine cycle receives 1000 Btu of energy at 540°F and rejects energy at a lower cycle temperature of 100°F.

(a) What is the entropy change of the engine due to the heat rejection process?

(b) What is the total energy rejected and the work output of the cycle for each 1000 Btu input?

4.15 The energy departing as heat from 3 lbm of furnace gases will be sufficient to warm 1 lbm of water initially at 80°F and 10 psia to 193.2°F and just vaporize it at that pressure and temperature. The associated cooling of the gases is from 1400°F to 680°F with an average specific heat of 0.26 Btu/lbm°F. Find:

(a) The heat necessary to just vaporize the water

(b) The entropy change of the gases

(c) The entropy change of the water

(d) The entropy growth for the isolated system (including gases and water).

4.16 Two large bodies at temperatures 55°F and 450°F are exchanging heat at the rate of 200 Btu/min. Assuming that the two bodies are large enough so that the temperature change in either one is negligible, compute the entropy change per minute of (a) the warmer body, (b) the cooler body, (c) the entire system.

4.17 Ten lbm of water at a temperature of 80°F are heated at a pressure of 67 psia to a temperature of 300°F, and are then evaporated at this temperature and pressure by heat interaction equal to 910.1 Btu/lbm. The vapor is then further heated at 67 psia to a final temperature of 480°F. Compute the change in entropy of the water.

$$c = 1.02 \text{ Btu/lbm}°\text{R} \quad \text{(liquid)}$$

$$c_p = 0.45 \text{ Btu/lbm}°\text{R} \quad \text{(vapor)}$$

4.18 A perfect gas undergoes isothermal expansion from state 1 to state 2 as shown in Fig. 4.29. It then undergoes an increase in pressure at constant volume from state 2 to state 3.

$$\text{Data: } \frac{p_2}{p_1} = \frac{1}{2}, \quad \frac{p_3}{p_2} = 2$$

$$T_3 = 1000°\text{R}$$

$$T_2 = 500°\text{R}$$

$$R = 53.3 \text{ ft-1bf/lbm}°\text{R}$$

$$\gamma = \frac{c_p}{c_v} = 1.4$$

Find the change of entropy between states 1 and 3.

4.19 Each of two rigid vessels contains 1 lbm of air. Initially, the state of the air in vessel A is identical with the state of the air in vessel B. A heat pump transfers heat from vessel A and rejects heat to vessel B. During a certain integral number of cycles of the heat pump, 665 ft-lbf of work are delivered to the pump. At the completion of the cycles, it is found that the air in vessel A has decreased in temperature by 50°F.

Assume air to be a perfect gas ($c_p = 0.24$ Btu/lbm°F, $c_v = 0.171$ Btu/lbm°F), and neglect heat interaction between the vessels and the environment.

(a) What is the increase in temperature of the air in vessel B?

(b) What is the entropy change for the entire system comprising the contents of vessels A and B and the heat pump during the process described?

(c) What is the initial temperature of the air in each vessel?

4.20 For a system consisting of a one-component substance in the absence of gravity, electricity, capillarity, magnetism, and motion, indicate by placing a check mark in the proper column under what condition the following equations apply:

	Reversible process (or cycle)	Irreversible process (or cycle)	Any process (or cycle)
$dQ + dW = dE$	____	____	____
$\oint \frac{dQ}{T} = 0$	____	____	____
$\int \frac{dQ}{T} = \int dS$	____	____	____
$dh = T\,ds + v\,dp$	____	____	____
$(s_2 - s_1)_p = c_p \ln \frac{T_2}{T_1}$	____	____	____
(perfect gas)			
$\oint T\,ds = \oint p\,dv$	____	____	____
$\oint T\,ds = -\oint dw$	____	____	____
$\oint ds = 0$	____	____	____
First law of thermodynamics	____	____	____
Second law of thermodynamics	____	____	____

4.21 Two reversible engines A and B reject heat to a common reservoir at a temperature T. Engine A receives heat from a reservoir at T_1, while B receives heat from a reservoir at T_2 $(T_2 < T_1)$. If both engines receive the same amount of heat, for engine A compared with engine B:

	Greater	Same	Less
The work is	____	____	____
The heat rejected is	____	____	____
$\oint ds$ is	____	____	____
$\oint \frac{dQ}{T}$ is	____	____	____
$\oint T\,ds$ is	____	____	____

4.22 Which is more effective in increasing the efficiency of a reversible engine operating between two thermal reservoirs
(a) Increasing the temperature of the high-temperature reservoir by an amount ΔT, keeping the temperature of the low-temperature reservoir constant, or
(b) Decreasing the temperature of the low-temperature reservoir by the same amount ΔT, keeping the temperature of the high-temperature reservoir constant?

4.23 Repeat Problem 4.22 for a reversible heat pump and compare the coefficients of performance.

4.24 By the use of the second law of thermodynamics show that:
(a) Mechanical friction is a source of irreversibility
(b) Throttling is an irreversible process
(c) The process of dropping a weight into a well containing water is irreversible.

NOMENCLATURE

B Darrieus function for steady flow

c_p Specific heat at constant pressure

c_v Specific heat at constant volume

E Total internal energy

e Total internal energy per unit mass

F Helmholtz function

G Gibbs function

g Acceleration due to gravity

g_c Constant of proportionality in Newton's second law

H Enthalpy

h Enthalpy per unit mass

I Irreversibility

m Mass

n Number of moles

p Pressure

Q Heat

q Heat per unit mass

S Entropy

s Entropy per unit mass

T Absolute temperature

t Temperature

U Internal energy

u Internal energy per unit mass

V Velocity or volume

v Specific volume

W Work

Z Compressibility factor

z Elevation

Φ Availability function for a closed system

Ψ Availability function for steady flow processes

μ Chemical potential

γ Ratio of specific heats

Subscripts:

c, h refer to cold and hot

(o) refers to environment conditions

i, r refer to irreversible and reversible processes

Superscript:

$(-)$ refers to property per mole

5

AVAILABILITY, THERMODYNAMIC POTENTIALS, AND CRITERIA OF EQUILIBRIUM

5-1
Introduction
By withdrawing heat from a system, work can be performed through the transformation of heat energy into mechanical energy. But as a consequence of the second law of thermodynamics, a continuous process for accomplishing this transformation will not produce a quantity of work that is exactly equivalent to the heat provided. Losses occur in such transformations, so that the problem lies in determining how to attain maximum efficiencies in converting internal energy into work and how to evaluate the quantity of energy available for work. As shown in Chapter 4, the best way to utilize internal energy to do work involves a reversible heat engine (Carnot engine). The second law indicates, however, that the efficiency of such conversions is always less than unity. In order to determine how much work-energy can be provided in a process, it is necessary to describe the available energy with respect to some reference datum. One choice could be the lowest temperature to which the system may be reduced. In the case of the Carnot cycle, for example, this datum is the constant temperature at which heat is rejected.

The concept of availability provides the information needed to determine the maximum work that a system in a given state can perform with respect to the environment. The internal energy of a system may be divided into two parts: available energy, which under ideal conditions may be completely converted to work, and unavailable energy, which is usually discarded from the system as heat. In the case of the Carnot engine, the quantity $[(T_h - T_c)/T_h]Q_{\text{supplied}}$ is the available energy and the quantity $(T_c/T_h)\ Q_{\text{supplied}}$ is the unavailable energy. As previously shown, these two quantities may be represented by rectangular areas for the Carnot cycle, on the T-S diagram.

In engines that are less efficient than the Carnot engine, only part of the available energy is converted into work, so that the degree of conversion depends also on the efficiency of the engine.

J. W. Gibbs is credited as the originator of the availability concept. He indicated that the environment plays an important part in evaluating the amount of work that can be performed by a system in any given state. According to Gibbs, the availability analysis of a process considers the system to interact with a stable environment of pressure p_o and temperature T_o. This environment may be thought of as an infinitely stable, homogeneous surrounding whose temperature, pressure, and composition are virtually unaffected by any process experienced by the system.

5-2
Reversible
Work
As a preliminary step in the process of developing an expression that shows the relationship between availability and the state of a system, it is first necessary to prove that a system produces maximum work during a process if it pursues a reversible path. Or, conversely, it would be

necessary to prove that, when work is done on a system, reversible work represents the minimum work required to attain a predetermined end state of the system.

Consider a closed system surrounded by an environment at T_o and p_o. When the system experiences a differential change from initial state 1 to final state 2, the change in internal energy dE is independent of the process. Thus for two processes, one reversible and the other irreversible, operating between states 1 and 2, the change in internal energy is a function of only states 1 and 2:

$$dE_r = dE_i \,,$$

where subscripts r and i refer to reversible and irreversible processes, respectively. But according to the first law, the change in internal energy dE is a result of interactions involving both heat and work, with the environment or,

$$dE = đQ + đW.$$

The sum would be identical for reversible and irreversible processes:

$$đQ_r + đW_r = đQ_i + đW_i. \tag{5.1}$$

In a reversible process, the change of entropy is given by

$$dS = \frac{đQ_r}{T_o} \quad \text{or} \quad đQ_r = T_o \, dS.$$

But in an irreversible process, the same entropy change is obtained with a smaller amount of heat supplied:

$$dS > \frac{đQ_i}{T_o} \quad \text{or} \quad đQ_i < T_o \, dS.$$

Hence, since the quantities of heat are different,

$$đQ_r > đQ_i,$$

therefore, from Eq. (5.1), the work required is different:

$$đW_r < đW_i. \tag{5.2}$$

The work done on a system during a reversible process is less than the work done during an irreversible process even though the same end states are involved in the two processes. In an irreversible process in which work is done on a system, some work must be done in overcoming the dissipative effects which cause irreversibility. If work is done by the system, the sense of the inequality is reversed, so that

$$-dW_r > -dW_i. \tag{5.3}$$

The work done by a system during a reversible process then is in excess of that done in an irreversible process connecting the same end states.

It may also be shown that all reversible processes operating between the same two states will produce identical amounts of work, provided that the system exchanges heat with the environment only. This can be proved by considering two reversible processes operating between states 1 and 2. If one of the processes is reversed, a complete cycle results. If the two reversible processes do not produce equal amounts of work, then reversal of one of the processes could result in a net amount of work done by the system. But since the environment is the only thermal reservoir with which the system exchanges heat, such a cycle would constitute a perpetual-motion machine of the second kind. Therefore the two reversible processes must produce equal amounts of work.

Consider, as an example, the expansion of a perfect gas during an adiabatic steady flow process from an initial state 1 at a pressure p_i to a final pressure p_f. Figure 5.1 shows two processes plotted on a T-S coordinate system. Process 1-2s is a reversible adiabatic expansion; process 1-2 is an irreversible adiabatic expansion. Although both processes have the same initial state, they have different final states. According to the first law, the work interaction in the irreversible process, in the absence of changes of kinetic and potential energies, is

$$W_i = W_{1-2} = H_2 - H_1,$$

whereas the work interaction during the isentropic process is

$$W_r = W_{1-2s} = H_{2s} - H_1.$$

Since $H_1 = H_3$, the work done by the system in the reversible process is

$$-W_r = H_1 - H_{2s} = H_3 - H_{2s} = mc_p(T_3 - T_{2s}) = \text{area } 2s\text{-}3\text{-}c\text{-}a,$$

whereas in the irreversible process the work done is

$$-W_i = H_1 - H_2 = H_3 - H_2 = mc_p(T_3 - T_2) = \text{area } 2\text{-}3\text{-}c\text{-}b.$$

The difference in work performed during the two processes is

$$-W_r - (-W_i) = H_2 - H_{2s} = mc_p(T_2 - T_{2s}) = \text{area } 2s\text{-}2\text{-}b\text{-}a.$$

This last quantity represents the "lost work" owing to the irreversibility of the process 1-2. There is, however, more available energy at state 2 with respect to a lower temperature system than there is at state 2s.

A similar procedure applies to adiabatic compression processes. Figure 5.2 shows an adiabatic steady flow compression of a perfect gas from p_i to

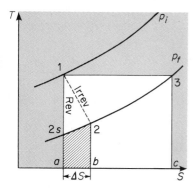

Fig. 5.1. *Maximum work during expansion.*

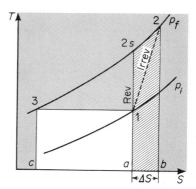

Fig. 5.2. *Minimum work during compression.*

p_f. Process 1-2s is reversible compression, whereas 1-2 is irreversible. The work done on the system during an irreversible process is more than during the reversible one, or

$$W_i > W_r,$$

and the quantity of work required by the two cases amounts to

$$W_r = H_{2s} - H_1, \quad W_i = H_2 - H_1.$$

The difference is

$$W_i - W_r = H_2 - H_{2s} = \text{area } 2s\text{-}2\text{-}b\text{-}a.$$

Area $2s$-2-b-a, shown in Fig. 5.2, represents the additional work that must be expended to compensate for the irreversibility of the compression process.

5-3 Reversible Work in a Nonflow Process

The preceding discussion described an adiabatic process in which irreversibility was involved. Such a process can be treated as though it took place in two separate steps, one a reversible, adiabatic process and the other a reversible, isothermal process in which heat is exchanged with the environment at a temperature T_o. Two cases are of particular interest, the nonflow process and the steady flow process.

Consider a closed system at an initial state defined by pressure p_1 and temperature T_1 surrounded by an environment at a pressure p_o and a temperature T_o. Let the system undergo a change from state 1 to state 2 along either of the two paths shown in Fig. 5.3(a) and 5.3(b). In both cases, the process involves a reversible adiabatic expansion to a pressure p' and then

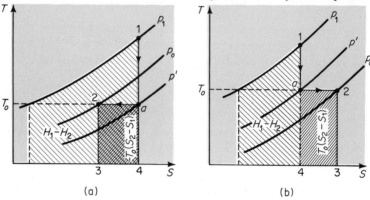

Fig. 5.3. *Maximum work in a nonflow process.*

reversible isothermal energy transfer that brings the system to point 2 (at the pressure p_o). The intermediate pressure p' may be either less than the final pressure, as in Fig. 5.3(a); or greater than the final pressure, as in Fig. 5.3(b). The total work involved is the algebraic sum of the work interactions in the two processes and represents the maximum work done by the system between states 1 and 2. For the reversible adiabatic process 1-a, the work done on the system according to the first law is

$$W_{1-a} = E_a - E_1.$$

For the reversible isothermal process a-2, the work done on the system is

$$W_{a-2} = (E_2 - E_a) - T_o(S_2 - S_a).$$

The total work is the sum of the work done during the two processes, or

$$(W_{\text{rev}})_{1-2} = W_{1-a} + W_{a-2}.$$

But since process 1-a is a reversible adiabatic (isentropic) process, then $S_1 = S_a$. Hence the preceding equation becomes

$$(W_{\text{rev}})_{1-2} = (E_2 - E_1) - T_o(S_2 - S_1). \tag{5.4}*$$

*The subscripts "max" or "min" may be used instead of the subscript "rev," depending upon whether work is done by or on the system.

Another method of arriving at Eq. (5.4) is to apply the first law directly to the over-all process 1-2, assuming reversible heat interaction with the environment at a temperature T_o. In the case of compression, Eq. (5.4) indicates the minimum work necessary for the entire process; and in the case of expansion, Eq. (5.4) shows the maximum work realized during the process. Note that both the change in the internal energy of the system and the heat interaction contribute to the magnitude of W_{rev}.

If a system in a gravitational field of strength g has a velocity V, then the total internal energy neglecting electrical, magnetic, and surface effects is given by

$$E = U + m\frac{V^2}{2g_c} + \frac{mg}{g_c}z. \tag{5.5}$$

When Eq. (5.5) is substituted into Eq. (5.4), the expression for the total work interaction for a reversible process becomes

$$(W_{\text{rev}})_{1-2} = (U_2 - U_1) - T_o(S_2 - S_1) + m\frac{(V_2^2 - V_1^2)}{2g_c} + \frac{mg}{g_c}(z_2 - z_1), \tag{5.6}$$

and per unit mass

$$(w_{\text{rev}})_{1-2} = (u_2 - u_1) - T_o(s_2 - s_1) + \frac{(V_2^2 - V_1^2)}{2g_c} + \frac{g}{g_c}(z_2 - z_1). \tag{5.7}$$

5-4
Reversible
Work in a
Flow Process
In developing an expression for reversible work in a flow process, suppose a control surface σ envelops an open system, as shown in Fig. 5.4. Let the boundary of the open system coincide with the control surface at those locations at which heat or mass is transferred. The heat transfer and mass transfer in the open system are then the

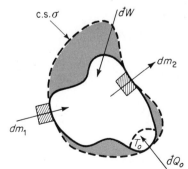

Fig. 5.4. *Flow system.*

same as in the control volume. Let dQ_o and dW be the heat and work interactions with the environment. The total work done on the system may consist of electrical, mechanical, and magnetic work, in addition to any flow work done on the fluid as it flows through the control surface. From the first law, the work done on the control volume other than flow work is

$$dW = -dQ_o - dm_1\left(h_1 + \frac{V_1^2}{2g_c} + \frac{gz_1}{g_c}\right) + dm_2\left(h_2 + \frac{V_2^2}{2g_c} + \frac{gz_2}{g_c}\right)$$
$$+ d\left(U + \frac{mV^2}{2g_c} + \frac{mg}{g_c}z\right)_\sigma. \tag{5.8}$$

Now consider the heat interaction between the system and the environment. Although the temperature may vary at different locations within the system, by assuming that heat is transferred only at those locations where the system and the environment are at the same temperature, reversible heat interaction is achieved. The reversible heat interaction is given by

$$dQ_o = T_o \, dS.$$

In a system where both heat and mass transfer occur across the control surface the total entropy change is

$$dS_\sigma = \frac{dQ_o}{T_o} + dm_1 \, s_1 - dm_2 \, s_2$$
$$= dS + dm_1 \, s_1 - dm_2 \, s_2.$$

Hence the reversible heat interaction is

$$dQ_o = T_o(dS_\sigma - dm_1 \, s_1 + dm_2 \, s_2). \tag{5.9}$$

Substituting for dQ_o from Eq. (5.9) into the first law gives the reversible work as

$$dW_{rev} = -T_o(dS_\sigma - dm_1 \, s_1 + dm_2 \, s_2) - dm_1\left(h_1 + \frac{V_1^2}{2g_c} + \frac{gz_1}{g_c}\right)$$
$$+ dm_2\left(h_2 + \frac{V_2^2}{2g_c} + \frac{gz_2}{g_c}\right) + d\left(U + \frac{mV^2}{2g_c} + \frac{mg}{g_c}z\right)_\sigma.$$

Rearranging terms, the last equation can be written as

$$dW_{rev} = dm_2\left((h_2 - T_o s_2 + \frac{V_2^2}{2g_c} + \frac{gz_2}{g_c}\right) - dm_1\left(h_1 - T_o s_1 + \frac{V_1^2}{2g_c}\right.$$
$$\left.+ \frac{gz_1}{g_c}\right) + d\left(U - T_o S + \frac{mV^2}{2g_c} + \frac{mg}{g_c}z\right)_\sigma. \tag{5.10}$$

Equation (5.10) gives the reversible work done on a system as a function of the inflow and outflow fluid properties, the initial and final states of the system as well as of the temperature of the environment.

Equation (5.10) may be readily adapted to the closed system by letting $dm_1 = dm_2 = 0$. Thus,

$$\text{\dj} W_{\text{rev}} = d\left(U - T_o S + \frac{mV^2}{2g_c} + \frac{mg}{g_c} z \right),$$

which, when integrated, gives Eq. (5.4).

**5-5
Reversible
Work in a
Steady Flow
Process**

Application of Eq. (5.10) to steady flow processes imposes two requirements. These are

$$dm_1 = dm_2 = dm,$$

and

$$d\left(U - T_o S + \frac{mV^2}{2g_c} + \frac{mg}{g_c} z \right)_\sigma = 0.$$

From Eq. (5.10), the reversible work in a steady flow process is then

$$W_{\text{rev}} = \left(H_2 - T_o S_2 + \frac{mV_2^2}{2g_c} + \frac{mg}{g_c} z_2 \right)$$
$$- \left(H_1 - T_o S_1 + \frac{mV_1^2}{2g_c} + \frac{mg}{g_c} z_1 \right). \tag{5.11}$$

The function $(H - T_o S)$ appearing in Eq. (5.11) is called the *Darrieus function* for steady flow (symbol B) such that

$$B \equiv H - T_o S. \tag{5.12}$$

The reversible work interaction in terms of the Darrieus function is

$$W_{\text{rev}} = \left(B_2 + \frac{mV_2^2}{2g_c} + \frac{mg}{g_c} z_2 \right) - \left(B_1 + \frac{mV_1^2}{2g_c} + \frac{mg}{g_c} z_1 \right). \tag{5.13}$$

If two or more streams enter or leave the system, the reversible work interaction in a steady flow process in which the system exchanges heat with the environment only is given by

$$W_{\text{rev}} = \sum_{\text{out}} \left(B + \frac{mV^2}{2g_c} + \frac{mg}{g_c} z \right) - \sum_{\text{in}} \left(B + \frac{mV^2}{2g_c} + \frac{mg}{g_c} z \right)$$
$$= -\sum_{\text{net}} \left(B + \frac{mV^2}{2g_c} + \frac{mg}{g_c} z \right). \tag{5.14}$$

As in the nonflow process, the reversible work in a steady flow process is defined by the end states of the system and by the temperature of the environment.

EXAMPLE 5.1: Find the maximum work per lbm of air that can be obtained from a piston-cylinder arrangement if the air expands from an initial state of $p_1 = 80$ psia, $T_1 = 800°R$ to a final state of $p_2 = 20$ psia, $T_2 = 600°R$. Neglect changes in potential and kinetic energies, and assume $T_o = 520°R$.

Solution: Using Eq. (5.7) for a nonflow process and assuming perfect gas yields

$$(w_{rev})_{1-2} = u_2 - u_1 - T_o(s_2 - s_1)$$

$$= c_v(T_2 - T_1) - T_o\left(c_p \ln\frac{T_2}{T_1} - R\ln\frac{p_2}{p_1}\right)$$

$$= 0.17(600 - 800) - 520\left(0.24\ln\frac{600}{800} - \frac{53.34}{778}\ln\frac{20}{80}\right)$$

$$= -47.7 \text{ Btu/lbm.}$$

EXAMPLE 5.2: A centrifugal compressor handles 50 lbm/min of dry air. The tabulated data give temperature, pressure, internal energy, and enthalpy of the air at the inlet and at the delivery. What is the actual work and the minimum work required per lbm of air? Find the actual and reversible horsepower. (Neglect heat interaction and changes in potential and kinetic energies between inlet and delivery. Assume the environment to be at a temperature of 70°F.)

Data:	p(psia)	T(°R)	u(Btu/lbm)	h(Btu/lbm)
Inlet:	14.7	520	88.62	124.27
Delivery:	30	660	112.67	157.92

Solution: Since this is a steady flow process, the work done per unit mass according to the first law is

$$w_{actual} = h_2 - h_1 = 157.92 - 124.27 = 33.65 \text{ Btu/lbm,}$$

and

$$P_{actual} = \frac{33.65 \times 50 \times 778}{33,000} = 39.7 \text{ hp.}$$

The minimum work of compression is equal to the reversible work. It is given by Eq. (5.13) as

$$w_{min} = w_{rev} = b_2 - b_1 = (h_2 - T_o s_2) - (h_1 - T_o s_1)$$

$$= (h_2 - h_1) - T_o\left(c_p \ln\frac{T_2}{T_1} - R\ln\frac{p_2}{p_1}\right)$$

$$= (157.92 - 124.27) - 530\left(0.24\ln\frac{660}{520} - \frac{53.34}{778}\ln\frac{39}{14.7}\right)$$

$$= 29.35 \text{ Btu/lbm,}$$

and

$$P_{rev} = \frac{29.35 \times 50 \times 778}{33,000} = 34.6 \text{ hp.}$$

The difference between the actual power and the reversible power is attributed to irreversibilities introduced by the compressor.

5-6
Availability
When heat interaction takes place between a system and the environment only, the maximum work that can be performed by the system indicates the energy availability of the system. Availability represents a composite property that depends on the state of both the system and the environment. In performing maximum work, the system undergoes only reversible processes before it finally reaches thermodynamic equilibrium with the environment. At this state no further interaction between the system and the environment occurs.

The concept of availability is used in determining the effectiveness of a process to perform work. As outlined by Darrieus, the effectiveness of a process during which work is produced is the ratio of the work done to the maximum possible work that can be obtained if the process were reversible. Reversible processes have an effectiveness equal to unity; actual processes have an effectiveness less than unity.

The expressions derived for reversible work in nonflow and in steady flow processes are used in defining availability of a system.

Consider a nonflow process in which the system exchanges heat with the environment only, which is at a temperature T_o. Let the state of the system change from an initial state 1 to a final state o, at which it is in equilibrium with the environment. In the absence of surface, electrical, and magnetic effects, the reversible work according to Eq. (5.4) is

$$(W_{rev})_{1-o} = (E_o - T_o S_o) - (E_1 - T_o S_1) = \Phi_o - \Phi_1, \qquad \textbf{(5.15)}$$

where Φ is called the *availability function for a nonflow process*. It is defined as

$$\Phi \equiv E - T_o S, \qquad \textbf{(5.16)}$$

and the reversible work is equal to the change in the availability function.

In differential form,

$$d\Phi = dE - T_o \, dS. \qquad \textbf{(5.17)}$$

The availability of a system to do work is equal to the decrease in the availability function. Thus

$$-(W_{rev})_{1-o} = \text{availability} = \Phi_1 - \Phi_o. \qquad \textbf{(5.18)}$$

Note that availability is a property which depends only on the initial state of the system, provided that the state of the environment remains unchanged and that the system reaches equilibrium with the environment.

When a system undergoes a change from state 1, representing an availability of $(\Phi_1 - \Phi_o)$, to state 2, representing an availability of $(\Phi_2 - \Phi_o)$, the reversible work that may be obtained is the difference between the two availability functions:

$$-(W_{rev})_{1-2} = (\Phi_1 - \Phi_o) - (\Phi_2 - \Phi_o) = \Phi_1 - \Phi_2. \tag{5.19}$$

In general,

$$-W_{1-2} \leqslant \Phi_1 - \Phi_2, \tag{5.20}$$

and in differential form,

$$-dW \leqslant -d\Phi, \tag{5.21}$$

where the inequality sign applies to irreversible processes.

The second case to be considered is a control volume experiencing a steady flow process. According to Eq. (5.13), the reversible work is the maximum (or minimum in case of compression) work interaction. In the absence of surface, electrical, and magnetic effects, the reversible work is

$$W_{rev} = \left(B_o + \frac{mV_o^2}{2g_c} + \frac{mg}{g_c}z_o \right) - \left(B_1 + \frac{mV_1^2}{2g_c} + \frac{mg}{g_c}z_1 \right) = \Psi_o - \Psi_1, \tag{5.22}$$

where Ψ is the *availability function for steady flow* and is defined as

$$\Psi \equiv B + \frac{mV^2}{2g_c} + \frac{mg}{g_c}z. \tag{5.23}$$

In differential form,

$$d\Psi = dH - T_o\, dS + d(KE) + d(\text{Pot } E). \tag{5.24}$$

The reversible work done by a flow system then is equal to the decrease in the availability function:

$$-(W_{rev})_{1-0} = \text{availability} = \Psi_1 - \Psi_o. \tag{5.25}$$

As in the nonflow process, the reversible work in a steady flow process going from state 1 to state 2 while exchanging heat with the environment is

$$-(W_{rev})_{1-2} = (\Psi_1 - \Psi_o) - (\Psi_2 - \Psi_o) = \Psi_1 - \Psi_2. \tag{5.26}$$

Substituting for Ψ gives

$$-(W_{rev})_{1-2} = \left(H_1 - T_o S_1 + \frac{mV_1^2}{2g_c} + \frac{mg}{g_c} z_1 \right)$$

$$- \left(H_2 - T_o S_2 + \frac{mV_2^2}{2g_c} + \frac{mg}{g_c} z_2 \right)$$

$$= (H_1 - H_2) - T_o(S_1 - S_2) + \frac{m(V_1^2 - V_2^2)}{2g_c}$$

$$+ \frac{mg}{g_c} (z_1 - z_2). \tag{5.27}$$

In general,

$$-W_{1-2} \leqslant \Psi_1 - \Psi_2 \tag{5.28}$$

or, in a differential form,

$$-dW \leqslant -d\Psi, \tag{5.29}$$

where the inequality sign applies to irreversible processes. When spontaneous changes in a system cannot occur, the system is at its minimum value of availability. Spontaneous changes can occur only if a system can go to a state of lower availability, and work can be obtained only if changes of state occur which result in a decrease in availability. As shown earlier, the reversible work which can be obtained from a system exchanging heat with the environment only represents the availability:

$$-W_{rev} = \Phi_1 - \Phi_{min} \quad \text{for a nonflow process,} \tag{5.30}$$

$$= \Psi_1 - \Psi_{min} \quad \text{for a steady flow process.} \tag{5.31}$$

Here, Φ_1 and Ψ_1 are the availability functions at some particular state, whereas Φ_{min} and Ψ_{min} are the availability functions at the most stable state of equilibrium. Stable equilibrium will be discussed in Section 5.12.

EXAMPLE 5.3: Calculate the availability in the initial and final states of Example 5.1. Check that the difference is equal to the reversible work for that process.

Solution: The availability in the initial state according to Eq. (5.18) is

$$\phi_1 - \phi_o = (u_1 - u_o) - T_o(s_1 - s_o)$$

$$= c_v (T_1 - T_o) - T_o \left(c_p \ln \frac{T_1}{T_o} - R \ln \frac{p_1}{p_o} \right)$$

$$= 0.17 (800 - 520) - 520 \left(0.24 \ln \frac{800}{520} - \frac{53.34}{778} \ln \frac{80}{14.7} \right)$$

$$= 54.6 \text{ Btu/lbm.}$$

The availability in the final state is

$$\phi_2 - \phi_0 = (u_2 - u_0) - T_0(s_2 - s_0)$$

$$= c_v(T_2 - T_0) - T_0\left(c_p \ln\frac{T_2}{T_0} - R\ln\frac{p_2}{p_0}\right)$$

$$= 0.17(600 - 520) - 520\left(0.24\ln\frac{600}{520} - \frac{53.34}{778}\ln\frac{20}{14.7}\right)$$

$$= 7.1 \text{ Btu/lbm}.$$

The reversible work is equal to the increase in the availability or

$$(w_{\text{rev}})_{1-2} = \phi_2 - \phi_1 = 7.1 - 54.6 = -47.5 \text{ Btu/lbm},$$

which agrees, to slide-rule accuracy, with the result of Example 5.1.

EXAMPLE 5.4: Find the unavailable energy resulting from the transfer of a quantity of heat Q between a thermal reservoir at temperature T and the environment at T_0.

Solution: The increase of entropy due to the heat transfer process is

$$\Delta S = \frac{Q}{T_0} - \frac{Q}{T} = Q\frac{T - T_0}{TT_0},$$

and the increase in unavailable energy is $= T_0\Delta S = Q[(T - T_0)/T]$. This energy represents the maximum work obtainable from a reversible engine operating between temperature T and the temperature of the environment, T_0. This work is referred to as *lost work* because it becomes unavailable as a result of the heat transfer process. Thus the *availability of a thermal reservoir* can be defined as the reversible work that can be obtained when a quantity of energy is withdrawn from the reservoir. Figure 5.5 shows the increase in the unavailable energy. Note that all the energy originally available is transformed in the process into unavailable energy.

EXAMPLE 5.5: The cycle of an engine is composed of two reversible isothermal processes and two irreversible adiabatic processes. The engine receives 1000 Btu of heat per lbm at the upper temperature of 1000°R. The low-temperature receiver is at 500°R. Due to fluid friction during the compression process and the expansion process, there is an increase in entropy during each of these processes equal to 5 per cent of the entropy increase during the heat transfer to the engine.

(a) Sketch a T-S diagram for the cycle and label the areas that represent the available and the unavailable energies.

(b) Calculate the thermal efficiency of the cycle.

Solution: (a) The increase in entropy is due to heat interaction and fluid friction. The entropy increase per cycle due to heat transfer to the engine is

$$\Delta s = 1000/1000 = 1 \text{ Btu/lbm}°R.$$

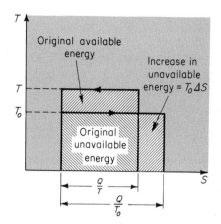

Fig. 5.5. *Example 5.4.*

As shown in Fig. 5.6, the available and unavailable energies are respectively 450 Btu/lbm and 500 × 1.1 = 550 Btu/lbm. Note that

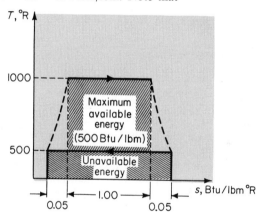

Fig. 5.6. *Example 5.5.*

$\Delta s_{\text{total}} = 1.0 + 2 \times (0.05 \times 1.0) = 1.1$ Btu/lbm°R.

(b) The thermal efficiency of the engine is

$$\eta = \frac{W_{\text{net out}}}{Q_{\text{in}}} = \frac{Q_{\text{in}} - Q_{\text{out}}}{Q_{\text{in}}}$$

$$= \frac{1000 - 1.1 \times 500}{1000}$$

$= 45$ per cent.

EXAMPLE 5.6: Two lbm of water at 105°F are mixed with 3 lbm of water at 210°F in a steady flow process.

(a) What is the temperature of the resulting mixture?

(b) Is the mixing isentropic? If not, what is the entropy change?

(c) What is the unavailable energy with respect to a receiver at 105°F?

Solution: (a) From the first law:

$$2h_1 + 3h_2 = 5h_3.$$

Assuming the specific heat of water is constant, then

$$2c(105 - 32) + 3c(210 - 32) = 5c(t_3 - 32),$$

from which the temperature of the mixture is

$$t_3 = 168°F.$$

(b) The increase in entropy due to the mixing process is

$$\Delta S = m_1 c \ln \frac{T_3}{T_1} + m_2 c \ln \frac{T_3}{T_2}$$

$$= 2 \times (1) \ln \frac{628}{565} + 3 \times (1) \ln \frac{628}{670} = 0.0164 \text{ Btu}/°R.$$

(c) Unavailable energy $= T_R \Delta S$

$$= (105 + 460) \times 0.0164$$

$$= 565 \times 0.0164 = 9.27 \text{ Btu}.$$

EXAMPLE 5.7: Water is evaporated at a constant temperature of 500°F as a result of heat interaction with combustion gases that are cooled from 2500°F to 600°F. The environment is at 80°F. Determine the decrease in available energy per lbm of gas due to the heat interaction process. What is the availability of the energy of the gas before and after the heat interaction? (c_p of the gas $= 0.24$ Btu/lbm°F: the latent heat of vaporization of the water is 456 Btu/lbm.)

Solution: The heat transfer per lbm of gas is

$$q = c_p(2500 - 600) = 0.24 \times 1900 = 456 \text{ Btu/lbm}.$$

Therefore, 1 lbm of water is evaporated per lbm of gas.

Decrease in available energy

$$= T_o(\Delta s_{\text{water}} - \Delta s_{\text{gas}})$$

$$= (80 + 460) \left(\frac{456}{500 + 460} - 0.24 \ln \frac{2500 + 460}{600 + 460} \right)$$

$$= 123.5 \text{ Btu/lbm gas}.$$

The unavailable energy before the heat transfer process is represented by area *a-b-c-d* of Fig. 5.7 and is equal to

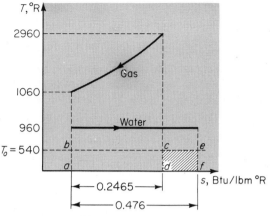

Fig. 5.7.   Example 5.7.

$T_0 \Delta s_{\text{gas}} = 540(0.2465) = 133.5$ Btu/lbm.

After the heat transfer process the unavailable energy (area a-b-e-f) is

$T_0 \Delta s_{\text{water}} = 540(0.476) = 257$ Btu/lbm.

Hence the increase in the unavailable energy due to the heat interaction (area d-c-e-f) is 123.5 Btu/lbm by difference. Note that the increase in the unavailable energy is the same as the decrease in the available energy obtained before.

The availability of energy per lbm of gas before the heat transfer is

$$- \Delta \psi = - (\Delta h - T_0 \Delta s)$$

$$= c_p(T_1 - T_0) - T_0 \left(c_p \ln \frac{T_1}{T_0} \right)$$

$$= 0.24\,(2960 - 540) - 540 \times 0.24 \ln \frac{2960}{540}$$

$$= 571 - 220 = 351 \text{ Btu/lbm.}$$

The availability after the heat transfer is

$$- \Delta \psi = c_p(T_2 - T_0) - T_0 \left(c_p \ln \frac{T_2}{T_0} \right)$$

$$= 0.24\,(1060 - 540) - 540 \times 0.24 \ln \frac{1060}{540}$$

$$= 37.3 \text{ Btu/lbm.}$$

5-7
Irreversibility   In order to obtain maximum work from a system in which the only heat interaction is with the environment, the system must change its state reversibly. But the actual work done by a system is always less than the idealized reversible work,

and the difference between the two is called the *irreversibility* of the process and is defined by the identity:

$$I \equiv (-W_{\text{rev}}) - (-W). \tag{5.32}$$

An expression for the irreversibility of a nonflow process is obtained as follows: Let a closed system receive an amount of heat Q from the environment and perform an amount of work W. The first law is

$$W = \Delta E - Q. \tag{5.33}$$

Combining this with Eq. (5.19) and (5.32) gives the following expression for irreversibility:

$$
\begin{aligned}
I &= \Phi_1 - \Phi_2 + (E_2 - E_1) - Q_{1-2} \\
&= (E_1 - T_o S_1) - (E_2 - T_o S_2) + (E_2 - E_1) - Q_{1-2}.
\end{aligned}
$$

If a system receives heat from an environment that is at a temperature T_o, the entropy change of the environment is

$$\Delta S_{\text{envir}} = -\frac{Q_{1-2}}{T_o}.$$

Substituting in the previous equation gives

$$
\begin{aligned}
I &= (E_1 - T_o S_1) - (E_2 - T_o S_2) + (E_2 - E_1) + T_o \Delta S_{\text{envir}} \\
&= T_o(S_2 - S_1) + T_o \Delta S_{\text{envir}} \\
&= T_o(\Delta S_{\text{sys}} + \Delta S_{\text{envir}}). \tag{5.34}
\end{aligned}
$$

According to this equation, the irreversibility of a process is the product of the environment temperature and the increase in entropy of both the system and the environment. Since neither the absolute temperature T_o nor the total change of entropy is negative, then

$$I \geqslant 0, \tag{5.35}$$

where the equality and inequality signs apply to reversible and irreversible processes respectively.

In a similar way, an expression for irreversibility in a flow process can be derived. Consider the open system of Fig. 5.4. The work done on the control volume enveloping the open system is

$$W_{1-2} = m_2 \left(h_2 + \frac{V_2^2}{2g_c} + \frac{gz_2}{g_c} \right) - m_1 \left(h_1 + \frac{V_1^2}{2g_c} + \frac{gz_1}{g_c} \right) - Q_{1-2} + \Delta E_\sigma. \tag{5.36}$$

By substituting for W_{rev} from Eq. (5.10) and for W_{1-2} from Eq. (5.36), Eq. (5.32) becomes

$$I = -\left[m_2\left(h_2 - T_o s_2 + \frac{V_2^2}{2g_c} + \frac{gz_2}{g_c}\right) - m_1\left(h_1 - T_o s_1 + \frac{V_1^2}{2g_c} + \frac{gz_1}{g_c}\right) \right.$$
$$+ \Delta\left(U - T_o S + m\frac{V^2}{2g_c} + \frac{mg}{g_c}z\right)_\sigma \Big]$$
$$+ \left[m_2\left(h_2 + \frac{V_2^2}{2g_c} + \frac{gz_2}{g_c}\right) - m_1\left(h_1 + \frac{V_1^2}{2g_c} + \frac{gz_1}{g_c}\right) - Q_{1-2} + \Delta E_\sigma \right],$$

which reduces to

$$I = T_o(m_2 s_2 - m_1 s_1 + \Delta S_\sigma) - Q_{1-2},$$

but the total increase of entropy of the system is

$$\Delta S_{\text{sys}} = \Delta S_\sigma + m_2 s_2 - m_1 s_1.$$

Also, the heat transferred to the system from the constant-temperature environment is

$$Q_{1-2} = -T_o \Delta S_{\text{envir}}.$$

These terms can now be substituted in the expression for irreversibility, so that

$$I = T_o(\Delta S_{\text{sys}} + \Delta S_{\text{envir}}). \tag{5.37}$$

Evidently, the same expression for irreversibility applies to both flow and nonflow processes.

The quantity $T_o(\Delta S_{\text{sys}} + S_{\text{envir}})$ represents an increase in unavailable energy. Note that the change of entropy $(\Delta S_{\text{sys}} + \Delta S_{\text{envir}})$ is the total production of entropy in the process. Also the increase in the unavailable energy in a process is equal in magnitude to the decrease in the available energy.

EXAMPLE 5.8: Calculate the rate of irreversibility involved in the heat transfer between a hot and a cold fluid with the following characteristics:

Fluid	t_1 (°F)	t_2 (°F)	c_p(Btu/lbm°F)	$\dot{m}$(lbm/sec)
Hot	275	100	1.03	0.12
Cold	80	220	1.11	—

The temperature of the environment $T_o = 530°R$. What is the rate of entropy production? (Assume constant specific heats.)

Solution: Assuming no pressure or heat losses, the mass flow rate of the cold fluid may be determined by the simple energy balance,

$$\dot{m}_c\, c_{p_c} (T_{2_c} - T_{1_c}) = \dot{m}_h\, c_{p_h} (T_{1_h} - T_{2_h}),$$

so that

$$\dot{m}_c = \frac{0.12 \times 1.03\,(275 - 100)}{1.11\,(220 - 80)} = 0.139 \text{ lbm/sec}.$$

The rate of increase of irreversibility, according to Eq. (5.37), is

$$\dot{I} = T_o (\Delta \dot{S}_c + \Delta \dot{S}_h) = T_o \left(\dot{m}_c\, c_{p_c} \ln \frac{T_{2_c}}{T_{1_c}} + \dot{m}_h\, c_{p_h} \ln \frac{T_{2_h}}{T_{1_h}} \right)$$

$$= 530 \left(0.139 \times 1.11 \ln \frac{680}{540} + 0.12 \times 1.03 \ln \frac{560}{735} \right)$$

$$= 0.98 \text{ But/sec}.$$

The rate of entropy production is

$$(\Delta \dot{S}_c + \Delta \dot{S}_h) = \frac{\dot{I}}{T_o} = 1.85 \times 10^{-3} \text{ Btu/sec}^\circ R.$$

5-8
Helmholtz and Gibbs Free Energies

Systems undergoing physical and chemical reactions often exist in an environment of constant temperature. These systems exchange heat with the environment during the course of the reaction, so that thermal equilibrium is maintained both initially and finally. The maximum work that can be obtained from a system under these conditions is discussed in this section.

Consider the heat interaction between a closed system and its environment at a pressure p_o and temperature T_o. The work done on this system, in the absence of kinetic, potential, electrical, magnetic, and surface energies, is given by the first law:

$$dW = dU - dQ, \tag{5.38}$$

where dW includes any p-V work done on the environment. If the system exchanges heat with the environment only, the change of entropy of the system, according to the second law, is

$$dS \geqslant \frac{dQ}{T_o}.$$

Substituting for dQ in the first law gives

$$dW \geqslant dU - T_o\, dS. \tag{5.39}$$

Integrating Eq. (5.39) for a finite process between two equilibrium states 1 and 2 gives

$$W_{1-2} \geqslant (U_2 - U_1) - T_o(S_2 - S_1). \tag{5.40}$$

If the initial and final temperatures of the system are equal to the temperature of the environment, Eq. (5.40) becomes

$$W_T \geqslant [(U_2 - T_2 S_2) - (U_1 - T_1 S_1)]_T$$
$$\geqslant (F_2 - F_1)_T, \tag{5.41}$$

where F is called the *Helmholtz function* or *Helmholtz free energy** and is defined as

$$F \equiv U - TS. \tag{5.42}$$

According to Eq. (5.41), the work done on a closed system whose initial and final temperatures are equal to that of the environment and which exchanges heat with the environment only is either equal to or greater than the change in the Helmholtz function. Note that if work is done by the system, Eq. (5.41) is written as

$$-W_T \leqslant (F_1 - F_2)_T, \tag{5.43}$$

and the work done by the system will be equal to or less than $-\Delta F_T$.

If, besides the foregoing restrictions, the initial and final volumes of the system are the same, the p-V work interaction with the environment is zero. Then Eq. (5.41) becomes

$$W_{T,V} \geqslant (F_2 - F_1)_{T,V}. \tag{5.44}$$

Equation (5.44), which is more restrictive than Eq. (5.41), applies to a constant-volume process in which the temperature at the beginning of the process, the temperature at the end of the process, and the temperature of the surrounding environment are all identical.

Consider next a system undergoing a steady flow process. In this system, too, heat is exchanged only with the environment, and the system exists in thermal equilibrium with the environment, both initially and ultimately. The *Gibbs free energy function* is defined as

$$G \equiv H - TS = U + pV - TS. \tag{5.45}$$

An equation analogous to Eq. (5.40), which applies to closed systems, applies to the steady flow process. Since the net flow work $(p_1 V_1 - p_2 V_2)$

*The term *free energy* refers to maximum energy that can be "freed" to do work.

at entry to and exit from the system affects the amount of work done, the following expression indicates work done on the steady flow system:

$$W \geqslant (U_2 - U_1) - T_o(S_2 - S_1) - (p_1 V_1 - p_2 V_2)$$
$$\geqslant (U_2 + p_2 V_2 - T_o S_2) - (U_1 + p_1 V_1 - T_o S_1). \tag{5.46}$$

Since the initial and final temperatures of the system were specified to be equal to the environment temperature,

$$W_T \geqslant (U_2 + p_2 V_2 - T_2 S_2)_T - (U_1 + p_1 V_1 - T_1 S_1)_T$$
$$\geqslant (G_2 - G_1)_T , \tag{5.47}$$

where G is the Gibbs function. In a steady flow process, when the initial and final temperatures are equal to that of the environment and when the system exchanges heat with the environment only, the work done is equal to or greater than the change in the Gibbs function. The equality and inequality signs refer to reversible and irreversible processes.

If, in addition to the preceding restrictions, the system is also in pressure equilibrium with the environment at the initial and final states, the flow work $(p_1 V_1 - p_2 V_2)$ is equal to the work done by the environment on the system, $p_o (V_1 - V_2)$. Thus the work done in a steady flow process is

$$W_{T,p} \geqslant (G_2 - G_1)_{T,p} . \tag{5.48}$$

The expression for work done described by Eq. (5.48) also applies to a nonflow, constant-temperature, constant-pressure process. If $-p_o \Delta V$ is subtracted from the expression given by Eq. (5.41), then

$$W_{T,p} \geqslant [(F_2 - F_1) + p_o(V_2 - V_1)]_{T,p}$$
$$\geqslant [F_2 + p_2 V_2) - (F_1 + p_1 V_1)]_{T,p}$$
$$\geqslant (G_2 - G_1)_{T,p} ,$$

which is the same as Eq. (5.48).

Both the Gibbs and the Helmholtz free energy functions establish criteria for thermodynamic equilibrium. At equilibrium, these functions are at their minimum values.

EXAMPLE 5.9: Steam expands isothermally from an initial state of 600°F and 500 psia to a final state of 600°F and 14.7 psia. The properties of steam at the initial and final states are given in the following table:

$t(°F)$	$p(psia)$	$u(Btu/lbm)$	$h(Btu/lbm)$	$s(Btu/lbm°R)$
600	500	1151.6	1298.6	1.5588
600	14.7	1218.2	1334.8	1.9734

What is the reversible work developed per unit mass of steam if the expansion process is (a) nonflow, (b) steady flow?

Solution: (a) The reversible work developed in a nonflow process is the change in the Helmholtz free energy:

$$(w_{rev})_T = (f_2 - f_1)_T$$
$$= [(u_2 - u_1) - T(s_2 - s_1)]_T$$
$$= (1218.2 - 1151.6) - 1060(1.9734 - 1.5588)$$
$$= -372.4 \text{ Btu/lbm.}$$

The reversible work is also given by

$$w_{rev} = -\int p \, dv.$$

No information, however, is provided on the variation of p with respect to v.

(b) The maximum work (other than $p\text{-}V$ work) developed in a steady flow process is the change in the Gibbs free energy:

$$(w_{rev})_T = (g_2 - g_1)_T$$
$$= [(h_2 - h_1) - T(s_2 - s_1)]_T$$
$$= (1334.8 - 1298.6) - 1060(1.9734 - 1.5588)$$
$$= -372.8 \text{ Btu/lbm.}$$

The foregoing result might also be obtained from the formula $\int v \, dp$ if $p\text{-}v$ data were available.

5-9
Chemical
Potential

The intensive state of a simple system is defined by two independent intensive properties. In the case of systems where changes in composition occur, or where phases are open for mass transfer, information is needed about concentrations of the components of the system. The composition of a homogeneous phase of a multicomponent system may be defined either by indicating the number of moles of each component or by indicating the relative molal concentration of each constituent and the total number of moles. In either case, if a system has k components, the composition is not adequately defined unless k independent variables are known. This means that, in order to define the thermodynamic state of a k-component system adequately, it is necessary to specify a total of $k + 2$ parameters. For example, the internal energy of a homogeneous phase of a system with k components is defined by

$$U = U(S, V, n_1, n_2, \ldots, n_k). \tag{5.49}$$

The differential of U is

$$dU = \left(\frac{\partial U}{\partial S}\right)_{V,n_i} dS + \left(\frac{\partial U}{\partial V}\right)_{S,n_i} dV + \sum_{i=1}^{i=k} \left(\frac{\partial U}{\partial n_i}\right)_{S,V,n_j} dn_i, \tag{5.50}$$

where $n_1, n_2, \ldots, n_k$ are the number of moles of the components of the system, and where the use of the subscript j implies that only one of the components is varied at a time. If the composition of the system does not change, the last term of the equation drops out, so that the differential of internal energy becomes

$$dU = \left(\frac{\partial U}{\partial S}\right)_{V,n_i} dS + \left(\frac{\partial U}{\partial V}\right)_{S,n_i} dV.$$

The combined first and second laws, however, give dU as

$$dU = T\,dS - p\,dV.$$

The coefficients of the independent variables S and V can be equated, yielding

$$\left(\frac{\partial U}{\partial S}\right)_{V,n_i} = T \tag{5.51}$$

and

$$\left(\frac{\partial U}{\partial V}\right)_{S,n_i} = -p. \tag{5.52}$$

The molal chemical potential $\bar{\mu}$ of component i is defined as

$$\bar{\mu}_i \equiv \left(\frac{\partial U}{\partial n_i}\right)_{S,V,n_j}. \tag{5.53}$$

When changes in composition are considered in the statements of the first and second laws, Eq. (5.50) becomes

$$dU = T\,dS - p\,dV + \sum_{i=1}^{i=k} \bar{\mu}_i\,dn_i. \tag{5.54}$$

In a similar manner, the Gibbs function $G\ (= H - TS)$ and its differential forms are given by

$$G = G(T, p, n_1, n_2, \ldots, n_k). \tag{5.55}$$

Changes in the free energy function result from changes in pressure, temperature, and composition:

$$dG = \left(\frac{\partial G}{\partial p}\right)_{T,n_i} dp + \left(\frac{\partial G}{\partial T}\right)_{p,n_i} dT + \sum_{i=1}^{i=k} \left(\frac{\partial G}{\partial n_i}\right)_{p,Tn_j} dn_i. \tag{5.56}$$

But the Gibbs free energy function can also be expressed as

$$dG = V\,dp - S\,dT + \sum_{i=1}^{i=k} \bar{\mu}_i\,dn_i. \tag{5.57}$$

Equating the coefficients of dp, dT, and dn_i yields

$$\left(\frac{\partial G}{\partial p}\right)_{T,n_i} = V, \tag{5.58}$$

$$\left(\frac{\partial G}{\partial T}\right)_{p,n_i} = -S, \tag{5.59}$$

and

$$\left(\frac{\partial G}{\partial n_i}\right)_{p,T,n_j} = \bar{\mu}_i. \tag{5.60}$$

The chemical potential $\bar{\mu}_i$, as indicated by Eqs. (5.53) and (5.60), can be expressed in terms of either the internal energy or the Gibbs function. The functions $(\partial U/\partial n_i)_{S,V,n_j}$ and $(\partial G/\partial n_i)_{p,T,n_j}$ can be shown to be equivalent by substituting $(U + pV - TS)$ for G in Eq. (5.57), then performing the indicated operations:

$$d(U + pV - TS) = V\,dp - S\,dT + \sum_{i=1}^{i=k} \bar{\mu}_i\,dn_i.$$

Therefore,

$$dU + p\,dV + V\,dp - T\,dS - S\,dT = V\,dp\ - S\,dT + \sum_{i=1}^{i=k} (\bar{\mu}_i\,dn_i).$$

And finally,

$$dU = T\,dS - p\,dV + \sum_{i=1}^{i=k} \bar{\mu}_i\,dn_i,$$

which is Eq. (5.54).

The chemical potential $\bar{\mu}$ is used as an index of chemical equilibrium in the same manner as temperature and pressure are used as indices of thermal and mechanical equilibria. It is an intensive property and may be expressed in terms of independent properties, such as

$$\bar{\mu}_i = \bar{\mu}_i(U, V, n_1, n_2, \ldots, n_k). \tag{5.61}$$

Analogous to U and G, the differentials of enthalpy and Helmholtz functions can be written in the forms:

$$dH = T\,dS + V\,dp + \sum_i \bar{\mu}_i\,dn_i, \tag{5.62}$$

$$dF = -S\,dT - p\,dV + \sum_i \bar{\mu}_i\,dn_i. \tag{5.63}$$

The chemical potential $\bar{\mu}$ can be expressed in terms of the preceding functions as

$$\bar{\mu}_i = \left(\frac{\partial H}{\partial n_i}\right)_{S,p,n_j} = \left(\frac{\partial F}{\partial n_i}\right)_{T,V,n_j} = \left(\frac{\partial U}{\partial n_i}\right)_{V,S,n_j} = \left(\frac{\partial G}{\partial n_i}\right)_{T,p,n_j}. \tag{5.64}$$

The chemical potential of a species is the partial differential of the internal energy, enthalpy, Helmholtz function, or Gibbs function with respect to the number of moles of that species, subject to the conditions indicated by subscripts in Eq. (5.64). The term *potential* arises from the analogous situation in which a force is exerted by a force field in a certain direction, and the force is the derivative of the force potential in that direction. Chemical potential is expressed on the basis of energy per lb-mole or energy per lbm.

5-10
Thermo-
dynamic
Relations
James Clerk Maxwell made many contributions to science; his main contribution to thermodynamics were the *Maxwell relations*. Consider the differential forms of the expressions for internal energy, Gibbs function, enthapy, and Helmholtz function given by Eqs. (5.54), (5.57), (5.62), and (5.63). These four properties can also be expressed in the form of Eqs. (5.50) and (5.56). By equating the coefficients of the independent variables S, V, p, and T, the following relations are obtained:

$$T = \left(\frac{\partial U}{\partial S}\right)_{V,n_i} = \left(\frac{\partial H}{\partial S}\right)_{p,n_i}, \tag{5.65}$$

$$p = -\left(\frac{\partial U}{\partial V}\right)_{S,n_i} = -\left(\frac{\partial F}{\partial V}\right)_{T,n_i}, \tag{5.66}$$

$$V = \left(\frac{\partial H}{\partial p}\right)_{S,n_i} = \left(\frac{\partial G}{\partial p}\right)_{T,n_i}, \tag{5.67}$$

$$S = -\left(\frac{\partial F}{\partial T}\right)_{V,n_i} = -\left(\frac{\partial G}{\partial T}\right)_{p,n_i}. \tag{5.68}$$

According to the properties of exact differentials outlined in Section 1-4, the following relations may be obtained for internal energy:

$$\left[\frac{\partial}{\partial V}\left(\frac{\partial U}{\partial S}\right)_{V,n_i}\right]_{S,n_i} = \left[\frac{\partial}{\partial S}\left(\frac{\partial U}{\partial V}\right)_{n_i,S}\right]_{V,n_i},$$

$$\left[\frac{\partial}{\partial n_i}\left(\frac{\partial U}{\partial V}\right)_{n_i,S}\right]_{S,V} = \left[\frac{\partial}{\partial V}\left(\frac{\partial U}{\partial n_i}\right)_{S,V}\right]_{n_i,S},$$

$$\left[\frac{\partial}{\partial S}\left(\frac{\partial U}{\partial n_i}\right)_{S,V}\right]_{n_i,S} = \left[\frac{\partial}{\partial n_i}\left(\frac{\partial U}{\partial S}\right)_{V,n_i}\right]_{S,V}.$$

Similar expressions for enthalpy, the Gibbs function, and the Helmholtz function can be derived from Eqs. (5.66)–(5.68). From them, the following Maxwell relations are readily obtained:

$$\left(\frac{\partial T}{\partial V}\right)_{S,n_i} = -\left(\frac{\partial p}{\partial S}\right)_{V,n_i}, \tag{5.69a}$$

$$-\left(\frac{\partial S}{\partial p}\right)_{T,n_i} = \left(\frac{\partial V}{\partial T}\right)_{p,n_i}, \tag{5.69b}$$

$$\left(\frac{\partial T}{\partial p}\right)_{S,n_i} = \left(\frac{\partial V}{\partial S}\right)_{p,n_i}, \tag{5.69c}$$

$$\left(\frac{\partial S}{\partial V}\right)_{T,n_i} = \left(\frac{\partial p}{\partial T}\right)_{V,n_i}. \tag{5.69d}$$

These Maxwell relations express the entropy of a simple system in terms of measurable properties, such as pressure, volume, and temperature. Other thermodynamic relations may be obtained in terms of the chemical potential.

From Eqs. (5.65) and (1.13), specific heats of a simple system may be expressed in terms of entropy:

$$c_v = \left(\frac{\partial u}{\partial T}\right)_v = \left(\frac{\partial u}{\partial s}\right)_v\left(\frac{\partial s}{\partial T}\right)_v = T\left(\frac{\partial s}{\partial T}\right)_v, \tag{5.70}$$

$$c_p = \left(\frac{\partial h}{\partial T}\right)_p = \left(\frac{\partial h}{\partial s}\right)_p\left(\frac{\partial s}{\partial T}\right)_p = T\left(\frac{\partial s}{\partial T}\right)_p. \tag{5.71}$$

Differentiating the constant volume specific heat with respect to v at constant T gives

$$\left(\frac{\partial c_v}{\partial v}\right)_T = T\left(\frac{\partial^2 s}{\partial v\,\partial T}\right).$$

From Eq. (5.69d), this becomes

$$\left(\frac{\partial c_v}{\partial v}\right)_T = T\left(\frac{\partial^2 s}{\partial v\,\partial T}\right) = T\left(\frac{\partial^2 p}{\partial T^2}\right)_v. \tag{5.72}$$

Similarly,

$$\left(\frac{\partial c_p}{\partial p}\right)_T = T\left(\frac{\partial^2 s}{\partial p \, \partial T}\right) = -T\left(\frac{\partial^2 v}{\partial T^2}\right)_p. \tag{5.73}$$

Equations (5.72) and (5.73) relate specific heat values to p-V-T information. The difference between c_p and c_v can be expressed in several different ways (see Problem 5.22):

$$c_p - c_v = T\left(\frac{\partial s}{\partial T}\right)_p - T\left(\frac{\partial s}{\partial T}\right)_v. \tag{5.74}$$

$$= T\left(\frac{\partial s}{\partial v}\right)_T \left(\frac{\partial v}{\partial T}\right)_p \tag{5.75}$$

$$= T\left(\frac{\partial p}{\partial T}\right)_V \left(\frac{\partial v}{\partial T}\right)_p \tag{5.76}$$

$$= -T\left(\frac{\partial v}{\partial T}\right)_p^2 \left(\frac{\partial p}{\partial v}\right)_T. \tag{5.77}$$

Using Eq. (1.13) the ratio of specific heats can be written as

$$\gamma = \frac{c_p}{c_v} = \frac{(\partial s/\partial T)_p}{(\partial s/\partial T)_V} = \frac{(\partial p/\partial v)_s}{(\partial p/\partial v)_T} = \left(\frac{\partial p}{\partial v}\right)_s \left(\frac{\partial v}{\partial p}\right)_T. \tag{5.78}$$

EXAMPLE 5.10:   The Gay-Lussac–Joule experiment, outlined in Chapter 3, indicates that the internal energy of a perfect gas is a function of temperature only. Using the appropriate Maxwell relation, give a mathematical proof of this statement.

Solution: The combined first and second laws can be written as

$$T \, dS = dU + p \, dV.$$

Dividing by dV and considering an isothermal change gives

$$T\left(\frac{\partial S}{\partial V}\right)_T = \left(\frac{\partial U}{\partial V}\right)_T + p.$$

Substituting for $(\partial S/\partial V)_T$ from the Maxwell relation (5.69d) and noting that for a perfect gas, $T(\partial p/\partial T)_V = p$, then

$$\left(\frac{\partial U}{\partial V}\right)_T = 0,$$

which means that the internal energy of a perfect gas is not a function of volume; hence it is a function of temperature only.

EXAMPLE 5.11: Using the Maxwell relation,

$$\left(\frac{\partial S}{\partial p}\right)_T = -\left(\frac{\partial V}{\partial T}\right)_p$$

and the equations

$$pV = Zn\mathscr{R}T, \qquad dH = T\,dS + V\,dp,$$

where Z is called the *compressibility factor*,* prove that the change of enthalpy and entropy between two states is given by the expressions

$$H_2 - H_1 = -n\mathscr{R}T^2 \int_{p_1}^{p_2} \left(\frac{\partial Z}{\partial T}\right)_p \frac{dp}{p}$$

and

$$S_2 - S_1 = -n\mathscr{R} \int_{p_1}^{p_2} \frac{Z}{p}\,dp + \frac{H_2 - H_1}{T}.$$

Solution: Differentiating the equation of state with respect to T at constant pressure gives

$$\left(\frac{\partial V}{\partial T}\right)_p = \frac{n\mathscr{R}Z}{p} + \frac{n\mathscr{R}T}{p}\left(\frac{\partial Z}{\partial T}\right)_p.$$

Using the Maxwell relation, then

$$\left(\frac{\partial S}{\partial p}\right)_T = -\frac{n\mathscr{R}}{p}\left[Z + T\left(\frac{\partial Z}{\partial T}\right)_p\right].$$

But

$$dH = T\,dS + V\,dp;$$

then,

$$\left(\frac{\partial H}{\partial p}\right)_T = T\left(\frac{\partial S}{\partial p}\right)_T + V = T\left(\frac{\partial S}{\partial p}\right)_T + \frac{Zn\mathscr{R}T}{p}$$

$$= -\frac{n\mathscr{R}T}{p}\left[Z + T\left(\frac{\partial Z}{\partial T}\right)_p - Z\right],$$

or

$$dH = -n\mathscr{R}T^2\left(\frac{\partial Z}{\partial T}\right)_p \frac{dp}{p} \quad (T = \text{constant}),$$

which when integrated gives

$$H_2 - H_1 = -n\mathscr{R}T^2 \int_{p_1}^{p_2} \left(\frac{\partial Z}{\partial T}\right)_p \frac{dp}{p}.$$

*See Chapter 6 for the definition of Z.

The change of entropy is given by

$$dS = \frac{dH}{T} - \frac{V\,dp}{T}.$$

Substituting from the foregoing expression of dH and the equation of state, then

$$dS = -n\mathscr{R}T\left(\frac{\partial Z}{\partial T}\right)_p \frac{dp}{p} - \frac{Zn\mathscr{R}}{p}\,dp.$$

Integration gives

$$S_2 - S_1 = -n\mathscr{R}T\int_{p_1}^{p_2}\left(\frac{\partial Z}{\partial T}\right)_p \frac{dp}{p} - n\mathscr{R}\int_{p_1}^{p_2}\frac{Z}{p}\,dp$$

$$= \frac{H_2 - H_1}{T} - n\mathscr{R}\int_{p_1}^{p_2}\frac{Z}{p}\,dp.$$

**5-11
Criteria of
Equilibrium**
When unrestrained thermodynamic potentials exist between a system and its environment, a flow of energy will occur. Energy may be expressed, as shown in Chapter 2, as the product of an intensive property and the differential of an extensive property. The intensive property may be considered as the thermodynamic potential effecting the transfer of energy, whereas the extensive property is a capacity term. Conversely, if a system is in equilibrium, the intensive properties and thermodynamic potentials of both the system and the environment must be in complete balance. Thermodynamic equilibrium also depends on constraints which prevent variations in the state of a system. A high-pressure gas confined in a rigid container, for example, is in pressure equilibrium with the environment, for the constant-volume container represents a constraint imposed on the variation of the system. It is obvious, of course, that if the container is suddenly removed, the system will not remain in equilibrium with the environment. A state of stable equilibrium is attained when spontaneous changes cannot occur, within the limits of constraint imposed on the system.

The equilibrium state of a system may be identified by the application of several criteria. The criteria may involve extensive properties, such as entropy, internal energy, enthalpy, Gibbs function, Helmholtz function, etc., or intensive properties, such as pressure, temperature, chemical potential, etc. Although the Gibbs function is the most important criterion in chemical thermodynamics, other potentials also help to describe aspects of the equilibrium state of a system, subject to certain conditions to be discussed. Chemical equilibrium is treated in more detail in Chapter 11.

According to the second law of thermodynamics, the entropy of an isolated system ($dE = 0$ and $dV = 0$) always increases, or remains constant, but never decreases, so that

$$dS_{\text{isolated}} \geqslant 0. \tag{5.79}$$

When an isolated system undergoes a real process, only those states which have a higher entropy than the initial state are possible. The second law further indicates that the isolated system never returns to the same state, but continuously proceeds in the same direction until it attains a state at which its entropy is a maximum. At this state no further change is possible and the system is then in a state of stable equilibrium. Thus the state of stable equilibrium of an isolated system is characterized by maximum entropy, consistent with the initial internal energy and the initial volume of the system. An additional criterion of the equilibrium state of an isolated system is that, under conditions of constant entropy and volume, the internal energy is at a minimum.

Suppose an isolated system is divided into two parts, a and b. If energy is transferred from one part to the other as they approach equilibrium, the total entropy change is the sum of the entropy changes of the two parts, or

$$dS = dS_a + dS_b.$$

Expressing S in terms of U and V, as given by the combined first and second laws, then

$$dS = \frac{1}{T_a}(dU_a + p_a\,dV_a) + \frac{1}{T_b}(dU_b + p_b\,dV_b),$$

since

$$dU_a = -dU_b \text{ and } dV_a = -dV_b;$$

therefore

$$dS = \left(\frac{1}{T_a} - \frac{1}{T_b}\right)dU_a + \left(\frac{p_a}{T_a} - \frac{p_b}{T_b}\right)dV_a.$$

But since $dS = 0$ when the system is in equilibrium, and since U and V are independent of each other, therefore,

$$T_a = T_b \quad \text{and} \quad p_a = p_b.$$

The foregoing result indicates that both the temperature and pressure must be uniform, which, in effect, are the conditions for thermal and mechanical equilibrium.

Consider next a multicomponent system defined by internal energy U, volume V, and molal concentrations. A change in the entropy of the system, according to Eq. (5.54), is

$$dS = \frac{1}{T}\left(dU + p\,dV - \sum_i \bar{\mu}_i\,dn_i\right).$$

The over-all change in entropy of the universe, that is, system plus environment, is

$$dS_{\text{sys}} + dS_{\text{envir}} \geqslant 0.$$

If the temperature of the environment remains essentially constant, the entropy change of the environment is given by

$$dS_{\text{envir}} = -\frac{dQ}{T_{\text{envir}}} = -\frac{dU + p\,dV}{T_{\text{envir}}}.$$

Hence,

$$dS_{\text{sys}} - \frac{dU + p\,dV}{T_{\text{envir}}} \geqslant 0.$$

In an isothermal, isobaric system, this relationship, when combined with Eq. (5.54), leads to

$$\sum_i \bar{\mu}_i\,dn_i \leqslant 0. \tag{5.80}$$

A multicomponent system, then, may proceed toward the equilibrium state through changes in composition which cause a decrease in the chemical potential of the system.

The relationship between the Helmholtz function and work interaction, as expressed in Eq. (5.44), can be indicated in differential form:

$$dF_{T,V} \leqslant dW_{T,V}. \tag{5.81}$$

The change in the Helmholtz function is less than or (under reversible conditions) equal to, the work done on the system. If there is no work interaction and the system undergoes an isothermal process, then

$$dF_{T,V} \leqslant 0. \tag{5.82}$$

The value of the Helmholtz function then decreases as the state of equilibrium is approached. At equilibrium, subject to constant-volume, constant-temperature conditions, the infinitesimal change in the Helmholtz function is zero:

$$dF_{T,V} = 0. \tag{5.83}$$

At this state, the system is in equilibrium with its environment.

Conditions for equilibrium in an isothermal, isobaric system can be determined by following a similar procedure. The differential of the Gibbs function, based on Eq. (5.48), is

$$dG_{T,p} \leqslant d W_{T,p}, \tag{5.84}$$

and if $d W_{T,p} = 0$, then

$$dG_{T,p} \leqslant 0. \tag{5.85}$$

The value of the Gibbs function then decreases as the state of equilibrium is approached. The smallest value of G that is possible under the imposed temperature and pressure conditions of the system corresponds to the state of equilibrium. Thus infinitesimal changes in a system that is in chemical equilibrium at constant temperature and pressure produce no change in the Gibbs free energy:

$$dG_{T,p} = 0. \tag{5.86}$$

This condition applies equally well to multicomponent, multiphase systems.

Equation (5.86) implies certain restrictions in addition to the specified constant-temperature and constant-pressure conditions. Consider, for example, a closed system consisting of a pure liquid and its vapor. Temperature and pressure are identical for both, since they must be in thermal and pressure equilibrium. Since the Gibbs function of the mixture depends on the proportions of liquid and vapor, the change in the Gibbs free energy of the mixture is a function of the change in quantity of each constituent:

$$dG_{T,p} = \left(\frac{\partial G}{\partial n_v}\right)_{n_l, T, p} dn_v + \left(\frac{\partial G}{\partial n_l}\right)_{n_v, T, p} dn_l.$$

The changes in quantity, however, are identical

$$dn_v + dn_l = 0.$$

Solving the two preceding equations simultaneously and noting that $dG_{T,p} = 0$ at equilibrium, then

$$\left(\frac{\partial G}{\partial n_v}\right)_{n_l,\,T,\,p} = \left(\frac{\partial G}{\partial n_l}\right)_{n_v,\,T,\,p}$$

or

$$\bar{\mu}_v = \bar{\mu}_l. \tag{5.87}$$

As will be shown in Chapter 10, when two or more phases are in equilibrium, the chemical potential $\bar{\mu}$ of each component is identical, irrespective of the phase in which it exists.

Similar considerations can be applied in analyzing the role of other criteria of equilibrium, such as internal energy and enthalpy. The following table summarizes the thermodynamic potentials used as critera for equilibrium, together with the corresponding constraints imposed on the variation of the system. The equilibrium state corresponds to the minimum value of the potential.

Properties held constant	Thermodynamic potential
S, V	U
S, p	H
T, V	F
T, p	G

5-12
Types of
Equilibrium

The thermodynamic potential which controls equilibrium in a system depends on the particular constraints which exist. This section discusses several types of equilibrium using the Gibbs function as the typical criterion for equilibrium. When a finite change of state occurs in a system at constant temperature and pressure, the Gibbs free energy may increase, remain unchanged, or decrease. This trend of change of the Gibbs function establishes four types of equilibrium: (a) stable, (b) neutral, (c) unstable, (d) metastable equilibrium defined as follows:

(a) A system is in a state of *stable equilibrium* if for any finite variation of the system at constant temperature and pressure the Gibbs free energy increases. This means that the stable equilibrium state of a system at constant temperature and pressure corresponds to the minimum value of Gibbs function so that

$$\delta G_{T,p} > 0. \tag{5.88}$$

The symbol δ in the foregoing equation represents a small but finite change. Analogous criteria of stable equilibrium, corresponding to thermodynamic conditions indicated by subscripts, are

$$\delta F_{T,v} > 0, \tag{5.89}$$

$$\delta U_{S,v} > 0, \tag{5.90}$$

$$\delta H_{S,p} > 0. \tag{5.91}$$

(b) A system is in a state of *neutral equilibrium* when the thermodynamic criterion of equilibrium remains at a constant value for all possible variations of finite magnitudes. For a system at constant temperature and pressure, the criterion of neutral equilibrium is

$$\delta G_{p,T} = 0. \tag{5.92}$$

This means that if the system can exist in two or more different states without any change in its free energy, the system is in neutral equilibrium. The change in state of the system may take place at an infinitesimally slow rate, and it involves no change in the value of the free energy. Analogous criteria for neutral equilibrium of other systems are

$$\delta F_{T,V} = 0, \tag{5.93}$$

$$\delta U_{S,V} = 0, \tag{5.94}$$

$$\delta H_{S,p} = 0. \tag{5.95}$$

(c) A system is in a state of *unstable equilibrium* when the appropriate thermodynamic criterion of equilibrium is neither a minimum nor a constant value for all possible variations of the system. In a system at constant temperature and pressure, the Gibbs free energy, for at least one variation, can be reduced:

$$\delta G_{T,p} < 0. \tag{5.96}$$

Criteria for unstable equilibrium in other systems are

$$\delta F_{T,V} < 0, \tag{5.97}$$

$$\delta U_{S,V} < 0, \tag{5.98}$$

$$\delta H_{S,p} < 0. \tag{5.99}$$

(d) A system is in a state of *metastable equilibrium* if it is stable to small but not to large disturbances. An example of metastable equilibrium is a mixture of oxygen and hydrogen. Since a spark may start a chemical reaction, such a mixture is not in its most stable thermodynamic equilibrium even though, in the absence of a spark, it appears to be stable. Figure 5.8 shows the different types of equilibrium, together with their mechanical analogies. As shown, entropy has been used as the criterion for equilibrium.

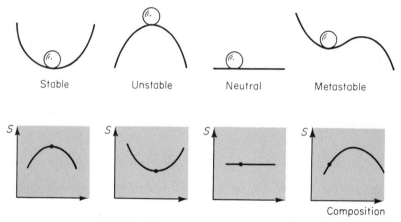

Fig. 5.8. Types of equilibrium.

REFERENCES

5.1 Coull, J., and E. B. Stuart; *Equilibrium Thermodynamics.* New York: John Wiley & Sons, Inc., 1964, chap. 1.

5.2 Darrieus, *Engineering*, **130** (1930), 283.

5.3 Keenan, J. H., *Thermodynamics.* New York: John Wiley & Sons, Inc., 1941, chap. 17.

5.4 ———, *Brit. J. Appl. Physics*, **2** (July, 1951), 183.

5.5 Kiefer, P. J., G. F. Kinney, and M. C. Stuart, *Principles of Engineering Thermodynamics.* New York: John Wiley & Sons, Inc., 1954, chap. 7.

5.6 Lee, J. F., and F. W. Sears, *Thermodynamics.* Reading, Mass.: Addison-Wesley Publishing Company, Inc., 1955, chap. 6.

5.7 Van Wylen, G. J., *Thermodynamics.* New York: John Wiley & Sons, Inc., 1959, chap. 10.

PROBLEMS

In the following problems, assume the temperature and pressure of the environment to be 530°R and 1 standard atmosphere, unless otherwise stated.

5.1 (a) What is the reversible work that can be obtained when 100 Btu are withdrawn from a thermal reservoir at 1000°R, in an environment at 100°R? (b) Suppose that the same quantity of heat flows by conduction from the reservoir at 1000°R to a second reservoir at 500°R. What is the reversible work that can now be obtained when the same amount of heat is withdrawn from the second reservoir? The temperature of the environment remains the same.

5.2 What is the reversible work that can be obtained from 1 lbm of air at 1000°F and atmospheric pressure?

5.3 A body of mass m and a constant pressure specific heat c_p is in equilibrium with the atmosphere at temperature T_a. What is the minimum possible work required to cool this body to a lower temperature T_b?

5.4 A perfect gas has a molecular weight of 27.6 and a constant pressure specific heat c_p of 0.252 Btu/lbm°F flows steadily through an open system. The inlet conditions are 100 psia and 700°F and the exit conditions are 20 psia and 200°F. If heat is exchanged only with the environment, what is the maximum work that can be obtained from this process?

5.5 A perfect gas having a constant pressure specific heat of 0.40 Btu/lbm°F and a molecular weight of 30, initially at a pressure of 1000 psia and a temperature of 800°F, undergoes a steady flow process until it reaches a pressure of 200 psia and a temperature of 300°F. With respect to atmospheric conditions of 14.7 psia and 70°F, find the maximum work, Btu/lbm, that could be obtained in this process.

5.6 A Carnot cycle operates between two thermal reservoirs at 1000°R and 700°R. If the increase in entropy during the heat interaction process is 2 Btu/°R, calculate the available and the unavailable energies. If the temperature of the cold reservoir is reduced to 600°R, other factors being the same, what will be the decrease in the unavailable energy? (Assume the environment temperature to be 520°R.)

5.7 Calculate the availability of a gas ($c_p = 0.26$ Btu/lbm°F) at 2000°F with respect to an environment at 70°F. What will be the maximum efficiency for an engine using the energy of this gas and rejecting part of it to the environment.

5.8 Find the change in the availability of 1 lbm of oxygen at atmospheric pressure and 40°F when it expands isothermally to double its volume.

5.9 600 Btu of heat are exchanged between two constant-temperature reservoirs at temperatures 1800°R and 800°R. Calculate
(a) The total change of entropy due to the heat transfer process
(b) The available energy before and after the heat transfer
(c) The increase in the unavailable energy.
Show parts (a) and (b) on a *T-s* diagram.

5.10 The increase of entropy due to stirring water at constant pressure is 0.12 Btu/lbm°R. If the water is initially at 80°F, calculate (a) the irreversibility of the process; (b) the final temperature of the water; (c) the change in the available energy.
Assume the specific heat of water at constant pressure $c_p = 1.0$ Btu/lbm°F and the temperature of the environment $T_o = 50$°F.

5.11 One lbm water is heated at constant pressure from 60°F to 340°F. ($c_p = 1$ Btu/lbm°F). Assuming steady flow, determine
(a) The heat interaction
(b) The unavailable energy based upon an environment temperature of 10°F
(c) Show the process on a *T-s* diagram and indicate various energies designated.

5.12 Air is heated at constant pressure from 40°F to 540°F. If the temperature of the environment is 40°F, what percentage of the heat transfer to the air represents an increase in the available energy of the air?

5.13 Air at 70°F and 14.7 psia is compressed isentropically to a temperature of 300°F and then heated at constant pressure to 1275°F. The specific heat at constant pressure, $c_p = 0.241$ Btu/lbm°F. The hot gas is then expanded isentropically to the initial pressure of 14.7 psia in a turbine, after which the gas is permitted to cool in the atmosphere to complete the cycle.
(a) How much energy is supplied during the heating process from 300°F to 1275°F?
(b) How much of this energy is available?
(c) How much of this energy is unavailable?
(d) What is the thermal efficiency of this ideal cycle?
(e) If 10 lbm of gas per second pass through this machine, what horsepower is developed?

5.14 One lbm of a fluid is warmed and vaporized at constant pressure.
If   Initial temperature $= 80°F$
Specific heat of fluid $= 0.60$ Btu/lbm°R
Heat for vaporization $= 700$ Btu/lbm
Entropy change during vaporization $= 1.06$ Btu/°R
Find
  (a) Temperature of vaporization
  (b) Entropy change during warming
  (c) Total entropy change
  (d) Total heat transfer
  (e) Amount of heat which is available as useful energy.

5.15 Water is heated at constant pressure from 80°F to 212°F, vaporized by supplying 970 Btu/lbm of water at 212°F and then superheated from 212°F to 300°F. The c_p of the liquid is 1.00 Btu/lbm°F and of the vapor is 0.47 Btu/lbm°F. The water receives the energy from furnace gas which is cooled from 1500°F to 900°F (c_p of the gas $= 0.24$ Btu/lbm°F).
(a) Determine the entropy change of the water per lbm.
(b) Determine the entropy change of the furnace gas per lbm of water.
(c) What is the net increase in unavailable energy per lbm of water referred to a 32°F receiver.

5.16 One lbm of oxygen and 1 lbm of hydrogen are allowed to mix adiabatically without change in total volume. Find the decrease in availability and irreversibility.

5.17 Calculate the irreversibility when air is throttled adiabatically from 300 psia to 14.7 psia. Neglect changes in kinetic energies and assume steady state.

5.18 A gas ($c_p = 0.26$ Btu/lbm°F) at 100 psia and 1000°F expands freely to atmospheric pressure. Calculate the decrease in availability ($R = 53.34$ ft-lbf/lbm°R).

5.19 Gas from the combustion chamber of a gas turbine plant enters the turbine at 1500°F and 75 psia and expands to 14.7 psia. Assuming the gas can be treated as air, and the environment is at 70°F, calculate:

(a) The availability of the gas entering the turbine
(b) The availability of the gas after isentropic expansion
(c) The availability of the gas after expanding with an expansion efficiency of 80 per cent
(d) The irreversibility of expansion (a) to (b)
(e) The irreversibility of the expansion (a) to (c).

5.20 Prove that the chemical potential of a perfect gas is given by

$$\bar{\mu} = \mathscr{R}T \ln p + f(T),$$

where $f(T)$ is a function of temperature only. What is the effect of pressure on $\bar{\mu}$ when the temperature is maintained constant?

5.21 Show that

$$U = F - T\left(\frac{\partial F}{\partial T}\right)_V$$

$$= G - T\left(\frac{\partial G}{\partial T}\right)_p - p\left(\frac{\partial G}{\partial p}\right)_T.$$

5.22 Using the functions $s = s(T, v)$, $v = v(T, p)$, and Eq. (5.74) derive Eqs. (5.75)–(5.78).

5.23 Show that

$$c_p - c_v = \frac{\beta^2 \, Tv}{K}$$

and

$$\left(\frac{\partial u}{\partial v}\right)_T = \frac{T\beta}{K} - p,$$

where β and K are the coefficients of volumetric expansion and isothermal compressibility.

NOMENCLATURE

a, b, c Constants

C Number of components or a constant

c_p Specific heat at constant pressure

c_v Specific heat at constant volume

e Internal energy per unit mass

F Number of degrees of freedom

f Function

k Boltzmann's constant

M Molecular weight

m Mass or mass per molecule

N Number of molecules

N_0 Avogadro's number

n Number of moles

P Number of phases

p Pressure

p_r Relative pressure

Q Heat

q Heat per unit mass

R Gas constant

$\mathcal{R}$ Universal gas constant

r Radius

T Absolute temperature

T_r Relative temperature

t Temperature

V Volume

V_r Relative volume

v Specific volume or speed

v_{rms} Root mean square speed

x Quality

Z Compressibility factor

β Coefficient of volumetric expansion

ϕ, ψ Function

γ Ratio of specific heats

μ_h Joule-Thomson coefficient

μ_T Isothermal coefficient

Subscripts

c Critical point

f, g Refer to fluid and gas

R Refers to reduced properties

r Refers to relative or residual properties

Superscripts

$*$ Refers to perfect gas

$(-)$ Means per mole

6

ONE-COMPONENT SYSTEM AND EQUATIONS OF STATE

6-1
One-component
System

The one-component system is a system which has a homogeneous and invariable chemical composition irrespective of the phase or phases in which it exists. The *phase* of a substance is the homogeneous, chemical and physical, state of aggregation of its molecules. A mixture of ice, water, and steam, for example, is a one-component system since the chemical composition of these three different phases is the same. A mixture of different gases may be treated as a one-component system, provided that its composition is uniform. If one of the gases condenses, the mixture can no longer be considered a one-component system since the condensed phase has a different composition than the original mixture.

Every substance can exist in at least three phases: solid, liquid, and gas. In addition, many substances, such as water and sulfur, have several crystalline structures. Ice, for example, exists in some seven different forms under high pressures.

All one-component systems exhibit the same qualitative behavior as far as coexisting phases and phase changes. Water is used in this section as a typical example. Consider the transfer of heat at constant pessure to a closed system of 1 lbm of water. Let the initial state of the water be at point *a* of Fig. 6.1. The constant pressure line *a-b-c-d* represents the relationship between the temperature and the volume during the course of heat inter-

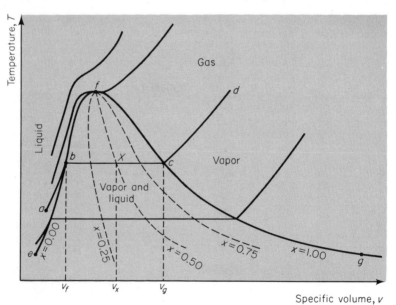

Fig. 6.1. Temperature-volume diagram of a one-component substance.

action. From *a* to *b*, heat transfer produces an increase in temperature and a small increase in volume. The amount of heat transfer is equal to the increase in enthalpy of the water. When point *b* is reached, part of the water begins to vaporize and a rapid increase in volume takes place. Although both the temperature and the pressure remain unaltered, the change of state is noted by the increase of the mass of the vapor and the decrease of the mass of the liquid. The intensive properties of both the liquid and the vapor states remain unchanged and the liquid is in equilibrium with its vapor. The liquid state corresponds to point *b*, whereas the vapor state corresponds to point *c*. When point *c* is reached, all the liquid has been converted into vapor. The vapor and liquid coexisting in equilibrium are called *saturated vapor* and *saturated liquid*, respectively. Points *b* and *c* are called *saturated liquid state* and *saturated vapor state*, respectively. The temperature of these states (which is identical with the evaporation temperature) is called the *saturation temperature*. For a one-component system in equilibrium, the pressure corresponding to the saturation temperature is called the *saturation pressure*. At point *c*, the change of phase from liquid to vapor is complete and further transfer of heat to the system increases both the temperature and the volume along portion *c-d* of the constant pressure curve. When the temperature of the vapor is higher than the saturation temperature, it is called *superheated vapor*. The term *superheat* denotes that the temperature of the vapor is in excess of the saturated value corresponding to the same pressure. In the superheated vapor region, the temperature and the pressure are independent and are, therefore, sufficient to determine the state of the system. In the case of a liquid, if the pressure is greater than the saturation pressure corresponding to its temperature, it is called *compressed* or *subcooled liquid*.

If the foregoing heating process is repeated at different pressures, curves similar to *a-b-c-d* are obtained. It is noted that there are two discontinuities in the slope of each of the constant-pressure lines (points *b* and *c*), with a constant temperature portion between them as shown in Fig. 6.1. If the pressure is increased beyond a certain value called the critical pressure, the discontinuities as well as the constant temperature portion disappear. In this case, there is no definite transition between the liquid and vapor phases, and the liquid changes to vapor without any discontinuity. The limiting state at which no discontinuities are noticeable is called the *critical state* and is represented by point *f* in Fig. 6.1. It is conventional to call the substance *vapor* if its temperature is below that of the critical point, and *gas* if above the critical point. In Fig. 6.1 line *e-b-f* is called the *saturation liquid line*, and line *f-c-g* is called the *saturation vapor line*. Both lines meet at the *critical point f*. Properties, such as temperature, pressure, and volume at the critical point, are identified as critical properties. For water the critical temperature pressure, and specific volume are: 705°F, 3206.2 psia, and 0.0503 ft³/lbm.

6-2
The Liquid-
Vapor Mixture

A state represented by a point under the dome e-b-f-c-g, such as X, corresponds to an equilibrium state of a mixture of liquid and vapor which is called *wet vapor*. The states of the vapor and liquid phases in the wet vapor region are represented by points c and b irrespective of the relative masses of each phase, that is, irrespective of the location of point X on line b-c. Let x be the ratio of the mass of the vapor to the mass of the mixture, then each pound mass of mixture contains x lbm of vapor and (1 − x) lbm of liquid. The property x is called the *quality* of the mixture and is defined by the equation:

$$x = \frac{m_g}{m_f + m_g},$$ (6.1)

where m_g and m_f are the masses of the vapor and the liquid in the mixture. Subscripts g and f refer to gas and fluid respectively. If $x = 0$, the mixture is completely liquid and its state is represented by point b, and if $x = 1$, the mixture is completely vapor and its state is represented by point c. Let v_f be the specific volume of the saturated liquid, v_g be the specific volume of the coexisting saturated vapor, and v_{fg} be the increase in the specific volume when the saturated liquid changes to saturated vapor. The specific volume v_x of a mixture is equal to the total volume of the mixture divided by the total mass. Its value depends on the relative amounts of the liquid and vapor present and on the specific volume of each phase. It is equal to the sum of the relative specific volumes of the liquid and the vapor.

$$v_x = (1 - x)v_f + xv_g.$$ (6.2a)

But, since

$$v_g = v_f + v_{fg},$$ (6.3)

then

$$v_x = v_f + xv_{fg},$$ (6.2b)

or

$$v_x = v_g - (1 - x)v_{fg}.$$ (6.2c)

Note that the specific volume of a mixture depends on the intensive properties of its phases as well as the mass proportions of each phase.

By means of Eq. (6.2a) or its equivalents (6.2b) or (6.2c), constant quality lines may be plotted as shown in Fig. 6.1. These lines meet at the critical point.

Expressions analogous to Eqs. (6.2) and (6.3) can be derived for enthalpy, internal energy, and entropy. These expressions per unit mass are

$$h_x = (1 - x)h_f + xh_g = h_f + xh_{fg} = h_g - (1 - x)h_{fg} \qquad (6.4)$$

$$u_x = (1 - x)u_f + xu_g = u_f + xu_{fg} = u_g - (1 - x)u_{fg} \qquad (6.5)$$

$$s_x = (1 - x)s_f + xs_g = s_f + xs_{fg} = s_g - (1 - x)s_{fg}. \qquad (6.6)$$

Note also that,

$$h_g = h_f + h_{fg} \qquad (6.7)$$

$$u_g = u_f + u_{fg} \qquad (6.8)$$

$$s_g = s_f + s_{fg}. \qquad (6.9)$$

6-3
Extension to the
Solid Phase

The foregoing liquid-vapor transition at constant pressure can be represented on the p-T plane as shown in Fig. 6.2. In this section the phase transition is extended to include the solid phase. Consider 1 lbm of ice at a pressure p and temperature T_a as represented by point a. The temperature T_a is below the fusion temperature T_b. Point b is located on the solid-

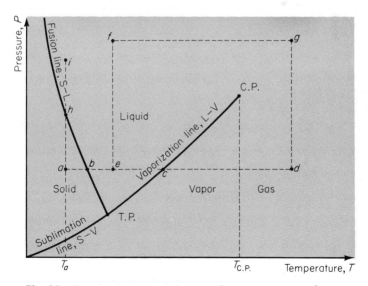

Fig. 6.2. *Pressure-temperature diagram of a one-component substance.*

liquid line (fusion line) and determines the state at which the solid is in equilibrium with its liquid. Heat transfer to the ice at constant pressure results in a temperature increase to T_b. With further transfer of heat, ice begins to liquify at a constant temperature T_b until all the substance is transformed to the liquid phase. During the melting process, the temperature is a function of pressure and remains constant at T_b. The change of the state of the system is accomplished by the increase of the amount of liquid and the decrease of the amount of solid during the heating process. The intensive state of each phase is, however, constant during the melting process. The transfer of heat to the liquid will increase its temperature to T_c, at which evaporation begins, and the temperature remains constant at T_c till all the liquid is evaporated. Point c is located on the liquid-vapor line (vaporization line) and determines the state at which the liquid is in equilibrium with its vapor. When all the liquid has evaporated, the temperature will rise again upon further transfer of heat along c-d.

If the preceding process is repeated at different pressures, the corresponding points b and c can be determined and the solid-liquid and liquid-vapor curves can be traced. These two curves meet at a point on the p-T plane called the *triple point*. Similarly the solid-vapor line can be determined for pressure values below the pressure of the triple point. Under such circumstances it is not possible to obtain a liquid state at a pressure lower than that of the triple point. In this case heat transfer to a solid will result first in raising its temperature to the solid-vapor line and then changing it directly into vapor. The solid-vapor line (sublimation line) represents the states in which the vapor is in equilibrium with its solid. The triple point defines a state in which the solid, liquid, and vapor phases of a substance coexist in equilibrium. It may be noted that, when two phases of a one-component system exist in equilibrium, a single intensive property is sufficient to define the intensive state of each phase. If this property is chosen as the saturation temperature, then the saturation pressure is a function of this temperature or

$$p = f(T). \tag{6.10}$$

The foregoing relation is represented by the solid-liquid, liquid-vapor, and solid-vapor curves in Fig. 6.2 for the corresponding phases in equilibrium. Note that the liquid-vapor curve extends from the triple point to the critical point and that three curves meet at the triple point. The intensive state of the phases of a one-component system at the triple point is fixed and no intensive properties are needed to determine their state. This means that in addition to temperature and pressure being fixed at the triple point, the specific volumes of the solid, liquid, and vapor phases are also fixed. To determine the intensive state of the system at the triple point, the relative proportions of two of the solid, liquid, and vapor phases are required. For pure water the temperature and pressure at the triple point are 32.018°F and 0.08854 psia. The triple point should not be confused with the ice point, the latter being defined as the state at which ice melts under 14.69 psia at a temperature of 32.0°F.

An alternate path to change a substance from the liquid to the gaseous state with a gradual change of phase is by following path *e-f-g-d* as shown in Fig. 6.2. Along path *e-f* the temperature is maintained constant while the pressure is raised to a value above the critical pressure. Path *f-g* is a constant pressure line in which the liquid changes to vapor without discontinuity. The final state is attained by lowering the pressure at constant temperature along path *g-d*. In a similar fashion a change from the solid to the liquid state may be achieved by path *a-h-i* in which an increase of pressure at constant temperature results, first in melting the solid at point *h*, and then proceeds to the final liquid state at point *i*.

The amount of heat necessary to change a unit mass from saturated liquid to saturated vapor at the same temperature and pressure is called the *latent heat of evaporation*. It is equal to the change in enthalpy between the liquid and vapor phases at the same temperature and pressure. The latent heat depends on the value of temperature and pressure at which the change of phase takes place. If the change is from solid to liquid, it is called the *latent heat of fusion*; and if the change is from solid directly to vapor, it is called the *latent heat of sublimation*. Each of these heats is equal to the change in enthalpy between the corresponding phases at the same temperature. It must be emphasized that both the temperature and the pressure remain constant during all phase transformations. An expression of the latent heat of vaporization is

$$\text{latent heat of vaporization} = h_g - h_f = (u_g + pv_g) - (u_f + pv_f)$$
$$= (u_g - u_f) + p(v_g - v_f). \qquad (6.11)$$

Therefore, the latent heat can be considered as the sum of the change in internal energy and the work of expansion of the vapor against the existing equilibrium pressure. Similar expressions for the latent heat of fusion and sublimation may be derived.

**6-4
Thermo-
dynamic
Surfaces**   In addition to providing values of thermodynamic properties, graphical representation permits one to visualize the progress of a change of a state of a system. Figure 6.3 shows a three-dimensional *p-V-T* surface for a substance which expands on freezing. On the same figure, the projections on the *p-T* and *p-V* planes are also shown. Figure 6.4 is the *p-V-T* surface for a substance which contracts on freezing.

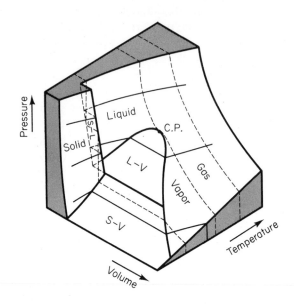

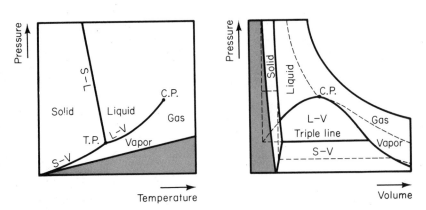

Fig. 6.3. *p-V-T surface and projections for a substance that expands on freezing.*

Also shown are the projections on the p-T and p-V planes. Any point on the p-V-T surface represents an equilibrium state of the substance and is determined by any two independent properties, such as p and T. In certain regions of the figures the substance exists in a single phase. These are labeled *solid*, *liquid*, and *gas* or *vapor*. When the substance has two phases, the region is labeled solid-liquid, solid-vapor, and liquid-vapor. The surfaces at which

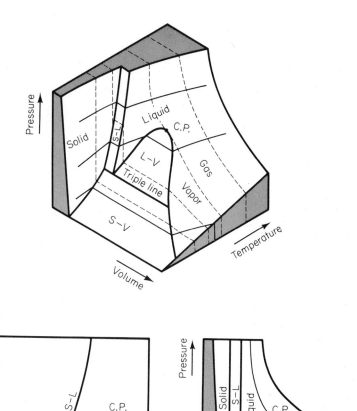

Fig. 6.4. *p-V-T surface and projections for a substance that contracts on freezing.*

two phases exist are ruled surfaces made up of straight lines parallel to the V coordinate. Therefore, when these surfaces are projected on the p-T plane, they appear as lines. The triple line shown on the p-V-T surface appears as a point on the p-T plane. Note that although both the pressure and the temperature are constant at the triple point, the specific volume can vary depending on the proportions of the three phases existing at that point.

Several isotherms and constant-pressure lines are shown on the p-V-T surfaces of Fig. 6.3 and 6.4. The different states of the substance carry the same label on the corresponding p-T and p-V diagrams.

Other thermodynamic properties, besides pressure, volume, and temperature, are often used to describe the state of a system. These properties are usually given in the form of charts, some of which will be briefly discussed.

The enthalpy-entropy diagram, also called the *Mollier** diagram, is extensively used for solving problems. As shown in Fig. 6.5, the constant-pressure and constant-temperature lines are identical in the liquid-vapor region. In the liquid and vapor regions, the temperature and pressure are

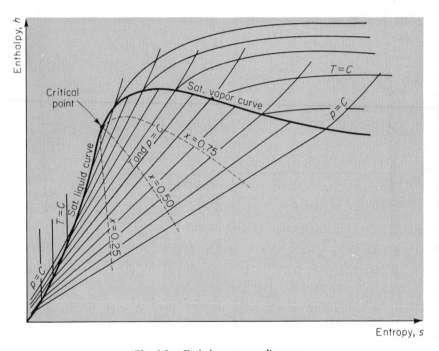

Fig. 6.5. *Enthalpy-entropy diagram.*

independent; hence, constant-temperature and constant-pressure curves are shown as independent curves. The slope of the constant-pressure curves at any point is a measure of the temperature. This is easily seen by noting that $(\partial h/\partial s)_p = 1/T$. In the wet region, constant-pressure lines are straight lines since the temperature remains the same at constant pressure. Note that isentropic processes are represented by vertical lines whereas constant-enthalpy lines are horizontal lines on this diagram.

*A Mollier chart for steam is given in Fig. A.1 inside the back cover.

Figure 6.6 is a *T-s* diagram. Figure 6.7 is a *p-h* diagram conveniently used in representing refrigeration cycles.

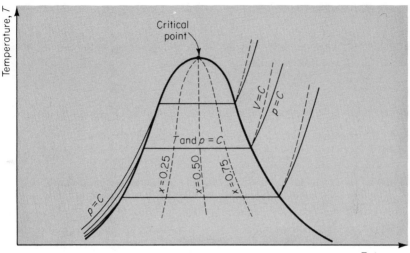

Fig. 6.6. *Temperature-entropy diagram.*

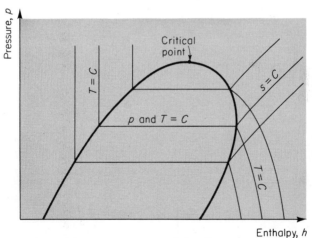

Fig. 6.7. *Pressure-enthalpy diagram.*

**6-5
Clapeyron
Relation**
Consider the change of state of a substance from the saturated liquid to the saturated vapor state. During the vaporization process both the temperature and the pressure are independent of the volume. Noting that during the change of phase each extensive property is linearly related to

the quality x, it follows that the extensive properties are linearly interrelated. The Maxwell relation, Eq. (5.69d), is

$$\left(\frac{\partial p}{\partial T}\right)_v = \left(\frac{\partial s}{\partial v}\right)_T.$$

For a phase change from the liquid to the gaseous state, the right-hand side of the preceding equation may be written

$$\left(\frac{\partial s}{\partial v}\right)_T = \frac{s_g - s_f}{v_g - v_f}.$$

Since the pressure is a function of temperature only, then

$$\left(\frac{\partial p}{\partial T}\right)_v = \frac{dp}{dT}.$$

Substituting the last two equations into the Maxwell relation and noting that $s_{fg} = s_g - s_f$, then

$$\frac{dp}{dT} = \frac{s_g - s_f}{v_g - v_f} = \frac{s_{fg}}{v_g - v_f}. \tag{6.12}$$

The change of entropy s_{fg} is equal to the enthalpy of vaporization divided by the absolute temperature, or

$$s_{fg} = \frac{h_{fg}}{T}, \tag{6.13}$$

which, when substituted in the previous equation, gives

$$\frac{dp}{dT} = \frac{h_{fg}}{T(v_g - v_f)}. \tag{6.14}$$

Equation (6.14) is called the *Clapeyron equation* and is conveniently used to determine the enthalpy of vaporization from the data of the rate of change of pressure with temperature, that is, the slope of the p-T curve of the substance and the specific volumes of the saturated liquid and saturated vapor.

Equations similar to Eq. (6.14) can be derived for any other two phases, such as the solid-vapor or solid-liquid ones. A simplification of Eq. (6.14) may be obtained by neglecting v_f in comparison with v_g and substituting for v_g from the perfect gas equation. Under these conditions, which are valid at low pressures, Eq. (6.14) becomes

$$\frac{dp}{dT} = \frac{h_{fg}}{Tv_g} = \frac{h_{fg}}{RT^2/p},$$

or

$$\frac{dp}{p} = \frac{h_{fg}\,dT}{RT^2},$$

which can be written in the form

$$\frac{d\ln p}{d(1/T)} = -\frac{h_{fg}}{R}. \tag{6.15}$$

Figure 6.8 shows a plot of $\ln p$ versus $1/T$, whose slope can be readily used to determine the enthalpy of vaporization.

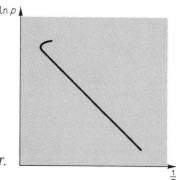

Fig. 6.8. *ln p versus* $1/T$.

**6-6
Tables of
Properties**

Properties of many substances are conveniently tabulated in thermodynamic tables. The most common examples are steam* and refrigerant tables in which the properties of the substance are given as functions of temperature and pressure. Tables 1 and 2 of the steam tables give the saturated properties of the liquid and vapor phases as a function of temperature or pressure. These include specific volume, enthalpy, entropy, and internal energy of the saturated liquid and saturated vapor states. Note that both the enthalpy and entropy values are calculated relative to their values at 32°F where both properties for saturated water are taken to be zero at this temperature. For the saturated states, the temperature and pressure are dependent and either one, together with a third property, such as specific volume or quality, is sufficient to determine the state. Table 3 of the steam tables gives the specific volume, enthalpy, and entropy of super-heated steam at different pressures and temperatures. Here, the temperature and pressure are independent properties and can therefore be used to determine the state. Table 4 gives the excess of specific volume, enthalpy,

*J. H. Keenan and F. G. Keyes, *Thermodynamic Properties of Steam* (New York: John Wiley & Sons, Inc., 1936). An abstract of steam tables is given in the Appendix.

and entropy of compressed liquid over their saturation values as a function of pressure and temperature. Finally, Table 5 gives properties of saturated solids and saturated vapors existing in equilibrium. The following examples illustrate the use of the steam tables.

EXAMPLE 6.1: One lbm of water initially at 800 psia and 200°F is heated at constant pressure. If the final state is superheated steam at 600°F determine:
(a) The initial specific volume of the water.
(b) v_f and v_g.
(c) The final specific volume of the superheated steam.
(d) If the final state were wet steam at 50 per cent quality, what is v_x?

Solution: (a) Since the initial pressure is higher than the saturation pressure corresponding to 200°F, the water is initially in the compressed liquid state.
From Table 4 of the steam tables, at 800 psia and 200°F,

$$v - v_f = -4.4 \times 10^{-5}, \quad \text{and} \quad v_f = 0.016634 \text{ ft}^3/\text{lbm}.$$

Therefore $v = 0.016634 - 0.000044 = 0.016590 \text{ ft}^3/\text{lbm}$.
(b) From Table A.4 at 800 psia,

$$v_f = 0.0209 \text{ ft}^3/\text{lbm}, \quad \text{and} \quad v_g = 0.5687 \text{ ft}^3/\text{lbm}.$$

(c) From Table A.5 at 800 psia and 600°F

$$v = 0.6779 \text{ ft}^3/\text{lbm}.$$

(d) $v_x = v_f + x v_{fg}$
$= 0.0209 + 0.5(0.5478) = 0.2948 \text{ ft}^3/\text{lbm}.$

EXAMPLE 6.2: A rigid vessel of volume 3 ft³ contains saturated water vapor at 50 psia. Owing to heat losses, the pressure drops to 40 psia. Calculate
(a) The quality of the mixture
(b) The mass of the vapor and liquid in the final state
(c) The amount of heat transferred from the vessel.

Solution: The following properties at 40 and 50 psia are extracted from Table A.4 of the Appendix:

p(psia)	t(°F)	Sat. liquid v_f(ft³/lbm)	Sat. vapor v_g(ft³/lbm)
40	267.25	0.01715	10.498
50	281.01	0.01727	8.515

(a) From the preceding table, the specific volume of saturated water vapor at 50 psia is 8.515 ft³/lbm. Therefore,

$$m = \frac{V}{v_g} = \frac{3}{8.515} = 0.352 \text{ lbm},$$

and

$$v_x = v_f + xv_{fg}$$
$$8.515 = 0.01715 + x(10.498 - 0.01715),$$

from which

$$x = \frac{8.4975}{10.48085} = 81 \text{ per cent.}$$

(b) $m_v = 0.81 \times 0.352 = 0.285$ lbm

and

$$m_f = 0.19 \times 0.352 = 0.067 \text{ lbm.}$$

(c) Since the heat transfer takes place at constant volume and $W = 0$,

$$\begin{aligned} Q = U_2 - U_1 &= m(u_f + xu_{fg})_2 - u_{g1} \\ &= 0.352(235.9 + 0.81 \times 856.1) - 1095.3 \\ &= -58.2 \text{ Btu.} \end{aligned}$$

EXAMPLE 6.3:   A rigid vessel of volume 5 ft³ initially contains a water-vapor mixture at 70 psia.

(a) If the quality of the mixture is 40 per cent, calculate the mass of the mixture.

(b) If the pressure in the vessel is raised to 100 psia by the transfer of heat, what will be the mass of the vapor and liquid?

Solution: The following properties at 70 and 100 psia are abstracted from Table A.4 of the Appendix:

p(psia)	t(°F)	Sat. liquid v_f(ft³/lbm)	Sat. vapor v_g(ft³/lbm)
70	302.92	0.01748	6.206
100	327.81	0.01774	4.432

(a) The specific volume of the mixture at 70 psia is given by,

$$\begin{aligned} v_x = v_f + xv_{fg} \\ = 0.01748 + 0.4(6.206 - 0.01748) = 2.49348 \text{ ft}^3/\text{lbm.} \end{aligned}$$

The mass of the mixture $m = \dfrac{V}{v_x} = \dfrac{5}{2.49348} = 2$ lbm.

(b) Since the volume and the mass of the water in the vessel remain unchanged, the specific volume must also remain constant. Therefore, at 100 psia,

$$v_x = 2.49348 = 0.01774 + x(4.432 - 0.01774),$$

from which $x = 56$ per cent. The respective masses of the vapor and liquid are

$$m_v = 0.56 \times 2 = 1.12 \text{ lbm} \quad \text{and} \quad m_f = 0.44 \times 2 = 0.88 \text{ lbm.}$$

EXAMPLE 6.4:   Wet steam at a pressure of 300 psia is throttled to a pressure of 14.7 psia. If the temperature after throttling is 240°F find the quality of the steam.

Solution: The enthalpies of the steam before and after throttling are equal. At 240°F and 14.7 psia, Table 3 of the steam tables gives

$$h = 1164.2 \text{ Btu/lbm,}$$

which is equal to the enthalpy of the wet steam at 300 psia. The latter is given by

$$h_x = h_f + x h_{fg}.$$

Therefore, using Table 2 of the steam tables or Table A.4 of the Appendix

$$h_x = 1164.2 = 393.84 + x(809.0),$$

from which

$$x = \frac{1164.2 - 393.84}{809.0} = \frac{770.36}{809} = 95.3 \text{ per cent.}$$

The foregoing result is more readily obtained by the use of the Mollier diagram by locating the final state and drawing a constant-enthalpy line (horizontal line) to the 300-psia line in the wet region. The quality of the steam can then be read from the chart.

6-7
Gas Tables

Gas tables* may conveniently be used to calculate property relations between different states of a system. Properties of a number of gases, including air at low pressure (based on perfect gas relations), are tabulated in gas tables for a wide range of temperature. The tabulated values take into consideration the variations of specific heat with temperature.

Gas tables may be used also to relate properties of systems undergoing isentropic processes. The change of entropy of a unit mass of a perfect gas in terms of temperature and pressure is

$$\Delta s = \int_{T_1}^{T_2} c_p \frac{dT}{T} - R \ln \frac{p_2}{p_1} .$$

In gas tables, a function ϕ is defined as

$$\phi = \int_{T_0}^{T} c_p \frac{dT}{T} . \tag{6.16}$$

Since c_p for a perfect gas is a function of temperature, ϕ is also a function of temperature only. ϕ is called the *entropy function*. Its value is tabulated

*For example, see J. H. Keenan and J. Kaye *Gas Tables* (New York: John Wiley & Sons, Inc., 1948). An abstract of these tables is given in the Appendix.

as a function of temperature and is chosen zero at $0°R$. The change of entropy can then be written

$$\Delta s = \phi_2 - \phi_1 - R \ln \frac{p_2}{p_1}. \tag{6.17}$$

For an isentropic process, such as compression or expansion, $\Delta s = 0$. Thus

$$\ln \left(\frac{p_2}{p_1} \right)_s = \frac{\phi_2 - \phi_1}{R}. \tag{6.18}$$

A *relative pressure* p_r is defined as the ratio of the pressure p to a reference pressure p_o such that

$$p_r \equiv \frac{p}{p_o}. \tag{6.19}$$

Substituting in Eq. (6.18) gives

$$\ln \left(\frac{p_2}{p_1} \right)_s = \ln \left(\frac{p_2/p_o}{p_1/p_o} \right)_s = \ln \frac{p_{r_2}}{p_{r_1}} = \frac{\phi_2 - \phi_1}{R} = f(T).$$

Also

$$\left(\frac{p_2}{p_1} \right)_s = \frac{p_{r_2}}{p_{r_1}}. \tag{6.20}$$

Equation (6.20) states that the isentropic pressure ratio is equal to the relative pressure ratio. Values of p_r are tabulated as a function of temperature.

A similar relation may be obtained for specific volumes. Starting with the equation

$$ds = c_v \frac{dT}{T} + R \frac{dv}{v},$$

and following the same procedure just outlined, leads to the following relation of relative specific volumes:

$$\left(\frac{v_2}{v_1} \right)_s = \frac{v_{r_2}}{v_{r_1}}, \tag{6.21}$$

where the *relative volume* v_r is defined as

$$v_r \equiv \frac{RT}{p_r}. \tag{6.22}$$

Another method of arriving at Eq. (6.21) is by substituting Eq. (6.22) into Eq. (6.20).

EXAMPLE 6.5: One lbm of air expands reversibly and adiabatically from an initial state of $p_1 = 100$ psia and $T_1 = 960°R$ to a final state of $p_2 = 15$ psia. If the process is steady flow and kinetic and potential energies are negligible, calculate the final temperature, volume, and the work developed.

Solution: From Table 1 of the gas tables or Table A.11, at $T_1 = 960°R$,

$$p_{r_1} = 10.61, \quad v_{r_1} = 33.52, \quad \text{and} \quad h_1 = 231.06 \text{ Btu/lbm.}$$

From Eq. (6.20)

$$p_{r_2} = p_{r_1}\left(\frac{p_2}{p_1}\right) = 10.61\left(\frac{15}{100}\right) = 1.592.$$

From gas tables, at $p_{r_2} = 1.59$,

$$T_2 = 562°R, \quad v_{r_2} = 130.61, \quad \text{and} \quad h_2 = 134.34 \text{ Btu/lbm.}$$

From Eq. (6.21)

$$v_2 = v_1\left(\frac{v_{r_2}}{v_{r_1}}\right) = \frac{RT_1}{p_1}\left(\frac{v_{r_2}}{v_{r_1}}\right) = \frac{53.34 \times 960}{100 \times 144} \times \left(\frac{130.61}{23.52}\right) = 13.85 \text{ ft}^3/\text{lbm.}$$

The work interaction according to the first law is

$$w = h_2 - h_1$$
$$= 134.34 - 231.06 = -96.72 \text{ Btu/lbm.}$$

6-8
The Phase
Rule

This section considers the conditions under which the different phases coexist and determines the minimum number of the properties of a system of several phases that can be varied independently. The discussion is extended to include systems of more than one constituent but excludes chemical reactions which are discussed in Chapter 11.

Consider a system composed of C components existing in equilibrium in P phases, and assume that the C components exist in all the phases.* In addition to temperature and pressure, the intensive state of each phase is defined if $(C - 1)$ parameters pertaining to composition, such as mole fractions or concentrations, are known. The composition of the system is defined by $(C - 1)$ mole fractions since the *last* mole fraction can be obtained by noting that the sum of the mole fractions of all components in each phase is equal to unity. The total number of parameters including the pressure and temperature that may vary independently is therefore $(C + 1)$ for each phase. For P phases there are $P(C + 1)$ parameters. Now consider the number of equations available to solve for the $P(C + 1)$

---

*It can be shown that the final result is the same whether one or more components is absent from one or more phases.

unknowns. These equations express the equilibrium between phases. Thus $(P - 1)$ equations are obtained by equating the temperature of the phases. An equal number of equations is also obtained by equating the pressures of the different phases. Finally, a set of $(P - 1)$ equations may be written for the concentration or chemical potential of each component in the P phases. Adding these equations gives a total number of $(P - 1)(C + 2)$ equations. When this number of equations is subtracted from the number of the unknowns, the number of independent intensive properties that could be varied to define the intensive properties of the phases of the system is obtained. These properties can be chosen arbitrarily and are usually referred to as *degrees of freedom*. If F represents the number of degrees of freedom of a system, then

$$F = P(C + 1) - (P - 1)(C + 2) = C + 2 - P. \tag{6.23}$$

Equation (6.23) is called the *Gibbs phase rule*. It applies to systems that are in a state of equilibrium. Note that the thermodynamic equilibrium of the phases of a system depends on composition and not on the relative amounts of each phase. Applying the phase rule to a single-phase single-component system, the number of intensive properties to define the state of the system is

$$F = C - P + 2 = 1 - 1 + 2 = 2.$$

Thus any two intensive properties, such as temperature, pressure or composition, that can be varied independently are sufficient to define the intensive state of a one-component substance. For a one-component substance existing in two phases $F = 1$; in three phases $F = 0$.

Figure 6.2 may be used to illustrate the foregoing examples. Two properties, such as temperature and pressure, can be varied independently and are sufficient to define the state of a one-component substance in a single phase. For the solid-liquid, solid-vapor, or liquid-vapor mixtures, if a property, such as pressure, is chosen, the temperature is fixed since there is only one pressure at which the two phases are in equilibrium. These systems are called *univariant* because one property is sufficient to define the intensive properties of the two phases. Note that, in order to define the intensive state of the system, it is necessary to define another independent property, such as mole fraction or specific volume. At the triple point $F = 0$; that is, the phases of the substance coexist only at unique values of temperature, pressure, and specific volumes of the three phases. This system is called *nonvariant*. Two independent properties, such as two mole fractions, completely define the intensive state of the system. It may be remarked from Eq. (6.23) that the number of phases cannot exceed the number of components by more than two. Another observation is that the maximum number of phases in equilibrium for a single component substance is three.

6-9
Perfect Gas
Law

A perfect or ideal gas is a hypothetical substance which obeys the laws of Boyle and Gay-Lussac (or Charles). Real gases at low pressures and high temperatures follow these laws very closely. At room temperatures and pressures, the representation of real gases by the perfect gas equation is satisfactory for monatomic and diatomic gases of low molecular weights.

Robert Boyle in 1662 observed that, when the temperature of a certain mass of a gas was maintained constant, the product of the pressure and the volume of the gas was a constant. Mathematically Boyle's law is expressed as

$$pV = \phi(T), \tag{6.24}$$

where p is the absolute pressure, V is the volume, T is the absolute temperature, and ϕ is a function.

Boyle's law is represented graphically in Fig. 6.9. The isotherms are

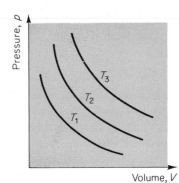

Fig. 6.9. p-V relation of a perfect gas at constant temperature.

rectangular hyperbolas on the p-V diagram. For any two points on an isotherm,

$$\frac{p_1}{p_2} = \frac{V_2}{V_1}. \tag{6.25}$$

Equation (6.25) states that, at constant temperature, the volume occupied by a certain mass of a perfect gas is inversely proportional to its pressure.

Charles in 1787, about a century after Boyle, observed that, at constant pressure, the volume of a given mass of a gas was proportional to its absolute temperature, or

$$\frac{V}{T} = \psi(p), \tag{6.26}$$

where ψ is a function.

In order to determine the nature of both the functions ϕ and ψ of Eq. (6.24) and (6.26), divide Eq. (6.24) by (6.26):

$$pT = \frac{\phi(T)}{\psi(p)}.$$

Separating the variables in the preceding equation gives

$$\frac{\phi(T)}{T} = p\psi(p).$$

But since T and p are independent variables and each appears on one side of the foregoing equation, each side of the equation must be equal to a constant C. Therefore,

$$\phi(T) = CT, \quad \text{and} \quad \psi(p) = \frac{C}{p}.$$

The foregoing result indicates that the product pV in Boyle's law varies linearly with temperature and, similarly, the quotient T/p in Charles' law varies linearly with volume.

Gay-Lussac's law (1802) states that, at constant pressure, the volumetric coefficient of expansion is constant for all gases. The variation of the volume of a gas with temperature at constant pressure is given by

$$V_t = V_o(1 + \beta t), \tag{6.27}$$

where V_t = volume occupied by the gas at temperature t.

V_o = volume occupied at some reference temperature ($t = 0$).

β = volumetric coefficient of expansion.

Equation (6.27) as shown in Fig. 6.10 is a straight-line relationship. The value of β varies slightly for different gases, but has the same value for all gases

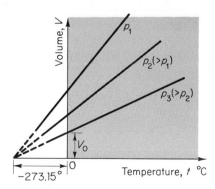

Fig. 6.10. *V-t relation of a perfect gas at constant pressure.*

at very low pressure, a condition which approximates a perfect gas. In perfect gas it is assumed that there is no interaction between the molecules. Only in this case is β considered to be constant. The value of β is found experimentally by plotting the volume versus temperature at low pressures and extrapolating to zero pressure. In this case $1 + \beta t = 0$ and if t is in °C, then

$$t = -\frac{1}{\beta} = -\frac{1}{0.0036609} = -273.15°C.$$

This means that $-273.15°C$ is the lowest temperature that can be attained: otherwise, a negative pressure will result. Actually the volume of the gas will never be zero at this temperature because the gas will liquify before such low temperatures are reached and Eq. (6.27) will no longer be valid.

The absolute temperature is equal to

$$T°K = 273.15°C + t°C,$$

which is in agreement with what was mentioned in Chapters 1 and 4. The volume of a gas at a temperature $t°C$ is given by

$$V_t = V_o\left(1 + \frac{t}{273.15}\right).$$

Therefore an alternate statement of Gay-Lussac's law is that, at constant pressure, the volume of a fixed mass of a gas increases by $1/273.15$ of its volume at 0°C for every degree of Celsius temperature rise. The preceding relation can be written as

$$\frac{V_t}{V_o} = 1 + \frac{t}{273.15} = \frac{273.15 + t}{273.15} = \frac{T}{T_o},$$

and for two states at the same pressure,

$$\frac{V_1}{V_2} = \frac{T_1}{T_2}, \tag{6.28}$$

which is Charles' law. Therefore Gay-Lussac's and Charles' laws are equivalent.

So far, variations of only two properties of a perfect gas have been considered. In order to explore the relation among temperature, pressure, and volume, consider a gas to change its state in two steps: the first at constant pressure and the second at constant temperature. For the first step, Charles' law gives

$$\frac{V_1}{V_2'} = \frac{T_1}{T_2},$$

where V_2' is the volume of the gas if the pressure is the maintained constant while its temperature is increased from T_1 to T_2. The second step is to change the state of the gas at constant temperature, for which Boyle's law gives

$$\frac{V_2'}{V_2} = \frac{p_1}{p_2} \quad \text{or} \quad V_2' = \frac{V_2 p_1}{p_2},$$

which when substituted in the previous equation yields

$$\frac{V_1}{V_2} = \frac{T_1}{T_2} \frac{p_2}{p_1}$$

or

$$\frac{pV}{T} = \text{constant.} \tag{6.29}$$

Equation (6.29) can also be obtained mathematically as follows: If the volume of a gas is expressed in terms of temperature and pressure, then

$$V = V(p, T),$$

and

$$dV = \left(\frac{\partial V}{\partial p}\right)_T dp + \left(\frac{\partial V}{\partial T}\right)_p dT. \tag{6.30}$$

Substituting

$$\left(\frac{\partial V}{\partial p}\right)_T = -\frac{V}{p}, \quad \text{(from Boyle's law)}$$

and

$$\left(\frac{\partial V}{\partial T}\right)_p = \frac{V}{T} \quad \text{(from Charles' law)}$$

into Eq. (6.30) and integrating gives,

$$\ln V + \ln p = \ln T + \ln \text{(constant)},$$

which is equivalent to Eq. (6.29). The preceding equation can be written as

$$\frac{p_1 V_1}{T_1} = \frac{p_2 V_2}{T_2} = mR$$

or

$$pV = mRT, \tag{6.31}$$

where R is the specific gas constant. Its value depends on the particular gas and the units used for pressure, specific volume, and absolute temperature. Equation (6.31) is called the *equation of state of a perfect gas*, and is represented on the p-V-T coordinates as shown in Fig. 6.11. Note that the pressure

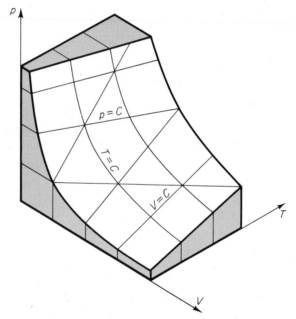

Fig. 6.11. *p-V-T surface for a perfect gas.*

and temperature in the perfect gas equation are absolute values. If both sides of Eq. (6.31) are divided by the mass, and since the volume V occupied by a mass m is equal to the product mv, then

$$pv = RT. \tag{6.32}$$

It is often convenient to express the equation of state on a mole basis. The mass m is equal to the product of the number of moles n and the molecular weight M. Therefore, substituting for m in Eq. (6.31) gives

$$pV = nMRT.$$

If $n = 1$, V is the volume occupied by 1 mole or the molal volume. Note that at equal temperature and pressure, perfect gases occupy the same molal volume (Avogadro's law). Considering two perfect gases a and b of equal volumes at the same temperature and pressure, then

$$p_a V_a = n_a M_a R_a T_a \quad \text{and} \quad p_b V_b = n_b M_b R_b T_b$$

or

$$\frac{p_a V_a}{n_a T_a} = \frac{p_b V_b}{n_b T_b} = M_a R_a = M_b R_b = \text{constant}.$$

The product MR is a constant for all perfect gases. It is called the *universal gas constant* and is denoted by $\mathscr{R}$. Since pV has the dimensions of energy, then $\mathscr{R}$ has the dimensions of energy per mole divided by the absolute temperature and its value depends on the units chosen. Therefore, the general form of the perfect gas law on a mole basis is

$$pV = n\mathscr{R}T. \tag{6.33}$$

Table 6.1 gives values of $\mathscr{R}$ in different units.

TABLE 6.1 VALUES OF THE UNIVERSAL GAS CONSTANT $\mathscr{R}$

1545.33 ft-lbf/lb-mole °R
1.98588 Btu/lb-mole °R
1.98588 cal/gm-mole °K
0.082054 liter-atm/gm-mole °K
8.3149×10^7 erg/gm-mole °K
8.3149×10^3 joule/kg-mole °K

EXAMPLE 6.6: A perfect gas occupies a volume of 1000 ft³ at a pressure of 13.0 psia and a temperature of 70°F. Calculate the volume of the gas when the pressure is 14.7 psia and the temperature is 40°F.

Solution: Using the relation

$$\frac{p_1 V_1}{T_1} = \frac{p_2 V_2}{T_2},$$

the volume V_2 of the gas is

$$V_2 = V_1 \frac{p_1}{p_2} \frac{T_2}{T_1} = 1000 \left(\frac{13}{14.7}\right)\left(\frac{40 + 460}{70 + 460}\right) = 835 \text{ ft}^3.$$

EXAMPLE 6.7: Find the volume in liters/gm-mole and ft³/lb-mole occupied by a perfect gas at a pressure of 1 atm and a temperature of 273.15°K(492°R).

Solution:

$$\bar{v} = \frac{\mathscr{R}T}{p} = \frac{0.082054 \times 273.15}{1} = 22.414 \text{ liters/gm-mole}$$

$$= \frac{1545 \times 492}{14.7 \times 144} = 359 \text{ ft}^3/\text{lb-mole.}$$

6-10
Molecular
Interpretation
of the Perfect
Gas Law

The equation of state of a perfect gas can be derived by making use of a mechanical model dictated by the kinetic theory of gases. As shown in Chapter 1, the product pV, according to Eq. (1.24), is

$$pV = \tfrac{1}{3} Nmv_{\text{rms}}^2,$$

where N is the number of molecules, m is the mass of each molecule, and v_{rms} is the root mean square speed.

Comparing the foregoing equation with Eq. (6.33) indicates that the absolute temperature, and consequently, the internal energy of a gas, is proportional to, and can be interpreted as, a measure of the translational kinetic energy of the molecules. The justification of the statement made in Chapter 1 regarding temperature not being a primary concept is now established. It should be remarked that reference to properties, such as temperature or pressure, apply to a large number of molecules and it is meaningless to refer to such properties for a single molecule.

Avogadro's number N_0 was defined in Chapter 1 as the number of molecules per gram-mole. The value of Avogadro's number is $N_0 = 6.0248 \times 10^{23}$ molecules/gm-mole. Noting that the number of moles n is equal to N/N_0, Eq. (6.33) can be written as

$$pV = \frac{N}{N_0} \mathscr{R}T = N\frac{\mathscr{R}}{N_0} T = NkT, \tag{6.34}$$

where k is the Boltzmann's constant.

The total kinetic energy of translation is the sum of the kinetic energies of the molecules or

$$U_{\text{trans}} = \frac{1}{2} \sum_i m_i v_i^2;$$

but, since

$$n\mathscr{R}T = \frac{1}{3} \sum_i m_i v_i^2, \quad \text{and} \quad nN_0 = N,$$

then

$$\frac{1}{2} \sum_i m_i v_i^2 = \frac{3}{2} n\mathscr{R}T = \frac{3}{2} NkT.$$

Therefore, the average kinetic energy of translation per molecule is

$$\epsilon_{\text{trans}} = \frac{\frac{1}{2} \sum_i m_i v_i^2}{N} = \frac{3}{2} kT = \frac{3}{2} \frac{\mathscr{R}T}{N_0}. \tag{6.35}$$

Equation (6.35) states that the average translational kinetic energy of a molecule of a perfect gas is a sole function of its absolute temperature. This means that in a mixture of perfect gases in thermal equilibrium, the value of ϵ_{trans} is the same for all the molecules of the mixture. Furthermore, at the same temperature, heavy molecules have a lower value of root mean square speed than lighter ones. Note from Eq. (6.35) that the translational motion of the molecules ceases at zero absolute temperature.

The perfect gas law states that at constant temperature the product pV is a constant. Under this condition, the preceding equations indicate that the mean translational kinetic energy of the molecules is independent of the pressure; it depends only on the temperature of the gas. Hence, the internal energy of a perfect gas, which is equal to the sum of the kinetic energies of its molecules, is a sole function of temperature. This is in accordance with Joule's law.

If the molecules of the gas are considered as point masses, then the translational energy per molecule, as given by Eq. (6.35), is equal to the internal energy of the molecules. Therefore the molal specific heat at constant volume $\bar{c}_v$ can be determined by differentiating Eq. (6.35) with respect to the temperature to give

$$\bar{c}_v = \tfrac{3}{2}\mathscr{R} \quad \text{(for monatomic gases).} \tag{6.36}$$

The ratio of specific heats is

$$\gamma = \frac{\bar{c}_p}{\bar{c}_v} = \frac{3/2\mathscr{R} + \mathscr{R}}{3/2\mathscr{R}} = \frac{5}{3} = 1.66. \tag{6.37}$$

A detailed discussion of the specific heats of perfect gases is postponed until Chapter 9; it suffices here to indicate that the value cited is in agreement with those observed for monatomic gases.

6-11
Equations of
State

Properties, such as pressure, temperature, volume, may be used to specify the state of a thermodynamic system in equilibrium. It is convenient to correlate the values of these properties as found experimentally through a functional relation called the *equation of state*. The equation of state may be expressed by means of a graph, tables of properties, or an equation of the form

$$f(p, V, T) = 0. \tag{6.38}$$

It has been shown previously that the thermodynamic state of a one-component system in the absence of electrical, magnetic, gravitational, surface, and motion effects is two-dimensional; that is, two independent properties are sufficient to describe the state of the system. A third property may be related to the two aforementioned independent properties by an equation of state.

In the case of a perfect gas the equation of state relating pressure, temperature, and specific volume is expressed by the simple relation

$$pv = RT. \tag{6.39}$$

As shown in Sections 6-9 and 6-10, the perfect gas equation was first deduced from the experiments of Charles and Boyle and can also be derived from the kinetic theory of gases. The latter case uses a highly idealized model of gas made up of perfectly elastic particles of negligible volume and no inter-particle forces. Therefore the perfect gas law is an approximation describing the behavior of real gases at nominal pressures and is an expression of the limiting behavior of real gases at high molal volumes. The perfect gas law becomes inadequate at low molal volumes or high pressure because molecular interaction cannot be neglected at high particle density.

Realizing the inherent inaccuracies in describing real gases by the perfect gas law, investigators have proposed numerous equations of state for real gases. The derivations are either empirical, according to experimental data, or have a physical interpretation based on the kinetic theory. Investigation of the gaseous state has received more attention than other states and has been an important factor in the development of present knowledge of the magnitude and nature of intermolecular forces. It has also helped in the analytical description of the behavior of high-pressure gases encountered in many industrial processes.

Deviations of a real gas from a perfect gas are readily displayed by plotting the deviation function $Z = pv/RT$ versus temperature, or pressure. Figure 6.12 shows the behavior of two real gases near room temperature. Note that as the pressure approaches zero, Z approaches unity. The ratio

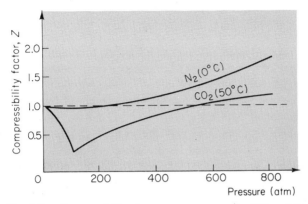

Fig. 6.12. Compressibility factor versus pressure for CO_2 and N_2.

pv/RT is called the *compressibility factor* and is discussed in detail in Section 6–12. Although graphical methods are used extensively for calculation, analytical methods seem to be superior where equations of state give accurate representation of the compressibility. Each equation, however, holds true in a specified range of density variations. Equations of state permit calculation of the variables involved along with their derivatives. Other thermodynamic properties, as well as conditions of equilibrium, can also be calculated with an accuracy comparable to the accuracy of the equation of state.

The following paragraphs discuss a few of these equations and investigate the principles of their derivations.

(a) *Van der Waals' equation of state:*   At low pressures the compressibility of real gases has a higher value than predicted by perfect gas analysis. Similarly, at high pressures real gases are found to be less compressible. The first observation is attributed to the attraction forces between the molecules and is more noticeable at low pressures. The second observation is attributed to the volume occupied by the molecules themselves. If the molecules of a gas are considered rigid spheres, only the space between the molecules is available for compression or expansion. At low pressures, where the mean free path of the molecules is large compared to the size of the molecules, the volume occupied by the molecules is relatively small and can be neglected. At high pressure, this volume cannot be neglected in comparison to the total volume occupied by the gas.

In order to find a correction term to compensate for the attraction forces between the molecules, consider the force of attraction on a single molecule hitting the wall of the confining vessel. When the molecule is not near the wall, it is surrounded by other molecules; consequently it is equally attracted in all directions, resulting in a zero net force on the molecule. This balance of forces is offset, however, when the molecule hits the wall, since it is then exposed to a net attraction force away from the wall toward the surrounding molecules. This attraction force reduces the pressure which otherwise would have been exerted by the molecule on the wall. The attraction force is proportional, among other factors, to the number of molecules per unit volume of the gas. The pressure is also proportional to the frequency of collision with the wall, which in turn is proportional to the number of molecules per unit volume. Therefore the attraction force is proportional to $(N/V)^2$ and since $N = nN_0$, it is proportional to $1/\bar{v}^2$, where $\bar{v}$ is the molal volume of the gas. The pressure exerted by the gas then equals a kinetic pressure p' as calculated by molecular change of momentum minus a correction term to compensate for the attraction forces so that

$$p = p' - \frac{a}{\bar{v}^2}$$

or

$$p' = p + \frac{a}{\bar{v}^2}, \tag{6.40}$$

where a is a proportionality constant.

The second correction due to the molecular sizes can be investigated by considering the collision of two identical molecules of the gas. If the molecular radius is r, the distance between the centers of identical molecules at the instant of collision is $2r$. Therefore, any molecule cannot come closer than a distance $2r$ to other identical molecules. This sets up a forbidden volume of $\frac{4}{3}\pi(2r)^3$ around each molecule, which is eight times the volume of the molecule itself. Only half of this volume, that is, only the hemisphere facing the incoming molecule, is effective in excluding the molecule from the forbidden volume. The latter is only four times the volume of the molecule. Denoting this volume per mole of the gas by the symbol b, the effective volume of the gas becomes $(\bar{v} - b)$.

Van der Waals, in 1879, realizing the foregoing deviations from the perfect gas law, proposed the following equation of state for a real gas,

$$\left(p + \frac{a}{\bar{v}^2}\right)(\bar{v} - b) = \mathscr{R}T. \tag{6.41}$$

When n moles of the gas are present, Eq. (6.41) becomes

$$\left(p + \frac{n^2 a}{V^2}\right)(V - nb) = n\mathscr{R}T. \tag{6.42}$$

Values of a and b for a few gases are listed in Table 6.2. Simplicity and ease of the constants' evaluation from limited data are the advantages of Van der Waals' equation; however, it gives only approximate results under many conditions. In general the accuracy with which Van der Waals' equation fits experimental data decreases at high densities.

TABLE 6.2 VALUES OF a AND b IN VAN DER WAALS' EQUATION

$$a \; \frac{\text{atm ft}^6}{(\text{lb-mole})^2} \qquad b \; \frac{\text{ft}^3}{\text{lb-mole}}$$

Gas	a	b	Gas	a	b
air	343.8	0.585	CH_4	578.9	0.684
O_2	349.5	0.510	C_3H_8	2374	1.446
N_2	346	0.618	C_4H_{10}	3675	1.944
H_2O	1397.1	0.487	NH_3	1076	0.598
CO	374.7	0.630	H_2	63.02	0.427
CO_2	924.2	0.685	Hg	5100	1.070

At low pressures, where the mean free path is large in comparison to the molecule's dimensions, the quantity b in Van der Waals' equation may be neglected. Hence Eq. (6.41) reduces to

$$\left(p + \frac{a}{\bar{v}^2}\right)(\bar{v}) = \mathscr{R}T$$

or

$$p\bar{v} = \mathscr{R}T - \frac{a}{\bar{v}}. \tag{6.43}$$

Equation (6.43) states that the product $p\bar{v}$ is less than $\mathscr{R}T$. This accounts for the shape of the curves of Fig. 6.12 at low pressures. Similarly at high pressures the term $a/\bar{v}^2$ can be neglected compared to p and Van der Waals' equation reduces to

$$p(\bar{v} - b) = \mathscr{R}T$$

or

$$p\bar{v} = \mathscr{R}T + bp. \tag{6.44}$$

Equation (6.44) is called the *Clausius equation of state*. Here the product $p\bar{v}$ is greater than $\mathscr{R}T$ and increases linearly with pressure.

Note that the Van der Waals' equation is cubic in V and, therefore, has three roots at each pressure. Figure 6.13 shows several isotherms plotted on a p-V diagram. Only one value of volume is obtained at temperatures equal to or above the critical isotherm; three values of specific volumes can be obtained at temperatures below the critical temperature. If thermodynamic equilibrium prevails, isothermal expansion will proceed from point a along

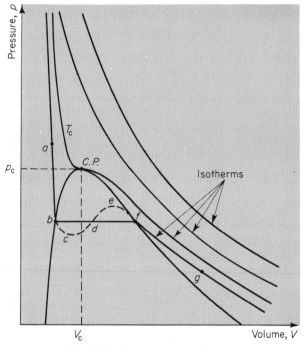

Fig. 6.13. *Pressure-volume diagram.*

path *a-b-f-g*. In this case both the liquid and vapor have the same pressure. If thermodynamic equilibrium does not prevail, the liquid state follows the metastable path *b-c* and vaporization is delayed. Note that the curve *b-c-d-e-f* is an isotherm but has different values of pressure. Along *b-c*, the temperature of the liquid exceeds the saturation temperature corresponding to the prevailing pressure. The liquid along *b-c* is then superheated liquid. In a similar fashion, isothermal compression of a gas under metastable condition follows path *g-f-e* and condensation is delayed. Along *e-f*, the temperature of the vapor is less than the saturation temperature corresponding to the prevailing pressure and the vapor is thus subcooled. Note that the stable conditions to which the metastable states at *c* or *e* eventually tend are along line *b-f*. The part of the curve *c-d-e* is unstable since its slope is positive, indicating that an increase in pressure results in an increase in volume.

The values of *a* and *b* of Van der Waals' equation can be calculated in terms of the properties at the critical point. To determine the critical values of Van der Waals' equation, the first and second derivatives of the pressure with respect to volume are equated to zero. This follows from the fact that the critical isotherm has an inflection point whose tangent is horizontal at the critical point. Therefore,

$$\left(\frac{\partial p}{\partial \bar{v}}\right)_c = 0 \quad \text{and} \quad \left(\frac{\partial^2 p}{\partial \bar{v}^2}\right)_c = 0,$$

where subscript c denotes critical point. The Van der Waals' equation at the critical point is

$$p_c = \frac{\mathscr{R}T_c}{\bar{v}_c - b} - \frac{a}{\bar{v}_c^2}. \tag{6.45}$$

Differentiating with respect to v and noting that T_c is a constant gives

$$\left(\frac{\partial p}{\partial \bar{v}}\right)_c = -\frac{\mathscr{R}T_c}{(\bar{v}_c - b)^2} + \frac{2a}{\bar{v}_c^3} = 0$$

and

$$\left(\frac{\partial^2 p}{\partial \bar{v}^2}\right)_c = \frac{2\mathscr{R}T_c}{(\bar{v}_c - b)^3} - \frac{6a}{\bar{v}_c^4} = 0.$$

Combining the last three equations, the critical properties, in terms of the coefficients a and b of the Van der Waals' equation are

$$p_c = \frac{a}{27b^2}$$

$$\bar{v}_c = 3b \tag{6.46}$$

$$T_c = \frac{8a}{27\mathscr{R}b}.$$

Alternatively, the coefficients of Van der Waals' equation can be determined in terms of the critical properties. The result is as follows:

$$a = 3p_c\bar{v}_c^2 = \frac{9}{8}\mathscr{R}T_c\bar{v}_c = \frac{27}{64}\frac{\mathscr{R}^2 T_c^2}{p_c}$$

$$b = \frac{\bar{v}_c}{3} = \frac{\mathscr{R}T_c}{8p_c} \tag{6.47}$$

and

$$\mathscr{R} = \frac{8}{3}\frac{p_c\bar{v}_c}{T_c}.$$

Checking the foregoing results is left as an exercise to the reader. Table 6.3 gives the critical properties for several gases.

TABLE 6.3 CRITICAL CONSTANTS FOR SEVERAL GASES

Gas	T_c (°R)	p_c (atm)	$\bar{v}_c$ (ft³/lb-mole)
Air	239	37.2	1.33
O_2	278	50.1	1.19
N_2	227	33.5	1.44
H_2	59.8	12.8	1.04
He	9.33	2.26	0.93
CO_2	548	72.9	1.53
H_2O	1165	218.2	0.91
NH_3	730	111.3	1.16

(b) *The Beattie-Bridgeman equation of state:* This equation has more constants than other equations of state; therefore, it is more successful in representing the compressibility of gases. The Beattie-Bridgeman equation is

$$p = \frac{\mathscr{R}T}{\bar{v}^2}(1 - e)(\bar{v} + B) - \frac{A}{\bar{v}^2}, \tag{6.48}$$

where $A = A_o\left(1 - \frac{a}{\bar{v}}\right)$

$$B = B_o\left(1 - \frac{b}{\bar{v}}\right)$$

$$e = \frac{c}{\bar{v}T^3}.$$

The five constants a, b, c, A_o, and B_o in Eq. (6.48) are given for several gases in Table 6.4. Data for many gases can be fitted to within 0.5 per cent accuracy over a wide range of temperature and pressure. The Beattie-Bridgeman equation is, however, inaccurate near the critical point.

TABLE 6.4 VALUES OF THE CONSTANTS IN THE BEATTIE-BRIDGEMAN EQUATION

Gas	A_o $\dfrac{\text{atm ft}^3}{\text{(lb-mole)}^2}$	B_o $\dfrac{\text{ft}^3}{\text{lb-mole}}$	a $\dfrac{\text{ft}^3}{\text{lb-mole}}$	$10^{-4}c$ $\dfrac{\text{ft}^3 \text{ °R}^3}{\text{lb-mole}}$	b $\dfrac{\text{ft}^3}{\text{lb-mole}}$
air	334.1	0.739	0.309	406	−0.176
O_2	382.5	0.741	0.410	448	0.0674
N_2	344.3	0.809	0.419	391.7	−0.111
H_2	50.57	0.336	−0.0811	4.7	−0.698
He	5.6	0.224	0.958	0.37	0.0
CO_2	1248.9	1.678	1.143	165	1.159
NH_3	613.9	0.547	2.729	44.560	3.062

(c) *Bertholet equation of state:*   Another classical equation of state is

$$\left(p + \frac{an^2}{TV^2}\right)(V - nb) = n\mathcal{R}T,$$ (6.49)

where a and b are constants. Bertholet made the additive pressure term proportional to $1/T$ and his equation reduces to Van der Waals' equation at high molal volumes.

(d) *Dieterici equation of state:*   In 1899, Dieterici proposed the following equation of state:

$$(pe^{an/V\mathcal{R}T})(V - nb) = n\mathcal{R}T,$$ (6.50)

where a and b are constants.

The Bertholet and Dieterici equations do not give accurate results over wide ranges of pressure and temperature. They give some insight, however, into the p-V-T relationships and have generated experimental and theoretical work in the field of intermolecular forces. Note that the Dieterici equation reduces to Van der Waals' equation of state at high molal volumes. The proof is left to the student as an exercise.

(e) *Virial* equation of state:*   Kammerlingh Onnes, in 1901, introduced the virial equation of state in the form of an infinite expansion of the product pV. Two forms are available:
In terms of V,

$$pV = n\mathcal{R}T\left(1 + \frac{nB}{V} + \frac{n^2 C}{V^2} + \cdots\right)$$ (6.51)

and in terms of p,

$$pV = n\mathcal{R}T(1 + nB'p + n^2 C'p^2 + \cdots).$$ (6.52)

The coefficients $B, C \ldots$ and $B', C' \ldots$ are called the second, third, etc., *virial coefficients.* These coefficients are functions of temperature and they relate the deviation of actual gases from perfect gases in terms of intermolecular forces. The virial equation applies to gases at low or medium densities only.

Comparison of accuracy of the various equations of state is difficult since accuracy of any equation depends on the nature of the gas under consideration, as well as on the method of constants' evaluation and the ranges of pressure and temperature. Quite often, the equation of state is suitable for thermodynamic calculations of functions such as p, V, and T

---

*The word "virial" comes from the Latin word for force, thus it refers to interaction forces between molecules.

but unsuitable for the evaluation of properties which depend on first and second derivatives of functions of p, V, and T.

EXAMPLE 6.8: Find the second and third virial coefficients of Van der Waals' equation of state when expressed in the expansion forms of Eq. (6.51) and (6.52).

Solution: (a) The Van der Waals equation is

$$\left(p + \frac{an^2}{V^2}\right)(V - nb) = n\mathscr{R}T.$$

Therefore,

$$pV + \frac{an^2}{V} - pnb - \frac{abn^3}{V^2} = n\mathscr{R}T$$

$$pV = n\mathscr{R}T\left(1 + \frac{pb}{\mathscr{R}T} - \frac{an}{V\mathscr{R}T} + \frac{abn^2}{V^2\mathscr{R}T}\right),$$

but

$$p = \frac{n\mathscr{R}T}{V - nb} - \frac{an^2}{V_2}.$$

Therefore,

$$pV = n\mathscr{R}T\left[1 + \frac{b}{\mathscr{R}T}\left(\frac{n\mathscr{R}T}{V - nb} - \frac{an^2}{V^2}\right) - \frac{an}{V\mathscr{R}T} + \frac{abn^2}{V^2\mathscr{R}T}\right]$$

$$= n\mathscr{R}T\left[1 + \frac{nb}{V - nb} - \frac{an}{V\mathscr{R}T}\right]$$

$$= n\mathscr{R}T\left[1 + \frac{nb}{V}\left(1 - \frac{nb}{V}\right)^{-1} - \frac{an}{V\mathscr{R}T}\right]$$

$$= n\mathscr{R}T\left[1 + \frac{nb}{V}\left(1 + \frac{nb}{V} + \frac{n^2b^2}{V_2} + \cdots\right) - \frac{an}{V\mathscr{R}T}\right]$$

$$= n\mathscr{R}T\left[1 + \frac{n}{V}\left(b - \frac{a}{\mathscr{R}T}\right) + \frac{n^2b^2}{V_2} + \frac{n^3b^3}{V_3} + \cdots\right].$$

Comparison with Eq. (6.51) gives the following virial coefficients:

second coefficient $B = b - \dfrac{a}{\mathscr{R}T}$

third coefficient $C = b^2$, etc.

(b) The Van der Waals equation, when expressed in the form of Eq. (6.52), gives

$$pV = n\mathscr{R}T + n\left(b - \frac{a}{\mathscr{R}T}\right)p.$$

Therefore, the second virial coefficient is $(b - a/\mathscr{R}T)$.

A similar procedure may be used to expand any equation of state into a series form.

**6-12
Compressi-
bility Factor**
From the perfect gas law, it can be seen that the specific volume of a gas becomes very large when the pressure is low or the temperature is high. Hence, specific volume cannot be conveniently used to represent the behavior of real gases at low pressure or high temperature. To surmount this difficulty, the properties of each real gas are indicated by means of a compressibility factor, which expresses the extent of deviation of the gas from a perfect gas. The compressibility factor Z is defined by

$$Z \equiv \frac{pv}{RT}. \tag{6.53}$$

The compressibility factor of a perfect gas has a value of unity under all conditions. Also, as the pressure is reduced, the compressibility factor of any gas approaches unity since a gas acts more like a perfect gas as the pressure is lowered:

$$\lim_{p \to 0} Z = 1. \tag{6.54}$$

The value of Z for any real gas may be less or more than unity, depending on the temperature and pressure of the gas, but must be finite.

Values of the compressibility factor of any gas may be determined experimentally. But it is also possible to determine values of Z from other properties of a gas, based on only a limited amount of data. This is accomplished by describing gases in terms of reduced properties, rather than in terms of properties alone. For example, by dividing pressure by the critical pressure of the gas under consideration, the reduced pressure is obtained:

$$p_R \equiv \frac{p}{p_c}.$$

Similarly,

$$T_R \equiv \frac{T}{T_c}, \tag{6.55}$$

and

$$v_R \equiv \frac{v}{v_c} = \frac{v}{RT_c/p_c}.$$

The compressibility factor of any one-component substance is a function of only two properties, usually temperature and pressure, so that

$$Z = f(T_R, p_R). \tag{6.56}$$

Equation (6.56) is called the *law of corresponding states* and is the basis for the generalized compressibility chart shown in Figures 6.14, 6.15, and 6.16.

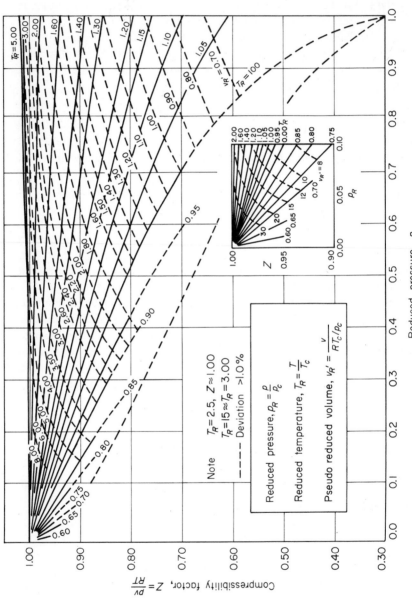

Fig. 6.14. *Generalized compressibility chart.* SOURCE: L. C. Nelson and E. F. Obert, "Generalized p,v,T Properties of

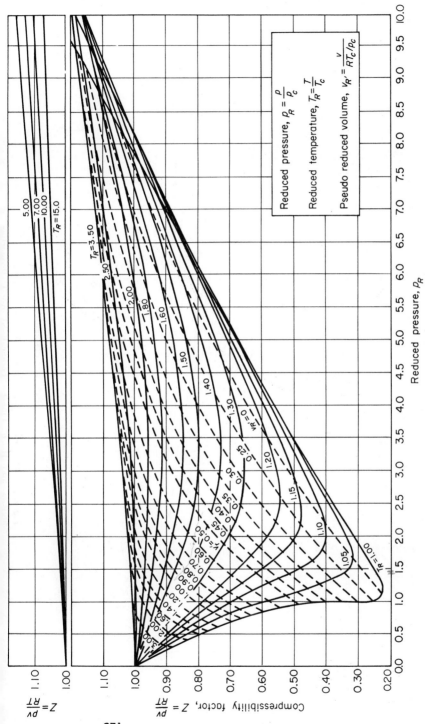

Fig. 6.15. *Generalized compressibility chart.* SOURCE: L. C. Nelson and E. F. Obert, "Generalized p-v-T Properties of Gases," trans. A.S.M.E., 76, 1057 (1954).

271

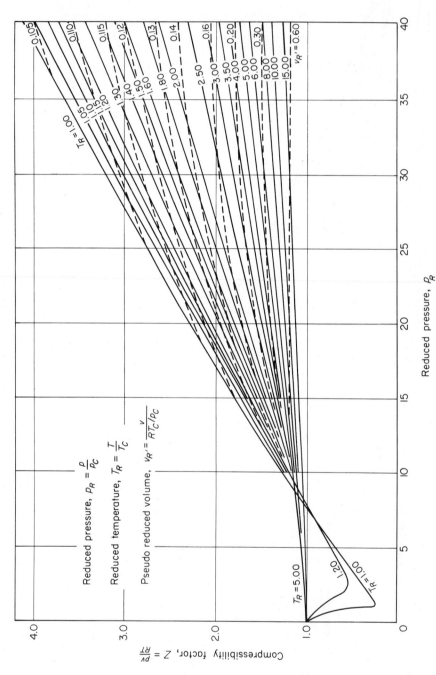

Fig. 6.16. *Generalized compressibility chart.* SOURCE: L. C. Nelson and E. F. Obert, "Generalized p-v-T Properties of

272

On these charts, the compressibility factor Z is plotted as a function of reduced temperature and reduced pressure. According to these charts, one-component substances which are at the same reduced pressure and temperature have the same compressibility factor.

The generalized compressibility chart provides one of the best means of expressing deviation from ideal behavior, and gives results with an accuracy of within 5 per cent. A gas that has a compressibility factor less than unity is more compressible than a perfect gas. The charts show that both temperature and pressure introduce deviations from ideal behavior. Note that the value of Z at the critical point is approximately 0.25.

The Van der Waals equation of state can be expressed in a more general form by introducing reduced properties into it. When the values of a, b, and $\mathscr{R}$ are expressed in terms of critical values, Eq. (6.41) becomes

$$p_R = \frac{8T_R}{3\bar{v}_R - 1} - \frac{3}{\bar{v}_R^2}. \tag{6.57}$$

Also, it is clear from Eq. (6.47) that for Van der Waals' gas at the critical point:

$$Z_c = \frac{p_c \bar{v}_c}{\mathscr{R}T_c} = \frac{3}{8}. \tag{6.58}$$

The constants a and b no longer appear in this Van der Waals equation, so that the equation can be used with any substance providing the critical properties are known.

The compressibility factor can be expressed in terms of the compressibility factor Z_c at the critical point. This relationship is derived by substituting Eq. (6.55) into Eq. (6.53):

$$Z = \frac{pv}{RT} = \frac{p_R v_R}{T_R} \frac{p_c v_c}{RT_c} = \frac{p_R v_R}{T_R} Z_c. \tag{6.59}$$

The compressibility factor at the critical point has a value between 0.2 and 0.3, the exact value depending on the substance under consideration. Because Z_c is not affected by the law of corresponding states, it can be treated as an independent variable. Therefore, the compressibility factor is a function of the critical compressibility factor, and the principle of corresponding states must be modified as follows:

$$Z = f(p_R, T_R, Z_c). \tag{6.60}$$

EXAMPLE 6.9: Determine the specific volume of steam at atmospheric pressure and 1000°F temperature by use of (a) steam tables; (b) the perfect gas law; (c) Van der Waals' equation; (d) compressibility chart.

Solution:
(a) From steam tables: $v = 59.13$ ft³/lbm.
(b) Perfect gas law:

$$v = \frac{RT}{p} = \frac{(1545/18.02)\,1460}{14.696 \times 144} = 59.2 \text{ ft}^3/\text{lbm}.$$

(c) Van der Waals' equation: For water the values of a and b, according to Table 6.2, are

$a = 20.6 \times 10^3$ (psi)(ft³/lb-mole)²
$b = 0.487$ ft³/lb-mole.

$$\left(p + \frac{a}{v^2}\right)(v - b) = RT$$

$$\left[14.696 + \frac{(20.6 \times 10^3)/(18.02)^2}{v^2}\right]\left(v - \frac{0.487}{18.02}\right) = \left(\frac{1545}{18.02}\right)1460,$$

from which $v = 59.1$ ft³/lbm.
(d) Compressibility chart:

$$T_R = \frac{T}{T_c} = \frac{1460}{1165.3} = 1.252$$

$$p_R = \frac{p}{p_c} = \frac{14.696}{3208} = 0.00457.$$

From the chart $Z = 1.0$ and $v = ZRT/p = 59.2$ ft³/lbm.
Note that results obtained by these different methods are practically identical. The perfect gas law proved valid, in this case, because of the low density of the gas.

6-13
Properties
of Real Gases
In previous sections, equations of state were developed which provided methods of correlating various properties of single-component gases. In this section, a method for evaluating thermodynamic properties of gases from *p-V-T* data is discussed.

A real gas behaves like a perfect gas when it is at a pressure much lower than its critical pressure, and at a temperature much higher than its critical temperature. The internal energy, or enthalpy, of a real gas is a function of two properties, such as pressure and temperature. Thus the enthalpy of a real gas may be expressed as

$$h = h(p, T), \tag{6.61}$$

and its differential is

$$dh = \left(\frac{\partial h}{\partial T}\right)_p dT + \left(\frac{\partial h}{\partial p}\right)_T dp. \tag{6.62}$$

The first term, which is equal to $c_p\, dT$, indicates the change of enthalpy of a perfect gas as the temperature changes. The second term is the change of enthalpy due to deviation of a real gas, at finite pressures, from perfect gas behavior. Thus the enthalpy of a real gas may be written as

$$h = h^* + h_r, \qquad\qquad (6.63)$$

where h^* is the enthalpy of the perfect gas and h_r is called *residual enthalpy*. The enthalpy change of a real gas between two states can be treated as the enthalpy change that a perfect gas undergoes and, in addition, the change in residual enthalpy that the real gas undergoes,

$$dh = dh^* + dh_r.$$

This can be rearranged as follows:

$$dh_r = d(h - h^*). \qquad\qquad (6.64)$$

According to the first and second laws, change of enthalpy for a simple system can be expressed as

$$dh = Tds + vdp.$$

This can be written in the form

$$\left(\frac{\partial h}{\partial p}\right)_T = T\left(\frac{\partial s}{\partial p}\right)_T + v. \qquad\qquad (6.65)$$

Now the following Maxwell relation (5.69b) applies:

$$\left(\frac{\partial s}{\partial p}\right)_T = -\left(\frac{\partial v}{\partial T}\right)_p.$$

With these substitutions, Eq. (6.62) now becomes

$$dh = \left(\frac{\partial h}{\partial T}\right)_p dT + \left[v - T\left(\frac{\partial v}{\partial T}\right)_p\right] dp. \qquad\qquad (6.66)$$

Residual enthalpy can now be equated with the last term in this equation:

$$dh_r = \left[v - T\left(\frac{\partial v}{\partial T}\right)_p\right] dp. \qquad\qquad (6.67)$$

Since the residual enthalpy is zero under vacuum conditions, integration leads to

$$h_r = \int_0^p \left[v - T\left(\frac{\partial v}{\partial T}\right)_p \right] dp. \tag{6.68}$$

The residual enthalpy can be readily evaluated from experimental p-V-T data. First, specific volume is plotted against temperature, and from the slopes, values of $(\partial v/\partial T)$ at constant pressure are obtained. Then the quantity $[v - T(\partial v/\partial T)_p]$ is calculated, and values are plotted against pressure. Numerical integration yields values of the residual enthalpy at any desired pressure.

From the equation of state it is possible to express residual enthalpy in terms of the compressibility factor. Specific volume is given by

$$v = \frac{ZRT}{p}. \tag{6.69}$$

Hence, by differentiation

$$\left(\frac{\partial v}{\partial T}\right)_p = \frac{R}{p}\left[Z + T\left(\frac{\partial Z}{\partial T}\right)_p \right]. \tag{6.70}$$

Substitutions can now be made in Eq. (6.67):

$$dh_r = \left\{ \frac{ZRT}{p} - \frac{RT}{p}\left[Z + T\left(\frac{\partial Z}{\partial T}\right)_p \right] \right\} dp$$

This reduces to

$$dh_r = -\frac{RT^2}{p}\left(\frac{\partial Z}{\partial T}\right)_p dp.$$

But it was shown that

$$dh_r = \left(\frac{\partial h}{\partial p}\right)_T dp.$$

Therefore,

$$\left(\frac{\partial h}{\partial p}\right)_T = -\frac{RT^2}{p}\left(\frac{\partial Z}{\partial T}\right)_p. \tag{6.71}$$

This can be expressed as an integral equation:

$$\int_{h^*}^h dh_r = h - h^* = -RT^2 \int_0^p \left(\frac{\partial Z}{\partial T}\right)_p \frac{dp}{p}. \tag{6.72}$$

To evaluate h_r, the compressibility factor is first plotted against temperature at various selected pressures. From this graph, values of $(\partial Z/\partial T)_p$ are

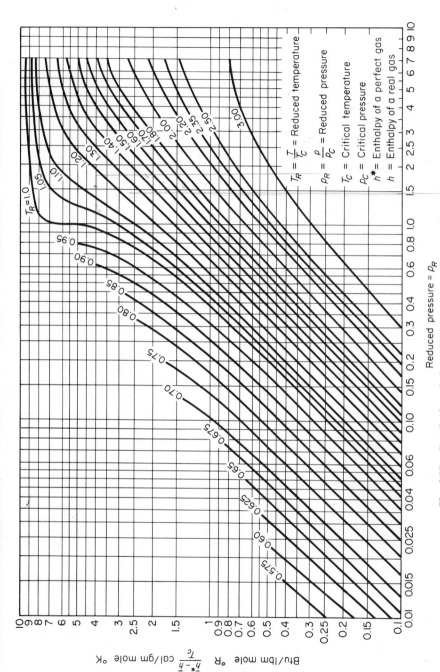

Fig. 6.17. *Residual enthalpy chart.* SOURCE: Hougen, O. A., K. M. Watson, and R. A. Ragatz, *Chemical Process Principles,* Part II, John Wiley & Sons, Inc., New York, 1947.

Reduced pressure = p_R

$T_R = \dfrac{T}{T_C}$ = Reduced temperature

$p_R = \dfrac{p}{p_C}$ = Reduced pressure

T_C = Critical temperature

p_C = Critical pressure

h^* = Enthalpy of a perfect gas

h = Enthalpy of a real gas

Btu/lbm mole °R $\dfrac{h^* - h}{T_c}$ cal/gm mole °K

obtained. Then values of $(RT^2/p)(\partial Z/\partial T)_p$ are plotted against pressure, and the area under the curve between the origin and a chosen pressure represents the residual enthalpy at that pressure.

The residual enthalpy can be expressed in a more general form as a function of reduced temperature and pressure, rather than in terms of absolute values. Since $T_R = T/T_c$ and $p_R = p/p_c$, substitution in Eq. (6.72) leads to

$$\int_{h^*}^{h} dh_r = -RT_R^2 T_c^2 \int_0^{p_R} \frac{1}{T_c}\left(\frac{\partial Z}{\partial T_R}\right)_{p_R} \frac{dp_R}{p_R},$$

From this, it follows that

$$-\frac{h_r}{T_c} = \frac{h^* - h}{T_c} = RT_R^2 \int_0^{p_R} \left(\frac{\partial Z}{\partial T_R}\right) \frac{dp_R}{p_R}. \tag{6.73}$$

The integral in the preceding equation is evaluated by using numerical and graphical techniques. The result is shown in Fig. 6.17 on a mole basis. In evaluating the change of enthalpy between two states, the following equation is used:

$$h_2 - h_1 = (h_2 - h_2^*) + (h_2^* - h_1^*) + (h_1^* - h_1).$$

The middle term (i.e., $h_2^* - h_1^*$) indicates the change of enthalpy of a perfect gas, and is equal to $c_p^*(T_2 - T_1)$. Values for the first and third terms are obtained from the enthalpy correction chart. These enthalpy changes, in a

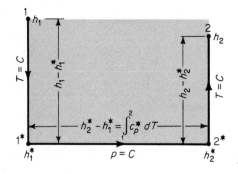

Fig. 6.18.   Changes of enthalpy.

process between states 1 and 2, are illustrated in Fig. 6.18, and involve the following steps:

(a) From state 1 of the real gas to state 1* of the perfect gas;
(b) From state 1* of the perfect gas to state 2* of the perfect gas;
(c) From state 2* of the perfect gas to the final state 2 of the real gas.

The *residual entropy* of a real gas may be evaluated by a procedure similar to that used for residual enthalpy. Residual entropy is defined by

$$s_r = s - s^*, \tag{6.74}$$

which is, in differential form,

$$ds_r = ds - ds^*. \tag{6.75}$$

The differential of entropy, expressed as a function of temperature and pressure, is

$$ds = \left(\frac{\partial s}{\partial T}\right)_p dT + \left(\frac{\partial s}{\partial p}\right)_T dp.$$

But according to the Maxwell relation (5.69b), $(\partial s/\partial p)_T = -(\partial v/\partial T)_p$. Also, from the combined first and second laws of thermodynamics

$$\left(\frac{\partial s}{\partial T}\right)_p = \frac{1}{T}\left(\frac{\partial h}{\partial T}\right)_p.$$

When these substitutions are made, then

$$ds = \frac{1}{T}\left(\frac{\partial h}{\partial T}\right)_p dT - \left(\frac{\partial v}{\partial T}\right)_p dp = \frac{c_p^* dT}{T} - \left(\frac{\partial v}{\partial T}\right)_p dp.$$

However, for a perfect gas

$$ds^* = \frac{c_p^* dT}{T} - \frac{R}{p} dp.$$

Therefore, residual entropy can be expressed in the form:

$$ds_r = ds - ds^* = -\left[\left(\frac{\partial v}{\partial T}\right)_p - \frac{R}{p}\right] dp.$$

In integral form, this becomes

$$s_r = -\int_{p \to 0}^{p} \left[\left(\frac{\partial v}{\partial T}\right)_p - \frac{R}{p}\right] dp, \tag{6.76}$$

since the entropy of a gas approaches zero as the pressure approaches zero. Substituting the Maxwell relation

$$\left(\frac{\partial s}{\partial p}\right)_T = -\left(\frac{\partial v}{\partial T}\right)_p,$$

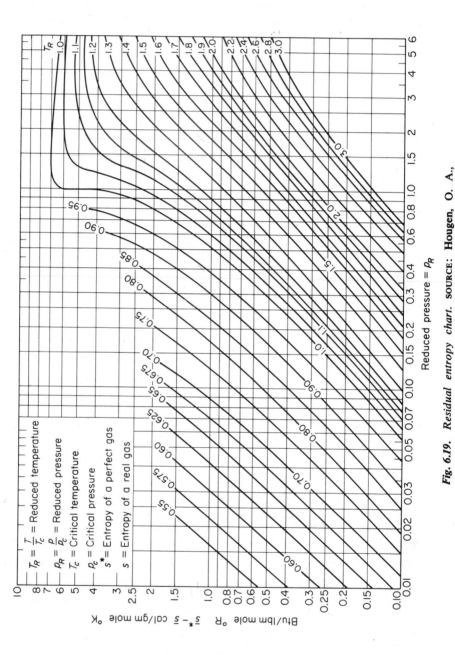

Fig. 6.19. Residual entropy chart. SOURCE: Hougen, O. A., K. M. Watson, and R. A. Ragatz, Chemical Process Principles,

into Eq. (6.70) gives

$$\left(\frac{\partial s}{\partial p}\right)_T = -\frac{R}{p}\left[Z + T\left(\frac{\partial Z}{\partial T}\right)_p\right].$$

(6.77)

Finally, temperature and pressure are expressed on the reduced scale basis. When these substitutions are made, the change of entropy of a real gas at constant temperature becomes

$$ds = -R\left[Z + T_R\left(\frac{\partial Z}{\partial T_R}\right)_{p_R}\right]_{T_R}\frac{dp_R}{p_R}.$$

(6.78)

For a perfect gas, however, the change of entropy at constant temperature is

$$ds^* = -R\left(\frac{dp_R}{p_R}\right)_{T_R}.$$

(6.79)

Therefore, residual entropy takes the form:

$$ds_r = ds - ds^* = -R\left[(Z-1) + T_R\left(\frac{\partial Z}{\partial T_R}\right)_{p_R}\right]_{T_R}\frac{dp_R}{p_R}.$$

(6.80)

In integral form, this becomes

$$-s_r = s^* - s = R\int_0^{p_R}\left[(Z-1) + T_R\left(\frac{\partial Z}{\partial T_R}\right)_{p_R}\right]_{T_R}\frac{dp_R}{p_R},$$

(6.81)

where the residual entropy disappears at low pressures. In Fig. 6.19, the function $\bar{s}^* - \bar{s}$ is plotted against reduced pressure for various reduced temperatures. In Fig. 6.20, the change of entropy between two states is shown as the sum of three changes:

$$s_2 - s_1 = (s_2 - s_2^*) + (s_2^* - s_1^*) + (s_1^* - s_1).$$

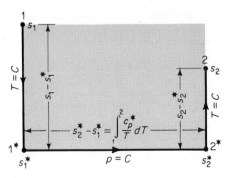

Fig. 6.20.   Changes of entropy.

EXAMPLE 6.10:   Superheated steam at 5000 psia and 800°F has the following properties: $h = 1047.1$ Btu/lbm, $s = 1.1622$ Btu/lbm°R and $v = 0.0593$ ft³/lbm. Determine the values of enthalpy, entropy, and specific volume of steam at 10,000 psia and 800°F. The critical temperature, T_c, is 1165.1°R; a pseudovalue of p_c for p-V-T computations from the generalized chart is 3330 psia.

Solution: Assume isothermal compression process from 5,000 to 10,000 psia. The reduced temperature and pressure at the initial and final states are

$$T_{R_1} = T_{R_2} = \frac{800 + 460}{1165.1} = 1.08$$

$$p_{R_1} = \frac{5000}{3330} = 1.5; \quad p_{R_2} = \frac{10,000}{3330} = 3.0 \,.$$

At $T_{R_1} = 1.08$ and $p_{R_1} = 1.5$, according to Figs. 6.17 and 6.19

$$\frac{\bar{h}_{r_1}}{T_c} = \frac{(\bar{h} - \bar{h}^*)_1}{T_c} = -5.5 \text{ Btu/lb-mole °R} \quad \text{and} \quad \bar{s}_{r_1} = -4.4 \text{ Btu/lb-mole °R}.$$

Similarly, at $T_{R_2} = 1.08$ and $p_{R_2} = 3$,

$$\frac{\bar{h}_{r_2}}{T_c} = \frac{(\bar{h} - \bar{h}^*)_2}{T_c} = -7.8 \text{ Btu/lb-mole °R} \quad \text{and} \quad \bar{s}_{r_2} = -5.4 \text{ Btu/lb-mole °R}.$$

Thus,

$$\frac{(\Delta \bar{h})_r}{T_c} = -7.8 + 5.5 = -2.3 \text{ Btu/lb-mole °R}$$

or

$$\Delta h_r = -\left(\frac{2.3}{18.02}\right) 1165.1 = -149 \text{ Btu/lbm}.$$

Since $T_1 = T_2$, then $h_1^* = h_2^*$. Thus,

$$\Delta h_r = \Delta h = h_2 - h_1$$

or

$$h_2 = 1047.1 - 149 = 898.1 \text{ Btu/lbm}.$$

The change of entropy may be calculated as follows:

$$\Delta \bar{s} = \Delta \bar{s}_r + \Delta \bar{s}^*.$$

Since the temperature is constant, $\Delta \bar{s}^*$ is a function of pressure alone,

$$\Delta \bar{s}^* = -\mathscr{R} \ln \frac{p_2}{p_1} = -(1.986) \ln 2 = -1.377 \text{ Btu/lb-mole °R}$$

$$\Delta \bar{s} = (-5.4 + 4.4) - 1.377 = -2.377 \text{ Btu/lb-mole °R}$$

$$= -0.1318 \text{ Btu/lbm °R}$$

and

$$s_2 = 1.1622 - 0.1318 = 1.0304 \text{ Btu/lbm } °R.$$

The specific volume may be determined from the equation

$$v_2 = \frac{Z_2 RT_2}{p_2}.$$

At $T_{R_2} = 1.08$ and $p_{R_2} = 3.0$, the value of Z obtained from Fig. 6.15 is 0.46. Thus,

$$v_2 = \frac{0.46 \times (1545/18.02) \times 1260}{10,000 \times 144} = 0.0345 \text{ ft}^3/\text{lbm.}$$

**6-14
Residual
Properties
in Terms
of Joule-
Thomson
Data**

The Joule-Thomson experiment described in Section 3.10 provides a precise method of determining residual properties. During an adiabatic throttling process, the enthalpy remains constant if only negligible changes in kinetic energy occur. Also, if the gas is perfect, the temperature remains unchanged. The *Joule-Thomson coefficient* has been defined as

$$\mu_h \equiv \left(\frac{\partial T}{\partial p}\right)_h, \tag{6.82}$$

while the *isothermal coefficient* has been defined as

$$\mu_T \equiv \left(\frac{\partial h}{\partial p}\right)_T. \tag{6.83}$$

The differential of enthalpy, as a function of temperature and pressure, is

$$dh = \left(\frac{\partial h}{\partial T}\right)_p dT + \left(\frac{\partial h}{\partial p}\right)_T dp.$$

In a throttling process, enthalpy does not change, and therefore

$$\left(\frac{\partial h}{\partial T}\right)_p dT = -\left(\frac{\partial h}{\partial p}\right)_T dp \quad \text{or} \quad \left(\frac{\partial h}{\partial T}\right)_p = \left(\frac{\partial h}{\partial p}\right)_T \left(\frac{\partial p}{\partial T}\right)_h.$$

By substituting the coefficients into this equation, according to Eqs. (6.82) and (6.83), this becomes

$$c_p = -\frac{\mu_T}{\mu_h}. \tag{6.84}$$

This equation provides a method of determining specific heat values from *h-p-T* data by means of Joule-Thomson experiments.

It was shown previously that the residual enthalpy is

$$dh_r = \left(\frac{\partial h}{\partial p}\right)_T dp.$$

By substituting the isothermal coefficient, this becomes

$$dh_r = \mu_T\, dp.$$

Since the residual enthalpy is zero at zero pressure, integration leads to

$$h_r = \int_0^p \mu_T\, dp. \tag{6.85}$$

It was shown that residual entropy can be expressed as

$$ds_r = \left[\frac{R}{p} + \left(\frac{\partial s}{\partial p}\right)_T\right] dp.$$

However, it can be shown that

$$\left(\frac{\partial s}{\partial p}\right)_T = \left(\frac{\partial h}{T \partial p}\right)_T = \frac{\mu_T}{T}.$$

Therefore,

$$ds_r = \left[\frac{R}{p} + \frac{\mu_T}{T}\right] dp.$$

When integrated, this equation becomes

$$s_r = \int_{p \to 0}^p \left[\frac{R}{p} + \frac{\mu_T}{T}\right] dp. \tag{6.86}$$

Equations (6.85) and (6.86) express the residual enthalpy and the residual entropy in terms of μ_T, p, and T.

6-15
Residual
Specific Heat
The specific heat of a real gas at constant temperature is a function of pressure, whereas the specific heat of a perfect gas is invariant. *Residual specific heat* is defined as:

$$(c_{p_r})_T = (c_p - c_p^*)_T\,, \tag{6.87}$$

where c_p^* is the constant-pressure specific heat of the perfect gas, or of a real gas at zero pressure. Also, specific heat can be defined by:

$$c_p = \left(\frac{\partial h}{\partial T}\right)_p = \left(\frac{T\partial s}{\partial T}\right)_p.$$

The change of specific heat as a function of change of pressure, at constant temperature, is

$$\left(\frac{\partial c_p}{\partial p}\right)_T = \left[\frac{T\partial(\partial s/\partial T)_p}{\partial p}\right]_T.$$

Since entropy is a property, the order of differentiation is immaterial, and so this equation can also be written

$$\left(\frac{\partial c_p}{\partial p}\right)_T = \left[\frac{T\partial(\partial s/\partial p)_T}{\partial T}\right]_p.$$

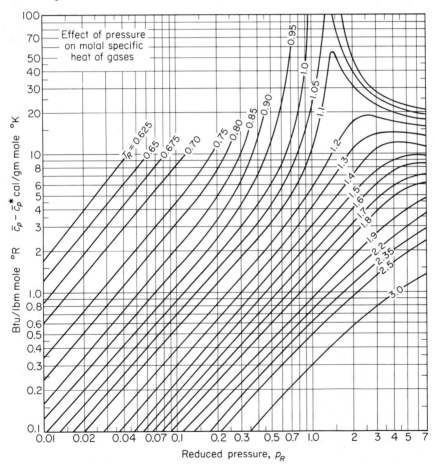

Fig. 6.21. *Residual specific heat chart.* SOURCE: Hougen, O. A., K. M. Watson, and R. A. Ragatz, *Chemical Process Principles,* Part II, John Wiley & Sons, Inc., New York, 1947.

But according to the Maxwell relation (5.69b),

$$\left(\frac{\partial s}{\partial p}\right)_T = -\left(\frac{\partial v}{\partial T}\right)_p.$$

Consequently, by substitution,

$$\left(\frac{\partial c_p}{\partial p}\right)_T = -T\left(\frac{\partial^2 v}{\partial T^2}\right)_p.$$

The integral form is

$$(c_p - c_p^*)_T = -T\int_{p\to 0}^{p}\left(\frac{\partial^2 v}{\partial T^2}\right)_p dp. \tag{6.88}$$

In Fig. 6.21, the function $\bar{c}_p - \bar{c}_p^*$ is shown plotted against reduced pressure at various reduced temperatures.

REFERENCES

6.1 Denbigh, K. G., *The Principles of Chemical Equilibrium*. Cambridge: Cambridge University Press, 1957, chap. 5.

6.2 Hougen, O. A., K. M. Watson, R. A. Ragatz, *Chemical Process Principles*, Part II. New York: John Wiley & Sons, Inc., 1959, chap. 14.

6.3 Keenan, J. H., and F. G. Kayes, *Thermodynamic Properties of Steam*. New York: John Wiley & Sons, Inc., 1936.

6.4 Lee, J. F., and F. W. Sears, *Thermodynamics*. Reading, Mass.: Addison-Wesley Publishing Company, Inc., 1955, chap. 2.

6.5 Obert, E. F., *Concepts of Thermodynamics*. New York: McGraw-Hill Book Company, 1960, chap. 9, 10.

6.6 Van Wylen, G. F., *Thermodynamics*. New York: John Wiley & Sons, Inc., 1959, chap. 2.

PROBLEMS

6.1 Calculate the specific volume and specific enthalpy of 35 per cent quality steam if the pressure is 3 psia.

6.2 How much heat must be transferred per lbm to raise the temperature of saturated steam to 500°F at a constant pressure of 144 psia? Check the result using the *h-s* diagram.

6.3 Water is compressed isentropically in a flow process from saturated state at 100°F to a pressure of 1000 psia. How much work is required?

6.4 A rigid vessel of volume 1.0 ft³ contains saturated water at 400 psia. What were the proportions by volume of liquid and vapor at the initial pressure of 14.7 psia?

6.5 Repeat Problem 6.4 if the final state was saturated steam at 400 psia.

6.6 Steam at 80 psia and a quality of 92 per cent occupies a rigid vessel of volume 10 ft³. Calculate the mass, internal energy, enthalpy, and entropy of the steam.

6.7 A rigid vessel of volume 2.2 ft³ contains 1 lbm of wet steam. What are the pressure and entropy of the steam if the temperature is 500°F?

6.8 A tank of 10 cu ft capacity is filled with steam at 300 psia and 480°F. The tank and contents are then cooled with negligible change in volume to 250°F.
(a) What will be the final amounts of vapor and water (in lbm), and what is the corresponding quality of the mixture?
(b) How much energy as heat was transferred during this process?

6.9 One lbm of steam at a quality of 40 per cent and a pressure of 200 psia is heated at a constant pressure to a temperature of 500°F. Neglecting changes in kinetic and potential energies, calculate the heat interaction, the work interaction, and the change of entropy.

6.10 One lbm water is heated at constant pressure from 60°F to 340°F ($c_p = 1$ Btu/lbm°F).
(a) Determine the quantity of heat supplied.
(b) Determine the amount of heat supplied that is unavailable for doing work based upon a receiver temperature of 10°F.
(c) Show the process on a T-S diagram and indicate the various quantities of heat designated.

6.11 Verify the value of the enthalpy of vaporization of water at 240°F as tabulated in the steam tables against the value computed according to Clapeyron's equation.

6.12 A steam main closed at both ends has an internal volume of 43.22 cu ft which is filled with dry saturated steam at 280°F.
(a) How much heat must be transferred from the steam to reduce the quality to 0.5?
(b) What will be the pressure in the main when the quality is 0.5?
(c) Show the process and end points on p-V and H-S plots.

6.13 Water at 200°F and atmospheric pressure enters a pump where it is compressed to 500 psia with no appreciable temperature increase and is then delivered to a boiler. It is evaporated and delivered to a steam main at 480 psia and 520°F. Calculate
(a) The work interaction per lbm of fluid during the pumping process
(b) The heat interaction per lbm of fluid.
Sketch the process on an H-S and on a T-S diagram.

6.14 One lbm of steam is confined in a piston-cylinder arrangement at 150 psia and 98 per cent quality. The piston is permitted to move in such a way that when the contained volume is six times as great as the initial volume, the pressure has dropped to 15 psia. At the same time, the heat transfer amounts to —4.50 Btu. Calculate the work interaction during the process.

6.15 An evacuated chamber is connected through a valve with a very large tank containing steam at 60 psia and 400°F. The valve is opened, and steam flows into the chamber until the pressure within the chamber is 50 psia. At the same time, heat is transferred from the chamber at the rate of 300 Btu per lbm of steam introduced. Determine the temperature and the quality of the steam in the chamber when the flow stops.

6.16 Using water as the fluid, it is proposed to compress a liquid-vapor mixture, initially at 20 psia and 90 per cent quality, to a final pressure of 300 psia, using a reversible adiabatic process.
(a) Show this process schematically on a *T-S* diagram.
(b) If this process is carried out in a piston-cylinder device having an initial total volume of 0.35 ft³, determine the work required.
(c) What will be the work interaction if the process is carried out under steady flow conditions?

6.17 Saturated water vapor at 100 psia and saturated water at 100 psia are delivered from separate lines (through throttling valves) to a 5-ft³ tank which is initially evacuated. It is desired to obtain, as a final condition in the tank, saturated vapor at a pressure of 50 psia. Calculate the mass of water and the mass of steam to be admitted from the separate lines. (Assume the tank is insulated and that the velocity terms are negligible.)

6.18 One lbm of saturated steam at 180 psia undergoes an irreversible steady flow, adiabatic process to 150°F, and 92 per cent quality. If there is no change in kinetic energy, find (a) the change of entropy; (b) the work interaction; (c) the increase in unavailable energy (considering the receiver temperature to be 150°F).

6.19 A throttle valve reduces the pressure of steam as it flows through a pipeline from 150 psia to 50 psia. The superheat is 10 degrees upstream of the throttle valve and the velocity is low. Some distance after the throttle valve, the steam fills the pipe and proceeds at negligible velocity. Find the temperature and the degree of superheat of the steam downstream of the valve. (Assume negligible heat loss from the pipe.) Show the process on *H-S* and *T-S* diagrams.

6.20 A sampling tube and a throttling calorimeter are installed in order to find the enthalpy of steam flowing in a steam main. The steam in the main is at 415°F, and after passing through the calorimeter is at 4 in. Hg gauge pressure and 280°F. The barometric reading is 30 in. Hg abs. Find (a) the enthalpy of steam in the main; (b) the specific volume of steam in the main.

6.21 Steam at 500 psia and 600°F enters an ideal nozzle with negligible initial velocity. It expands adiabatically and with negligible friction to 100 psia. Compute by use of steam tables (a) the pressure and temperature at which the steam will become (dry) saturated; (b) all terminal properties, including the velocity of the departing jet. Show the process on a *T-S* diagram.

6.22 Air undergoes a steady flow, reversible adiabatic process. The initial conditions are 100 psia and 800°F, and the final pressure is 20 psia. Assume that changes in kinetic and potential energies are negligible. Making use of gas tables, calculate
(a) The final temperature
(b) The final specific volume
(c) The change in internal energy per lbm
(d) The change in enthalpy per lbm
(e) The work interaction per lbm.

6.23 An axial-flow compressor operates adiabatically but with an isentropic efficiency of 78 per cent. The fluid is air entering at 70°F and 15 psia, and discharging at 75 psia. Making use of gas tables, find
(a) The enthalpy change enroute through the compressor
(b) The temperature of the leaving air
(c) The power required per 1000 cu ft of air per minute at entering conditions
(d) The rate of delivery at exit conditions.
(Assume kinetic and potential energy changes to be negligible.)

6.24 Noting that $(\partial p/\partial v)_T = (\partial^2 p/\partial v^2)_T = 0$ at the critical point, show that the constants in the Dieterici equation are

$$a = \frac{4\mathscr{R}^2 T_c^2}{e^2 p_c} \quad \text{and} \quad b = \frac{\mathscr{R} T_c}{e^2 p_c}.$$

Find an expression for the isothermal compressibility.

6.25 Repeat Problem 6.24 for the Berthelot equation and find the constants a and b of that equation.

6.26 The equation of state for a particular vapor is given by the following relationship:

$$p(v - C) = RT + \frac{A}{T},$$

where C and A are constants, and R is the gas constant. Find the coefficient of volumetric expansion in terms of R, C, A, T, and p.

6.27 Calculate the specific volume of oxygen at a pressure of 20 atm and a temperature of 130°K. Compare the result with that obtained by the perfect gas law. The critical temperature and pressure of oxygen are $T_c = 154.78$°K and $p_c = 50.1$ atm.

6.28 A spherical tank 1 ft in diameter contains nitrogen initially at a pressure of 3000 psia and a temperature of −100°F. The heat interaction with the environment is 5 Btu/sec. Find the time elapsed till the temperature reaches 0°F. What is the final pressure?

6.29 Using the compressibility chart calculate
(a) The density of nitrogen at 4000 psia and 60°F.
(b) The temperature of 3 lbm of CO_2 gas in a container of volume 1 ft³ at a pressure of 3000 psia.

6.30 Prove that

$$(Z - Z_0)_p = -\frac{p}{R} \int_{T_o}^{T} \left(\frac{\mu_T}{T^2}\right)_p dT,$$

where Z_o is the compressibility factor at a pressure p and temperature T_o.

6.31 One lbm of ethane gas in a piston-cylinder is compressed isothermally from initial conditions of 100 psia and 100°F to a final pressure of 1200 psia. What is the Δh, Δu, and Δs for the process, considering ethane to be a nonideal gas. ($T_c = 549.8°R$, $p_c = 708$ psia.)

6.32 CO_2 enters a compressor at 115°F and 20 psia, at the rate of 100 lbm/min, and is compressed reversibly and isothermally to 2000 psia. Velocities are negligible. For CO_2, T_c is 547.7°R and p_c is 1072 psia.
(a) Find the change in entropy and the change in enthalpy between the inlet and outlet of the compressor, using the generalized residual charts.
(b) Find the heat interaction and the work interaction for the process per lbm of CO_2.
(c) Calculate the volumetric flow rate of CO_2 leaving the compressor.

NOMENCLATURE

A	Area	v_{avg}	Average speed
C	Number of molecules striking an area	v_{mp}	Most probable speed
$f(v)$	Speed distribution function	v_{rms}	Root mean square speed
h	Planck's constant	W	Thermodynamic probability
k	Boltzmann's constant	x, y, z	Cartesian coordinates or functions
M	Molecular weight	Z	Collision frequency between molecules
m	Molecular mass		
N	Number of molecules	α	Constant
N_0	Avogadro's number	$\beta =$	$\sqrt{\lambda/2}$
n	Number of molecules per unit volume	ϕ	Function
P	Collision probability	Γ	Gamma function
p	Pressure	λ	Lagrange's multiplier
R	Gas constant	ϵ	Internal energy per molecule
r	Radius	Λ	Molecular free path
$\mathscr{R}$	Universal gas constant	ω	Solid angle
S	Entropy	ρ	Density
T	Absolute temperature	σ	Collision cross section
U	Internal energy	τ	Time
V	Volume	θ, ϕ	Angles
$\vec{v}$	Velocity	$\sum_i$	Summation over indices i

7

KINETIC THEORY
OF GASES

7-1
Introduction
From a microscopic point of view, matter is not continuous but consists, rather, of discrete invisible particles. Although this concept was hypothesized by the ancient philosophers, it was only at the beginning of the nineteenth century that this hypothesis acquired a scientific form and served as the basis on which the atomic theory was built. The kinetic theory of gases attempts to explain the macroscopic properties of a gas in terms of the motion of its molecules. Kinetic theory is applicable to all matter, but it has been applied more extensively, so far, to gases than to solids or liquids.

The kinetic theory of gases was developed in the middle of the nineteenth century when the dynamic theory of heat was beginning to receive acceptance. The historical development of both theories reflects the struggle of primary hypotheses against established mathematical theories. In his book, *Hydrodynamics* (1738), Daniel Bernoulli presented an account of the kinetic theory of gases, but his work passed unnoticed and had, at the time, little or no influence on investigation in this area. Scientists during that period favored the static theory of gases, in which atoms are considered to repel each other, thus exerting pressure on the walls of the confining vessel. Over a century later, in 1859, Bernoulli's theory was revived, and the kinetic theory developed rapidly, mainly because of the work of Maxwell, Clausius, and Boltzmann. Planck, in 1901, formulated the quantum theory which helped to explain certain aspects of kinetic theory. According to quantum theory, the energy (and momentum) of very small particles, such as molecules and electrons, is subject to quantum restrictions so that the particles can have only certain discrete values of energy.

Kinetic theory states that the movement of the molecules of a gas is extremely complex, and it is pointless to describe in detail the motion of each of the molecules. Through statistical methods it is possible to describe the motion of numerous molecules in terms of the average motion of these molecules in space and/or time. Molecular motion is studied because it is closely associated with the macroscopic characteristics of a gas, such as pressure and temperature. The applications of statistical techniques to relate the behavior of individual molecules to the observable behavior of material systems is called *statistical thermodynamics.*

Kinetic theory is considered one of the great developments of theoretical physics because of the simplicity of its concepts and the wide application of its results.

7-2
Perfect Gas
Model
The main assumption of the kinetic theory of gases lies in its definition of the gaseous state. The gas of a single-component substance is assumed to consist of a large number of identical, discrete particles called *molecules,* a molecule being the smallest unit with the chemical properties

of the substance. The number of molecules is extremely large. For example, in 1 cu cm of a gas at standard conditions (273°K and standard atmospheric pressure) there are 2.69×10^{19} molecules; at a pressure of 10^{-10} atm, 1 cu mm contains 2.69 million molecules.

The volume occupied by the molecules is negligibly small compared to the total volume of the gas. At atmospheric temperature and pressure, for example, the molecules occupy one thousandth of the volume of the gas. The distance between molecules is therefore much larger than the molecules themselves, so that on a molecular scale a gas is neither continuous nor homogeneous. Matter appears to be continuous on a macroscopic scale because of the large number of molecules in a small volume and because properties of matter are continuously subjected to an averaging effect owing to the contributions of the numerous molecules. The molecules are constantly in random motion and may be visualized as point masses, or small elastic spheres that move in straight lines until they collide with each other or with the walls of the confining vessel. Kinetic theory postulates that the molecules exert no force on each other except when they collide. The collisions are assumed perfectly elastic, and each collision changes both the magnitude and the direction of movement of the two colliding molecules. The relative velocities of the molecules of a gas vary from small values at the instant of collision to very large values. No attractive forces are considered to be exerted by the molecules, whereas repulsive forces are assumed to act only during collision contact.

Experimental proof that molecules are in continuous motion was given when Brownian motion was discovered in liquids by Robert Brown in 1827 and in gases by De Broglie in 1908. Microscopic observations reveal that macroscopic masses (large by molecular standards) are in continuous and irregular motion due to the collisions between molecules.

Kinetic theory assumed that motion of molecules was governed by the classical laws of mechanics. It was found later that this assumption is invalid for molecular-scale systems. When the quantum theory was developed, it became possible to explain the detailed motion of microscopic particles.

Although the position and velocity of molecules constantly change because of the large number of molecules, the number of molecules per unit volume of the gas remains essentially constant. Similarly, motion of the molecules occurs uniformly in all directions, so that all magnitudes and directions of molecular velocities are equally probable. By statistical laws, the number of molecules having a velocity between any two limits can be predicted with a known accuracy. It is thus seen that the concept of mechanical equilibrium of a gas is replaced by the concept of *statistical equilibrium* based on use of statistical laws. Properties evaluated by means of statistical equilibrium represent average properties; properties measured experimentally on a macroscopic scale are also average properties.

7-3
Analogy
Between
Kinetic Theory
and Thermo-
dynamics

The relationship between kinetic theory and thermodynamics arises from the molecular velocity distribution of a gas at the equilibrium state. The law governing the velocity distribution will be derived later in this chapter. This section discusses some preliminary kinetic interpretations of energy and thermodynamic properties.

Each molecule of mass m travels at a velocity $\vec{v}$ and possesses a kinetic energy $mv^2/2$. The internal energy of translation of the gas is equal to the sum of the translational kinetic energy of its individual molecules, or

$$U = \sum_{i=1}^{N} \frac{m_i v_i^2}{2}$$

$$= Nm\frac{v_{\mathrm{rms}}^2}{2} \quad \text{(for identical molecules)}, \tag{7.1}$$

where v_{rms} is the root mean square speed, $mv_{\mathrm{rms}}^2/2$ is the average kinetic energy of a single molecule, and N is the number of molecules.

The root mean square speed of molecules of a perfect gas is related to pressure. This was shown in Chapter 1 with a derivation based on the laws of mechanics. Pressure was interpreted as the momentum transmitted by the molecules to a unit surface area in a unit time. The expression was given by Eq. (1.24) as

$$pV = \tfrac{1}{3}Nm\,v_{\mathrm{rms}}^2. \tag{7.2}$$

From Eq. (7.2), and the perfect gas law relationship, the root mean square speed is obtained

$$v_{\mathrm{rms}} = \sqrt{\frac{3pV}{Nm}} = \sqrt{\frac{3\mathscr{R}T}{M}} = \sqrt{\frac{3kT}{m}}. \tag{7.3}$$

Note that v_{rms} is proportional to the square root of the absolute temperature of the gas and is inversely proportional to the square root of the molecular weight. Equation (7.3) serves also as a definition of absolute temperature in terms of average microscopic properties; for it is a measure of the average translational kinetic energy of the molecules:

$$T = \frac{m}{3k} v_{\mathrm{rms}}^2.$$

It was shown in Chapter 6 that the average kinetic energy of a perfect gas is independent of pressure, depending only on the temperature of the gas. The average kinetic energy of translation of molecules of different gases at a given temperature is the same for all the gases irrespective of molecular mass as expressed by

$$KE_{avg} = \frac{mv_{rms}^2}{2} = \frac{3}{2}\frac{\mathcal{R}}{N_0}T = \frac{3}{2}kT. \tag{7.4}$$

This result, when generalized, will be shown later to lead to the *principle of equipartition of energy.*

When heat is transferred to a gas at constant volume, the kinetic energy of its molecules is increased and the temperature rises in accordance with Eq. (7.4). Conversely, if heat is transferred from the gas, the temperature decreases because the kinetic energy of the molecules is diminished. When two gases at different temperatures (different average kinetic energies) come in contact, the collisions between their molecules tend to equalize their momenta. When thermal equilibrium is attained, the molecules of both gases have the same average kinetic energy. According to the first law, the decrease in kinetic energy of the molecules of the hot gas is equal to the increase in kinetic energy of the molecules of the cold gas. A similar situation occurs when heat is transferred between two gases separated by a heat-conducting wall. The molecules on the hot side, when colliding with the wall, impart some of their kinetic energy to the wall, molecules of the wall in turn transmit this energy to molecules of the cold gas. The process continues until the average kinetic energies of the molecules on both sides are equal.

Energy interaction as just described excludes heat as a distinct form of energy. It may be considered as a form of microscopic work which eventually appears as kinetic energy. This form of kinetic energy must, however, be distinguished from macroscopic mechanical kinetic energy in the sense that it is *disordered* kinetic energy exhibited by the agitation of the molecules in all directions and at different speeds.

Consider now the adiabatic compression of a gas in an insulated piston-cylinder arrangement. As the piston does work on the gas it imparts additional kinetic energy to the molecules that collide with its face. This additional energy is subsequently transmitted and distributed by molecular collisions to the other molecules, resulting in an increase in the average kinetic energy of the molecules. The increase in temperature of the gas due to compression is thus a consequence of the increase in the average kinetic energy of the molecules. The temperature of the piston and cylinder walls also increases as a result of the collisions between the molecules of the gas and the atoms of the piston and cylinder walls. Work done on a gas is therefore accomplished by doing work on the molecules and may be interpreted as an increase in the kinetic energy of the molecules in a *predetermined* or a fixed direction. When work is converted to heat, molecular motion in a certain direction is transferred into motion in an entirely disordered pattern. The reverse process, of re-coordination of molecular collisions, can also be accomplished, but some loss of efficiency occurs, as described by the second law.

EXAMPLE 7.1: Calculate the root mean square speed of oxygen and hydrogen molecules at 70°C. What is the kinetic energy per molecule?

Solution: Assume O_2 and H_2 may be treated as perfect gases, then

$$(v_{rms})_{O_2} = \sqrt{\frac{3\mathscr{R}T}{M}} = \sqrt{\frac{3(8.314 \times 10^7 \text{ erg/gm-mole }°\text{K})(343.15°\text{K})}{32.0 \text{ gm/gm-mole}}}$$

$$= 51,600 \text{ cm/sec} = 516 \text{ m/sec}$$

and

$$(v_{rms})_{H_2} = \sqrt{\frac{3(8.314 \times 10^7 \text{ erg/gm-mole }°\text{K})(343.15°\text{K})}{2.0160 \text{ gm/gm-mole}}}$$

$$= 206,000 \text{ cm/sec} = 2060 \text{ m/sec}.$$

From Eq. (7.4), the kinetic energy of either molecule is

$$KE = \tfrac{3}{2} kT = \tfrac{3}{2}(1.38 \times 10^{-23} \text{ joule/}°\text{K})(343.15°\text{K})$$

$$= 7.09 \times 10^{-21} \text{ joule}.$$

**7-4
Distribution
of Trans-
lational
Velocities**   The rms velocity of the molecules of a gas has been shown to be related to the temperature of the gas; it is now to be shown that the rms velocity is a useful parameter. If all particles at the same temperature are moving at the same speed, then the rms value describes the velocity magnitude of all particles perfectly. But if their speeds differ significantly, then the rms value provides only limited information, and the problem of determining the velocity of all the particles still exists. It then becomes necessary to determine velocity distribution, so that the number of particles moving with any particular velocity can be determined. In practice, such statistical details do not lend themselves to direct use in subsequent calculations; excessive data in this case are not much more useful than meager data. When, however, the expression for velocity distribution is known, it is possible to derive various velocity parameters which can be used.

In determining the velocity distribution, a model is first established which is based on *velocity space*. Consider a volume of gas at constant temperature whose particles are moving at different velocities. The instantaneous velocity vector of each molecule can be resolved into components v_x, v_y, and v_z. If the three velocity directions serve as axes, the velocity of each molecule may be represented as a vector originating at the origin. The surface of a sphere centered at the origin therefore represents, at some instant of time, all particles of identical speed. Furthermore, all particles of identical speed are assumed to be uniformly distributed since large numbers of particles are involved. Finally, the number of particles in each concentric shell is assumed to bear a simple relationship to the velocity.

Consider an infinitesimal volume $dv_x\, dv_y\, dv_z$ in the velocity space shown in Fig. 7.1. Let this volume lie within a thin spherical shell of inner and

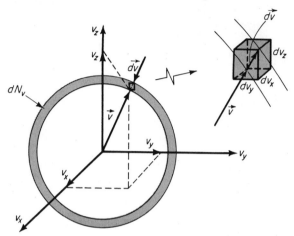

Fig. 7.1.   *Velocity density in a thin spherical shell is constant.*

outer radii v and $v + dv$. If N is the total number of molecules of the gas, the spherical shell contains dN_v points, each moving at a velocity between v and $v + dv$ in magnitude. Assume that the number of points in the volume $dv_x\, dv_y\, dv_z$ is large, so that the volume is of uniform density. Note that the velocity components in the v_x, v_y, and v_z directions of the points in the volume $dv_x\, dv_y\, dv_z$ lie between v_x and $v_x + dv_x$, v_y and $v_y + dv_y$, and v_z and $v_z + dv_z$. Consider a narrow zone bounded by two infinite planes parallel to the v_y-v_z plane at a distance v_x from it and dv_x apart. As shown in Fig. 7.2(a) the molecules whose velocity vectors terminate between the planes v_x and $v_x + dv_x$ all have their x component of velocity lying between v_x and $v_x + dv_x$. If dN_{v_x} represents the number of these points, then the fraction dN_{v_x}/N depends on both the distance dv_x between the planes and the location of the planes. Since the location of the planes is a function of v_x, this may be expressed mathematically as

$$\frac{dN_{v_x}}{N} = f(v_x)\, dv_x, \tag{7.5a}$$

where $f(v_x)$ is a function of v_x, and is called the *distribution function* for the x component of velocity. The product $f(v_x)\, dv_x$ represents the fraction of molecules with velocities in the x direction between v_x and $v_x + dv_x$. The

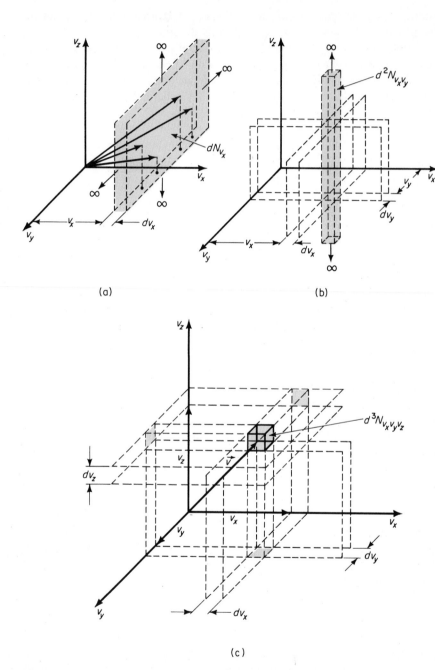

(a)

(b)

(c)

Fig. 7.2.   *Velocity space diagram.*

term $f(v_x)\, dv_x$ also expresses the probability that a molecule chosen at random will have an x component of velocity lying between v_x and $v_x + dv_x$.

The same procedure may be applied to the v_y and v_z directions. Since all directions are equally probable, the fraction of molecules having components between v_y and $v_y + dv_y$ and between v_z and $v_z + dv_z$ can be described as

$$\frac{dN_{v_y}}{N} = f(v_y)\, dv_y, \tag{7.5b}$$

and

$$\frac{dN_{v_z}}{N} = f(v_z)\, dv_z. \tag{7.5c}$$

The foregoing equations imply that the distribution of each component of velocity is independent of the other two.

All the molecules represented by dN_{v_x} have velocities whose v_x components lie between v_x and $v_x + dv_x$; however, only a fraction of these points have velocities whose v_y components lie between v_y and $v_y + dv_y$. If this fraction is denoted by $d^2N_{v_x v_y}/dN_{v_x}$ then $d^2N_{v_x v_y}$ denotes the number of molecules whose components of velocities in the v_x and v_y directions lie between v_x and $v_x + dv_x$ and between v_y and $v_y + dv_y$. (The superscript 2 indicates that it is a second-order term.) As shown in Fig. 7.2(b), $d^2N_{v_x v_y}$ is equal to the number of points in the vertical cylinder of cross section $dv_x\, dv_y$ extending between $v_z = \pm\infty$.

Since a gas has a large number of molecules and since there is no preference for any particular direction, the fractions $dN_{v_x}/N, dN_{v_y}/N, \ldots$ (and also second-order fractions) can be expected to be the same throughout the entire volume of the gas. Therefore any small volume of gas contains a representative sample of the velocities of the molecules for the entire volume of the gas. Consequently, the following equality can be expressed:

$$\frac{d^2N_{v_x v_y}}{dN_{v_x}} = \frac{dN_{v_y}}{N}.$$

Combining this equation with Eq. (7.5b) gives

$$d^2N_{v_x v_y} = dN_{v_x} f(v_y)\, dv_y.$$

But

$$dN_{v_x} = Nf(v_x)\, dv_x,$$

so that

$$d^2N_{v_x v_y} = Nf(v_x)f(v_y)\, dv_x\, dv_y. \tag{7.6}$$

The foregoing procedure may be extended to the v_z direction. If $d^3N_{v_x v_y v_z}$ denotes the number of molecules which have velocity components lying between v_x and $v_x + dv_x$, v_y and $v_y + dv_y$, and v_z and $v_z + dv_z$, then

$$d^3 N_{v_x v_y v_z} = Nf(v_x)f(v_y)f(v_z) \, dv_x \, dv_y \, dv_z. \tag{7.7}$$

These points appear in the parallelepiped of volume $dv_x \, dv_y \, dv_z$ of Fig. 7.2(c). The density of these velocity points is equal to the number of points divided by the volume, or

$$\rho(v_x, v_y, v_z) = \frac{d^3 N_{v_x v_y v_z}}{dv_x \, dv_y \, dv_z} = Nf(v_x)f(v_y)f(v_z). \tag{7.8}$$

Since density in the volume $dv_x \, dv_y \, dv_z$ is a continuous function, the differential of density can be written as

$$d\rho = \left(\frac{\partial \rho}{\partial v_x}\right) dv_x + \left(\frac{\partial \rho}{\partial v_y}\right) dv_y + \left(\frac{\partial \rho}{\partial v_z}\right) dv_z.$$

But the density in the volume $dv_x \, dv_y \, dv_z$ is uniform, so that $d\rho = 0$ irrespective of the location of the volume $dv_x \, dv_y \, dv_z$ within the shell. Therefore, when Eq. (7.8) is differentiated with respect to the direction variables, the following results:

$$d\rho = 0 = Nf'(v_x)f(v_y)f(v_z) \, dv_x + Nf'(v_y)f(v_x)f(v_z) \, dv_y$$
$$+ \, Nf'(v_z)f(v_x)f(v_y) \, dv_z,$$

where the primes denote differentiation with respect to the argument. This equation reduces to

$$\frac{f'(v_x)}{f(v_x)} dv_x + \frac{f'(v_y)}{f(v_y)} dv_y + \frac{f'(v_z)}{f(v_z)} dv_z = 0. \tag{7.9}$$

Since all the points in the volume $dv_x \, dv_y \, dv_z$ lie within the spherical shell, the magnitude of the velocity vector v is a constant. This constraint can be expressed as

$$v^2 = v_x^2 + v_y^2 + v_z^2 = \text{constant}.$$

Differentiation of the preceding equation gives

$$v_x \, dv_x + v_y \, dv_y + v_z \, dv_z = 0. \tag{7.10}$$

To solve Eq. (7.9) subject to the constraint of Eq. (7.10), *Lagrange's method of undetermined multipliers*, which is outlined in the appendix of this chapter, is applied. Note that there are three unknowns v_x, v_y, and v_z but only two equations. By multiplying Eq. (7.10) by λ and adding the result to Eq. (7.9), the following is obtained

$$\left(\frac{f'(v_x)}{f(v_x)} + \lambda v_x\right) dv_x + \left(\frac{f'(v_y)}{f(v_y)} + \lambda v_y\right) dv_y + \left(\frac{f'(v_z)}{f(v_z)} + \lambda v_z\right) dv_z = 0,$$

where λ is called *Lagrange's undetermined multiplier*.

Since the components of velocity v_x, v_y, and v_z may be considered independent variables, the coefficients of dv_x, dv_y, and dv_z can be individually equated to zero. Therefore,

$$\frac{f'(v_x)}{f(v_x)} + \lambda v_x = 0,$$

$$\frac{f'(v_y)}{f(v_y)} + \lambda v_y = 0,$$

$$\frac{f'(v_z)}{f(v_z)} + \lambda v_z = 0.$$

Integration yields

$$f(v_x) = \alpha e^{-\lambda v_x^2/2},$$

$$f(v_y) = \alpha e^{-\lambda v_y^2/2},$$

and

$$f(v_z) = \alpha e^{-\lambda v_z^2/2},$$

where α is a constant of integration. Note that symmetry indicates that the three foregoing equations have the same integration constant. Although only two equations were available to start with, the proper value of the constant λ makes v_x, v_y, and v_z independent of each other so that four equations rather than only two become available. When the preceding values of $f(v_x)$, $f(v_y)$, and $f(v_z)$ are substituted into Eq. (7.8), the density of velocity points becomes

$$\rho(v) = N\alpha^3 e^{(-\lambda/2)(v_x^2 + v_y^2 + v_z^2)} = N\alpha^3 e^{(-\lambda/2)(v^2)}.$$

Denoting $\lambda/2$ by β^2, then

$$\rho(v) = N\alpha^3 e^{-\beta^2 v^2}. \tag{7.11}$$

Equation (7.11) is the *Maxwell velocity distribution function* Note that density is a function of the magnitude, but not the direction, of the velocity. This is in accordance with the assumption that the gas is isotropic.

7-5
The Functions
α and β

Before Eq. (7.11) can be used, the nature of the two constants that appear in it, α and β, must be established. The total number of molecules is described by

$$N = \int_{v=0}^{\infty} dN_v = \int_0^{\infty} 4\pi v^2 \rho \, dv,$$

where dN_v is the number of molecules in a spherical shell of radius v and thickness dv in velocity space. Using Eq. (7.11), then

$$N = \int_0^{\infty} dN_v = 4\pi N \alpha^3 \int_0^{\infty} v^2 e^{-\beta^2 v^2} \, dv. \qquad (7.12)$$

To integrate the preceding expression, first let $x = \beta^2 v^2$, then

$$\int_0^{\infty} v^2 e^{-\beta^2 v^2} \, dv = \int_0^{\infty} \left(\frac{x}{\beta^2}\right) e^{-x} \frac{dx}{2x^{1/2}\beta}$$

$$= \frac{1}{2\beta^3} \int_0^{\infty} x^{(3/2)-1} e^{-x} \, dx = \frac{1}{2\beta^3} \Gamma\left(\frac{3}{2}\right) = \frac{1}{2\beta^3} \frac{\sqrt{\pi}}{2},$$

where $\Gamma(n) = \int_0^{\infty} x^{n-1} e^{-x} \, dx$ $(n > 0)$, is called the *gamma function*. Values of the gamma function are tabulated in Table 7.1. The expression for N, then becomes

$$N = \left(\frac{2\pi N \alpha^3}{\beta^3}\right)\left(\frac{\sqrt{\pi}}{2}\right) = \pi^{3/2} N \left(\frac{\alpha}{\beta}\right)^3,$$

from which

$$\alpha = \frac{\beta}{\sqrt{\pi}}. \qquad (7.13)$$

TABLE 7.1

$$\Gamma^*(n) = \int_0^{\infty} x^{n-1} e^{-x} \, dx \qquad (n > 0)$$

n	$\Gamma(n)$	n	$\Gamma(n)$
$\frac{1}{2}$	$\sqrt{\pi}$	3	2
1	1	$\frac{7}{2}$	$\frac{15}{8}\sqrt{\pi}$
$\frac{3}{2}$	$\frac{\sqrt{\pi}}{2}$	4	6
2	1	$\frac{9}{2}$	$\frac{105}{16}\sqrt{\pi}$
$\frac{5}{2}$	$\frac{3}{4}\sqrt{\pi}$	5	24

*It may be shown that $\Gamma(n+1) = n\Gamma(n)$.

The function β still remains to be determined. The translational kinetic energy of the molecules of a gas is described by

$$U = \int_0^\infty \tfrac{1}{2} m v^2 \, dN_v.$$

But from Eq. (7.12) and (7.13)

$$dN_v = \frac{4}{\sqrt{\pi}} v^2 N \beta^3 e^{-\beta^2 v^2} \, dv.$$

Therefore,

$$U = \int_0^\infty \frac{1}{2} m v^2 \frac{4}{\sqrt{\pi}} v^2 N \beta^3 e^{-\beta^2 v^2} \, dv = \frac{2mN\beta^3}{\sqrt{\pi}} \int_0^\infty v^4 e^{-\beta^2 v^2} \, dv.$$

Again letting $x = \beta^2 v^2$ gives

$$U = \frac{2mN\beta^3}{\sqrt{\pi}} \int_0^\infty \left(\frac{x}{\beta^2}\right)^2 e^{-x} \frac{dx}{2\beta^2 (x^{1/2}/\beta)}$$

$$= \frac{mN}{\sqrt{\pi} \, \beta^2} \int_0^\infty x^{(5/2)-1} e^{-x} \, dx$$

$$= \left(\frac{mN}{\sqrt{\pi} \, \beta^2}\right) \Gamma\left(\frac{5}{2}\right) = \frac{3mN}{4\beta^2}.$$

But the total translational energy U according to Eq. (7.4) is

$$U = \tfrac{3}{2} N k T.$$

Equating the two previous equations gives the function β as

$$\beta = \sqrt{\frac{m}{2kT}}. \tag{7.14}$$

From Eq. (7.13) the value of α is therefore

$$\alpha = \sqrt{\frac{m}{2\pi kT}}. \tag{7.15}$$

Substituting the foregoing values of α and β into Eq. (7.12) gives

$$\frac{dN_v}{dv} = \frac{4N}{\sqrt{\pi}} \left(\frac{m}{2kT}\right)^{3/2} v^2 e^{-(m/2kT)v^2}. \tag{7.16}$$

The function dN_v/dv is called the Maxwell-Boltzmann *speed distribution function*. It represents the number of molecules having a speed v per unit

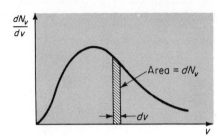

Fig. 7.3. *Maxwell-Boltzmann speed distribution.*

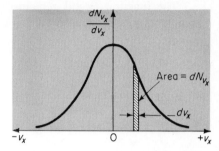

Fig. 7.4. *Maxwell-Boltzmann distribution for one component of velocity.*

range of speed. A plot of dN_v/dv versus v is shown in Fig. 7.3. An area dv-wide underneath the curve represents the number dN_v, that is, the number of molecules having speeds between v and $v + dv$.

The speed distribution function for each of the three velocity components may now be indicated. In the x direction, for example, Eq. (7.5a) gives

$$\frac{dN_{v_x}}{dv_x} = Nf(v_x) = \frac{N}{\sqrt{\pi}}\left(\frac{m}{2kT}\right)^{1/2} e^{-(m/2kT)v_x^2}. \tag{7.17}$$

A plot of dN_{v_x}/dv_x versus v_x is presented in Fig. 7.4. The curve is symmetric about the zero-speed axis and has a maximum value of $N(m/2\pi kT)^{1/2}$ at $v_x = 0$. The Maxwell-Boltzmann speed distribution according to Eq. (7.16) may be written in the form

$$\frac{dN_v}{N} = f(v)\,dv = \frac{4}{\sqrt{\pi}}\left(\frac{m}{2kT}\right)^{3/2} v^2 e^{-mv^2/2kT}\,dv. \tag{7.18}$$

Figure 7.5 shows a plot of the Maxwell-Boltzmann speed distribution law.

An expression for the Maxwell-Boltzmann distribution law for the different energies of the molecules is obtained as follows: In a coordinate space diagram let the number of molecules having energies between ϵ and $\epsilon + d\epsilon$ be dN_ϵ. The kinetic energy of a molecule is

$$\epsilon = \tfrac{1}{2}mv^2,$$

and

$$d\epsilon = mv\,dv = m\sqrt{\frac{2\epsilon}{m}}\,dv = \sqrt{2m\epsilon}\,dv,$$

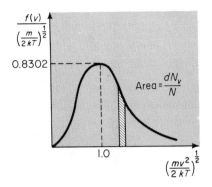

Fig. 7.5. *Maxwell-Boltzmann speed distribution.*

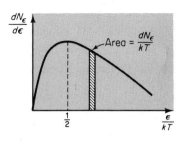

Fig. 7.6. *Maxwell energy distribution.*

or

$$dv = \frac{d\epsilon}{\sqrt{2m\epsilon}}.$$

Substituting for dv from the preceding equation into Eq. (7.16) gives

$$dN_\epsilon = \frac{4N}{\sqrt{\pi}} \left(\frac{m}{2kT}\right)^{3/2} \frac{2\epsilon}{m} e^{-\epsilon/kT} \frac{d\epsilon}{\sqrt{2m\epsilon}}$$

or

$$\frac{dN_\epsilon}{d\epsilon} = \frac{2N}{\sqrt{\pi}} \frac{\epsilon^{1/2}}{(kT)^{3/2}} e^{-\epsilon/kT}. \tag{7.19}$$

A plot of $dN_\epsilon/d\epsilon$ versus ϵ/kT is shown in Fig. 7.6. The maximum value of $dN_\epsilon/d\epsilon$ corresponds to ϵ equal to $kT/2$.

7-6
The Distribu-
tion Function

The speed distribution function $f(v)$ when multiplied by dv represents the fraction of the molecules with speeds in the interval between v and $v + dv$. Since the number of molecules in that interval is $Nf(v)\,dv$, the function $f(v)$ can be considered as a statistical proportionality factor, so that the following equation is satisfied

$$\int_0^\infty f(v)\,dv = 1. \tag{7.20}$$

The function f at any instant in time depends on the location of the molecules as well as on their velocities, so that

$$f(v) = \phi(x, y, z, v_x, v_y, v_z, \tau). \tag{7.21}$$

When the gas is in statistical equilibrium, the position of the molecules is completely random, and the distribution function can be considered to depend only on v_x, v_y, and v_z; that is,

$$f(v) = \phi(v_x, v_y, v_z). \tag{7.22}$$

The previous section outlined the importance of the velocity distribution function as a useful parameter in describing the velocities of the molecules of a gas. The concept of the distribution function may be extended to describe the distributions in other properties, such as density, energy, and square of speeds.

The distribution function can now be used in establishing three characteristic molecular speeds: the average speed, the root mean square speed, and the most probable speed.

The *average speed* is defined as the sum of the speeds of all molecules divided by the number of molecules. If x is any function of molecular speed, the average value of x is given by the equation

$$x_{avg} = \int_0^\infty x f(v) \, dv. \tag{7.23}$$

Thus,

$$v_{avg} = \frac{1}{N} \int_0^\infty v \, dN_v = \int_0^\infty v f(v) \, dv.$$

Substituting for $f(v)$ from Eq. (7.18) gives

$$v_{avg} = \int_0^\infty \frac{4}{\sqrt{\pi}} \left(\frac{m}{2kT}\right)^{3/2} v^3 e^{-(m/2kT)v^2} \, dv$$

$$= \frac{4}{\sqrt{\pi}} \left(\frac{m}{2kT}\right)^{3/2} \int_0^\infty v^3 e^{-(m/2kT)v^2} \, dv.$$

Let

$$x = \frac{m}{2kT} v^2$$

$$dx = \frac{m}{kT} v \, dv = \sqrt{\frac{2m}{kT}} x^{1/2} \, dv.$$

Substituting for v and dv, the expression for v_{avg} becomes

$$v_{avg} = \sqrt{\frac{2}{\pi}} \left(\frac{m}{kT}\right)^{3/2} \int_0^\infty \left(\frac{2xkT}{m}\right)^{3/2} e^{-x} \sqrt{\frac{kT}{2m}} \frac{1}{x^{1/2}} \, dx$$

$$= 2\sqrt{\frac{2kT}{\pi m}} \int_0^\infty x^{2-1} e^{-x} \, dx = 2\sqrt{\frac{2kT}{\pi m}} \Gamma(2) = 2\sqrt{\frac{2kT}{\pi m}}. \tag{7.24}$$

The *root mean square speed* is defined as the sum of velocity squares of all molecules divided by the number of molecules. Thus

$$v_{\mathrm{rms}}^2 = \frac{1}{N} \int_0^\infty v^2 \, dN_v = \int_0^\infty v^2 f(v) \, dv.$$

Substituting from Eq. (7.18) gives

$$
\begin{aligned}
v_{\mathrm{rms}}^2 &= \int_0^\infty \frac{4}{\sqrt{\pi}} \left(\frac{m}{2kT}\right)^{3/2} v^4 e^{-(m/2kT)v^2} \, dv \\
&= \frac{4}{\sqrt{\pi}} \left(\frac{m}{2kT}\right)^{3/2} \int_0^\infty \frac{4k^2 T^2}{m^2} e^{-x} x^{3/2} \sqrt{\frac{kT}{2m}} \, dx \\
&= \frac{4kT}{\sqrt{\pi}\, m} \Gamma\left(\frac{5}{2}\right) \\
&= \frac{4kT}{\sqrt{\pi}\, m} \frac{3\sqrt{\pi}}{4} = \frac{3kT}{m}.
\end{aligned}
$$

Hence

$$v_{\mathrm{rms}} = \sqrt{\frac{3kT}{m}}, \qquad\qquad (7.25)$$

which is the same as Eq. (7.3).

The *most probable speed* is the speed at which the largest number of molecules is moving, so that it is the speed which occurs most frequently. It is obtained by differentiating the expression of dN_v/dv with respect to v and equating the result to zero.

From Eq. (7.16), we have

$$\frac{4N}{\sqrt{\pi}} \left(\frac{m}{2kT}\right)^{3/2} \frac{d}{dv}\left(v^2 e^{-(m/2kT)v^2}\right) = 0,$$

or

$$v^2 e^{-(m/2kT)v^2} \left(-\frac{m}{2kT}\right)(2v) + e^{-(m/2kT)v^2}(2v) = 0,$$

from which

$$v_{\mathrm{mp}} = \sqrt{\frac{2kT}{m}}. \qquad\qquad (7.26)$$

The relative magnitudes of the three foregoing speeds are shown in Fig. 7.7 and their values are in the following proportions:

$$v_{\mathrm{mp}} : v_{\mathrm{avg}} : v_{\mathrm{rms}} = 1 : 1.128 : 1.224.$$

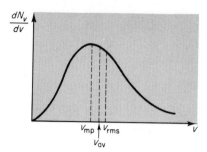

Fig. 7.7. *Relative magnitudes of* v_{mp}, v_{av}, *and* v_{rms}.

To calculate the number of molecules with speeds or velocities in a certain range, it is necessary to integrate the speed distribution function between the limits of that range. For example, the number of molecules having speeds between 0 and v is

$$N_{0 \to v} = \int_0^v dN_v.$$

But dN_v, according to Eq. (7.16), is

$$dN_v = \frac{4N}{\sqrt{\pi}} \left(\frac{m}{2kT}\right)^{3/2} v^2 e^{-(m/2kT)v^2} \, dv$$

$$= \frac{4N}{\sqrt{\pi}} \beta^3 v^2 e^{-\beta^2 v^2} \, dv.$$

Letting $x = \beta v = v/v_{mp}$, then

$$N_{0 \to v} = \frac{4N}{\sqrt{\pi}} \int_0^x x^2 e^{-x^2} \, dx = -\frac{2N}{\sqrt{\pi}} \int_0^x x \, de^{-x^2}.$$

Integration by parts gives

$$N_{0 \to v} = -\frac{2N}{\sqrt{\pi}} \left[xe^{-x^2} - \int_0^x e^{-x^2} \, dx \right]$$

$$= N \left[\frac{2}{\sqrt{\pi}} \int_0^x e^{-x^2} \, dx - \frac{2}{\sqrt{\pi}} xe^{-x^2} \right]$$

$$= N \left[erf(x) - \frac{2}{\sqrt{\pi}} xe^{-x^2} \right], \tag{7.27}$$

where $x = (m/2kT)^{1/2} v$.

The function $erf(x)$ appearing in Eq. (7.27) is called the *error function* and is defined as

$$erf(x) \equiv \frac{2}{\sqrt{\pi}} \int_0^x e^{-x^2} \, dx. \tag{7.28}$$

Values of $erf(x)$ as a function of x are given in Table 7.2.

TABLE 7.2 VALUES OF THE ERROR FUNCTION

$$erf(x) = \frac{2}{\sqrt{\pi}} \int_0^x e^{-x^2}\, dx$$

x	$erf(x)$	x	$erf(x)$	x	$erf(x)$
0	0	1.0	0.8427	2.0	0.9953
0.2	0.2227	1.2	0.9103	2.2	0.9981
0.4	0.4284	1.4	0.9523	2.4	0.9993
0.6	0.6039	1.6	0.9763	2.6	0.9998
0.8	0.7421	1.8	0.9891	2.8	0.9999

EXAMPLE 7.2: Calculate the average speed, root mean square speed, and most probable speed for oxygen at 0°C.

Solution: The mass of an oxygen molecule is

$$m = \frac{M}{N_0} = \frac{32.0}{6.025 \times 10^{23}} = 5.31 \times 10^{-23} \text{ gram/molecule,}$$

and

$$k = 1.38 \times 10^{-16} \text{ erg/molecule °K.}$$

The average speed, according to Eq. (7.24), is

$$v_{avg} = 2\sqrt{\frac{2kT}{\pi m}} = 2\sqrt{\frac{2(1.38 \times 10^{-16})\, 273}{\pi (5.31 \times 10^{-23})}} = 42{,}600 \text{ cm/sec} = 426 \text{ m/sec.}$$

The root mean square speed according to Eq. (7.25) is

$$v_{rms} = \sqrt{\frac{3kT}{m}} = \sqrt{\frac{3(1.38 \times 10^{-16})\, 273}{5.31 \times 10^{-23}}} = 46{,}100 \text{ cm/sec} = 461 \text{ m/sec.}$$

The most probable speed according to Eq. (7.26) is

$$v_{mp} = \sqrt{\frac{2kT}{m}} = \sqrt{\frac{2(1.38 \times 10^{-16})\, 273}{5.31 \times 10^{-23}}} = 37{,}600 \text{ cm/sec} = 376 \text{ m/sec.}$$

**7-7
Number of
Molecules
Striking a Unit
Surface in a
Unit Time**

Closely associated with pressure is the number of molecules that strike a surface in a unit time. In order to determine the rate of such collisions, it is first necessary to determine the number of molecules that have a certain speed and are moving in a certain direction. Integration of this expression over the total range of speeds and directions leads to an expression of the collision rate. The derivation is done in two steps: first, the number of molecules moving in a certain direction is determined; second, the fraction of these molecules which have a speed v is determined.

Consider a sphere in velocity space, as shown in Fig. 7.8. Let the velocity vector of each molecule be drawn from the origin. The radial pro-

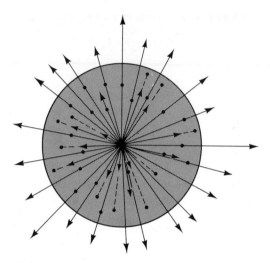

Fig. 7.8. *Molecular velocity vectors drawn from a common origin.*

jection of each vector on the surface of the sphere is represented by a point. The surface of the sphere will then have N points if N particles are considered. Because of the uniform distribution of points in velocity space, the number of points per unit area will be the same* irrespective of the position of the surface chosen. If the sphere has a radius r, the number of points per unit

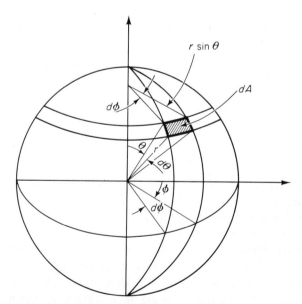

Fig. 7.9. *Molecular velocity vectors in the $\theta\phi$ direction.*

*This assumption is valid, provided that the unit area is not too small.

area of surface is $N/4\pi r^2$. Consider now a small area dA on the surface of the sphere as shown in Fig. 7.9. This area subtends a solid angle* at the origin defined in terms of the small angles $d\theta$ and $d\phi$ and the radius of the sphere. The elementary area dA expressed in polar coordinates is

$$dA = r^2 \sin \theta \, d\theta \, d\phi.$$

Let the number of points on dA be denoted by $dN_{\theta\phi}$, where the subscripts indicate the direction of dA with respect to the origin. Since the number of points on any portion of the surface of the sphere is proportional to the area, therefore

$$\frac{dN_{\theta\phi}}{N} = \frac{dA}{4\pi r^2}.$$

When the equivalent expression for dA is substituted in this equation, the number of molecules of gas traveling between the directions θ and $\theta + d\theta$ and between ϕ and $\phi + d\phi$ is

$$dN_{\theta\phi} = \frac{N}{4\pi r^2} (r^2 \sin \theta \, d\theta \, d\phi) = \frac{N}{4\pi} d\omega, \tag{7.31}$$

where $d\omega = \sin \theta \, d\theta \, d\phi$ and represents the solid angle at the origin subtended by the area dA. If $dn_{\theta\phi} = dN_{\theta\phi}/V$ represents the number of molecules per unit volume (number density), then

$$dn_{\theta\phi} = \frac{n}{4\pi} d\omega. \tag{7.32}$$

In order to determine the fraction of the $dN_{\theta\phi}$ molecules that have a speed between v and $v + dv$, consider a sphere of radius v in velocity space. Take the solid angle subtended by a small area dA_v to be the same for both velocity space and ordinary space. The fraction of the molecules moving with a speed v in the direction bounded by the angles θ and $\theta + d\theta$ and ϕ and $\phi + d\phi$ is equal to the ratio of the area dA_v to the total area of the sphere, or

$$\frac{dN_{\theta\phi v}}{dN_v} = \frac{dA_v}{4\pi v^2} = \frac{dA}{4\pi r^2} = \frac{dN_{\theta\phi}}{N}.$$

Therefore,

$$dN_{\theta\phi v} = \frac{dN_{\theta\phi}}{N} dN_v. \tag{7.33}$$

*The *solid angle* is defined as the area on the surface of a sphere of unit radius subtended at the center of a sphere.

The foregoing expression could also be obtained from the definition of the distribution function which, in this case, gives the fraction of the $(\theta\phi)$ molecules moving at speeds between v and $v + dv$. Substituting for $dN_{\theta\phi}$ from Eq. (7.31) gives

$$dN_{\theta\phi v} = \frac{N}{4\pi} d\omega \frac{dN_v}{N} = \frac{N}{4\pi} d\omega f(v)\, dv. \tag{7.34}$$

Dividing both sides of Eq. (7.34) by the volume V gives

$$dn_{\theta\phi v} = \frac{n}{4\pi} d\omega f(v)\, dv, \tag{7.35}$$

where n is the number of molecules per unit volume. Equation (7.35) describes the number of molecules per unit volume which start at the origin of the coordinate system and are confined within a cone of a solid angle $d\omega$ and have a speed between v and $v + dv$.

In an analogous manner the number of molecules with speeds between v and $v + dv$ starting from a small volume dV in ordinary space and

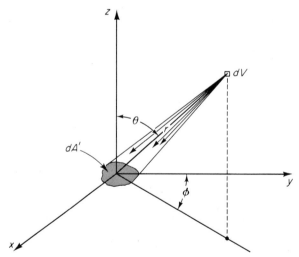

Fig. 7.10. *Molecular collisions with dA' in the θφ direction.*

moving in the direction of a small surface dA' at the origin of the coordinate system may be determined. Using Eq. (7.35) and referring to Fig. 7.10, the number of these molecules is

$$dn_{\theta\phi v}\, dV = \left(\frac{n}{4\pi} d\omega' f(v)\, dv\right) dV,$$

where $d\omega' = dA' \cos \theta / r^2 =$ the solid angle of cone whose vertex lies in the volume dV and whose base occupies the area dA'. The volume dV is given by

$$dV = r^2 \sin \theta \, d\theta \, d\phi \, dr \quad \text{and} \quad dr = v \, d\tau.$$

These expressions for $d\omega'$ and dV can now be substituted in Eq. (7.35) to determine the number of molecules from dV striking the area dA' in time $d\tau$:

$$dC_{\theta\phi v} = dn_{\theta\phi v} \, dV = \left(\frac{n}{4\pi} \frac{dA' \cos \theta}{r^2} f(v) \, dv \right) r^2 \sin \theta \, d\theta \, d\phi \, v \, d\tau.$$

Since $d\tau$ represents the time required for a molecule to travel a distance dr, the number of molecules per unit area and per unit time that travel this path is

$$\frac{dC_{\theta\phi v}}{dA' d\tau} = \frac{n}{4\pi} \sin \theta \cos \theta \, v f(v) \, dv \, d\phi \, d\theta. \tag{7.36}$$

The total number of molecules that will strike the wall per unit area per unit time is obtained by integrating the preceding expression in the hemisphere above the xy plane and over all positive velocities, or

$$\frac{C}{dA' d\tau} = \int_{\phi=0}^{2\pi} \int_{\theta=0}^{\pi/2} \int_{v=0}^{\infty} \frac{n}{4\pi} \sin \theta \cos \theta \, v f(v) \, dv \, d\theta \, d\phi.$$

The result can be expressed in terms of the average speed:

$$\dot{c} = \frac{C}{dA' d\tau} = \frac{n}{4} \int_0^{\infty} v f(v) \, dv = \frac{1}{4} n v_{\text{avg}}. \tag{7.37}$$

Since v_{avg} can be evaluated from Eq. (7.24), the rate at which the molecules strike a wall per unit area is

$$\dot{c} = n \sqrt{\frac{kT}{2\pi m}}. \tag{7.38}$$

By substituting p/kT for n in Eq. (7.38), the frequency of collision with a unit area of wall can be expressed in terms of pressure:

$$\dot{c} = \frac{p}{\sqrt{2\pi m k T}}. \tag{7.39}$$

Equation (7.39) may be used to calculate the pressure force on an area. Each collision of a particle with an area A results in a change in momentum of the particle:

$$\text{momentum change due to collision} = 2 \, mv \cos \theta.$$

But the total rate of change of momentum per unit area is equal to the pressure. Therefore,

$$dp = \frac{dC_{\theta\phi v}}{dA'd\tau}(2mv\cos\theta)$$

$$= \frac{n}{4\pi} v \sin\theta \cos\theta \, d\theta \, d\phi (2mv\cos\theta) f(v) \, dv.$$

This expression is then integrated over θ from 0 to $\pi/2$, over ϕ from 0 to 2π and over v from 0 to ∞ to give

$$p = \tfrac{1}{3} mn \int_0^\infty v^2 f(v) \, dv = \tfrac{1}{3} mn v_{\text{rms}}^2. \tag{7.40}$$

This is the same as Eq. (1.24) obtained in Chapter 1.

EXAMPLE 7.3: Calculate the wall collision frequency per square meter for oxygen at 1 atm and 0°C. Appropriate constants are given in the Appendix.

Solution:

$$1 \text{ atm} = 1.01 \times 10^5 \frac{\text{kg}}{\text{m}^2} \frac{\text{m}}{\text{sec}^2}$$

$$m_{O_2} = \frac{32.0 \text{ gm/gm-mole}}{6.025 \times 10^{23} \text{ molecules/gm-mole}} = 5.31 \times 10^{-26} \text{ kg/molecule}$$

$$k = 1.38 \times 10^{-23} \text{ kg m}^2/\text{sec}^2 {}^\circ\text{K}$$

$$T = 273 {}^\circ\text{K}.$$

The wall collision frequency according to Eq. (7.39) is

$$\dot{c} = \frac{p}{\sqrt{2\pi mkT}}$$

$$= \frac{1.01 \times 10^5}{\sqrt{2\pi (5.31 \times 10^{-26})(1.38 \times 10^{-23}) \, 273}}$$

$$= 2.84 \times 10^{27} \text{ collisions/sec-m}^2.$$

7-8
Molecular
Collisions
and Mean
Free Path

The velocities at which the molecules of a gas move are described by equations derived previously. But the microscopic view is still not complete since the paths taken by the molecules are yet to be determined. If the particles collide to an appreciable extent with each other, then their diffusional characteristics are different than if they collide only with the walls of the container. Some indication of the collision tendencies comes from two parameters, the *mean free path* and the molecular *collision frequency*.

The mean free path of a molecule is the average distance it travels

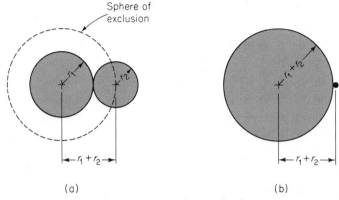

Fig. 7.11.   Collision of two molecules.

between collisions with other molecules. Consider the collision between two molecules of radii r_1 and r_2 as shown in Fig. 7.11(a). If the molecules are assumed to be small elastic spheres* rather than point masses, the distance between the centers of the molecules is $r_1 + r_2$ when they collide. One of the two molecules may therefore be considered to have an effective radius $r_1 + r_2$, whereas the other molecule is a point of zero radius, as shown in Fig. 7.11(b). All molecules except one may be considered motionless or "frozen" in their respective positions in the gas. Now consider the movement of a single molecule of radius $r_1 + r_2$ as it travels in a gas containing stationary molecules of zero radius. The cross-sectional area of the cylindrical volume swept out by the moving molecule is

$$\sigma = \pi(r_1 + r_2)^2,$$

where σ is the *collision cross section*. The number of collisions that occur as the molecule travels through this stationary matrix depends on the number of molecules per unit volume that lie within the cylindrical volume. The molecular *collision frequency Z*, that is, the number of collisions of molecules per unit time irrespective of path deflections, is given by

$$Z = \left(\frac{N}{V}\right)\sigma v_{avg} = n\sigma v_{avg},$$

where v_{avg} represents the average velocity of the molecules. Assuming identical molecules each of mass m, v_{avg} is

$$v_{avg} = \sqrt{\frac{8kT}{\pi m}}.$$

*Although it was previously assumed that the molecules are point masses, it may be shown that statistical laws apply to other models and are therefore independent of the assumption of point masses.

Therefore,

$$Z = \frac{N}{V} \sigma \sqrt{\frac{8kT}{\pi m}} .$$

Since the mean free path is the average distance that the molecule travels between collisions with other molecules, the mean free path is given by

$$\Lambda_m = \frac{v_{\text{avg}} \tau}{Z \tau} = \frac{V}{N\sigma} = \frac{1}{n\sigma} ,$$

where τ represents time interval.

In the preceding derivation, only one molecule was assumed to be moving, and the motion of other molecules was ignored. Because of the motion of other molecules, the average velocity of the original molecule when considered in relation to the other molecules is, in effect, larger than originally considered. The relative average velocity, then, is found to be $\frac{4}{3} v_{\text{avg}}$. When this correction is taken into account, the foregoing expressions for collision frequency and mean free path become

$$Z = \frac{4}{3} n\sigma \sqrt{\frac{8kT}{\pi m}} = \frac{4}{3} n\sigma v_{\text{avg}} \qquad (7.41)$$

and

$$\Lambda_m = \frac{3V}{4N\sigma} = \frac{3}{4\sigma n} . \qquad (7.42)$$

Although the molecular collision frequency depends on the velocity of the molecules, the mean free path is independent of velocity; instead, it depends on the dimensions of the molecules and their number per unit volume. According to Avogadro's law, the concentration of molecules depends only on pressure and temperature. Also, the dimensions of the molecules of all perfect gases are nearly equal, being small compared to the mean free path. Consequently, the mean free path is approximately the same for all gases under the same conditions. For example, the mean free path of oxygen at standard conditions is 8×10^{-6} cm. This is approximately 10 times the intermolecular distance and 100 times the molecular diameter.* Since the mean free path at a given temperature is inversely proportional to pressure, the mean free path of oxygen at 0.01 mm Hg pressure (at 0°C) is of the order of 1 cm.

7-9 ~~SKIPPED~~
Distribution of
Free Paths

A molecule, at times, will travel a distance larger than the mean free path before it collides; at other times, it will travel a shorter distance. The magnitude of these free paths will show a typical distribution pattern. An expression describing the distribution of free paths of molecules of a gas

*Molecular diameters are approximately 3Å (3×10^{-8} cm).

is derived as follows: The number of molecules which collide during a time interval $d\tau$ is proportional to the number of molecules in the gas and to their relative velocities. It is given by

$$dN = -PNv\, d\tau,$$

where P is a proportionality factor called the *collision probability*, N is the number of molecules that do not experience a collision in time $d\tau$, and v is velocity. This can be expressed in terms of distance as

$$dN = -PN\, dx.$$

Integration of the foregoing equation gives

$$N = N_0 e^{-Px},$$

where N_0 is the total number of molecules (Avogadro's number if one mole is considered). Now the mean free path Λ_m represents the average distance traveled by any molecule until it experiences one collision, and can be evaluated from

$$\Lambda_m = \frac{1}{N_0} \int_0^{N_0} x\, dN. \tag{7.43}$$

It can be shown that $\Lambda_m = 1/P$, so that the collision probability P is the reciprocal of the mean free path. Thus the number of molecules which travel a path x without collision can be expressed in terms of the mean free path rather than probability:

$$N = N_0 e^{-x/\Lambda_m}. \tag{7.44}$$

Figure 7.12 gives the distribution of free paths, that is, the fraction of the original molecules, N/N_0, which travel a path equal to x/Λ_m without collision.

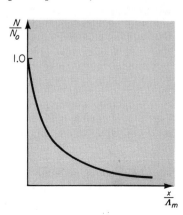

Fig. 7.12.   *Distribution of free paths.*

7-10
Equipartition
of Energy

The molecules of a gas possess four types of energy: translational, rotational, vibrational, and electronic. The translational energy is attributed to the Brownian motion of the molecules and is given by

$$U = \sum_i N_i (\epsilon_{\text{trans}})_i = N \frac{m v_{\text{rms}}^2}{2} = N (\epsilon_{\text{trans}})_{\text{avg}}.$$

Substituting for v_{rms} from Eq. (7.25) gives

$$U = \tfrac{3}{2} NkT. \tag{7.45}$$

Therefore the average translational energy per molecule is

$$(\epsilon_{\text{trans}})_{\text{avg}} = \frac{U}{N} = \frac{3}{2} kT. \tag{7.46}$$

The translational energy of a molecule, which is a form of kinetic energy, may be described in terms of its velocity components in the three perpendicular directions x, y, and z. It is equal to the sum of its translational energies in the three directions so that

$$\epsilon_{\text{trans}} = \frac{m v^2}{2} = \frac{m v_x^2}{2} + \frac{m v_y^2}{2} + \frac{m v_z^2}{2}.$$

Since all three directions are equally probable, the average kinetic energy is the same for each of the three directions. Consequently, the average kinetic energy of a molecule associated with each direction is equal to one-third of the average translational energy, or

$$\epsilon_{x, y, \text{ or } z} = \tfrac{1}{2} kT. \tag{7.47}$$

This equipartition of translational energy means that the kinetic energy is equally divided among three degrees of freedom each contributing an average value of $\tfrac{1}{2} kT$. According to the *principle of equipartition of energy*, each degree of freedom is associated with an equal amount of energy, in this case $\tfrac{1}{2} kT$. The magnitude of the average translational energy of a molecule at 25°C in any one direction is

$$\tfrac{1}{2} kT = \tfrac{1}{2} (1.38 \times 10^{-16})(298) = 2.06 \times 10^{-14} \text{ erg,}$$

and its total translational kinetic energy is

$$\tfrac{3}{2} kT = 6.18 \times 10^{-14} \text{ erg.}$$

Since $\mathcal{R} = N_0 k$, the average kinetic energy due to translational motion on a mole basis is

$\frac{3}{2} \mathcal{R}T = \frac{3}{2}$ (1.987)(298) = 890 cal/gm-mole.

The principle of equipartition of energy applies also to other manifestations of kinetic energy. Considering rotational energy, a molecule may rotate about three perpendicular axes through its center of gravity and thus possesses three rotational degrees of freedom. In the case of a *linear* molecule, the atoms lie on the same axis, so that contribution to rotational energy is a result of rotation about two axes that are mutually perpendicular to each other and to the line connecting the centers of the atoms. Diatomic molecules are in this category and have only two rotational degrees of freedom. Since each degree of freedom of rotational energy adds $\frac{1}{2} kT$ to the energy of the molecule, the translational and rotational energies of a diatomic molecule are specified by five degrees of freedom, whereas the kinetic energy of a monatomic molecule is specified by only three degrees.

The third type of molecular energy is vibrational energy. The atoms comprising a molecule tend to vibrate about their equilibrium positions. If a molecule has N atoms, each atom may independently vibrate in three directions and the molecule may have $3N$ degrees of freedom. Some of this vibrational motion results in translational and rotational motion of the entire molecule. Consequently, vibrational motion of a nonlinear molecule shows $(3N - 6)$ degrees of freedom, whereas vibrational motion of a linear molecule shows $(3N - 5)$ degrees of freedom. Since a vibrating molecule possesses both kinetic and potential energies, each contributing $\frac{1}{2} kT$, the vibrational energy per molecule per degree of freedom is kT. Considering a diatomic molecule, the total average energy of a diatomic molecule should be $\frac{7}{2} kT (=\frac{3}{2} kT + kT + kT)$. This result contradicts experimental observations because vibrations do not occur in the molecules until high temperatures are reached. As will be shown in Chapter 8, the restrictions imposed by the quantum theory limit the conformity of the vibrational motion with the principle of equipartition of energy except at very high temperatures. Finally, energy of a molecule may be in the form of electronic energy. This is associated with the structural arrangement of the electrons in the molecule. A change in the electronic energy of a molecule arises from a change in the kinetic and potential energy of one or more of its electrons. No degrees of freedom are assigned to electronic energy but rather the total change of electronic energy is computed. Information about the electronic energy inherent in a molecule is obtained by means of spectroscopy. Through measurements of the radiation absorbed or emitted by a molecule, the allowed energy states of the molecule can be determined, and this is related to the molecular structure.

The application of the principle of equipartition of energy to calculate specific heat values will be discussed in Chapter 9.

Appendix:
Lagrange's
Method of
Undetermined
Multipliers

Lagrange's method of undetermined multipliers is a mathematical tool for finding stationary values of a function, subject to conditions of constraint. Stationary values of a function occur at a maximum, a minimum, or a point of inflection. The function is stable only when it is stationary at a minimum value. Consider the problem of finding a stationary value of a function of several variables given by

$$f(x_1, x_2, \ldots, x_n) = 0. \tag{1}$$

The variables $x_1, x_2, \ldots, x_n$, n in number, are related according to the equations of constraint given by

$$\phi_1 (x_1, x_2, \ldots, x_n) = 0$$
$$\phi_2 (x_1, x_2, \ldots, x_n) = 0 \tag{2}$$
$$\cdot$$
$$\cdot$$
$$\cdot$$
$$\phi_m (x_1, x_2, \ldots, x_n) = 0,$$

where m is the number of equations of constraint. Note that $m \leqslant n$.

When there are as many conditions of constraint as there are variables (that is, $m = n$), then the value of the function f is unique and can readily be determined by solving simultaneously n equations in n unknowns. But when $m < n$, the equations must be combined in such a way that f is maximized (or minimized). Note that $(n - m)$ equations are then needed; when added to the existing m constraint equations, they give a total of n equations.

If the function f and its derivatives are continuous, then the differential of f is given by

$$df = \frac{\partial f}{\partial x_1} dx_1 + \frac{\partial f}{\partial x_2} dx_2 + \cdots + \frac{\partial f}{\partial x_n} dx_n = \sum_{i=1}^{n} \frac{\partial f}{\partial x_i} dx_i. \tag{3}$$

In the vicinity of a stationary point of the function f, the change of f must be equal to zero, or

$$df = 0 = \sum_{i=1}^{n} \frac{\partial f}{\partial x_i} dx_i. \tag{4}$$

The differentials of Eq. (2) are

$$d\phi_j = 0 = \sum_{i=1}^{n} \frac{\partial \phi_j}{\partial x_i} dx_i, \qquad j = 1, 2, \ldots, m. \tag{5}$$

Lagrange's method consists of multiplying $d\phi_1$ by λ_1, $d\phi_2$ by λ_2, . . . , etc., where $\lambda_1, \lambda_2, . . . , \lambda_m$ are arbitrary functions called *undetermined multipliers*, and adding these expressions to Eq. (4). A single equation is obtained, in which all the variables (rather than $n - 1$) may be treated as independent.

$$
\frac{df}{\partial x_1} dx_1 + \frac{\partial f}{\partial x_2} dx_2 + \cdots + \frac{\partial f}{\partial x_n} dx_n
$$

$$
+ \lambda_1 \left(\frac{\partial \phi_1}{\partial x_1} dx_1 + \frac{\partial \phi_1}{\partial x_2} dx_2 + \cdots + \frac{\partial \phi_1}{\partial x_n} dx_n \right)
$$

$$
+ \lambda_2 \left(\frac{\partial \phi_2}{\partial x_1} dx_1 + \frac{\partial \phi_2}{\partial x_2} dx_2 + \cdots + \frac{\partial \phi_2}{\partial x_n} dx_n \right)
$$

$$
\cdot
$$
$$
\cdot
$$

$$
+ \lambda_m \left(\frac{\partial \phi_m}{\partial x_1} dx_1 + \frac{\partial \phi_m}{\partial x_2} dx_2 + \cdots + \frac{\partial \phi_m}{\partial x_n} dx_n \right) = 0,
$$

or

$$
\left(\frac{\partial f}{\partial x_1} + \lambda_1 \frac{\partial \phi_1}{\partial x_1} + \lambda_2 \frac{\partial \phi_2}{\partial x_1} + \cdots + \lambda_m \frac{\partial \phi_m}{\partial x_1} \right) dx_1
$$

$$
+ \left(\frac{\partial f}{\partial x_2} + \lambda_1 \frac{\partial \phi_1}{\partial x_2} + \lambda_2 \frac{\partial \phi_2}{\partial x_2} + \cdots + \lambda_m \frac{\partial \phi_m}{\partial x_2} \right) dx_2
$$

$$
\cdot
$$
$$
\cdot
$$

$$
+ \left(\frac{\partial f}{\partial x_n} + \lambda_1 \frac{\partial \phi_1}{\partial x_n} + \lambda_2 \frac{\partial \phi_2}{\partial x_n} + \cdots + \lambda_m \frac{\partial \phi_m}{\partial x_n} \right) dx_n = 0.
$$

(6)

Only those values of $\lambda_1, \lambda_2, . . . , \lambda_m$ are acceptable which make the coefficients of $dx_1, dx_2, . . . , dx_n$ in Eq. (6) vanish separately, so that n separate equations are obtained from Eq. (6). This is essentially equivalent to treating each x as independent. After the m equations are solved for the λ's, the remaining $(n - m)$ equations are solved for the unknowns $x_1, x_2, . . . , x_n$.

REFERENCES

7.1 Sears, F. W., *Thermodynamics*. Reading, Mass.: Addison-Wesley Publishing Company, Inc., 1952, chap. 11, 12.

7.2 Sheehan, W. F., *Physical Chemistry*. New York: Allyn & Bacon, Inc., 1961, Chap. 1.

PROBLEMS

7.1 The magnitude of molecular velocities of a perfect gas is, according to the following distribution,

Number of Molecules	Speed in m/sec
10	20
20	50
40	100
60	125
80	150
100	200
60	300
40	350

Draw a graph showing the speed distribution among the molecules and compute the average and the root mean square speeds.

7.2 Calculate the density and root mean square speed for the following gases at 0°C and 100°C. Avogadro's number $= 6.023 \times 10^{23}$ molecules/gm-mole and $k = 1.38 \times 10^{-16}$ erg/molecule°K. Assume atmospheric pressure.

Gas	Molecular Weight (gm/gm-mole)
A	39.94
H_2	2.02
He	4.00
N_2	28.02
CO_2	44.00

7.3 Plot the Maxwell-Boltzmann speed and velocity distributions for 1 kg-mole of nitrogen at temperatures of 100°K and 1000°K.

7.4 The molecules of a gas have a Maxwellian speed distribution given by

$$f(v) = \frac{4}{\sqrt{\pi}} \left(\frac{m}{2kT} \right)^{3/2} v^2 e^{-mv^2/2kT}.$$

(a) Check that $\int_0^\infty f(\epsilon)d\epsilon = 1$, where $\epsilon = \frac{1}{2}mv^2$.

(b) Show that the most probable and average kinetic energies are $\frac{1}{2}kT$ and $\frac{3}{2}kT$.

7.5 Prove that the Maxwell-Boltzmann distribution law is valid for a mixture of perfect gases in thermal equilibrium if the law holds true for each gas separately.

7.6 Compute the average speed, root mean square speed, the most probable speed in m/sec for hydrogen and carbon monoxide at 0°C and 500°C.

7.7 What is the fractional number of molecules of a perfect gas with speeds between 0 and v_{mp}? Plot the Maxwell-Boltzmann speed distribution for 1 kg-mole of oxygen at 1000°K.

7.8 Repeat Problem 7.7 if the fractional number of molecules having velocities with x components between $-v_{mp_x}$ and $+v_{mp_x}$ is required. Plot the Maxwell-Boltzmann velocity distribution.

7.9 Calculate the average speed of a perfect gas in the ranges of 0 to v_{mp} and v_{mp} to ∞.

7.10 Determine the fractional number of molecules of a perfect gas with
(a) Speeds between $v = v_{mp}$ and $v = 1.1 \, v_{mp}$. What fraction is moving with a speed greater than v_{mp}?
(b) Velocities of x Cartesian components lying in the same range, that is, between v_{mp} and $1.1 \, v_{mp}$.

7.11 What is the number of oxygen molecules per mole having speeds between 900 and 1000 m/sec at 1000°K?

7.12 Calculate the time rate of molecular impacts on a surface of a square centimeter exposed to air at 300°K if the pressure is (a) atmospheric, (b) 10^{-5} mm Hg.

7.13 A cubical box, 1 cm on each side, contains hydrogen at 0°C and 1 atm. If the number of molecules in the box is approximately 2.7×10^{19}, calculate the number of collisions made with the walls in each second.

7.14 Calculate the mean free paths for the gases listed in Problem 7.2 for 0°C and 100°C. Assume atmospheric pressure. The molecular diameters follow:

Gas	Molecular Diameter (cm)
A	3.64×10^{-8}
H_2	2.18×10^{-8}
He	2.74×10^{-8}
N_2	3.75×10^{-8}
CO_2	4.59×10^{-8}

7.15 Helium at a pressure of 1 atm and 20°C occupies a sphere 20 cm in diameter. The outside of the sphere is evacuated and the molecules escape through a pinhole in the sphere of 10^{-7} cm diameter. Assuming isothermal conditions, how long will it take for the pressure to drop to 0.1 atm? (Assume that the wall of the sphere is very thin and is planar in the vicinity of the pin hole.)

7.16 Air at atmospheric pressure and 300°K leaks into a vacuum system through a small hole. The pressure in the vacuum system is low enough for leakage back to the outside to be negligible. Find the ratio of the number of O_2 to N_2 molecules leaking into the system. If the cross-sectional area of the hole is 10^{-7} cm^2, find the mass of air entering the system per second. Assume mean molecular weight of air 28.97.

7.17   Two vessels containing a perfect gas at different pressures p_1 and p_2 are initially at the same temperature T. It is discovered that gas leaks through a small hole connecting the two constant pressure vessels. Assuming steady state and adiabatic conditions calculate:

(a) The rms speed of the leaking gas in each vessel
(b) The rate of leakage per second
(c) The mean energy per molecule of the leaking gas.
(d) How would you maintain the vessels at constant temperature?

NOMENCLATURE

$A, B, C,$ D, K	Constants		S	Entropy
a, b, c	Distances		T	Absolute temperature
c	Wave velocity		U	Internal energy
E	Total internal energy		V	Volume or voltage
F	Force		v	Velocity or a function
g_i	Degeneracy of ith level		W	Thermodynamic probability
h	Planck's constant		x, y, z	Cartesian coordinates
I	Moment of inertia		$\mathcal{Z}$	Partition function
K	Spring constant		Z	Molecular partition function
k	Boltzmann's constant or a constant		α, β, B	Lagrange's multipliers
l	Length		Ψ	Wave function
m	Molecular mass		ω	Circular frequency
m, n, j	Integers		ϵ	Internal energy per molecule
N	Number of molecules		ν	Frequency
N_0	Avogadro's number		ρ	Density per unit length
n	Number of molecules per unit volume		τ	Time
P	Legendre's polynomial		Θ, Φ	Functions
p	Pressure or momentum		$\sum_i$	Summation over indices i
R	Gas constant		$\prod_i$	Product over indices i
$\mathcal{R}$	Universal gas constant			
r	Distance			

8

STATISTICAL
AND QUANTUM
MECHANICS

8-1
Introduction
Classical thermodynamics is based on a model which, because of its simplifications, cannot explain certain phenomena adequately. For example, it treats a gas as though all the atoms were identical not only in mass but also in dynamic qualities (that is, energy, momentum, velocity). There is evidence that marked differences or fluctuations in dynamic qualities do exist. When these differences are incorporated in the model, and the system is then analyzed, valuable information is derived. In the domain of statistical mechanics, then, substances are considered from the microscopic, not the macroscopic standpoint, and furthermore, differences between atoms (and molecules) in their dynamic qualities are considered.

It is possible, in principle, to apply the laws of mechanics to each individual molecule of a gas and thus determine the behavior of the system. But the behavior of individual particles, such as the molecules of a gas, is complicated, time dependent, and difficult to follow. Furthermore, the macroscopic properties of a substance are determined by the average behavior of a large number of molecules rather than by the behavior of a single molecule at a certain time. A molecule of a gas can show a wide spectrum of velocities ranging, in a short period of time, from zero to very high values. But the average velocity of the molecules in the gas is of more interest in interpreting the thermodynamic properties of the gas than is the velocity of each molecule.

Statistical methods lead to the prediction of the distribution of particles among available energy levels. When a very large number of particles is present, the most probable macrostate of particle distribution is far more common than any other, and the energy distribution of particles of the system can be determined with *almost* total certainty.

8-2
Thermodynamic
Probability
A substance can be considered to consist of a large number of atoms which, although identical in mass, are still not necessarily all alike. The atoms may be considered to be distributed over a number of different states which readily transform from one to another. It is possible to calculate the number of different ways that a system consisting of numerous particles in different states can be arranged. Furthermore, it is possible to predict which of the various arrangements will be the most probable. Such a treatment, in which the most probable distribution is determined from mathematical statistics, can be correlated with certain classical thermodynamic properties.

The approach used in calculating macroscopic properties is based on the theory of probability. A major assumption in the analysis is that all conceivable microstates* of a system have the same a priori probability of occurrence. A system in which the energy U, the volume V, and the number of particles N are specified can exist in several different macrostates. The problem lies in determining how many microstates exist in each macrostate and in determining which particular macrostate is the most probable, and therefore, the one that imparts the macroscopic properties to the system.

Suppose it is required to arrange N *distinguishable*† particles into several different groups, with $N_1, N_2, \ldots N_i \ldots$ particles in each group. The groupings may be thought of, more conveniently, in terms of physical compartments, although what is really involved here is a grouping in terms of discrete energy levels. Before examining the number of different ways in which this can be done, the number of ways in which N particles can be arranged in N distinct positions may be first considered. The first particle can occupy any one of the N possible positions. This means that the first particle has a choice of N positions. The second particle has a choice of the remaining $(N - 1)$ positions, since one position is already occupied by the first particle. With two positions filled, the third particle has a choice of $(N-2)$ positions, etc. This leads to a total of $N(N - 1)(N - 2) \ldots (2)(1) = N!$ possible arrangements of the N particles in the N positions (or energy levels). This is essentially a *permutation process* of the N particles among themselves.

Now suppose that the N particles are arranged so that there are $N_1, N_2, \ldots N_i \ldots$ particles in each group, rather than only one particle in each group. If the number of particles in the first group is N_1 then there are $N_1!$ different arrangements for the particles in that group. Similarly for the ith group, the number of arrangements is $N_i!$. The total number of ways of arranging all the particles is therefore $(N_1!)(N_2!) \ldots (N_i!) \ldots$.

If, however, the particles within a group are indistinguishable from each other, the interchange of particles within a group does not result in a new arrangement. Therefore, the permutations within each group cannot be considered to contribute to the total number of possible arrangements. Since $N!$ represents the number of ways of arranging N particles in N positions, $(N_1!)(N_2!) \ldots (N_i!) \ldots$ represents the number of ways of distributing N particles in N_i groups when the particles are distinguishable from each other, then the total number of ways of arranging N particles in N_i groups when the particles within a group cannot be distinguished from each other is

---

*A microstate or a microscopic state of a system is described by the instantaneous state of each particle, whereas a macrostate is described by the instantaneous properties of the total collection of particles.

†Quantum statistics counts all particles and considers it possible to distinguish between identical particles when they are at different energy levels. When they are at the same energy level, however, they are not necessarily distinguishable.

$$W = \frac{N!}{N_1! N_2! \ldots N_i! \ldots} = \frac{N!}{\prod_i N_i!}. \tag{8.1}$$

W is called the *thermodynamic probability* of a macrostate. It is equal to the number of microstates corresponding to a given macrostate where each arrangement of particles defines a microstate. The larger the value of W, the more probable the corresponding macrodistribution occurs. Thermodynamic probability should not be confused with *mathematical probability*, the latter being the ratio of the number of favorable events to the total number of events. The sum of all mathematical probabilities of the various possibilities of an event to occur is 1. Therefore, mathematical probabilities lie between 0 and 1, the former impossibility and the latter certainty. Note that the ratio of thermodynamic probabilities corresponding to two distributions gives the relative frequency (or probability) with which they occur.

Consider the example of arranging the letters a, b, and c. There are six ways (3!) in which the three letters may be distributed in three separate groups, with only one letter in each group. These are:

$$\boxed{a}\ \boxed{b}\ \boxed{c} \qquad \boxed{b}\ \boxed{c}\ \boxed{a} \qquad \boxed{c}\ \boxed{a}\ \boxed{b}$$
$$\boxed{a}\ \boxed{c}\ \boxed{b} \qquad \boxed{b}\ \boxed{a}\ \boxed{c} \qquad \boxed{c}\ \boxed{b}\ \boxed{a}$$

A number of arrangements are possible, depending on whether the three letters can be distributed in three groups, two groups, or one group. When only two groups are available for the three letters the arrangements are

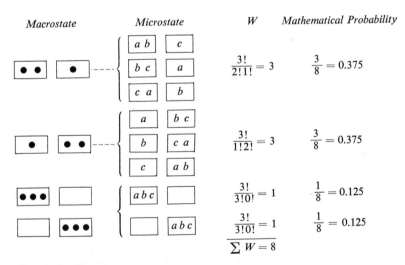

Macrostate	Microstate	W	Mathematical Probability
	ab c		
$\boxed{\bullet\ \bullet}\ \boxed{\bullet}$	bc a	$\dfrac{3!}{2!1!} = 3$	$\dfrac{3}{8} = 0.375$
	ca b		
	a bc		
$\boxed{\bullet}\ \boxed{\bullet\ \bullet}$	b ca	$\dfrac{3!}{1!2!} = 3$	$\dfrac{3}{8} = 0.375$
	c ab		
$\boxed{\bullet\bullet\bullet}\ \boxed{\ }$	abc $\boxed{\ }$	$\dfrac{3!}{3!0!} = 1$	$\dfrac{1}{8} = 0.125$
$\boxed{\ }\ \boxed{\bullet\bullet\bullet}$	$\boxed{\ }$ abc	$\dfrac{3!}{3!0!} = 1$	$\dfrac{1}{8} = 0.125$
		$\sum W = 8$	

Note that a change in the order of the letters within a group does not represent another arrangement of the group. The number, rather than the order, of the letters is important in these arrangements, just as the number of particles at each energy level is the significant factor.

The maximum value of W corresponds to the most probable arrangement of particles. The proof of this statement will be presented subsequently. At the maximum value of W, the rate of change in W must be zero; that is, $dW = 0$. Since W is usually a large number it is more convenient to maximize the logarithm of W, rather than W itself.

EXAMPLE 8.1: Answers to each of four questions may be either right or wrong. Find the distribution of the answers when each choice is as likely to be right as wrong.

Solution: The number of possible arrangements is $2^4 = 16$. If the correct and incorrect arrangements are denoted by $+$ and $-$, the following table can be formulated.

TABLE 8.1

Number of Correct Answers	Arrangement	Thermodynamic Probability or Relative Frequency of Occurrence	Mathematical Probability
4	$+ + + +$	$\dfrac{4!}{4!0!} = 1$	$\dfrac{1}{16}$
3	$\left.\begin{array}{l} + + + - \\ + + - + \\ + - + + \\ \\ - + + + \end{array}\right\}$	$\dfrac{4!}{3!1!} = 4$	$\dfrac{4}{16}$
2	$\left.\begin{array}{l} + + - - \\ + - - + \\ - - + + \\ + - + - \\ - + + - \\ - + - + \end{array}\right\}$	$\dfrac{4!}{2!2!} = 6$	$\dfrac{6}{16}$
1	$\left.\begin{array}{l} + - - - \\ - + - - \\ - - + - \\ - - - + \end{array}\right\}$	$\dfrac{4!}{1!3!} = 4$	$\dfrac{4}{16}$
0	$- - - -$	$\dfrac{4!}{0!4!} = 1$	$\dfrac{1}{16}$
Total		$\overline{16}$	$\overline{1.000}$

EXAMPLE 8.2: Consider a system of 3 particles a, b, and c and 4 energy levels

ϵ, 2ϵ, 3ϵ and 4ϵ. If the total energy of the particles is 9ϵ, find the number of possible arrangements.

Solution: Representing the energy levels horizontally, the possible arrangements are

Energy	Macrostate									
	A	B			C					
4ϵ		ab	ac	bc	a	a	b	b	c	c
3ϵ	abc				b	c	c	a	a	b
2ϵ					c	b	a	c	b	a
ϵ		c	b	a						

In the foregoing distribution there are 3 different macrostates and 10 microstates. Note that the mathematical probability of each microstate is 0.1 and for the macrostates A, B, and C they are 0.1, 0.3, and 0.6 as obtained by the following calculation:

Macrostate	W	Mathematical Probability
A	$\dfrac{3!}{3!0!} = 1$	$\dfrac{1}{10} = 0.10$
B	$\dfrac{3!}{2!1!} = 3$	$\dfrac{3}{10} = 0.30$
C	$\dfrac{3!}{1!1!1!} = 6$	$\dfrac{6}{10} = 0.60$
	$\sum W = 10$	

If the particles were indistinguishable, only the 3 macrostates and 3 microstates exist. These macrodistributions are

Energy	Macrostate		
	A	B	C
4ϵ		• •	•
3ϵ	• • •		•
2ϵ			•
ϵ		•	

8-3
Maxwell-
Boltzmann
Statistics

From the mathematical statistics approach, it can be shown that numerous particles, when capable of distributing themselves in several alternative arrangements, will tend to distribute themselves among the various alternatives in the most random way possible. Orderly distributions also occur, but they occur with less probability. The most probable distribution is one which is associated with the least "order."

In real systems, another factor controls the distribution. Different arrangements of atoms are associated with different quantities of energy. In the energy-limited system, the energy levels of the atoms tend to cluster about the same particular value. The clustering effect—owing to the averaging of energy levels—competes with the distributive effect which arises from the disorder associated with probability. Consequently, the final distribution is a resultant determined by these two competing effects.

In the Maxwell-Boltzmann model of the microstate, particles are distinguishable from each other and there is no limit to the number of particles per quantum state. The collection of the microstates forms the macrostates of the system.

In order to find the most probable macrostate of a system of particles, it is necessary to maximize the number of ways of forming a macrostate by maximizing the expressions describing the particle distribution while imposing applicable conditions of constraint. Since the number of particles is large, it is more convenient, from the arithmetic standpoint, to calculate the logarithm of probability than to calculate probability itself.

The thermodynamic probability W according to Eq. (8.1) is

$$W = \frac{N!}{\prod_i N_i!}.$$

The natural logarithm of the foregoing equation is

$$\ln W = \ln N! - \sum_i \ln N_i!.$$

Applying Stirling's approximation formula (see Appendix to this chapter),

$$\ln N! = N \ln N - N, \quad N \gg 1.$$

Therefore,

$$\ln W = N \ln N - N - \sum_i (N_i \ln N_i) + \sum_i N_i$$
$$= N \ln N - \sum_i N_i \ln N_i.$$

Using the symbol δ to denote a small change in $\ln W$ due to particle shifting between energy levels then,

$$\delta(\ln W) = -\delta \sum_i (N_i \ln N_i). \tag{8.2}$$

Equation (8.2) is subject to two conditions of constraint prescribed by the macroscopic state of the system: that the total number of molecules and the internal energy of the system remain unchanged. Thus,

$$\sum_i \delta N_i = dN = 0, \tag{8.3}$$

and

$$\sum_i \epsilon_i \, \delta N_i = dU = 0. \tag{8.4}$$

Equation (8.2) can then be written

$$\delta(\ln W) = -\delta \sum_i (N_i \ln N_i)$$

$$= -\sum_i N_i \frac{\delta N_i}{N_i} - \sum_i \ln N_i \, \delta N_i = 0 - \sum_i (\ln N_i) \, \delta N_i \,,$$

and for the maximum value of ln W(or of W), variation of ln W must vanish for small variations of N_i's,

$$\sum_i \ln N_i \, \delta N_i = 0. \tag{8.5}$$

We apply Lagrange's method of undetermined multipliers to Eq. (8.5), subject to the conditions of constraint given by Eq. (8.3) and (8.4). First, multiply Eq. (8.3) by $-\ln \alpha$, Eq. (8.4) by β and add the result to Eq. (8.5). Then,

$$-\ln \alpha \sum_i \delta N_i + \beta \sum_i \epsilon_i \, \delta N_i + \sum_i \ln N_i \, \delta N_i = 0,$$

or

$$\sum_i (-\ln \alpha + \beta \epsilon_i + \ln N_i) \, \delta N_i = 0.$$

Since α and β are yet to be determined, the δN_i's are regarded as independent. Thus the bracketed term in the summation must vanish for each value of δN_i in order to satisfy the preceding equation. Therefore

$$-\ln \alpha + \beta \epsilon_i + \ln N_i = 0,$$

or

$$N_i = \alpha e^{-\beta \epsilon_i}. \tag{8.6}$$

N_i in Eq. (8.6) indicates the most probable number of particles having energy ϵ_i. Equation (8.6) is called the *Maxwell-Boltzmann distribution law*. The total number of particles N is given by

$$N = \sum_i N_i = \alpha \sum_i e^{-\beta \epsilon_i}. \tag{8.7}$$

The sum in Eq. (8.7) is known as the state-sum or *partition function** of the system and is given the symbol Z. Thus

$$Z = \sum_i e^{-\beta \epsilon_i}. \tag{8.8}$$

The summation in the expression of Z is taken over all the states of energy of the system. For the most probable macrostate the number of particles N_i with quantum states in the ith group can now be written in terms of the partition function as

$$N_i = N \frac{e^{-\beta \epsilon_i}}{\sum_i e^{-\beta \epsilon_i}} = \frac{N}{Z} e^{-\beta \epsilon_i}. \tag{8.9}$$

As will be shown later, all thermodynamic properties may be correlated, either directly or indirectly to the partition function.

EXAMPLE 8.3:   Twenty-six particles are arranged in 4 cells according to the following table:

Cell	Number of Particles	Unit Energy
1	$N_1 = 8$	$1.0\,\epsilon$
2	$N_2 = 8$	$1.1\,\epsilon$
3	$N_3 = 6$	$1.2\,\epsilon$
4	$N_4 = 4$	$1.3\,\epsilon$

(a) If $\delta N_4 = -1$ and $\delta N_3 = 0$, find the new distribution subject to the conditions $\delta N = 0$ and $\delta U = 0$. (b) If the unit energy for each cell remains the same, which distribution would be most probable?

Solution: (a) The total energy is

$$U = (8 \times 1.0 + 8 \times 1.1 + 6 \times 1.2 + 4 \times 1.3)\epsilon = 29.2\epsilon.$$

Since $\delta N = 0$ and $\delta U = 0$, we have

$$N_1' + N_2' + 6 + 3 = 26 \quad \text{or} \quad N_1' = 17 - N_2', \tag{a}$$

and

$$(N_1' \times 1.0 + N_2' \times 1.1 + 6 \times 1.2 + 3 \times 1.3)\epsilon = 29.2\epsilon,$$

or

$$N_1' + 1.1 N_2' = 18.1. \tag{b}$$

From Eq. (a) and (b), $N_1' = 6$ and $N_2' = 11$.

(b) The probabilities of the two arrangements are

*It is called *partition function* because the atoms comprising the system at equilibrium may be considered to be partitioned among the different energy states.

$$W = \frac{26!}{8!8!6!4!} \quad \text{and} \quad W' = \frac{26!}{6!11!6!3!}.$$

Their ratio is

$$\frac{W}{W'} = 4.42.$$

Only 3 of the 26 particles are involved in the shift described here, but the probability that this change of configuration will occur is unfavorable, as indicated by the value of 4.42. It may, however, be shown that, when the particles are arranged in their most probable distribution, a shifting of a few of the particles between energy levels changes probability by only a small amount.

8-4
Entropy and
Probability
When an isolated system undergoes an irreversible process, such as the free expansion of a gas or the mixing of two gases, the number of possible microstates of the system is increased. In effect there is an increase in the value of the probability W. In a free expansion, the increase in probability is attributed to the larger volume and to the additional energy states, which are then available to the particles of the system. The molecules of the gas have a larger "choice" of locations or energy levels in the newly acquired volume. At the same time less is known about the location of a particular molecule after the expansion, for it is then free to move in a larger volume. Similarly, when two gases mix adiabatically, the number of microstates increases, and the molecules are distributed in a greater degree of randomness and disorder. At the same time the lack of knowledge about the states of the molecules increases.

When a system proceeds from a nonequilibrium state to an equilibrium state, its entropy increases. This increase in entropy parallels the increase in molecular disorder and the greater probability of attaining the equilibrium state. In other words the natural trend is for entropy to increase. We further note that both entropy and probability are properties of the system. Therefore, it may be postulated that entropy is related to the probability associated with a state and with the information that may be known about a system. A system reaches a stable equilibrium state when its entropy is at a maximum, and this state is the one of maximum thermodynamic probability and greatest disorder. Boltzmann conceived of this parallelism between entropy and probability and identified the state of maximum probability or least information with maximum entropy. Entropy may therefore be written as

$$S = f(W), \tag{8.10}$$

where f is a function to be determined according to the following reasoning:

In calculating the probability W of a system composed of two independent subsystems A and B, we note that each microstate of subsystem A may be chosen in combination with any microstate of subsystem B. The total number of microstates of the combined subsystems A and B is therefore

$$W = W_A W_B. \tag{8.11}$$

On the other hand, the entropy S of the system is the sum of the entropies of subsystems A and B,

$$S = S_A + S_B. \tag{8.12}$$

The two preceding relations dictate that, in seeking the nature of the function f of Eq. (8.10), one must take into account the respective multiplicative and additive natures of probability and entropy.

The entropy of the foregoing system, according to Eq. (8.10), may be written as

$$S = f(W_A W_B) = f(W_A) + f(W_B).$$

Differentiation of the preceding equation with respect to W_A gives

$$W_B f'(W_A W_B) = f'(W_A),$$

where the primes stand for differentiation with respect to the argument so that

$$f'(W_A W_B) = \frac{\partial f(W_A W_B)}{\partial(W_A W_B)} \quad \text{and} \quad f'(W_A) = \frac{\partial f(W_A)}{\partial W_A}.$$

A second differentiation with respect to W_B gives

$$W_A W_B f''(W_A W_B) + f'(W_A W_B) = 0,$$

or

$$W f''(W) + f'(W) = 0,$$

for which the general solution is

$$f(W) = S = C_1 \ln W + C_2. \tag{8.13}$$

To determine the constant C_1, consider a free expansion process in which $2N_0$ molecules of a perfect gas at a pressure p expand from a volume V_1 to V_2 where $V_2 = 2V_1$. Before expansion, the probability of finding all the $2N_0$ molecules in V_1 is $W_1 = 1$; also, the entropy is given by

$$S_1 = -2\mathscr{R} \ln p + S_0,$$

where p is the pressure measured in units of a standard pressure (say atmospheres), and S_0 is a constant depending only on temperature. After expansion, the $2N_0$ molecules occupy both the volumes V_1 and $V_2 - V_1$ and each volume contains N_0 molecules. Also, the pressure is $p/2$. The probability and entropy at this state are

$$W_2 = \frac{(2N_0)!}{N_0! \, N_0!},$$

and

$$S_2 = -2\mathscr{R} \ln \frac{p}{2} + S_0.$$

In evaluating the change in probability, the factorials in W_2 may be calculated, using Stirling's approximation formula. Thus,

$$\ln W_2 - \ln W_1 = \ln(2N_0!) - 2 \ln (N_0!) = 2N_0 \ln 2.$$

But the entropy change is

$$S_2 - S_1 = 2\mathscr{R} \ln 2.$$

Substituting for S and W in Eq. (8.13) gives

$$C_1 = \frac{S_2 - S_1}{\ln W_2 - \ln W_1} = \frac{\mathscr{R}}{N_0} = k. \tag{8.14}$$

The arbitrary additive constant C_2 can be chosen zero since at $W = 1$, $S = 0$. Equation (8.13) can then be written

$$S = k \ln W, \tag{8.15}$$

where k is Boltzmann's constant. Equation (8.15) states that the entropy of an isolated system at a certain state is equal to the natural logarithm of the thermodynamic probability of that state multiplied by Boltzmann's constant. Note that Eq. (8.15) satisfies the additive nature of entropy and the multiplicative nature of probability.

Equation (8.15) provides an interesting interpretation of the second law of thermodynamics. The second law, which, when considered as a consequence of the kinetic theory, indicates that an increase in entropy of a system means that the system changes from a less to a more probable state. This interpretation limits the application of the second law to systems containing large numbers of particles and also, it becomes a statement of a very high probability but not complete certainty.

The foregoing treatment has shown that molecules distribute themselves among several energy states according to certain patterns, and that in any particular system, a certain distribution is the most probable one, even though many distributions are possible. It is then pertinent to consider whether—and how—this most probable configuration differs in some thermodynamic way from the other configurations. Such differences may then indicate the relationship between thermodynamic properties and energy distribution.

8-5
Evaluation of
the Parameter β In the derivation of the Maxwell-Boltzmann distribution law, a Lagrange multiplier β was used. In order to utilize the resultant equation, it is necessary to determine the nature of this constant β. This is done by combining the expression derived by the statistical approach with expressions based on classical thermodynamics. When β is adequately defined, it becomes possible to evaluate all the thermodynamic functions from statistical mechanical relationships (that is, from considerations of energy distribution).

To find an expression for the Lagrange multiplier β, we proceed as follows:

The logarithm of the probability is given by

$$\ln W = N \ln N - \sum_i N_i \ln N_i.$$

But according to Eq. (8.9),

$$N_i = \frac{N}{Z} e^{-\beta \epsilon_i},$$

so that

$$\begin{aligned}\ln W &= N \ln N - \sum_i N_i (\ln N - \ln Z - \beta \epsilon_i) \\ &= N \ln N - \ln N \sum_i N_i + \sum_i N_i \ln Z + \beta \sum_i N_i \epsilon_i \\ &= N \ln Z + \beta U.\end{aligned}$$

By introducing entropy, from Eq. (8.15) into this expression, the following expression is obtained:

$$S = Nk \ln Z + k\beta U. \tag{8.16}$$

Classical thermodynamics gives the change in the internal energy of a simple system as

$$dU = T \, dS - p \, dV.$$

Also,

$$dU = \left(\frac{\partial U}{\partial S}\right)_V dS + \left(\frac{\partial U}{\partial V}\right)_S dV.$$

Since S and V are independent, then, equating the coefficients of dS gives

$$\left(\frac{\partial U}{\partial S}\right)_V = T \quad \text{or} \quad \left(\frac{\partial S}{\partial U}\right)_V = \frac{1}{T}. \tag{8.17}$$

Note that this equation may be considered a thermodynamic definition of absolute temperature, in which entropy is a thermodynamic potential function. The internal energy of a system of N particles is equal to the sum of the energies of the individual particles so that

$$U = \sum_i \epsilon_i N_i$$
$$= \sum_i \epsilon_i \frac{N}{Z} e^{-\beta \epsilon_i} = \frac{N}{Z} \sum_i \epsilon_i e^{-\beta \epsilon_i} = -\frac{N}{Z} \left(\frac{\partial Z}{\partial \beta}\right)_V,$$

or

$$\left(\frac{\partial Z}{\partial \beta}\right)_V = -\frac{ZU}{N}. \tag{8.18}$$

Differentiating Eq. (8.16) with respect to U at constant volume gives

$$\left(\frac{\partial S}{\partial U}\right)_V = kN \left(\frac{\partial \ln Z}{\partial U}\right)_V + k\beta + kU \left(\frac{\partial \beta}{\partial U}\right)_V.$$

Noting that $\partial \ln Z = \partial Z / Z$ and making use of Eq. (8.18), the foregoing equation becomes

$$\left(\frac{\partial S}{\partial U}\right)_V = \frac{kN}{Z} \left(\frac{\partial Z}{\partial \beta}\right)_V \left(\frac{\partial \beta}{\partial U}\right)_V + k\beta + kU \left(\frac{\partial \beta}{\partial U}\right)_V$$
$$= \frac{kN}{Z} \left(-\frac{UZ}{N}\right) \left(\frac{\partial \beta}{\partial U}\right)_V + k\beta + kU \left(\frac{\partial \beta}{\partial U}\right)_V,$$

or

$$\left(\frac{\partial S}{\partial U}\right)_V = k\beta. \tag{8.19}$$

Equating the right-hand sides of Eq. (8.17) and (8.19) gives

$$\beta = \frac{1}{kT}. \tag{8.20}$$

Note that β is directly related to the absolute temperature T. Replacing the value of β by $1/kT$ in the previous equations in which β appeared gives the following expressions:

$$N_i = \frac{N}{Z} e^{-\epsilon_i/kT}, \tag{8.21}$$

$$Z = \sum_i e^{-\epsilon_i/kT}, \tag{8.22}$$

$$S = Nk \ln Z + \frac{U}{T}. \tag{8.23}$$

The internal energy is given by

$$U = \frac{N}{Z} \sum_i \epsilon_i e^{-\epsilon_i/kT}.$$

But

$$\frac{dZ}{dT} = \frac{1}{kT^2} \sum_i \epsilon_i e^{-\epsilon_i/kT},$$

so that

$$U = \frac{NkT^2}{Z} \frac{dZ}{dT} = NkT^2 \left(\frac{\partial \ln Z}{\partial T}\right)_{N,V}. \tag{8.24}$$

The Helmholtz function is

$$F = U - TS = -NkT \ln Z. \tag{8.25}$$

The pressure of the system can be expressed by the relation

$$p = -\left(\frac{\partial F}{\partial V}\right)_{T,N}$$

$$= NkT \left(\frac{\partial \ln Z}{\partial V}\right)_{T,N}, \tag{8.26}$$

and so on for the other thermodynamic functions.

8-6
Degeneracy of
Energy Levels
The previously presented solution considered situations where particles are distributed among different energy levels. A specialized case occurs frequently where two (or more) energy states differ from each other, from the standpoint of configuration, but their energy values and number of particles are identical. Such cases mean that a greater number of different arrangements is possible. The method of evaluating this effect will now be considered.

If several states of a system have the same energy level, this energy level is said to be *degenerate*. We shall denote the number of discrete quantum energy states corresponding to an energy level ϵ_i, by g_i; the ϵ_ith level of energy is then said to be g_i-fold degenerate. In the case of a monatomic gas, for example, if N_i is the number of molecules in the ϵ_ith level,

$g_i \gg N_i$ at room temperature (or higher) and the degree of degeneracy increases rapidly with the increase of energy. At low temperatures, the lower energy states become more populated and N_i is not much different from g_i. The following analysis will lead to an expression of the Maxwell-Boltzmann distribution law, taking the degeneracy of energy levels into account.

Suppose it is required to arrange N particles into groups with $N_1, N_2, \ldots N_i, \ldots$ particles in the respective groups. Let the energy level of the first group of N_1 particles be ϵ_1 with a degeneracy g_1, the energy level of the second group of N_2 particles be ϵ_2 with a degeneracy g_2, etc. Starting with the first group, since any one of the N particles may occupy any one of the g_1 states of the energy level, there are $g_1 N$ possible arrangements for the first of the N particles. Since any one of the remaining $(N - 1)$ particles may occupy any one of the g_1 states, then there are $g_1(N - 1)$ arrangements for the second particle, and so on for the rest of the N_1 particles. The number of possible arrangements in the first group of N_1 particles, taking into account the indistinguishability of particles, is then

$$\frac{g_1 N g_1(N - 1)g_1(N - 2) \ldots g_1(N - N_1 + 1)}{N_1!} = \frac{g_1^{N_1} N!}{(N - N_1)!N_1!}.$$

For the second group of N_2 particles having an energy level ϵ_2 and a degeneracy g_2, there are $g_2(N - N_1)$ possible arrangements for the first particle, $g_2(N - N_1 - 1)$ for the second, etc. The number of arrangements in the second group of N_2 particles is then

$$\frac{g_2(N - N_1)g_2(N - N_1 - 1)g_2(N - N_1 - 2) \ldots g_2(N - N_1 - N_2 + 1)}{N_2!}$$

$$= \frac{g_2^{N_2}(N - N_1)!}{(N - N_1 - N_2)!N_2!}.$$

In general for the ith group, the number of arrangements is

$$\frac{g_i(N - N_1 - N_2 - \cdots N_{i-1})g_i(N - N_1 - N_2 - \cdots N_{i-1} - 1) \ldots g_i(N - N_1 - N_2 - N_i + 1)}{N_i!}$$

$$= \frac{g_i^{N_i}(N - N_1 - N_2 - \cdots N_i - 1)!}{(N - N_1 - N_2 - \cdots - N_i)!N_i!}.$$

Multiplying the preceding expressions gives the total number of arrangements as

$$W = \frac{(g_1^{N_1} g_2^{N_2} g_3^{N_3} \ldots g_i^{N_i} \ldots)N!}{N_1!N_2!N_3! \ldots N_i! \ldots} = N! \prod_i \frac{g_i^{N_i}}{N_i!}. \tag{8.27}$$

Equation (8.27) thus replaces Eq. (8.1) if degeneracy, that is the number of quantum states in the ith level, is taken into consideration.

Applying Stirling's approximation to Eq. (8.27) gives

$$\ln W = \ln N! + \sum_i N_i \ln g_i - \sum_i \ln N_i!$$
$$= N \ln N - N + \sum_i N_i \ln g_i - \sum_i N_i \ln N_i + \sum_i N_i,$$

or

$$\ln W = N \ln N + \sum_i N_i \ln \frac{g_i}{N_i}. \tag{8.28}$$

Equation (8.28) is subject to the two following conditions of constraint:

$$\sum_i \delta N_i = dN = 0, \tag{8.29}$$

and

$$\sum_i \epsilon_i \, \delta N_i = dU = 0. \tag{8.30}$$

For the maximum value of W (at which $dg_i = 0$), we write

$$\delta \ln W = \sum_i \ln \left(\frac{g_i}{N_i} \right) \delta N_i = 0. \tag{8.31}$$

Multiplying Eq. (8.29) and (8.30) by the Lagrange multipliers $\ln \alpha$ and $-\beta$ and adding the result to Eq. (8.31) gives

$$\sum_i \left[\ln \alpha - \beta \epsilon_i + \ln \frac{g_i}{N_i} \right] \delta N_i = 0.$$

Since the δN_i's may be treated as independent, then

$$\ln \frac{\alpha g_i}{N_i} = \beta \epsilon_i,$$

or

$$N_i = \alpha g_i e^{-\beta \epsilon_i}. \tag{8.32}$$

Equation (8.32) is called the *general Maxwell-Boltzmann distribution law.* It differs from Eq. (8.6) by the weighing factor g_i which accounts for the degeneracy of the energy levels.

The partition function Z now takes the more general form,

$$Z = \sum_i g_i e^{-\epsilon_i/kT}. \tag{8.33}$$

Summation in the foregoing expression is taken over all the levels of energy.

8-7
Other Kinds of
Statistics
Equally important as the Maxwell-Boltzmann distribution law are the Fermi-Dirac and Bose-Einstein statistics. All three statistics apply probability theory to determine the distribution of properties of particles. Each develops a distribution function which gives the average number of particles at a given energy state. At statistical equilibrium, the relative number of molecules at any particular energy level is essentially constant, even though the energy states of individual molecules may be constantly changing owing to particle collisions. Which statistical approach to use depends on the nature and the behavior of particles considered. The Maxwell-Boltzmann statistics, for example, describe a classical system composed of identical particles in thermal equilibrium that are distinguishable. A perfect gas in which there is a distribution of particle energies over a wide range is described by a modified Maxwell-Boltzmann statistics which corrects for the indistinguishability of the molecules. Discrepancies appear, however, when Maxwell-Boltzmann statistics are applied to electrons in a metal. One of these discrepancies is the difference between the observed and the predicted electrical conductivity of a metal. Fermi-Dirac statistics resolve these difficulties.

8-8
Fermi-Dirac
Statistics
The essential difference between Fermi-Dirac and Maxwell-Boltzmann statistics arises from the method of defining and counting microstates. Fermi-Dirac statistics are particularly appropriate for a system in which the particles are charged, such as electrons in a metal. Free electrons in a metal, sometimes called *perfect electron gas*, can move throughout the entire volume of the system. Unlike molecules, electrons in a metal show a considerable amount of interaction among themselves because of their high density, and this effect cannot be ignored. As a result, no two particles may occupy the same energy state; that is, they may not have the same quantum states, which is a statement of the Pauli exclusion principle.* Thus, Fermi-Dirac statistics apply to systems of identical indistinguishable particles, such as electrons and protons which obey the Pauli exclusion principle. The following paragraph outlines the derivation of Fermi-Dirac statistics:

Suppose it is required to arrange N indistinguishable particles between energy levels $\epsilon_1, \epsilon_2, \ldots$, etc., having the respective degeneracies $g_1, g_2, \ldots$, etc. The number of energy states g_i of any energy level ϵ_i is assumed to be larger than the number of particles N_i in that level. Furthermore, only one particle is allowed in each energy state. Let N_1 be the number of particles assigned to energy level ϵ_1. The first particle has a choice of g_1 states $(g_1 > N_1)$; the second has a choice of $(g_1 - 1)$ states; etc. The total number of arrangements, taking into account the indistinguishability of the N_1 particles, is

---

*The Pauli exclusion principle states that no two particles can occupy the same quantum state.

$$\frac{g_1(g_1 - 1)(g_1 - 2) \ldots (g_1 - N_1 + 1)}{N_1!} = \frac{g_1!}{N_1!(g_1 - N_1)!}.$$

For the ith energy level the foregoing expression takes the form

$$W_i = \frac{g_i!}{N_i!(g_i - N_i)!}.$$

The total number of arrangements for all energy states is the product of the individual arrangements of the N_i groups, or

$$W = \prod_i \frac{g_i!}{N_i!(g_i - N_i)!}. \tag{8.34}$$

Taking the natural logarithm of Eq. (8.34) and making use of Stirling's approximation for $g_i!$ and $(g_i - N_i)!$ gives

$$\ln W = \sum_i [\ln g_i! - \ln N_i! - \ln(g_i - N_i)!]$$
$$= \sum_i [g_i \ln g_i - g_i - N_i \ln N_i + N_i - (g_i - N_i)\ln(g_i - N_i) + (g_i - N_i)]$$
$$= \sum_i [g_i \ln g_i - N_i \ln N_i - (g_i - N_i)\ln(g_i - N_i)]$$

and

$$\delta(\ln W) = \sum_i \left[-\ln \frac{N_i}{(g_i - N_i)} \right] \delta N_i.$$

To determine the most probable distribution, the value of $\ln W$ is maximized:

$$\sum_i \left[\ln\left(\frac{g_i - N_i}{N_i} \right) \right] \delta N_i = 0. \tag{8.35}$$

In addition, the following two equations of constraint apply:

$$\sum_i \delta N_i = dN = 0, \tag{8.36}$$

$$\sum_i \epsilon_i \delta N_i = dU = 0. \tag{8.37}$$

Multiplying Eq. (8.36) by $(-\ln B)$ and Eq. (8.37) by $(-\beta)$, then adding the result to Eq. (8.35), gives

$$\sum_i \left[-\ln B - \beta \epsilon_i + \ln \frac{g_i - N_i}{N_i} \right] \delta N_i = 0.$$

Since each coefficient of δN_i in the summation must be equal to zero, then

$$\frac{g_i - N_i}{N_i} = B e^{\beta \epsilon_i},$$

or

$$N_i = \frac{g_i}{B e^{\beta \epsilon_i} + 1}. \tag{8.38}$$

Equation (8.38), which describes the distribution of particles according to Fermi-Dirac statistics, was derived by Fermi and was applied by Dirac to electrons in metal.

8-9 Bose-Einstein Statistics

Bose-Einstein statistics are most appropriate for systems consisting of identical indistinguishable particles, such as light quanta or photons. Unlike Fermi-Dirac statistics, the Bose-Einstein distribution law imposes no limit on the number of particles which can occupy the same energy state, and therefore, the Pauli exclusion principle is not applicable.

Proceeding as in Fermi-Dirac statistics, the first particle of the group N_1 has a choice of g_1 states of energy level ϵ_1. The second particle has a choice of $(g_1 - 1)$ states, in addition to the state occupied by the first particle. This means that there are g_1 arrangements if both particles are at the same state and $[g_1(g_1 - 1)/2]$ arrangements if they are at different states. Therefore, the total number of possible arrangements of the first two particles is

$$W_2 = g_1 + \frac{g_1(g_1 - 1)}{2} = \frac{g_1(g_1 + 1)}{2}.$$

The addition of a third particle will give rise to g_1 arrangements when all the particles are in one state, $g_1(g_1 - 1)$ arrangements when two particles are in one state and the third particle is in a different state, and $\{[g_1(g_1 - 1)/2][(g_1 - 2)/3]\}$ arrangements when the three particles are in different states. Thus, the total number of possible arrangements is

$$W_3 = g_1 + g_1(g_1 - 1) + \frac{g_1(g_1 - 1)}{2}\frac{(g_1 - 2)}{3} = \frac{g_1(g_1 + 1)(g_1 + 2)}{3!}.$$

To generalize, then, the number of possible arrangements of N_i particles in the g_i states of the energy level ϵ_i is

$$W_i = \frac{g_i(g_i + 1)(g_i + 2) \ldots (g_i + N_i - 1)}{N_i!} = \frac{(g_i + N_i - 1)!}{N_i!(g_i - 1)!}.$$

The total number of the possible arrangements for all energy levels is equal to the product of all of the W_i's, or

$$W = \prod_i W_i = \prod_i \frac{(g_i + N_i - 1)!}{N_i!(g_i - 1)!}. \tag{8.39}$$

Taking the natural logarithm of Eq. (8.39) and neglecting the term 1 compared to $(g_i + N_i)$ or g_i gives

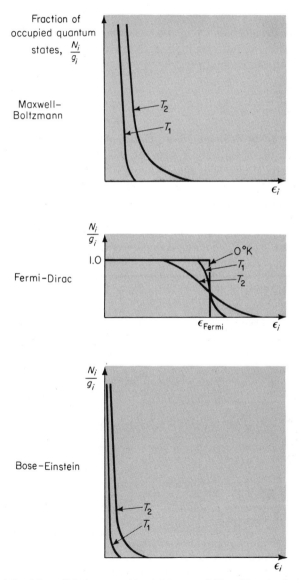

Fig. 8.1. *Maxwell-Boltzmann, Fermi-Dirac, and Bose-Einstein distributions.*

$$\ln W = \sum_i [\ln (g_i + N_i)! - \ln N_i! - \ln g_i!]$$

$$= \sum_i [(g_i + N_i) \ln (g_i + N_i) - N_i \ln N_i - g_i \ln g_i]$$

and

$$\delta(\ln W) = \sum_i \left[\ln \frac{g_i + N_i}{N_i} \right] \delta N_i.$$

By maximizing the probability in the preceding equation and by imposing the two conditions of constraint, the following expression, for the Bose-Einstein distribution, is obtained:

$$N_i = \frac{g_i}{B e^{\beta \epsilon_i} - 1}, \quad (g_i \gg 1). \tag{8.40}$$

The Maxwell-Boltzmann, Fermi-Dirac, and Bose-Einstein distribution differ from each other only by a term of ± 1 in the denominator. They become essentially identical in value when $B e^{\beta \epsilon_i}$ is large compared to unity. In this case $N_i/g_i \ll 1$, and only one particle is found in the same quantum state. This condition, which greatly simplifies mathematical procedure,

TABLE 8.2 Comparison between Maxwell-Boltzmann, Fermi-Dirac, and Bose-Einstein Statistics

	Maxwell-Boltzmann	Fermi-Dirac	Bose-Einstein
Characteristic model	Large number of identical particles that are distinguishable.	Large number of identical indistinguishable particles that conform to the Pauli exclusion principle.	Large number of identical indistinguishable particles.
Thermodynamic probability	$W = N! \prod_i \dfrac{g_i^{N_i}}{N_i!}$	$W = \prod_i \dfrac{g_i!}{N_i!(g_i - N_i)!}$	$W = \prod_i \dfrac{(g_i + N_i - 1)!}{N_i!(g_i - 1)!}$
Distribution law	$N_i = \dfrac{g_i e^{-\epsilon_i/kT}}{B}$	$N_i = \dfrac{g_i}{B e^{\epsilon_i/kT} + 1}$	$N_i = \dfrac{g_i}{B e^{\epsilon_i/kT} - 1}$
Examples of systems which follow the statistics	Gas molecules* (except near 0°K); electrons at extremely high temperatures.	Electrons in metal (except at very high temperatures).	Photons of radiation; gas molecules near 0°K.

*provided that $N_i/g_i \ll 1$ and the value of W is divided by $N!$ to discount the distinguishability of the N particles.

exists in a perfect gas in which the predominant energies are translational (except at low temperatures). The three distributions are compared in Fig. 8.1 and in Table 8.2.

At a temperature of absolute zero, the energy level predicted by the Maxwell-Boltzmann distribution and the Bose-Einstein distribution is zero. On the other hand, the Fermi-Dirac law shows a finite energy level at a temperature of absolute zero. At this temperature, the low energy levels become well populated; however, all the electrons cannot be at zero energy level because of the Pauli exclusion principle. This leads to an energy distribution in which all of the lowest energy levels are completely filled, but no more than one electron is contained in any state. Thus the number of the occupied energy states starting from zero up to an energy level ϵ_f is equal to the number of electrons ($N_i = g_i$), where ϵ_f is called the *Fermi level of energy* and represents the maximum energy at the absolute zero of temperature. States of higher energies are empty.

EXAMPLE 8.4: It is required to compare the Fermi-Dirac, Bose-Einstein, and the Maxwell-Boltzmann statistics when three particles are arranged in two energy levels. Two particles are at energy level ϵ_1 having a degeneracy $g_1 = 2$ and one particle at energy level ϵ_2 having a degeneracy $g_2 = 1$.

Solution
Fermi-Dirac:

$$W = \prod_i \frac{g_i!}{N_i!(g_i - N_i)!}$$

$$= \frac{2!}{2!0!} \cdot \frac{1!}{1!0!} = 1.$$

Bose-Einstein:

$$W = \prod_i \frac{(g_i + N_i - 1)!}{N_i!(g_i - 1)!}$$

$$= \frac{3!}{2!1!} \cdot \frac{1!}{1!0!} = 3.$$

Maxwell-Boltzmann:

$$W = N! \prod_i \frac{g_i^{N_i}}{N_i!} = \frac{3! \cdot (2^2 \cdot 1^1)}{2!1!} = 12.$$

Here the particles are called a, b, and c since they are distinguishable.

$$N_1 = 2: \quad \begin{matrix} n_1 = 2 \\ n_2 = 0 \end{matrix} \quad \text{or} \quad \begin{matrix} n_1 = 1 \\ n_2 = 1 \end{matrix} \quad \text{or} \quad \begin{matrix} n_1 = 0 \\ n_2 = 2 \end{matrix}$$

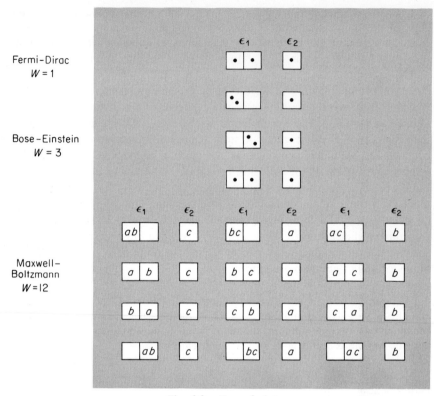

Fig. 8.2. *Example 8.4.*

$$W = \frac{3!}{2!0!1!} + \frac{3!}{1!1!1!} + \frac{3!}{0!2!1!} = 3 + 6 + 3 = 12 \quad \text{(as before)}.$$

Therefore,

$$W_{FD} : W_{BE} : W_{MB} = 1 : 3 : 12.$$

Figure 8.2 illustrates the particle distributions for the three statistics.

**8-10
Partition
Functions**
The expressions for partition function which were derived in previous sections applied to an individual molecule. To describe the properties of a gas consisting of N molecules, an expression of the partition function for a system that consists of N particles is developed. This section outlines the relationship between these two partition functions.

According to Maxwell-Boltzmann statistics, the thermodynamic probability given by Eq. (8.27) is

$$W = N! \prod_i \frac{g_i^{N_i}}{N_i!}.$$

352

Taking the logarithm of the preceding equation and using Stirling's approximation gives

$$\ln W = N \ln N + \sum_i N_i \ln \frac{g_i}{N_i}.$$

Substituting from the expression,

$$N_i = \frac{N}{Z} g_i e^{-\epsilon_i/kT},$$

into the previous equation gives

$$\ln W = N \ln N + \sum_i \left[\left(\frac{N}{Z} g_i e^{-\epsilon_i/kT} \right) \ln \frac{g_i}{\frac{N}{Z} g_i e^{-\epsilon_i/kT}} \right]$$

$$= N \ln N + \frac{N}{Z} \ln \frac{Z}{N} \sum_i \left(g_i e^{-\epsilon_i/kT} \right) - \frac{N}{Z} \sum_i \left(g_i e^{-\epsilon_i/kT} \ln e^{-\epsilon_i/kT} \right)$$

$$= N \ln N + \frac{N}{Z} \ln \frac{Z}{N} \sum_i \left(g_i e^{-\epsilon_i/kT} \right) + \frac{N}{Z} \sum_i \left(g_i \frac{\epsilon_i}{kT} e^{-\epsilon_i/kT} \right).$$

But

$$Z = \sum_i g_i e^{-\epsilon_i/kT} \quad \text{and} \quad U = \frac{N \sum_i g_i \epsilon_i e^{-\epsilon_i/kT}}{Z},$$

which, when substituted in the preceding equation, gives

$$\ln W = \ln Z^N + \frac{U}{kT}. \tag{8.41}$$

Therefore, the partition function $\mathcal{Z}$ of N distinguishable particles in terms of the molecular partition function Z may be written in the form

$$\mathcal{Z} = (Z)^N. \tag{8.42}$$

When the particles are indistinguishable, the expression for W given by Eq. (8.27) must be divided by $N!$ so that

$$W = \prod_i \frac{g_i^{N_i}}{N_i!}. \tag{8.43}$$

Taking the logarithm of Eq. (8.43) and using Stirling's approximation gives

$$\ln W = \sum_i [N_i \ln g_i - N_i \ln N_i + N_i] = \sum_i N_i \left[\ln \frac{g_i}{N_i} + 1\right].$$

Substituting for N_i gives

$$\ln W = \sum_i N_i \left[\ln \frac{g_i}{(N/Z)g_i e^{-\epsilon_i/kT}} + 1\right]$$

$$= \sum_i N_i \left[\ln \frac{Z}{N} + \frac{\epsilon_i}{kT} + 1\right]$$

$$= N \ln \frac{Z}{N} + \frac{U}{kT} + N$$

$$= N \ln Z - N \ln N + \frac{U}{kT} + N$$

$$= N \ln Z - \ln N! + \frac{U}{kT}$$

$$= \ln \left(\frac{Z^N}{N!}\right) + \frac{U}{kT}. \tag{8.44}$$

Therefore, the partition function $\mathcal{Z}$ for indistinguishable particles may be written in terms of the molecular partition function Z as

$$\mathcal{Z} = \frac{(Z)^N}{N!}. \tag{8.45}$$

The foregoing result indicates that when Maxwell-Boltzmann statistics are applied to a gas, the expression for W_{MB} must be divided by $N!$. This division is necessary, since the molecules of a gas are identical, so that from a quantum statistics point of view they are indistinguishable except for their energy levels. Note, however, that the expression W_{MB} (when divided by $N!$) does not give the correct number of microstates of indistinguishable particles.

8-11
Statistics of a
Monatomic Gas
The Maxwell-Boltzmann velocity distribution law, which was derived in Chapter 7, can also be derived from the foregoing statistics. Consider a volume V containing a perfect monatomic gas of indistinguishable atoms. Let more than one atom be allowed in any energy level; that is, the gas is degenerate; furthermore, let the number of the allowable quantum states g_i in the ith level be much larger than the number of molecules in that level, that is, $g_i/N_i \gg 1$. According to Bose-Einstein statistics, the number of atoms of energy ϵ_i is

$$N_i = \frac{g_i}{Be^{\beta\epsilon_i} - 1}, \tag{8.40}$$

But since $g_i/N_i \gg 1$, therefore $Be^{\beta \epsilon_i} \gg 1$. Consequently, the 1 in the denominator of Eq. (8.40) may be neglected. This is a fairly good approximation even at low energies because B is large (except at very low temperature). The Bose-Einstein distribution law then becomes

$$N_i = \frac{g_i}{Be^{\beta \epsilon_i}} = g_i \, \alpha \, e^{-\beta \epsilon_i}, \tag{8.46}$$

which is the Boltzmann distribution law where $\alpha = 1/B$.

Consider next a *momentum space* of coordinates p_x, p_y, and p_z and let the momentum of each atom in a volume V be represented by a momentum vector starting at the origin. The momentum of atoms having energies between ϵ_i and $\epsilon_i + \Delta \epsilon_i$ lies in a momentum shell of radius p_i and thickness Δp_i. The volume of this shell is

$$V = (4\pi p_i^2) \, \Delta p_i.$$

Although momentum space is analogous to velocity space, the distribution of the end points of the vectors does not follow the same pattern. In velocity space, changes in magnitude occur in a continuous way, the increments in velocity being infinitesimally small. In momentum space, however, increments in momentum occur in discrete steps, owing to the quantum restrictions imposed on energy. The spacing between the end points of the momentum vectors is still small, so that the number of points in a small volume in momentum space can be calculated.

The quantum cell in the six-dimensional phase space of coordinates x, y, z, p_x, p_y, and p_z defines the location of an atom. The Heisenberg uncertainty principle discussed in Section 8.15 imposes the condition that the quantum cell cannot be less than h^3, where h is Planck's constant. An atom whose momentum lies in the spherical shell may be at any location within the volume V, and the number of possible quantum states in the shell (degeneracy) is then:

$$g_i = (4\pi p_i^2 \Delta p_i)\left(\frac{V}{h^3}\right).$$

Since $p = mv$, then

$$g_i = \frac{4\pi m^3 v_i^2 V \, dv_i}{h^3}.$$

Also,

$$\alpha^* = \frac{N}{Z} = \frac{N}{V}\left(\frac{h^2}{2\pi mkT}\right)^{3/2}.$$

*See Eq. (9.3) of Chap. 9.

Substituting for g_i and α in Eq. (8.46) and noting that $\epsilon_i = \frac{1}{2}mv_i^2$, then

$$dN = N_i = \left(\frac{4\pi m^3 v_i^2 V \, dv_i}{h^3}\right) \frac{N}{V} \left(\frac{h^2}{2\pi mkT}\right)^{3/2} e^{-m_i v_i^2/2kT}$$

or

$$\frac{dN}{dv_i} = \frac{4N}{\sqrt{\pi}} \left(\frac{m}{2kT}\right)^{3/2} v_i^2 e^{-mv_i^2/2kT}. \tag{8.47}$$

Equation (8.47) indicates the speed distribution function and is the same as Eq. (7.16).

**8-12
Wave Mechanics and Internal Energy Levels**
In the previous sections, formulas were derived for calculating various thermodynamic functions. These are based on partition functions, which describe how a multitude of atoms (or molecules) capable of existing at different energy levels will distribute themselves among the various levels. The remaining problem is to determine these energy values. For this, it becomes necessary to delve into wave mechanics.

Although Newtonian mechanics can describe large-scale or macroscopic systems, it cannot describe the behavior of particles at the atomic scale adequately. Microscopic particles are subject to *quantum restrictions*, which allow the particles to have only discrete values of energy. The behavior of these microscopic particles is described by the Schrödinger wave equation.

Certain phenomena, such as the diffraction of electrons by a crystal lattice, photoelectric* effects, and the radiation emitted from an isothermal enclosure, suggested that these particles can have only definite energy levels. Furthermore, there was evidence that microscopic particles behave in a wave-like manner, operating at definite and discrete values of frequency. This wave-particle duality led Planck to propose that energy emitted from, or absorbed by, a heated surface takes place in small quanta called *photons*. The energy of a photon of radiation is proportional to the frequency of radiation according to Planck's equation:

$$\epsilon = h\nu, \tag{8.48}$$

where h is Planck's constant (equal to 6.624×10^{-27} erg-sec). Note that the energy of a photon associated with radiation of a given frequency has a single distinct value; that is, it is quantized.

In 1925 De Broglie postulated that a particle of momentum p has associated with it a wave of wavelength λ given by the relation

*The emission of elections from a metal due to incident photons is called photoelectric emission.

$$\lambda = \frac{h}{p}. \tag{8.49}$$

Equation (8.49) is called the *De Broglie equation* which is based on Eq. (8.48) and on the classical result that the ratio of energy to momentum in an electromagnetic plane wave equals the velocity of the wave. Equation (8.49) was derived for a photon but applies equally well to material particles. In 1927 Davisson and Germer using electrons, and Stern and Estermann using atoms confirmed the validity of Eq. (8.49) by diffraction experiments with a crystal lattice. For macroscopic particles, the wavelength is so small that the wavelike properties are very difficult to observe, and thus classical mechanics is sufficient to describe the motion of macroscopic particles to a very high degree of precision.

The foregoing experiments among many others confirmed the dual character of atomic particles and suggested that the behavior of matter on an atomic scale is associated with a field having a wavelike character. This field may be described by a function called the *wave function*. A good example is electromagnetic radiation which behaves like waves, having length and frequency, and also like particles of definite energy and momentum.

EXAMPLE 8.5: Compare the wavelengths of an electron (mass = 9.1086 $\times$ 10^{-28} gram) when accelerated through a potential of 10,000 volts and a mass of 1 gram moving at a velocity of 5000 cm/sec.

Solution: Since 1 electron volt is the energy necessary to accelerate an electron through a potential of 1 volt, the kinetic energy acquired by the electron is

$$\epsilon = e\,V\,\text{erg},$$

where $e = 4.8025 \times 10^{-10}$ electrostatic units of charge and V is the voltage drop, (1 volt $= 1/299.776$ esu). The kinetic energy of the electron is

$$\epsilon = (4.8025 \times 10^{-10})\,\frac{10,000}{299.776} = 1.6 \times 10^{-8}\ \text{gm-cm}^2/\text{sec}^2 = 1.6 \times 10^{-8}\ \text{erg},$$

but

$$p = \sqrt{2m\epsilon} = \sqrt{2\,(9.1086 \times 10^{-28})\,(1.6 \times 10^{-8})} = 5.4 \times 10^{-18}\ \text{gm-cm/sec}.$$

Therefore, the wavelength of the electron is

$$\lambda = \frac{h}{p} = \frac{(6.624 \times 10^{-27})\ \text{gm-cm}^2/\text{sec}}{(5.4 \times 10^{-18})\ \text{gm-cm/sec}} = 11.12 \times 10^{-10}\ \text{cm}.$$

In the case of the mass of 1 gram,

$$\lambda = \frac{h}{p} = \frac{6.624 \times 10^{-27}}{1 \times 5000} = 1.325 \times 10^{-30}\ \text{cm}.$$

This example demonstrates that, in the case of heavy particles, the wavelengths are so small that classical mechanics is sufficient to describe the motion.

8-13   Many of the characteristic properties of a sub-
Wave Equation   stance are associated with the motion of its molecules so that a knowledge of the kinetic behavior of the molecules of a gas should lead to prediction of properties of the gas. But when very large velocities and very small particles are involved, the classical methods of describing the motion do not adequately explain properties. Methods based on a wave interpretation, however, have proved useful, and therefore the wave mechanics equations will now be examined.

Consider the small transverse vibration of a homogeneous string stretched between two points on the x axis as shown in Fig. 8.3. Let the vibration of the string be confined to the $x\psi$ plane; that is, there is no lateral vibration. It is assumed that the mass density ρ per unit length is

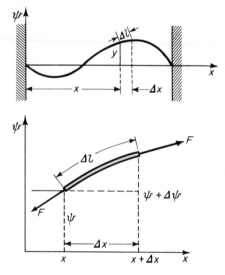

Fig. 8.3. *Vibration of a string.*

uniform and the displacements of the string are small, such that $\Delta l \approx \Delta x$. Let F be the uniform tension in the string. The ψ component of the tension force in the string at the end (x, ψ) is given by

$$-F\frac{\partial \Psi}{\partial l} = -F\frac{\partial \Psi}{\partial x}\frac{\partial x}{\partial l} \approx -F\frac{\partial \Psi}{\partial x},$$

while at the end $(x + \Delta x, \psi + \Delta\psi)$ it is given by

$$F\frac{\partial \Psi}{\partial x} + F\frac{\partial^2 \Psi}{\partial x^2}\Delta x.$$

In the last expression, the remaining terms in Taylor's expansion* have been neglected. Equating the net force in the ψ direction to the mass of element Δl multiplied by its acceleration gives

$$F\frac{\partial^2 \Psi}{\partial x^2}\Delta x = \rho\,\Delta x \frac{\partial^2 \Psi}{\partial \tau^2},$$

and therefore,

$$\frac{\partial^2 \Psi}{\partial x^2} = \frac{\rho}{F}\frac{\partial^2 \Psi}{\partial \tau^2}.$$

Denoting ρ/F by $1/c^2$ gives the *wave equation* as

$$\frac{\partial^2 \Psi}{\partial x^2} = \frac{1}{c^2}\frac{\partial^2 \Psi}{\partial \tau^2}, \tag{8.50}$$

where c is called the *wave velocity* of the vibrating string. Equation (8.50) is a homogeneous partial differential equation whose solution may be written as the product of two separate functions, one dependent only on time and the other dependent only on position, so that

$$\Psi(x,\tau) = f(x)g(\tau)$$

Substituting the foregoing expression for Ψ into Eq. (8.50) gives

$$\frac{\partial^2 [f(x)g(\tau)]}{\partial x^2} = \frac{1}{c^2}\frac{\partial^2 [f(x)g(\tau)]}{\partial \tau^2}$$

$$g(\tau)\frac{d^2 f(x)}{dx^2} = \frac{1}{c^2}f(x)\frac{d^2 g(\tau)}{d\tau^2}$$

$$\frac{1}{f(x)}\frac{d^2 f(x)}{dx^2} = \frac{1}{c^2}\left[\frac{1}{g(\tau)}\right]\frac{d^2 g(\tau)}{d\tau^2}. \tag{8.51}$$

Through separation of variables, each side of Eq. (8.51) must be equal to the same constant since the two functions are independent of each other. Assuming harmonic waves, the function Ψ must repeat itself for each period of vibration or at time intervals equal to $2\pi/\omega$. Therefore, the time-dependent function $g(\tau)$ may be expressed in the form

$$g(\tau) = Ae^{-i\omega\tau},$$

*Taylor's expansion

$$f(x+h) = f(x) + hf'(x) + \frac{h^2}{2!}f''(x) + \frac{h^3}{3!}f'''(x) + \cdots$$

(primes indicate differentiation with respect to the argument).

where A is a constant, $i = \sqrt{-1}$ and ω is the angular frequency equal to $2\pi\nu$. Substituting for $g(\tau)$ in Eq. (8.51) gives the position-dependent equation as

$$\frac{d^2 f(x)}{dx^2} = -\frac{\omega^2}{c^2} f(x),$$

(8.52)

or in terms of wavelength

$$\frac{d^2 f(x)}{dx^2} = -\frac{(2\pi)^2}{\lambda^2} f(x).$$

(8.53)

The propagation of longitudinal waves along an elastic homogeneous bar may be described by the wave equation (8.50) in which Ψ is interpreted as the longitudinal displacement from the equilibrium position. For longitudinal waves in a fluid such as air, the wave function Ψ represents the density of the medium in which the waves propagate. In such cases, the vibrations occur in three perpendicular directions rather than in only one direction. Three equations analogous to Eq. (8.50) can be formulated, and when they are combined, the three-dimensional wave equation results:

$$\frac{\partial^2 \Psi}{\partial x^2} + \frac{\partial^2 \Psi}{\partial y^2} + \frac{\partial^2 \Psi}{\partial z^2} = \frac{1}{c^2} \frac{\partial^2 \Psi}{\partial \tau^2}.$$

(8.54)

**8-14
Schrödinger's
Wave Equation** At this point, the objective lies in determining how the energy of a molecule is distributed. Classically, the energy of a particle is in the form of kinetic and potential energy, so that

$$\epsilon = \epsilon_{kin} + \epsilon_{pot} = \frac{p^2}{2m} + \epsilon_{pot}.$$

The momentum of a particle is associated with wavelength according to the De Broglie equation

$$p = \frac{h}{\lambda}.$$

This expression, relating to wave motion, can be combined with the classical energy equation to give

$$p^2 = \left(\frac{h}{\lambda}\right)^2 = 2m(\epsilon - \epsilon_{pot}).$$

Introducing the foregoing result into the one-dimensional wave equation (8.53) gives

$$\frac{d^2 f(x)}{dx^2} = -\left(\frac{2\pi}{\lambda}\right)^2 f(x) = -(2\pi)^2 \left[\frac{2m(\epsilon - \epsilon_{pot})}{h^2}\right] f(x)$$

$$= -\frac{8\pi^2 m}{h^2}(\epsilon - \epsilon_{pot}) f(x).$$

If the time-dependency of the wave function can be ignored, then $f(x)$ can be replaced by Ψ, giving Schrödinger's time-independent wave equation for a single particle in one dimension:

$$\frac{d^2\Psi}{dx^2} + \frac{8\pi^2 m}{h^2}(\epsilon - \epsilon_{pot})\Psi = 0. \tag{8.55}$$

Equation (8.55) is an ordinary second-order differential equation with a variable coefficient (since ϵ_{pot} is in general a function of x). It gives the allowable values of the discrete energy ϵ of a particle of mass m for which solutions exist.

In three dimensions, the Schrödinger equation takes the form:

$$\frac{\partial^2\Psi}{\partial x^2} + \frac{\partial^2\Psi}{\partial y^2} + \frac{\partial^2\Psi}{\partial z^2} + \frac{8\pi^2 m}{h^2}(\epsilon - \epsilon_{pot})\Psi = 0, \tag{8.56}$$

or

$$\nabla^2\Psi + \frac{8\pi^2 m}{h^2}(\epsilon - \epsilon_{pot})\Psi = 0, \tag{8.56a}$$

where ∇^2 is the Laplacian operator.

The Schrödinger wave equation in spherical polar coordinates may be obtained by making the following substitutions in Eq. (8.56),

$$x = r \sin\theta \cos\phi$$

$$y = r \sin\theta \sin\phi$$

$$z = r \cos\theta,$$

and has the form,

$$\frac{1}{r^2}\frac{\partial}{\partial r}\left(r^2\frac{\partial\Psi}{\partial r}\right) + \frac{1}{r^2\sin\theta}\frac{\partial}{\partial\theta}\left(\sin\theta\frac{\partial\Psi}{\partial\theta}\right) + \frac{1}{r^2\sin^2\theta}\frac{\partial^2\Psi}{\partial\phi^2} + \frac{8\pi^2 m}{h^2}(\epsilon - \epsilon_{pot}) = 0. \tag{8.57}$$

Now the intensity of a wave is proportional to the square of its amplitude. In the case of particle waves, the square of the amplitude of the wave function is related to particle density, or to the probability of finding a particle in a volume element $dx\,dy\,dz$. But the wave function Ψ may be a complex function; on the other hand, probability must be a positive real value. Consequently, statistical probability density is expressed by means of the product of both the wave function and its conjugate*:

$$\Psi\Psi^* = |\Psi|^2. \tag{8.58}$$

The expression $|\Psi|^2\,dx\,dy\,dz$, can be interpreted to indicate the probability of finding a particle in a given element of volume of the system. In a system of volume V, the probability of finding any particle somewhere in that volume is certain. This criterion serves to determine the probability density according to the normalizing condition,

$$\int_V \Psi\Psi^*\,dV = 1. \tag{8.59}$$

8-15
The Uncertainty
Principle
According to quantum mechanics, there is a definite limit to the precision to which the position and momentum of small particles may simultaneously be measured experimentally. The degree of precision is indicated by the *Heisenberg uncertainty principle*. Suppose it is required to measure the momentum and position of an atomic-scale particle, such as an electron. This may be done by observing at least one photon of light emitted by, or bounced off, the electron. The measuring device might be an ideal optical microscope using light of a short wavelength λ. Since the resolving power of the microscope is inversely proportional to the wavelength of the light used, the degree of accuracy in measuring the position is limited to the wavelength with which the electron is observed. Therefore, shorter wavelengths improve the resolving power and locate the electron's position more accurately. The momentum of the photon, however, changes the momentum of the electron and consequently its position, so that absolute accuracy of simultaneous measurement of both position and momentum can never be achieved. The energy of a photon is $h\nu$ and therefore the error in measuring the momentum would be $h\nu/c = h/\lambda$. The Heisenberg uncertainty principle shows that the product of the uncertainty in position and the uncertainty in momentum has a minimum value:

$$\Delta p_x\,\Delta x \geqslant \frac{h}{4\pi}, \tag{8.60}$$

---

*The conjugate of a complex number $(a + ib)$ is $(a - ib)$, where $i = \sqrt{-1}$ and $|a + ib| = |a - ib| = \sqrt{a^2 + b^2}$.

where Δp_x and Δx are the uncertainties in measuring the conjugate momentum and position respectively of a particle and h is Planck's constant. This means that a point in phase space cannot be accurately specified but can only be located within a volume equal to or greater than h^3. Note that at the limiting value indicated by the Eq. (8.60) (that is, $\Delta p \, \Delta x = h/4\pi$), an increased accuracy in measuring momentum can be achieved only at the expense of a decreased knowledge of position. Furthermore, when momentum or position is known precisely, that is, either Δp or Δx is zero, nothing at all is known about the other parameter.

Although this inherent uncertainty exists also in classical mechanics, its effects are unnoticed since the method of measurement has practically no effect on the measured properties. Certainty in measurement in classical mechanics is equivalent to only a high probability in wave mechanics.

EXAMPLE 8.6: Compare the uncertainties in the velocities of a hydrogen atom and an electron if the position of either particle can be determined with an uncertainty of 100Å (1 angstrom $= 10^{-8}$ cm). We have

$$\Delta p \geqslant \frac{h}{4\pi \, \Delta x}$$

$$\Delta p \geqslant \frac{6.624 \times 10^{-27}}{4\pi(100 \times 10^{-8})} \quad \text{or} \quad \Delta p \geqslant 0.524 \times 10^{-21} \text{ gm-cm/sec.}$$

$$\Delta v_H = \frac{\Delta p}{m_H} = \frac{0.524 \times 10^{-21}}{1838 \times 9.1086 \times 10^{-28}} = 0.315 \times 10^3 \text{ cm/sec.}$$

$$\Delta v_{\text{electron}} = \frac{\Delta p}{m_{\text{electron}}} = \frac{0.524 \times 10^{-21}}{9.1086 \times 10^{-28}} = 0.578 \times 10^6 \text{ cm/sec.}$$

Note that for the same uncertainty in position, the uncertainty of velocities is in the ratio of

$$\frac{\Delta v_{\text{electron}}}{\Delta v_H} = 1838,$$

which is also the ratio of the mass of a hydrogen atom to the mass of an electron.

8-16
Internal Energy
Levels

The energy of the molecules of a system may be considered to be associated with translational, rotational, vibrational, electronic, and potential (due to external force fields) modes of motion. If intermolecular forces are considered, a sixth contribution to the total energy is introduced. If it is assumed that there is no interaction between the molecules comprising a perfect gas, the total energy of a molecule is the sum of these energies:

$$\epsilon = \epsilon_{\text{trans}} + \epsilon_{\text{rot}} + \epsilon_{\text{vib}} + \epsilon_{\text{elec}} + \epsilon_{\text{pot}} . \qquad (8.61)$$

The Schrödinger equation describes the movement of a wavelike particle as a function of position for different values of the total energy of the particle. Various modes of motion of the molecule may occur, corresponding to these various kinetic and potential energy terms which may be included in the Schrödinger equation. To a first approximation, these different motions may be treated as though they were independent of each other, so that each particular motion is then described by its own Schrödinger equation.*

According to quantum theory, the internal energies of a system are quantized; that is, only discrete values are possible. The enumeration of the allowed quantum states constitutes the first step in the statistical analysis of the system.

8-17
Translational
Energy

Consider the motion of a molecule of a monatomic gas in a box of dimensions a, b, and c. Although Fig. 8.4 shows only the dimension a, along the x axis, it is understood that similar behavior occurs along the y and z axes. The molecule is confined between the walls of the box which

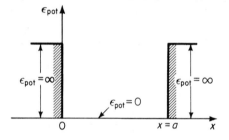

Fig. 8.4. Particle in a box.

bound a potential region identified by a uniform potential energy ϵ_{pot} within the box. Since the motion is unchanged by change in the zero of potential energy, we may take $\epsilon_{pot} = 0$ for convenience inside the box and $\epsilon_{pot} = \infty$ outside. In order to separate the Schrödinger equation into three differential equations, one for each of the axial directions, assume a solution in which the time-independent wave function Ψ is expressed in the form:

$$\Psi(x, y, z) = X(x)\, Y(y)\, Z(z),$$ (8.62)

where $X(x)$ is a function of x only, $Y(y)$ a function of y only, and $Z(z)$ a function of z only. When X, Y, and Z are substituted in the Schrödinger equation (8.56), the following is subsequently obtained:

$$\frac{1}{X}\frac{d^2 X}{dx^2} + \frac{1}{Y}\frac{d^2 Y}{dy^2} + \frac{1}{Z}\frac{d^2 Z}{dz^2} + \frac{8\pi^2 m}{h^2}\epsilon = 0.$$ (8.63)

*A more refined calculation introduces interaction between, for example, rotational and vibrational modes.

The energy ϵ can be expressed in terms of its components in each of the three directions:

$$\epsilon = \epsilon_x + \epsilon_y + \epsilon_z.$$

Since translational motion, and energies, in the x, y, and z directions are independent of each other, the wave equation may be expressed separately for each direction:

$$\frac{1}{X}\frac{d^2X}{dx^2} + \frac{8\pi^2 m}{h^2}\,\epsilon_x = 0, \tag{8.64}$$

$$\frac{1}{Y}\frac{d^2Y}{dy^2} + \frac{8\pi^2 m}{h^2}\,\epsilon_y = 0, \tag{8.65}$$

$$\frac{1}{Z}\frac{d^2Z}{dz^2} + \frac{8\pi^2 m}{h^2}\,\epsilon_z = 0. \tag{8.66}$$

Since Eq. (8.64), (8.65), and (8.66) have the same form, it is sufficient to solve any one of them. The components of potential energy are subject to boundary conditions imposed by the walls of the box, since the walls constitute barriers confining the particles to the box. This is equivalent to saying that a particle has no potential energy when inside the box but infinite potential energy when outside. In the region $0 < x < a$ Eq. (8.64) becomes

$$\frac{d^2X}{dx^2} + (M\epsilon_x)X = 0, \tag{8.67}$$

where

$$M = \frac{8\pi^2 m}{h^2}. \tag{8.68}$$

Equation (8.67) is a second-order differential equation in $X(x)$ whose solution is of the form:

$$X = A \sin \sqrt{M\epsilon_x}\, x + B \cos \sqrt{M\epsilon_x}\, x, \tag{8.69}$$

where A and B are constants.

The boundary conditions are introduced into Eq. (8.69):

At $x = 0$, $X = 0$, therefore $B = 0$ and $X = A \sin \sqrt{M\epsilon_x}x$.

At $x = a$, $X = 0$, therefore $\sqrt{M\epsilon_x}\, a = n_x\pi$,

where n_x must be positive integer. These integers are termed the *translational quantum numbers*. From this condition, the x component of the energy may be written

$$\epsilon_x = \frac{n_x^2 h^2}{8ma^2}, \quad n_x = 1, 2, 3, \ldots \tag{8.70}$$

and

$$X = A \sin \left(\frac{n_x \pi}{a}\right) x.$$

Since the translational quantum number n_x is an integer, the energy ϵ_x can have only certain discrete values, corresponding to specific forms of the wave function. Even though an infinite number of energy values, corresponding to all positive integer values of n_x, give rise to translational motion, these energy values can be at only certain discrete levels. Thus, the energy of a particle in a box is *quantized*.

Similar expressions may be obtained for translational energies in the y and z directions. The total translational energy is then

$$\epsilon = \epsilon_x + \epsilon_y + \epsilon_z = \frac{h^2}{8m}\left[\left(\frac{n_x}{a}\right)^2 + \left(\frac{n_y}{b}\right)^2 + \left(\frac{n_z}{c}\right)^2\right]. \tag{8.71}$$

Translational energy is highly degenerate as there are many combinations of $(n_x/a)^2$, $(n_y/b)^2$ and $(n_z/c)^2$ which add to the same value. Such degenerate quantum states have the same energy and can be distinguished only by the set of quantum numbers. The solution of Eq. (8.71) is given by a set of wave functions as

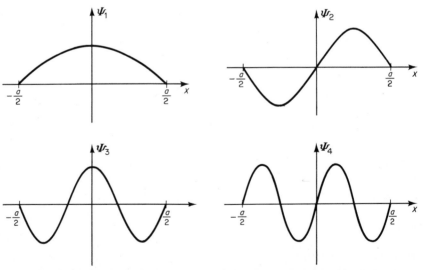

Fig. 8.5. Ψ as a function of x for a particle in a box.

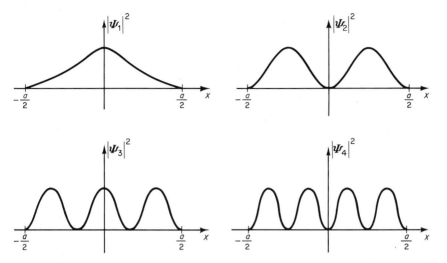

Fig. 8.6. *Probability density as a function of x for a particle in a box.*

$$\Psi = A \sin\left(n_x \pi \frac{x}{a}\right) \sin\left(n_y \pi \frac{y}{b}\right) \sin\left(n_z \pi \frac{z}{c}\right), \qquad (8.72)$$

which represents a series of standing waves with even and odd half-waves. Figure 8.5 shows Ψ as a function x for $n_x = 1, 2, 3,$ and 4 for constant values of y and z equal to $b/2$ and $c/2$ respectively. Figure 8.6 shows the corresponding values of $|\Psi|^2$, indicating the probability associated with the location of the particle in any particular position.

**8-18
Rotational
Energy**

Another type of motion of the molecule is rotational motion. To describe rotational motion, the Schrödinger equation must be expressed in the polar coordinate system.

Consider a model of a "dumbbell" diatomic molecule composed of two atoms as shown in Fig. 8.7. The masses of the atoms, m_1 and m_2, may be assumed to be point masses so that the moment of inertia of the molecule about the line joining the two atoms is zero. Perpendicular to the line joining the two atoms, and along axes that pass through the center of gravity, the molecule has two equal moments of inertia. Assume also that the distance between the atoms is constant and thus treat the molecule as a *rigid rotator*.

Let the origin of the Cartesian coordinates be located at the center of gravity of the molecule. In considering the rotation of the molecule about its cg, the angles θ and ϕ determine the orientation of the molecule with

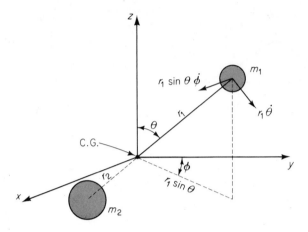

Fig. 8.7. *Dumbbell molecule.*

respect to the coordinate axes as shown in Fig. 8.7. The velocity of the mass m_1, at a distance r_1 from the origin is given by

$$v_{m_1} = \sqrt{v_\theta^2 + v_\phi^2} = \sqrt{(r_1\dot\theta)^2 + (r_1\dot\phi\sin\theta)^2} = r_1\sqrt{\dot\theta^2 + \dot\phi^2\sin^2\theta},$$

where $\dot\theta$ and $\dot\phi$ are the time rate of change of the angles θ and ϕ. Similarly, the velocity of the mass m_2 at a distance r_2 from the origin is given by

$$v_{m_2} = r_2\sqrt{\dot\theta^2 + \dot\phi^2\sin^2\theta}.$$

The kinetic energy of the molecule can thus be written,

$$\epsilon_{\text{rot}} = \tfrac{1}{2}m_1 v_{m_1}^2 + \tfrac{1}{2}m_2 v_{m_2}^2$$

$$= \left(\frac{m_1 r_1^2 + m_2 r_2^2}{2}\right)(\dot\theta^2 + \dot\phi^2\sin^2\theta).$$

The term $(m_1 r_1^2 + m_2 r_2^2)$ is the moment of inertia, I, of the masses m_1 and m_2 about the cg of the molecule. The kinetic energy of the molecule then is

$$\epsilon_{\text{rot}} = \frac{I}{2}(\dot\theta^2 + \dot\phi^2\sin^2\theta). \tag{8.73}$$

Note that the term $(\dot\theta^2 + \dot\phi^2\sin^2\theta)$ is equal to the square of the velocity of a particle that is located at a unit distance from the cg. Therefore, the moment of inertia I can be considered to represent the mass of a particle separated from the cg by a radial distance of unity.

When the kinetic energy associated with rotational motion is expressed by Eq. (8.73); is substituted in the Schrödinger equation (8.57) expressed in polar coordinates, the following equation is obtained:

$$\frac{1}{\sin \theta} \frac{\partial}{\partial \theta} \left(\sin \theta \frac{\partial \Psi}{\partial \theta} \right) + \frac{1}{\sin^2 \theta} \frac{\partial^2 \Psi}{\partial \phi^2} + \frac{8\pi^2 I \epsilon}{h^2} \Psi = 0. \qquad (8.74)$$

Again, the potential energy may be taken to be zero. The solution to Eq. (8.74) is accomplished by assuming a product solution of the form:

$$\Psi(\theta, \phi) = \Theta(\theta) \, \Phi(\phi),$$

where $\Theta(\theta)$ and $\Phi(\phi)$ are independent functions of θ and ϕ respectively. After these values for the wave function are substituted into Eq. (8.74), the variables can be separated in the form

$$\frac{\sin \theta}{\Theta} \frac{\partial}{\partial \theta} \left(\sin \theta \frac{\partial \Theta}{\partial \theta} \right) + \frac{8\pi^2 I \epsilon}{h^2} \sin^2 \theta = -\frac{1}{\Phi} \frac{\partial^2 \Phi}{\partial \phi^2}.$$

Since the functions Θ and Φ are independent, each side of the preceding equation can be set equal to a constant, say, m^2. The solution to the equation,

$$-\frac{1}{\Phi} \frac{\partial^2 \Phi}{\partial \phi^2} = m^2, \qquad (8.75)$$

has the form

$$\Phi = A \sin m\phi + B \cos m\phi.$$

The function Φ must be single-valued, and must repeat itself at 2π intervals. Therefore,

$$\sin m \phi = \sin m(\phi + 2\pi) = \sin m\phi \cos 2\pi m + \cos m\phi \sin 2\pi m$$

and

$$\cos m\phi = \cos m(\phi + 2\pi) = \cos m\phi \cos 2\pi m - \sin m\phi \sin 2\pi m.$$

It can be shown, from these equations, that the conditions $\cos 2\pi m = 1$ and $\sin 2\pi m = 0$ must be simultaneously satisfied. This is possible only if m is an integer.

In order to solve the equation,

$$\frac{\sin \theta}{\Theta} \frac{\partial}{\partial \theta} \left(\sin \theta \frac{\partial \Theta}{\partial \theta} \right) + \frac{8\pi^2 I \epsilon}{h^2} \sin^2 \theta = m^2, \qquad (8.76)$$

substitutions are made as follows:

$$D = \frac{8\pi^2 I \epsilon}{h^2}, \tag{8.77}$$

$$x = \cos \theta, \tag{8.78}$$

and

$$\Theta(\theta) = (1 - x^2)^{\frac{m^2}{2}} v(x). \tag{8.79}$$

These substitutions lead to

$$(1 - x^2)v'' - 2(m + 1)v' + [D - m(m + 1)]v = 0, \tag{8.80}$$

where primes denote differentiation with respect to the argument x. The general solution to this second-order equation is a sum of two independent functions multiplied by arbitrary constants. The solution which is finite for $\theta = 0$, can be expressed as a polynomial in x, and presented in the form of an infinite series:

$$v = \sum_{n=0}^{\infty} a_n x^n. \tag{8.81}$$

Substituting from Eq. (8.81) into Eq. (8.80) ultimately leads to

$$\sum_{n=0}^{\infty} a_n n(n - 1)x^{n-2} - \sum_{n=0}^{\infty} [n + m)(n + m + 1) - D]a_n x^n = 0.$$

If the normalization condition is to be satisfied, the series must terminate with a finite number of terms. At some finite value of n, the coefficient of x^n must equal zero, and this occurs when

$$D = (n + m)(n + m + 1) = j(j + 1), \tag{8.82}$$

where $j = m + n$, is an integer since both m and n are integers. This equation for D leads, through Eq. (8.77), to the following expression for rotational energy:

$$\epsilon_{\text{rot}} = \frac{h^2}{8\pi^2 I} j(j + 1), \quad j = 0, 1, 2, 3 \ldots . \tag{8.83}$$

Note that $j \geq |m|$ and the allowed rotational energy levels are specified by the *rotational quantum number* j. Figure 8.8 shows the allowed rotational energies of diatomic molecules at different values of j. Since the ratio

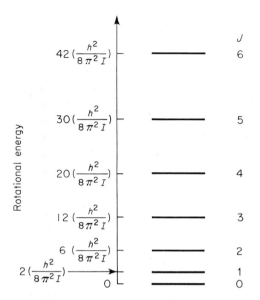

Fig. 8.8. *Allowed rotational energies of a diatomic molecule.*

ϵ_i/kT, as indicated by the Boltzmann law, determines the population of the quantum states, it is readily seen that kT may be used as a reference amount of energy. Figure 8.9 compares the magnitude of rotational energies with

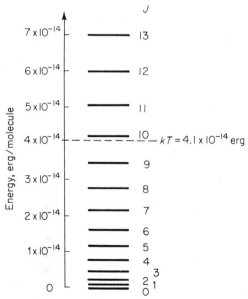

Fig. 8.9. *Allowed rotational energies for CO at 25°C ($m_e = 11.4 \times 10^{-24}$ gm, r = 1.13Å and I = 14.5 × 10⁻⁴⁰ gm-cm²).*

kT for CO at 25°C. Consequently, several energy levels will be appreciably occupied at 25°C.

Finally, the solution to Eq. (8.76) may be given:

$$\Psi_{\rm rot} = (A \sin m\phi + B \cos m\phi) CP_j^m (\cos \theta), \tag{8.84}$$

where P_j^m is called the *associated Legendre polynomial* of degree j and order m, and C is a constant.

The minimum energy of rotation corresponds to the zero value of j. The quantum number m determines the allowed quantum states for each allowed energy level and for a given value of j, m can assume any quantum state corresponding to any integer value between $-j$ and $+j$ (including zero). Therefore the degeneracy of each allowed rotational energy level is $(2j + 1)$.

8-19
Harmonic
Oscillator

A third type of motion of the molecule is vibrational motion. In this case, the two atoms of a diatomic molecule are considered to oscillate relative to each other. The potential energy of the two atoms then varies with the relative displacement. The vibration of atoms in crystals may be shown to be equivalent to the behavior of a quantum-mechanical system called a *harmonic oscillator*. This model will now be used to determine the quantum-mechanical vibrational energy levels.

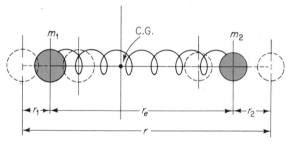

Fig. 8.10. *Harmonic oscillator.*

Small amplitude sinusoidal oscillation of two atoms of masses m_1 and m_2 along the axis of a diatomic molecule is shown in Fig. 8.10. Let r_e be the distance between the atoms at equilibrium and r_1 and r_2 be the instantaneous displacement of masses m_1 and m_2 from their equilibrium positions measured positively away from the cg in each case. The distance r between the atoms at any time is equal to

$$r = r_e \pm (r_2 + r_1). \tag{8.85}$$

Since no external forces are involved in the oscillations and therefore momentum is conserved, the mass of one atom multiplied by its velocity must be equal to the mass of the second mutliplied by its corresponding velocity, or

$$m_1 \dot{r}_1 = m_2 \dot{r}_2. \tag{8.86}$$

When Eq. (8.85) is differentiated with respect to time, and the results introduced into Eq. (8.86), the following is obtained:

$$m_1 \dot{r}_1 = m_e \dot{r},$$

where $m_e = (m_1 m_2)/(m_1 + m_2)$ is an equivalent or "reduced" mass. The motion of an oscillating, elastic body of mass m_e is described by

$$m_e \ddot{r} = -Kr, \tag{8.87}$$

where K is the spring constant. The solution to this equation is

$$r = A \sin \sqrt{\frac{K}{m_e}} \tau + B \cos \sqrt{\frac{K}{m_e}} \tau. \tag{8.88}$$

Boundary conditions are as follows:

at $\quad \tau = 0, \quad r = r_o;$

at $\quad \tau = 0, \quad \dot{r} = 0.$

The resultant solution is

$$r = r_o \cos \sqrt{\frac{K}{m_e}} \tau.$$

Apparently, the frequency of oscillation ν is given by

$$\nu = \frac{1}{2\pi} \sqrt{\frac{K}{m_e}}. \tag{8.89}$$

These are all results of classical mechanics. But the correct quantum analysis of the harmonic oscillator leads to certain modifications. The Schrödinger equation for simple vibrational motion of a molecule is

$$\frac{d^2 \Psi}{dr^2} + \frac{8\pi^2 m_e}{h^2} (\epsilon - \epsilon_{\text{pot}}) \Psi = 0.$$

The potential energy ϵ_{pot} is equal to the work done on the oscillator to stretch it through a distance r, or

$$\epsilon_{pot} = -\int_0^r -Kr\, dr = \tfrac{1}{2} Kr^2.$$

Substituting the foregoing value of ϵ_{pot} into the Schrödinger equation gives

$$\frac{d^2\Psi}{dr^2} + \frac{8\pi^2 m_e}{h^2}\left(\epsilon - \tfrac{1}{2}Kr^2\right)\Psi = 0, \tag{8.90}$$

or

$$\frac{d^2\Psi}{dr^2} + (A - B^2 r^2)\Psi = 0. \tag{8.91}$$

From the following substitution,

$$Br^2 = x^2, \tag{8.92}$$

Eq. (8.90) becomes

$$\frac{d^2\Psi}{dx^2} + (C - x^2)\Psi = 0; \tag{8.93}$$

where $C = A/B$.

If the solution to Eq. (8.93) is of the form

$$\Psi = e^{-x^2/2}v(x),$$

then substitution into Eq. (8.93) leads to

$$v'' - 2xv' + (C - 1)v = 0. \tag{8.94}$$

Equation (8.94) is called the *Hermite equation*. Its appropriate solution is expressed in the form of the polynomial:

$$v = \sum_{n=0}^{\infty} a_n x^n. \tag{8.95}$$

Substituting this polynomial in Eq. (8.94) gives

$$\sum_{n=0}^{\infty} a_n n(n-1)x^{n-2} - 2\sum_{n=0}^{\infty} a_n n x^n + (C-1)\sum_{n=0}^{\infty} a_n x^n = 0.$$

Letting $k = n - 2$, the following results:

$$2a_2 + \sum_{k=1}^{\infty} \{[(k + 2)(k + 1)a_{k+2}x^k] - [2(k + 2) - (C - 1)]a_k x^{k+2}\}$$

$$+ (C - 1)a_0 = 0. \qquad (8.96)$$

To satisfy the normalization condition, the series must terminate with a finite number of terms, and this consideration leads to the following condition:

$$C = 2n + 1 = 2(n + \tfrac{1}{2}).$$

Since $C = A/B$, and since the values of A and B are given in Eq. (8.90) and (8.91), substitution leads to the following:

$$\epsilon = \frac{h}{2\pi} \sqrt{\frac{K}{m_e}} \left(n + \frac{1}{2}\right).$$

But it was shown in Eq. (8.89) that the spring constant K can be related to the classical frequency of vibration, and therefore the vibrational energy can be expressed as

$$\epsilon_{\text{vib}} = (n + \tfrac{1}{2})h\nu, \quad n = 0, 1, 2, \ldots . \qquad (8.97)$$

The integer n is called the *vibrational quantum number*. Equation (8.97) gives the allowable energy levels of a harmonic oscillator. Starting from a minimum value of $\tfrac{1}{2}h\nu$, the allowable levels of vibrational energy are separated from each other by a constant value of $h\nu$. Also, there is a definite quantum energy for each quantum state, and therefore there is no degeneracy of the vibrational quantum states of a single harmonic oscillator. The allowed vibrational energies of a diatomic molecule are plotted in Fig. 8.11. The magnitude of lower

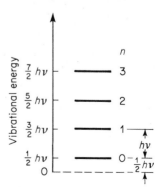

Fig. 8.11. *Allowed vibrational energies of a diatomic molecule.*

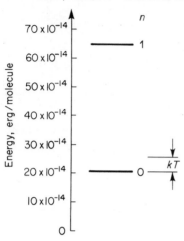

Fig. 8.12. *Allowed vibrational energies of CO at 25°C.*

energy states is compared with the value of kT at 25°C for CO in Fig. 8.12. Finally, the wave-function solution to Eq. (8.90) is

$$\Psi_{\text{vib}}(r) = D_n e^{-x^2/2} H_n(x), \tag{8.98}$$

where $H_n(x)$ is the *Hermite polynomial* of degree n and D_n is a normalization constant which may be evaluated by means of the condition (8.59). In Fig.

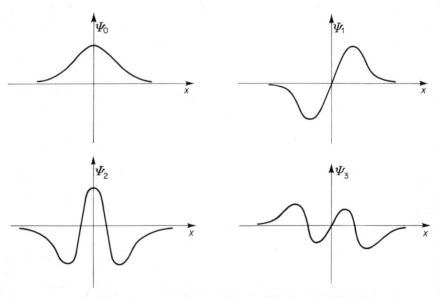

Fig. 8.13. Ψ *as a function of x for a simple harmonic oscillator.*

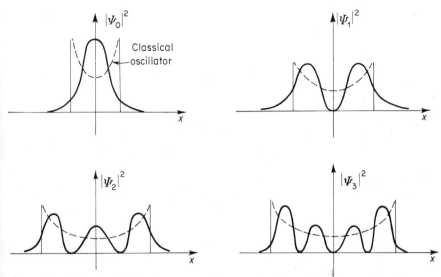

Fig. 8.14. *Probability density as a function of x for a simple harmonic oscillator.*

8.13 and Fig. 8.14, the wave function Ψ and the probability $|\Psi|^2$ are shown as a function of x.

8-20 Electronic Energy   A fourth energy term involves the motion of electrons in orbits in a molecule. Here, too, the Schrödinger equation serves as the starting point. Since the motion is of a rotational nature (rather than translational), the Schrödinger equation describing its motion is first expressed in the polar coordinate system. But a multitude of solutions results, since both the radial distance from the center of the sphere and the angular displacements along the surface of the sphere can vary. In addition, the electron can also rotate about its own center, and discrete energy levels are associated with this motion, also. When the interactions between electrons and nuclei, and between the electrons, are considered, the Schrödinger equation becomes difficult to solve exactly for most atoms and molecules, and various approximation techniques are employed.

Appendix: Stirling's Formula   Stirling's formula provides a useful approximation for the logarithm of a factorial of a large number. The logarithm of the factorial $N!$ is given by

$$\ln (N!) = \ln 2 + \ln 3 + \cdots + \ln N.$$

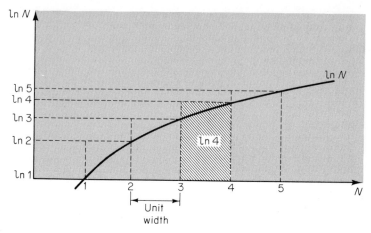

Fig. 8A. *Stirling's approximation.*

Figure 8A shows ln N plotted versus N. If the abscissa is divided into unit intervals, the rectangular areas defined by the dotted contours are (1)(ln 2), (1)(ln 3), ... (1)(ln N).

Sum of rectangular-shaped areas

$$= (1)(\ln 2) + (1)(\ln 3) + \ldots + (1)(\ln N)$$
$$= (1)(\ln N!)$$

Area under logarithmic curve

$$= \int_1^N \ln (N) \, dN$$

If N is large, the area under the logarithmic curve is approximately equal to the steplike series of areas so that

$$\ln N! \approx \int_1^N \ln N \, dN.$$

Performing the integration by parts gives

$$\ln N! \approx N \ln N - \int_1^N dN \approx N \ln N - N + 1.$$

If $N \gg 1$, the preceding equation can be reduced to

$$\ln N! \approx N \ln N - N = N \ln N - N \ln e$$

or

$$N! \approx \left(\frac{N}{e}\right)^N. \tag{1}$$

Equation (1) is called *Stirling's approximation formula*. It may be shown that a better approximation for $N!$ is given by

$$N! \approx \sqrt{2\pi N}\left(\frac{N}{e}\right)^N. \tag{2}$$

Note that Eq. (2) reduces to Eq. (1) when $N \gg 1$. Table (8A.1) gives a comparison of Eq. (1) and (2), together with the exact value of $\ln N!$ Note that Stirling's approximation is quite good for large values of N where the relative error approaches zero although the absolute error is not zero.

TABLE 8A.1

	ln $N!$		
N	Exact Value	Eq. (1)	Eq. (2)
5	4.78	3.05	4.77
10	15.10	13.03	15.10
20	42.3	39.9	42.31
30	74.6	72.1	74.72
40	110.3	107.6	110.36
50	148.3	145.6	148.37
100	363.2	360.0	363.22

REFERENCES

8.1 Crawford, F. H., *Heat, Thermodynamics and Statistical Physics.* New York: Harcourt, Brace & World, Inc., 1963, chap. 15, 17, 18.

8.2 Denbigh, K. G., *The Principles of Chemical Equilibrium.* Cambridge: Cambridge University Press, 1957, chap. 1.

8.3 Dole, M., *Introduction to Statistical Thermodynamics.* Englewood Cliffs, N.J.: Prentice-Hall, Inc., 1954.

8.4 Howerton, M. T., *Engineering Thermodynamics.* Princeton, N. J.: D. Van Nostrand Co., Inc., 1962, chap. 2, 3.

8.5 Sears, F. W., *Thermodynamics.* Reading, Mass.: Addison-Wesley Publishing Company, Inc., 1952, chap. 14.

8.6 Sommerfeld, A., *Thermodynamics and Statistical Mechanics.* New York: Academic Press, Inc., 1956, chap. 3, 4.

PROBLEMS

8.1 Find the number of ways of distributing three distinguishable particles a, b, and c in three energy levels. What is the thermodynamic probability of all three particles lying in a single energy level? Assume particles to be indistinguishable if they lie in a single energy level.

8.2 A box contains 3 black, 4 white, and 5 red balls. What is the mathematical probability of drawing:
(a) Two black balls in succession if the first ball is replaced after drawing
(b) Two black balls in succession if the first ball is not replaced after drawing
(c) Either a black or a white ball if one ball is drawn?

8.3 Find the number of ways in which 10 distinguishable particles can be arranged in 3 groups such that the groups contain 2, 3, and 5 particles. What will be the number of arrangements if the particles in each group are indistinguishable?

8.4 It is required to arrange 6 black and 6 white particles in 2 compartments of 6 positions each. Each particle occupies one of these positions and each compartment has the same number of particles. Assuming that the black (as well as the white) particles are indistinguishable among themselves, complete the following table and determine the thermodynamic probabilities of each distribution.

Particles in compartment 1	Particles in compartment 2	Number of arrangements
6B	—	—
5B + 1W	—	—
4B + 2W	—	—
3B + 3W	—	—
2B + 4W	—	—
1B + 5W	—	—
6W	—	—

8.5 In a cu cm there are approximately 2.7×10^{19} molecules at standard conditions. What is the mathematical probability if the molecules occupy one-half of the volume leaving the other half empty? What is the probability if the molecules occupy only one-quarter of the volume?

8.6 Calculate the change of entropy when H_2 gas (at 0°C and 1 atm) occupying a volume of 1 cm³ expands freely and adiabatically to a final volume of 10 cm³. Check your result by classical thermodynamics.

8.7 Assume that the possible energy levels of an N-particle system are ϵ, 2ϵ, 3ϵ, 4ϵ ... $n\epsilon$, where n varies from zero to infinity and ϵ is a constant. Assuming the N particles are distributed among the energy levels according to a Boltzmann distribution, determine the expressions for the number of particles in the ith energy level and the partition function. What is the total energy and the constant volume specific heat of the system?

8.8 Assume a perfect gas obeying Boltzmann's statistics in a force field which acts on each particle of the gas according to the equation $F = -a - bz$, where a and b are constants and z is the distance above the plane $z = 0$. The particles are all held above the plane $z = 0$. Find the average potential energy of the gas at temperature T in the z direction.

8.9 The total energy of two identical harmonic oscillators is $7h\nu$. What is the degeneracy of the combined system of the two oscillators?

8.10 Five particles are arranged in two energy levels each of degeneracy 3. What is the thermodynamic probability of each possible macrostate according to Fermi-Dirac and Bose-Einstein statistics?

8.11 Compare F-D, B-E, and M-B statistics when four particles are distributed among two energy level groups having degeneracies $g_1 = 2$ and $g_2 = 3$. Only one particle is allowed in each state.

8.12 The equation of a translational system,

$$\frac{n_x^2}{a^2} + \frac{n_y^2}{b^2} + \frac{n_z^2}{c^2} = \frac{8m\epsilon_i}{h^2} \qquad \begin{matrix} a, b, c \\ n_x, n_y, n_z \end{matrix} \quad \begin{matrix} \text{dimensions} \\ \text{integers} \end{matrix} \quad ,$$

is analogous to the equation of an ellipsoid,

$$\frac{x^2}{a^2} + \frac{y^2}{b^2} + \frac{z^2}{c^2} = r^2,$$

where r^2 is identified as $8m\epsilon_i/h^2$. Realizing that only $\frac{1}{8}$ of the volume of the ellipsoid is defined by positive values of the variables necessary to determine the number of states of energies between 0 and ϵ,

(a) Prove that the number of states between ϵ and $\epsilon + d\epsilon$ is

$$g_i = \frac{4\pi mV}{h^3}\sqrt{2m}\ \epsilon_i^{1/2}\,d\epsilon_i\,,$$

where $V = $ volume of the gas.

(b) Find an expression for the partition function.

(c) Using the results of (a) and (b) and the Maxwell-Boltzmann distribution law prove that

$$d\left(\frac{N_i}{N}\right) = \frac{2}{kT\sqrt{\pi}}\frac{(\epsilon_i/kT)^{1/2}}{e^{\epsilon_i/kT}}\,d\epsilon_i$$

(d) Plot $[d(N_i/N)]/[d(\epsilon_i/kT)]$ versus ϵ_i/kT and evaluate the fraction of the molecules between kT and $2kT$.

NOMENCLATURE

A, B, C	Constants	V	Volume
a, b, c	Dimensions	v	Velocity
c_p	Specific heat at constant pressure	W	Thermodynamic probability
c_v	Specific heat at constant volume	x, y, z	Cartesian coordinates
E	Internal energy	$\mathscr{Z}$	Partition function
F	Helmholtz function	Z	Molecular partition function
f	Number of degrees of freedom	α, β	Lagrange's multipliers
G	Gibbs function	ψ	Wave function
g_i	Degeneracy of the ith level	ω	Circular frequency
H	Enthalpy	ϵ	Internal energy per molecule
h	Planck's constant	ν	Frequency
I	Moment of inertia	γ	Ratio of specific heats
k	Boltzmann's constant	τ	Time
m	Molecular mass		

A, B, C Constants V Volume

$\theta_E = \dfrac{h\nu_E}{k} =$ Einstein characteristic temperature

$\theta_D = \dfrac{h\nu_D}{k} =$ Debye characteristic temperature

$\theta_r = \dfrac{h^2}{8\pi^2 Ik} =$ Rotational characteristic temperature

$\theta_v = \dfrac{h\nu}{k} =$ Vibrational characteristic temperature

m, n, j	Integers	σ	Symmetry number
N	Number of molecules	μ	Chemical potential
N_0	Avogadro's number		
n	Number of moles		

Subscripts

$m =$ per molecule

p	Pressure	
R	Gas constant	
$\mathscr{R}$	Universal gas constant	
r	$\dfrac{\epsilon_i}{kT}$ or distance	
S	Entropy	
T	Absolute temperature	
U	Internal energy	

Superscripts

$(-) =$ per mole

9

APPLICATIONS
OF STATISTICAL
AND QUANTUM
MECHANICS

9-1

Introduction

The concepts of quantum mechanics and statistical mechanics lend themselves to many applications, and in the field of thermodynamics, they are particularly useful, for they help to explain the average statistical properties of macroscopic physical systems.

Thermodynamic properties may be expressed in terms of the partition function and its derivatives. It was previously shown that the explicit form of the partition function indicates how the energy of a system is partitioned among the possible energy levels. Consequently, the first step in evaluating these properties is to compute the value of the partition function. The partition function for a single particle according to Eq. (8.8) is

$$Z = \sum_i e^{-\beta \epsilon_i},$$

where ϵ_i is the total energy of the particle in the ith state. If there is no interaction between the different forms of energy, the total energy of the particle is equal to the sum of the contributing energies or

$$\epsilon_i = \epsilon_{\text{trans}} + \epsilon_{\text{rot}} + \epsilon_{\text{vib}} + \epsilon_{\text{elec}} + \cdots.$$

The partition function for one particle then becomes

$$Z = \sum e^{-\beta(\epsilon_{\text{trans}} + \epsilon_{\text{rot}} + \epsilon_{\text{vib}} + \epsilon_{\text{elec}} + \cdots)}$$
$$= Z_{\text{trans}} Z_{\text{rot}} Z_{\text{vib}} Z_{\text{elec}} \cdots,$$

(9.1)

or the partition function is equal to the product of the contributing partition functions. Equation (9.1) serves as a key equation in determining thermodynamic properties.

In the following sections, thermodynamic properties of monatomic gases, diatomic gases, and simple crystals are determined by application of techniques described in Chapter 8. Particular attention is given to values of specific heat. Cases where only translational, rotational, and vibrational energies contribute to the total energy of the molecules are treated in these applications. The latter part of this chapter discusses the third law of thermodynamics.

9-2

Perfect

Monatomic Gas

The translational energy of the molecules of a perfect monatomic gas constitutes the main energy of the gas. Consider a system of indistinguishable molecules of a monatomic gas in a box of volume V and side dimensions $a, b,$ and c. The energy levels in each of the x, y, and z directions are highly degenerate and the quantized ith energy state is given by Eq. (8.71) as $\epsilon_i = \dfrac{h^2}{8m}\left[\left(\dfrac{n_x}{a}\right)^2 + \left(\dfrac{n_y}{b}\right)^2 + \left(\dfrac{n_z}{c}\right)^2\right],$

where the translational quantum numbers n_x, n_y, and n_z are integers (excluding zero) having values 1, 2, 3, ... Since the molecules of the gas are indistinguishable and more than one molecule is allowed in any single quantum state, Bose-Einstein statistics can be applied. The distribution of molecules among the quantum states, for the most probable macrostate, is

$$\frac{N_i}{g_i} = \frac{1}{Be^{\beta\epsilon_i} - 1}, \tag{9.2}$$

where $B = Z/N$. The translational partition function Z is the product of the component partition functions in the three coordinates axes, Z_x, Z_y, Z_z:

$$Z_{\text{trans}} = \sum_i e^{-\epsilon_i/kT} = \left[\sum_{n_x=0}^{\infty} e^{-h^2 n_x^2/8mkTa^2}\right]\left[\sum_{n_y=0}^{\infty} e^{-h^2 n_y^2/8mkTb^2}\right]\left[\sum_{n_z=0}^{\infty} e^{-h^2 n_z^2/8mkTc^2}\right].$$

Since the coefficients of n_x^2, n_y^2, and n_z^2 in the exponents of the foregoing equation are small for sufficiently high temperatures*, the summation signs may be approximated by integration signs. The preceding equation then takes the form

$$Z_{\text{trans}} = \left[\int_0^{\infty} e^{-h^2 n_x^2/8mkTa^2}\, dn_x\right]\left[\int_0^{\infty} e^{-h^2 n_y^2/8mkTb^2}\, dn_y\right]\left[\int_0^{\infty} e^{-h^2 n_z^2/8mkTc^2}\, dn_z\right].$$

Each of the terms in brackets can be integrated, leading to the following expression for the translational partition function:

$$Z_{\text{trans}} = abc\left(\frac{\sqrt{2\pi mkT}}{h}\right)^3.$$

But since the volume $V = abc$, the partition function per molecule becomes

$$Z_{\text{trans}} = V\left(\frac{2\pi mkT}{h^2}\right)^{3/2}. \tag{9.3}$$

According to Eq. (8.45) the partition function for N identical, indistinguishable molecules is

$$Z_{\text{trans}} = \frac{1}{N!}Z^N = \frac{1}{N!}V^N\left(\frac{2\pi mkT}{h^2}\right)^{(3/2)N} \tag{9.4}$$

Equation (9.4) serves as a basis for the determination of the thermodynamic properties of a monatomic gas.

*Mainly due to the small numerical value of Planck's constant.

First, the Helmholtz function can be determined. According to Eq. (8.25), this free energy is

$$F = -kT \ln Z.$$

Substituting for Z, the Helmholtz function becomes

$$F = -kT\left[-\ln N! + N \ln V + \frac{3}{2} N \ln \frac{2\pi mk}{h^2} + \frac{3}{2} N \ln T\right],$$

and therefore

$$F = -NkT\left[-\ln N + 1 + \ln V + \frac{3}{2} \ln \frac{2\pi mk}{h^2} + \frac{3}{2} \ln T\right]. \qquad (9.5)$$

Since $p = -(\partial F/\partial V)_{T,N}$, therefore,

$$p = NkT\frac{1}{V}, \qquad (9.6)$$

which is the equation of state of a perfect gas, in agreement with the result obtained from the kinetic theory.

The internal energy according to Eq. (8.24) is given by

$$U = NkT^2\left(\frac{\partial \ln Z}{\partial T}\right)_V = -Nk\left(\frac{\partial \ln Z}{\partial(1/T)}\right)_V.$$

From Eq. (9.3), the internal energy of N molecules then is

$$U = NkT^2\left(\frac{3}{2}\frac{1}{T}\right) = \frac{3}{2}NkT = \frac{3}{2}n\mathcal{R}T. \qquad (9.7)$$

On a mole basis the internal energy is

$$\bar{u} = \tfrac{3}{2}N_0 kT = \tfrac{3}{2}\mathcal{R}T. \qquad (9.8)$$

Enthalpy per mole can be obtained from internal energy:

$$\bar{h} = \bar{u} + \mathcal{R}T = \tfrac{5}{2}\mathcal{R}T. \qquad (9.9)$$

Molal specific heat at constant volume is therefore,

$$\bar{c}_v = \left(\frac{\partial \bar{u}}{\partial T}\right)_V = \frac{\mathcal{R}}{T^2}\left[\frac{\partial^2 \ln Z}{\partial(1/T)^2}\right]_V = \frac{3}{2}\mathcal{R}, \qquad (9.10)$$

whereas molal specific heat at constant pressure is

$$\bar{c}_p = \left(\frac{\partial \bar{h}}{\partial T}\right)_p = \frac{5}{2}\mathscr{R}, \tag{9.11}$$

and the ratio of specific heats is

$$\gamma = \frac{\bar{c}_p}{\bar{c}_v} = \frac{(5/2)\mathscr{R}}{(3/2)\mathscr{R}} = \frac{5}{3} = 1.67. \tag{9.13}$$

The entropy of the most probable macrostate is obtained by substituting Eq. (9.4) into Eq. (8.16),

$$S = Nk \ln Z + \frac{U}{T},$$

which resolves to

$$S = NK\left[-\ln N + \ln V + \frac{3}{2}\ln\frac{2\pi mk}{h^2} + \frac{3}{2}\ln T + \frac{5}{2}\right]. \tag{9.14}$$

Equation (9.14) is called the *Sackur-Tetrode equation* for the absolute entropy of a monatomic gas.

An expression for the chemical potential is

$$\mu = \left(\frac{\partial F}{\partial N_i}\right)_{T,N_j},$$

where the subscript j indicates that all N_i's are constant except one. From Eq. (9.5), μ becomes

$$\mu = -kT\left[-\ln N + \ln V + \frac{3}{2}\ln\frac{2\pi mk}{h^2} + \frac{3}{2}\ln T\right]. \tag{9.15}$$

The Gibbs free energy can be defined as

$$G = F + pV.$$

Substituting from Eq. (9.5) and (9.6) leads to the following:

$$G = -NkT\left[-\ln N + \ln V + \frac{3}{2}\ln\frac{2\pi mk}{h^2} + \frac{3}{2}\ln T\right]. \tag{9.16}$$

9-3
Perfect
Diatomic Gas

In addition to translational energy, diatomic molecules show both rotational energy and vibrational energy. The total energy of the molecule is the sum of energies from these sources (as well as from electronic and potential sources). The partition function of a diatomic molecule is the product of the partition functions associated with the translation, rotation and vibration. Effects on specific heat of a diatomic molecule can be ascribed primarily to translational, rotational, and vibrational motion. Since the modes of excitation of a perfect gas can be assumed to be independent of each other, the total constant-volume specific heat is equal to the sum of the translational, rotational, and vibrational specific heats, or

$$\bar{c}_v = \bar{c}_{v_{\text{trans}}} + \bar{c}_{v_{\text{rot}}} + \bar{c}_{v_{\text{vib}}}. \tag{9.17}$$

The translational molal specific heat, of a diatomic gas, as for a monatomic gas, is

$$\bar{c}_{v_{\text{trans}}} = \tfrac{3}{2}\mathscr{R}. \tag{9.10}$$

The translational partition function for a diatomic molecule is the same as that for a monatomic molecule and is given by Eq. (9.3). The rotational partition function per molecule, as shown previously, is

$$Z_{\text{rot}} = \sum_{j=0}^{\infty} (2j + 1)e^{-[j(j+1)/T](h^2/8\pi^2 Ik)}, \tag{9.18}$$

where the degeneracy, g_i, of each allowed energy level ϵ_i, is indicated by the $(2j + 1)$ term. When various constants in the exponent are lumped together,

TABLE 9.1 CHARACTERISTIC TEMPERATURES FOR ROTATION AND VIBRATION OF DIATOMIC MOLECULES

Substance	$\theta_r, °K$	$\theta_v, °K$
H_2	85.5	6140
OH	27.5	5360
HCl	15.3	4300
CH	20.7	4100
N_2	2.86	3340
HI	9.0	3200
CO	2.77	3120
NO	2.47	2740
O_2	2.09	2260
Cl_2	0.347	810
K_2	0.081	140

the result is a constant which is specific for each molecule, θ_r, the *rotational characteristic temperature*, where

$$\theta_r = \frac{h^2}{8\pi^2 Ik}, \tag{9.19}$$

θ_r has the dimensions of absolute temperature. Values of θ_r for several gases are given in Table 9.1.

The rotational partition function, when expanded in an infinite series, is

$$Z_{\text{rot}} = \sum_{j=0}^{\infty} (2j + 1)e^{-j(j+1)(\theta_r/T)}$$

$$= 1 + 3e^{-2\theta_r/T} + 5e^{-6\theta_r/T} + 7e^{-12\theta_r/T} + \cdots$$

At low temperatures (that is, $T \ll \theta_r$), only the first term of the series is significant, so that $Z_{\text{rot}} \approx 1$, and therefore $\bar{u}_{\text{rot}} = \mathscr{R}T^2[\partial(\ln Z_{\text{rot}})/\partial T] = 0$. Therefore only a negligible amount of rotational motion occurs at low temperatures. To evaluate the rotational partition function at high temperatures, where $T \gg \theta_r$, the summation operation of Eq. (9.18) is treated as an integration, so that

$$Z_{\text{rot}} = \int_0^{\infty} (2j + 1) \, e^{-j(j+1)(\theta_r/T)} \, dj.$$

When the integration is performed, the following result is obtained:

$$Z_{\text{rot}} = \frac{T}{\theta_r}.$$

One additional factor that affects the rotational partition function must be considered, and this is the symmetry effect. If a molecule is symmetrical, the number of different modes of rotation is only half of that which would occur if it were asymmetrical. This effect is introduced into the partition function through the symmetry number, σ, so that the rotational partition function, therefore, is

$$Z_{\text{rot}} = \frac{8\pi^2 IkT}{\sigma h^2}. \tag{9.20}$$

The value of σ is equal to 1 for asymmetrical molecules and is equal to 2 for symmetrical ones.

From the rotational partition function it is now possible to calculate the internal energy due to rotation, at high temperatures, which is

$$\bar{u}_{\text{rot}} = \mathcal{R}T^2 \frac{\partial(\ln Z_{\text{rot}})}{\partial T} = \mathcal{R}T. \tag{9.21}$$

At high temperatures, the internal energy of rotation is a simple function of temperature, and such factors as symmetry or distinguishability have no effect. From the rotational internal energy, the corresponding constant-volume molal specific heat at high temperatures can be obtained:

$$\tag{9.22}$$

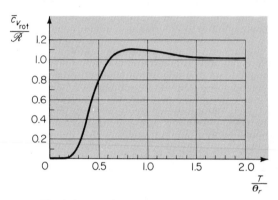

Fig. 9.1. $\bar{c}_{v_{\text{rot}}}/\mathcal{R}$ versus T/θ_r for a diatomic gas.

From a plot of $\bar{c}_{v_{\text{rot}}}/\mathcal{R}$ against T/θ_r, as in Fig. 9.1, it is seen that the value of $\bar{c}_{v_{\text{rot}}}$ is zero at low temperatures, and $\mathcal{R}$ at high temperatures, but at $(T/\theta_r) = 0.8$, the molal specific heat reaches a maximum of $1.1\,\mathcal{R}$.

The energy of vibration of a diatomic molecule according to Eq. (8.97) is

$$\epsilon_{\text{vib}} = (n + \tfrac{1}{2})h\nu, \qquad n = 0, 1, 2, 3, \dots \ .$$

The partition function of vibration then is

$$Z_{\text{vib}} = e^{-h\nu/2kT} \sum_{n=0}^{\infty} e^{-nh\nu/kT}. \tag{9.23}$$

Here, too, it is convenient to combine constants into a single one, the *vibrational characteristic temperature*, θ_v, so that

$$Z_{\text{vib}} = e^{-\theta_v/2T} \sum_{n=0}^{\infty} e^{-n\theta_v/T}. \tag{9.24}$$

Values of θ_v, expressed in units of temperature, are listed for various molecules in Table 9.1.

The sum of the infinite series in Eq. (9.24) can be reduced to a single fraction, and therefore the vibrational partition function becomes

$$Z_{\text{vib}} = \frac{e^{-\theta_v/2T}}{1 - e^{-\theta_v/T}}. \tag{9.25}$$

The internal energy of vibration per mole can then be derived from this partition function:

$$\bar{u}_{\text{vib}} = \mathscr{R}T^2 \frac{\partial}{\partial T} (\ln Z_{\text{vib}}) = \mathscr{R}\theta_v \left[\frac{1}{2} + \frac{1}{e^{\theta_v/T} - 1} \right]. \tag{9.26}$$

From this equation it is evident that even at low temperatures, vibrational effects contribute to internal energy, the amount being $\mathscr{R}\theta_v/2$. The constant-volume specific heat can be calculated from internal energy:

$$\bar{c}_{v_{\text{vib}}} = \left(\frac{\partial \bar{u}_{\text{vib}}}{\partial T} \right)_v = \mathscr{R} \left(\frac{\theta_v}{T} \right)^2 \frac{e^{\theta_v/T}}{(e^{\theta_v/T} - 1)^2}. \tag{9.27}$$

At low temperatures, since $e^{\theta_v/T} \gg 1$, the specific heat reduces to

$$\bar{c}_{v_{\text{vib}}} = \mathscr{R} \left(\frac{\theta_v}{T} \right)^2 e^{-\theta_v/T} \longrightarrow 0.$$

At high temperatures, on the other hand, since the exponential term can be replaced by an infinite series, the specific heat can be shown to reduce to

$$\bar{c}_{v_{\text{vib}}} = \mathscr{R} \left(\frac{\theta_v}{T} \right)^2 \frac{[1 + (\theta_v/T) + (\theta_v^2/2T^2) + \cdots]}{[(\theta_v/T) + (\theta_v^2/2T^2) + \cdots]^2}.$$

A plot of $\bar{c}_{v_{\text{vib}}}/\mathscr{R}$ versus T/θ_v is shown in Fig. 9.2.

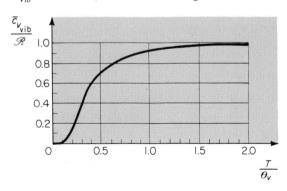

Fig. 9.2. $\bar{c}_{v_{\text{vib}}}/\mathscr{R}$ versus T/θ_v for a diatomic gas.

The contributions to molal specific heat made by the translational, rotational and vibrational motion of a diatomic molecule may now be added together:

$$\bar{c}_v = \frac{3}{2}\mathscr{R} + \frac{\mathscr{R}}{T^2}\left(\frac{\partial^2 \ln Z_{\text{rot}}}{\partial(1/T)^2}\right)_v + \mathscr{R}\left(\frac{\theta_v}{T}\right)^2 \frac{e^{\theta_v/T}}{(e^{\theta_v/T}-1)^2}. \tag{9.28}$$

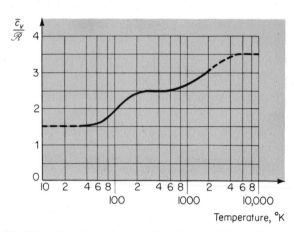

Fig. 9.3.   *Experimental values of $\bar{c}_v/\mathscr{R}$ versus T for hydrogen.*

In Fig. 9.3, $\bar{c}_v/\mathscr{R}$ is plotted against T for a diatomic gas (hydrogen). Because of the individual contributions made by translational, rotational, and vibrational effects, the curve does not show a simple shape.

The partition function of a diatomic molecule, as the product of the partition functions due to translation, rotation and vibration, is

$$Z = V\left(\frac{2\pi mkT}{h^2}\right)^{3/2}\left(\frac{8\pi^2 IkT}{\sigma h^2}\right)\left(\frac{e^{-\theta_v/2T}}{1-e^{-\theta_v/T}}\right). \tag{9.29}$$

As in the case of monatomic gases, Eq. (9.29) may be used to determine expressions for the thermodynamic properties as will be illustrated in the following examples. Table 9.2 summarizes some general formulas used to derive thermodynamic properties.

EXAMPLE 9.1: Hydrogen is a diatomic molecule composed of two symmetrical atoms and has a rotational characteristic temperature $\theta_r = 85.5°$K. Calculate the most probable distribution of rotational and vibrational energies at 25°C. Plot your results as energy versus particle percentages. Take the vibrational energy level $\epsilon_i = h\nu(n)$, that is, relative to the zero-point energy.

TABLE 9.2   Summary of some formulas of thermodynamic properties

General

$$Z = \sum_i g_i e^{-\epsilon_i/kT}$$

$$N_i = \frac{N}{Z} g_i e^{-\epsilon_i/kT}$$

$$p = kT \left(\frac{\partial \ln Z}{\partial V}\right)_T$$

$$U = \sum_i \epsilon_i N_i = kT^2 \left(\frac{\partial \ln Z}{\partial T}\right)_V$$

$$H = kT \left[T\left(\frac{\partial \ln Z}{\partial T}\right)_V + V\left(\frac{\partial \ln Z}{\partial V}\right)_T \right]$$

$$S = k \left[\ln Z + T\left(\frac{\partial \ln Z}{\partial T}\right)_V \right]$$

$$S_{\text{trans}} = Nk \left(\frac{5}{2} + \ln \frac{Z_{\text{trans}}}{N}\right) = Nk \left[\frac{3}{2} \ln M + \frac{5}{2} \ln T - \ln p - 1.155\right],$$

where M is the gram molecular weight, $T°K$ and p in atmospheres.

$$S_{\text{rot}} = Nk(1 + \ln Z_{\text{rot}}) = Nk[\ln I' + \ln T - \ln \sigma - 2.2],$$

where $I' = I(6.023 \times 10^{23})(10^{16})$ and I is in (gm/gm-mole) Å²*.

$$S_{\text{vib}} = Nk \left[\frac{\theta_v/T}{e^{\theta_v/T} - 1} - \ln (1 - e^{-\theta_v/T})\right]$$

$$F = -kT \ln Z$$

$$G = -kT \left[\ln Z - V\left(\frac{\partial \ln Z}{\partial V}\right)\right]$$

$$\theta_r = \frac{h^2}{8\pi^2 I k}$$

$$\theta_v = \frac{hv}{k}$$

Perfect monatomic gas

$$Z = V\left(\frac{2\pi kTm}{h^2}\right)^{3/2}$$

Perfect diatomic gas

$$Z_{\text{trans}} = V\left(\frac{2\pi kTm}{h^2}\right)^{3/2}$$

$$Z_{\text{rot}} = \frac{8\pi^2 I kT}{\sigma h^2}, \quad \text{when } T \gg \theta_{\text{rot}}$$

$$Z_{\text{vib}} = \frac{e^{-\theta_v/2T}}{1 - e^{-\theta_v/T}}$$

*The angstrom unit Å $= 10^{-8}$ cm.

Solution: The Maxwell-Boltzmann distribution law is

$$\frac{N_i}{N} = \frac{g_i e^{-\epsilon_i/kT}}{\sum_i g_i e^{-\epsilon_i/kT}}.$$

For the rotational energy distribution:

$$\frac{N_i}{N} = \frac{(2j+1)e^{-j(j+1)(\theta_r/T)}}{Z_{\text{rot}}}.$$

At 25°C,

$$\frac{\theta_r}{T} = \frac{85.5}{298.15} = 0.287.$$

Therefore,

$$\frac{N_i}{N} = \frac{(2j+1)e^{-j(j+1)(0.287)}}{Z_{\text{rot}}}.$$

To evaluate the foregoing expression the following table is prepared:

j	$\frac{\epsilon_i}{kT}$	$e^{-j(j+1)(0.287)}$	$g_i e^{-\epsilon_i/kT}$	$\frac{N_i}{N}$
0	0	1.000	1.000	0.262
1	0.574	0.564	1.690	0.443
2	1.722	0.179	0.895	0.234
3	3.444	0.0322	0.224	0.058
4	5.74	0.0032	0.029	0.0076
5	8.61	0.00018	0.002	0.0005
			$Z_{\text{rot}} = 3.840$	1.000

For the vibrational energy distribution,

$$\frac{N_i}{N} = \frac{(1)e^{-[h\nu(n)]/kT}}{Z_{\text{vib}}} = \frac{e^{-(\theta_v/T)(n)}}{Z_{\text{vib}}},$$

where

$$\frac{\theta_v}{T} = \frac{6140}{298.15} = 20.6.$$

The following table can then be prepared:

n	$\left(\frac{\theta_v}{T}\right)(n)$	$g_i e^{-\epsilon_i/kT}$	$\frac{N_i}{N}$
0	0	1	1
1	20.6	1.13×10^{-9}	0
2	41.2	0	0
		$Z_{\text{vib}} \approx 1.0$	

This means that essentially all the particles are at their lowest vibrational energy level. Figure 9.4 shows the distribution of rotational energy and vibrational energy over the range of energy levels.

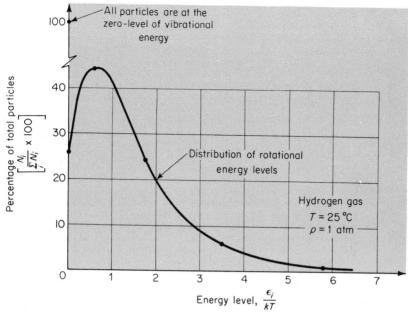

Fig. 9.4. *Example 9.1.*

EXAMPLE 9.2:   Oxygen molecules have the following physical properties

$$\theta_r = \frac{h^2}{8\pi^2 Ik} = 2.09°K$$

$$\theta_v = \frac{hv}{k} = 2260°K.$$

Considering only translational, rotational, and vibrational energies, calculate the following properties per gm-mole at 273°K:

(a) The translational, rotational, and vibrational partition functions
(b) Internal energy
(c) Enthalpy
(d) Helmholtz and Gibbs functions
(e) Entropy

Solution: (a) The translational partition function is

$$Z_{\text{trans}} = \frac{V}{h^3}(2\pi kTm)^{3/2}$$

$$= \frac{22400}{2.91 \times 10^{-79}}\left[(2\pi)(1.38 \times 10^{-16})(273)(5.31 \times 10^{-23})\right]^{3/2}$$

$$= 34.3 \times 10^{29}.$$

The rotational partition function is

$$Z_{\text{rot}} = \frac{8\pi^2 IkT}{\sigma h^2} = \frac{T}{\sigma \theta_r} = \frac{273}{2(2.09)} = 65.3.$$

The vibrational partition function is

$$Z_{\text{vib}} = \frac{e^{-\theta_v/2T}}{1 - e^{-\theta_v/T}} = 0.0159.$$

(b) The internal energy is

$$\bar{u} = \frac{3}{2} \mathscr{R}T + \mathscr{R}T + \mathscr{R}\theta_v \left(\frac{1}{2} + \frac{1}{e^{\theta_v/T} - 1} \right)$$

$$= \frac{5}{2} (1.986)(273) + 1.986(2260)\left(\frac{1}{2} + 0 \right) = 3600 \text{ cal/gm-mole.}$$

(c) The enthalpy is

$$\bar{h} = \bar{u} + \mathscr{R}T = 3600 + (1.986)(273) = 4142 \text{ cal/gm-mole.}$$

(d) The Helmholtz and Gibbs functions are

$$\bar{f} = -\mathscr{R}T\left(\ln \frac{Z_{\text{trans}}}{N_0} + \ln Z_{\text{rot}} + \ln Z_{\text{vib}} + 1 \right)$$

$$= -\mathscr{R}T(15.54 + 4.18 - 4.14 + 1) = -9000 \text{ cal/gm-mole}$$

$$\bar{g} = -\mathscr{R}T \ln \frac{Z}{N_0} = -\mathscr{R}T \ln \frac{35.6 \times 10^{29}}{6.025 \times 10^{23}} = -8450 \text{ cal/gm-mole.}$$

(e) The entropy values, according to Table 9.2, are

$$\bar{s}_{\text{trans}} = \mathscr{R}\left(\frac{5}{2} + \ln \frac{Z_{\text{trans}}}{N_0} \right) = 1.986\left(\frac{5}{2} + \ln \frac{34.3 \times 10^{29}}{6.025 \times 10^{23}} \right)$$

$$= 35.85 \text{ cal/gm-mole}^\circ\text{K}$$

$$\bar{s}_{\text{rot}} = \mathscr{R} \ln \left(\frac{8\pi^2 IkT}{\sigma h^2} \right) + \mathscr{R} = \mathscr{R}(1 + \ln Z_{\text{rot}})$$

$$= 1.986(1 + \ln 65.3) = 8.5 \text{ cal/gm-mole}^\circ\text{K}$$

$$\bar{s}_{\text{vib}} = \mathscr{R}\left[\frac{\theta_v/T}{e^{\theta_v/T} - 1} - \ln (1 - e^{-\theta_v/T}) \right]$$

$$= 1.986\left[\frac{2260/273}{e^{2260/273} - 1} - \ln (1 - e^{-2260/273}) \right]$$

$$= 1.986(2.1 \times 10^{-3} - 1 \times 10^{-4}) = 0.00397 \text{ cal/gm-mole}^\circ\text{K.}$$

The total entropy is

$$\bar{s}_{\text{total}} = 35.85 + 8.5 + 0.004 = 44.354 \text{ cal/gm-mole}^\circ\text{K.}$$

9-4
Specific Heat of
Perfect Gases

From Sections 9–2 and 9–3, it appears that the average molal specific heat at constant volume can be written as

$$\bar{c}_v = \tfrac{1}{2} f \mathcal{R}, \qquad (9.30)$$

where f is the number of fully developed *degrees of freedom* of the gaseous molecule. For monatomic gases, the value of f is 3, corresponding to the translational kinetic energy of the molecule in three orthogonal directions. The dumbbell model of the diatomic molecule has a nonzero moment of inertia about two of its axes of rotation. Thus, it possesses, in addition to the three degrees of translational freedom, two degrees of rotational freedom. Furthermore, since the atomic bond is not perfectly rigid, the atoms can vibrate along the line joining them. At high temperature the vibrational movement of two atoms along the line joining them contributes two additional degrees of freedom; one corresponding to the vibrational kinetic energy and the other to the vibrational potential energy of the oscillator. For polyatomic gases, the value of f is 6; three translational and three rotational; the vibrational degrees are again unexcited except at elevated temperatures.

According to the principle of equipartition of energy, each degree of freedom of a gas in thermal equilibrium at temperature T, contributes $\tfrac{1}{2}kT$ per molecule to the kinetic energy, and also each degree of freedom contributes $\tfrac{1}{2}kT$ per molecule to the potential energy. Therefore the average energy associated with the vibration of a diatomic molecule is kT.

The corresponding contribution to the constant volume specific heat is $\tfrac{1}{2}\mathcal{R}$ per mole. Thus for a monatomic gas with 3 degrees of freedom, the internal energy per mole is $\tfrac{3}{2}\mathcal{R}T$ and $\bar{c}_v$ is $\tfrac{3}{2}\mathcal{R}$. For a diatomic gas with 5 degrees of freedom, the internal energy per mole is $\tfrac{5}{2}\mathcal{R}T$ and $\bar{c}_v$ is $\tfrac{5}{2}\mathcal{R}$.

The molal constant pressure specific heat is

$$\bar{c}_p = \bar{c}_v + \mathcal{R} = (1 + \tfrac{1}{2}f)\mathcal{R}, \qquad (9.31)$$

and the ratio of specific heats γ is

$$\gamma = \frac{\bar{c}_p}{\bar{c}_v} = \frac{f+2}{f}. \qquad (9.32)$$

Equation (9.32) predicts γ to be 1.67 for monatomic gases, 1.40 for diatomic gases, and 1.33 for polyatomic gases. At high temperatures, the vibrational modes become excited, predicting a value of $\bar{c}_v = \tfrac{7}{2}\mathcal{R}$ and $\gamma = 1.29$ for diatomic molecules. In general, the more complex the molecule, the higher the values of its specific heats and the smaller the value of γ. The value of γ, however, can never be greater than 1.67 ($f = 3$) or less than 1.0 ($f = \infty$).

The equipartition theorem implies that the specific heat of a perfect gas is independent of temperature. Experiments, however, show that, for a diatomic gas, $\bar{c}_v$ varies with T and approaches the predicted value of $\frac{7}{2}\mathscr{R}$ only at very high temperatures. Therefore the principle of equipartition of energy does not hold until a sufficiently high temperature is reached such that kT is much larger than the separation between the quantized energy levels. Evidently the disagreement arises because classical kinetic theory does not predict the temperature at which the various degrees of freedom become excited, corresponding to the quantized vibrational and rotational energy levels.

According to Eq. (8.97), vibrational oscillations above the ground level require that multiple values of the energy quanta $h\nu$ be supplied. At low temperature, the energy, kT, is small compared to $h\nu$ and since the energy of oscillation can never be less than $h\nu/2$, no change of internal energy is possible and the vibrational contribution to c_v is zero. Therefore, the diatomic molecule exhibits an average value of c_v of only $\frac{5}{2}k$ per molecule. As the temperature is raised, kT approaches $h\nu$ in magnitude. At very high temperatures, $kT > h\nu$, and c_v then agrees with the principle of equipartition of energy.

A similar situation occurs with the rotation of the molecule. The energy of rotation requires multiple values of $k\theta_r$ such that

$$\epsilon_{\mathrm{rot}} = \frac{h^2}{8\pi^2 I} j(j+1) = k\theta_r j(j+1).$$

For the rotation of a diatomic molecule about an axis perpendicular to the line joining the two atoms, the energy, kT, must equal or exceed a minimum value of rotational energy. At high temperatures, the available energy, kT, exceeds this minimum value by a large enough amount to permit rotation at several energy levels, so that the principle of equipartition does apply and $\bar{c}_v$ assumes the classical value of $\mathscr{R}$. Variation of $\bar{c}_v$ versus temperature for a typical diatomic gas (hydrogen) is shown in Fig. 9.3. At low temperature only translational motion is exhibited and the value of $\bar{c}_v$ is $\frac{3}{2}\mathscr{R}$. At 50°K, rotational motion begins to absorb energy so that, when room temperature is reached, rotational motion is fully developed and $\bar{c}_v = \frac{5}{2}\mathscr{R}$. At about 600°K, vibrational motion begins to occur, and the classical equilibrium value of $\frac{7}{2}\mathscr{R}$ is attained, ultimately, at still higher temperatures.

Experimentally determined values of specific heat, and specific heat ratios, of various gases are listed in Table 9.3. The agreement between predicted and measured values is quite good, especially for monatomic gases. The last column of the table gives an indication of the departure of the gas from perfect gas behavior.

TABLE 9.3   VALUES OF SPECIFIC HEATS OF VARIOUS GASES AT 1 ATM
AND 15°C, UNLESS OTHERWISE STATED

Gas		$\dfrac{\bar{c}_v}{\mathscr{R}}$	$\dfrac{\bar{c}_p}{\mathscr{R}}$	γ	$\dfrac{\bar{c}_p - \bar{c}_v}{\mathscr{R}}$
Monatomic	He	1.519	2.520	1.659(18°)	1.001
	Ne			1.64 (19°)	
	A	1.509	2.517	1.66	1.008
	Kr			1.68 (19°)	
	Xe			1.66 (19°)	
Diatomic	H_2	2.438	3.438	1.410	0.9995
	N_2	2.448	3.453	1.404	1.005
	CO	2.488	3.493	1.404	1.005
	O_2	2.504	3.508	1.401	1.004
	NO	2.152	3.517	1.400	1.005
	Cl_2	3.02	4.11	1.36	1.09
Triatomic	H_2O	3.3	4.36	1.32 (100°)	1.06
	CO_2	3.38	4.407	1.304	1.027
	SO_2	3.79	4.89	1.29	1.10
Polyatomic	NH_3	3.42	4.48	1.31	1.06
	C_2H_4	4.04	5.07	1.25	1.03

EXAMPLE 9.3:   Using the data of Example 9.1 for hydrogen, calculate the rotational and vibrational constant-volume specific heats at (a) 25°C and atmospheric pressure; (b) 1000°C and atmospheric pressure.

Solution: (a) The rotational characteristic temperature θ_r, according to Table 9.1, is

$$\theta_r = 85.5°\text{K}.$$

At $T = 25°$C,

$$\frac{\theta_r}{T} = \frac{85.5}{298.15} = 0.287 \quad \text{and} \quad r = j(j+1)(0.287),$$

and at $T = 1000°$C,

$$\frac{\theta_r}{T} = \frac{85.5}{1273.15} = 0.0671 \quad \text{and} \quad r = j(j+1)(0.0671).$$

Internal energy is given by

$$U = \frac{N \sum_i g_i \epsilon_i e^{-\epsilon_i/kT}}{\sum_i g_i e^{-\epsilon_i/kT}}.$$

Differentiating internal energy with respect to temperature yields the following:

$$(\bar{c}_v)_{\text{rot}} = \mathscr{R}\left[\frac{\sum\limits_{j=0,1...}^{\infty} g_i r^2 e^{-r}}{\sum\limits_{j=0,1...}^{\infty} g_i e^{-r}} - \left(\frac{\sum\limits_{j=0,1...}^{\infty} g_i r e^{-r}}{\sum\limits_{j=0,1...}^{\infty} g_i e^{-r}}\right)^2\right],$$

where

$$r = \frac{\epsilon_i}{kT} = \frac{j(j+1)}{T}(\theta_r) \quad \text{and} \quad g_i = 2j+1.$$

To calculate the value of $\bar{c}_v$ at 25°C, the following table may be formulated:

j	$j+1$	$r =$ $j(j+1)(0.287)$	e^{-r}	$g_i =$ $2j+1$	$g_i e^{-r}$	$r(g_i e^{-r})$	$r(rg_i e^{-r})$
0	1	0	1	1	1	0	0
1	2	0.574	0.564	3	1.690	0.970	0.556
2	3	1.722	0.179	5	0.895	1.542	2.66
3	4	3.444	0.0320	7	0.224	0.772	2.66
4	5	5.74	0.0032	9	0.029	0.166	0.953
5	6	8.61	0.00018	11	0.002	0.017	0.146
					3.840	3.467	6.975

At 25°C,

$$(\bar{c}_v)_{\text{rot}} = \mathscr{R}\left[\frac{6.975}{3.840} - \left(\frac{3.467}{3.840}\right)^2\right] = 1.986 \text{ cal/gm-mole°K.}$$

At 25°C, $(\bar{c}_v)_{\text{rot}}$ has already reached the classical equilibrium value, and therefore, at 1000°C, $(\bar{c}_v)_{\text{rot}}$ is the classical value.

(b) The vibrational constant-volume specific heat is given by

$$(\bar{c}_v)_{\text{vib}} = \mathscr{R}(e^{\theta_v/T})\left[\frac{\theta_v/T}{e^{\theta_v/T} - 1}\right]^2,$$

where the vibrational temperature θ_v is equal to 6140°K. At 25°C, $\theta_v/T = 20.6$, and

$$(\bar{c}_v)_{\text{vib}} = \mathscr{R}(e^{20.6})\left[\frac{20.6}{e^{20.6} - 1}\right]^2 \approx 0.$$

At 1000°C, $\theta_v/T = 4.82$,

and

$$(\bar{c}_v)_{\text{vib}} = \mathscr{R}(e^{4.82})\left[\frac{4.82}{e^{4.82} - 1}\right]^2$$
$$= 0.379 \text{ cal/gm-mole°K.}$$

EXAMPLE 9.4: The interatomic distance of carbon monoxide is 1.128 Å. What is the constant-volume specific heat at 300°K and atmospheric pressure?

Solution:

$$(\bar{c}_v)_{\text{trans}} = \frac{3}{2}\,\mathscr{R}.$$

$$I = \left(\frac{m_1 m_2}{m_1 + m_2}\right)r^2 = (1.448 \times 10^{-39})\,\frac{\text{gm-cm}^2}{\text{molecule}}.$$

Therefore (see also Table 9.1),

$$\theta_r = \frac{h^2}{8\pi^2 Ik} = \frac{(6.6254 \times 10^{-27})^2 \left(\frac{\text{erg-sec}}{\text{molecule}}\right)^2}{(8\pi^2)(1.448 \times 10^{-39})\,\frac{\text{gm-cm}^2}{\text{molecule}}\,(1.38049 \times 10^{-16})\,\frac{\text{erg}}{\text{°K molecule}}} = 2.77\text{°K},$$

and

$$\frac{\theta_r}{T} = 0.00923.$$

At 300°K, even very high rotational energy levels are filled (since θ_r corresponds to such a low temperature). Consequently, the classical value for rotational specific heat is reached long before 300°K.

Vibrational effects do not appear for CO at 300°K; much higher temperatures are required, therefore

$$(\bar{c}_v)_{300°K} = \tfrac{3}{2}\mathscr{R} + \mathscr{R} = 4.97 \text{ cal/gm-mole°K}.$$

9-5
Simple
Crystals

Atoms in a simple crystal cannot be treated as independent entities owing to the strong restoring forces between them. Because of the strong constraints imposed by the lattice, atoms in a simple crystal cannot translate or rotate; on the other hand, they are free to vibrate in three coordinate directions. These vibrations constitute the sole contribution to the crystal internal energy. The oscillations can be treated as small vibrations about equilibrium positions if the temperature is not too high. It is assumed that the vibrations involve both kinetic and potential energy.

Each atom in a crystalline solid has three translational degrees of freedom. An N-particle crystal then has $3N$ independent and equivalent degrees of freedom, (only $3N - 6$ degrees of freedom if movement of the entire body is excluded). The partition function is obtained by summation over these degrees of freedom. Although the kinetic energy summation is readily written in terms of the Cartesian coordinate system, the summation of the potential energy of the particles due to their mutual interactions becomes a very complex function in Cartesian coordinates. To simplify the form of the potential energy, one may introduce *normal* coordinates.* This coordinate transformation enables separation of the Schrödinger equation into simpler differential equations, each of them with a smaller number of variables. Such a transformation is based on the assumption: when a system of harmonic oscillators is excited along one normal coordinate, the system vibrates in simple harmonic motion only along that coordinate and does not transfer energy to the other normal coordinates.

The Schrödinger equation may be separated into $3N$ equations, each in terms of an individual normal coordinate, or mode of vibration, corresponding to a particular energy level. Each equation is of the form of a simple harmonic oscillator equation and the non-degenerate vibrational energy levels obtained from this treatment have the form:

$$\epsilon_i = (n + \tfrac{1}{2})h\nu_i, \quad n = 0, 1, 2, \ldots .$$

Thus, for small amplitude oscillations, an N-particle crystal may be regarded as an ensemble of $3N - 6$ independent harmonic oscillators. Since the oscillators are distinguishable because of their identification with the lattice points, the statistics follow the Maxwell-Boltzmann model. The partition function is obtained by the usual summation over all independent quantum states. The energy ϵ_i is summed up over the $3N$ normal modes:

$$Z = g_0 \sum_{i=1}^{3N} e^{-[(E_0 + \Sigma \epsilon_i)/kT]} = g_0 \sum_{i=1}^{3N} e^{-E_0/kT} e^{-\Sigma(\epsilon_i/kT)}.$$

But

$$\frac{\epsilon_i}{kT} = \left(n + \frac{1}{2}\right)\frac{h\nu_i}{kT} = \left(n + \frac{1}{2}\right)\frac{\theta_v}{T},$$

therefore

$$Z = g_0 e^{-E_0/kT} \prod_{i=1}^{3N} e^{-\theta_v/2T}[1 - e^{-\theta_v/T}]^{-1}, \tag{9.33}$$

where E_0 is the zero-point energy of the crystal (potential energy) and g_0 is the degeneracy due to different orientation of the atoms in the lattice.

The partition function indicated in Eq. (9.33) is that of the whole crystal consisting of N atoms. No division by $N!$ is required here, since the atoms in the immediate vicinity of the fixed lattice points are not free to exchange positions with each other, so that they are not indistinguishable, even though they are identical. Note also that ϵ_i's are the energies of the normal modes referenced to the zero-point energy.

*See reference 8.2.

The most probable distribution of the atoms according to Maxwell-Boltzmann distribution is

$$\frac{N_i}{3N} = \frac{g_0}{Z} e^{-[(E_0 + \Sigma \epsilon_i)/kT]} . \tag{9.34}$$

The thermodynamic properties of the crystal may then be obtained as with a gas, by means of the partition function. The internal energy, Helmholtz function, and entropy are related to the partition function by

$$U = kT^2 \left(\frac{\partial \ln Z}{\partial T}\right)_V,$$

$$F = -kT \ln Z,$$

$$S = k \ln Z + kT \left(\frac{\partial \ln Z}{\partial T}\right)_V.$$

If the expression for the partition function, Eq. (9.33), is substituted in these equations, then

$$U = U_0 + h \sum_{i=1}^{3N} \nu_i [e^{h\nu_i/kT} - 1]^{-1}, \tag{9.35}$$

$$F = -kT \ln Z = -kT \ln g_0 + U_0 + kT \sum_{i=1}^{3N} \ln [1 - e^{-h\nu_i/kT}], \tag{9.36}$$

$$S = \frac{U - F}{T} = k \ln g_0 - k \sum_{i=1}^{3N} \left\{ \ln [1 - e^{-h\nu_i/kT}] - \frac{h\nu_i}{kT} [e^{h\nu_i/kT} - 1]^{-1} \right\}, \tag{9.37}$$

where U_0 represents the minimum internal energy of the crystal and is equal to

$$U_0 = E_0 + \sum_{i=1}^{3N} \frac{h\nu_i}{2}. \tag{9.38}$$

The specific heat of the crystal at constant volume is

$$c_v = k \sum_{i=1}^{3N} \left(\frac{h\nu_i}{kT}\right)^2 e^{h\nu_i/kT} [e^{h\nu_i/kT} - 1]^{-2}. \tag{9.39}$$

9-6
Einstein Model
The difficulty of evaluating the preceding thermodynamic quantities lies in predicting the $3N$ frequencies of the crystal. In general, some approximations must be made in order to obtain any results. Both Einstein and Debye developed methods

of solution. The approximation made at high temperature will be examined first.

At high temperatures, the value of $h\nu/kT$ becomes much less than unity; although the frequency of vibration can increase as the temperature rises, tending to counterbalance the temperature effect, the frequency cannot increase indefinitely. The reason is that frequency can increase only as wavelength diminishes, and the wavelength cannot be smaller than the atomic spacing. Therefore, the term $e^{h\nu/kT}$ which can be expressed as an infinite series, at high temperatures is equivalent to only the first two terms of the series—that is, $[1 + (h\nu/kT)]$. Then the internal energy and specific heat of the crystal are

$$U = U_0 + h3N\nu\left[1 + \frac{h\nu}{kT} - 1\right]^{-1} = U_0 + 3NkT \tag{9.40}$$

$$\bar{c}_v = 3N_0k \approx 6 \text{ cal/gm-mole}°\text{K}. \tag{9.41}$$

Similarly,

$$F = -kT\ln g_0 + U_0 + 3N_0kT\ln(h\nu/kT) \tag{9.42}$$

and

$$S = k\ln g_0 + 3N_0k[1 - \ln(h\nu/kT)]. \tag{9.43}$$

The results of the foregoing equations are in agreement with those obtained by classical mechanics. According to the principle of equipartition of energy, each of the $3N$ coordinates and momenta associated with vibrational motion contributes $\frac{1}{2}kT$ to the internal energy, so that the molal specific heat of a crystal should be $3\mathscr{R}$. According to the law of Dulong and Petit, which was postulated in 1819, the molal constant-volume specific heat of any element in the crystalline solid state is 6.4 cal/gm-mole°K. Experimental work on atomic and simple ionic crystals shows that specific heat values at room temperatures generally do fall in this range.

But at lower temperatures, specific heats fall below this classical value and, in fact, approach zero. A simple approximation proposed by Einstein in 1907 led to a solution that indicated the correct trend. For a monatomic crystal of identical atoms, Einstein assumed that all $3N$ frequencies of all atoms of the crystal are identical and independent, so that Eq. (9.35) becomes

$$U = U_0 + 3Nk\theta_E[e^{\theta_E/T} - 1]^{-1}, \tag{9.44}$$

where $\theta_E = h\nu_E/k$ is called the *Einstein characteristic temperature*. Then molal specific heat at constant volume is

$$\bar{c}_v = 3\mathscr{R}\left(\frac{\theta_E}{T}\right)^2 e^{\theta_E/T}[e^{\theta_E/T} - 1]^{-2}. \qquad (9.45)$$

By suitable selection of ν_E, the assumed frequency calculates confirmed specific heat values, measured at temperatures as low as $\theta_E/3$ (about 20°K). At lower temperatures, however, the deviations are significantly larger. It may be noted that at high temperatures, the value of $\bar{c}_v$ calculated by the Einstein method, approaches the classical value of $3\mathscr{R}$.

9-7
Debye Model
Debye analyzed the thermodynamic behavior of crystals by comparing their vibration character-istics with those of an isotropic (independent of direction) elastic continuum. He then was able to derive an expression for the *frequency distribution* of a crystal lattice. In an elastic medium, the frequency density of standing waves is proportional to the square of the frequency:

$$dN = C\nu^2\, d\nu, \qquad (9.46)$$

where C is a proportionality constant depending on volume and wave veloci-ty, and dN is the number of modes whose frequencies lie between ν and $\nu + d\nu$. Debye assumed that this distribution can be employed to describe the crystal vibration frequencies. At the maximum frequency the total number of normal modes is $3N_0$ for 1 mole. Then,

$$dN = \frac{9N_0}{\nu_{\max}^3}\, \nu^2\, d\nu. \qquad (9.47)$$

The internal energy of the crystal according to Eq. (9.35) and (9.38) is

$$U = E_0 + h\sum_{i=1}^{3N}\left[\frac{\nu_i}{2} + \nu_i(e^{h\nu_i/kT} - 1)^{-1}\right]$$

$$= E_0 + h\int_0^{3N}\left(\frac{\nu}{2} + \nu(e^{h\nu/kT} - 1)^{-1}\right)dN, \qquad (3N \gg 1).$$

Substituting for dN from Eq. (9.47) gives

$$U = E_0 + \frac{9N_0}{\nu_{\max}^3}h\int_0^{\nu_{\max}}\left[\frac{\nu^3}{2} + \nu^3(e^{h\nu/kT} - 1)^{-1}\right]d\nu,$$

which may be rewritten as

$$U = E_0 + \frac{9}{8}N_0 k\theta_D + 9N_0 kT\left(\frac{T}{\theta_D}\right)^3\int_0^{\theta_D/T}\frac{x^3}{e^x - 1}\, dx, \qquad (9.48)$$

where $\theta_D = h\nu_D/k$ is the *Debye characteristic temperature*, $\nu_D = \nu_{max}$ and $x = h\nu/kT$. Table 9.4 gives values of θ_D for several solids.

TABLE 9.4 DEBYE TEMPERATURES FOR SEVERAL SOLIDS

Substance		Temperature range, °K	θ_D, °K
Lead	Pb	14–573	88
Mercury	Hg	31–232	97
Iodine	I	22–298	106
Cadmium	Cd	50–380	168
Sodium	Na	50–240	172
Silver	Ag	35–873	215
Calcium	Ca	22–62	226
Zinc	Zn	33–673	235
Copper	Cu	14–773	315
Aluminum	Al	19–773	398
Iron	Fe	32–95	453
Diamond	C	30–1169	1860

The molal specific heat at constant volume is

$$\bar{c}_v = 9N_0 k\left[4\left(\frac{T}{\theta_D}\right)^3 \int_0^{\theta_D/T} \frac{x^3}{e^x - 1}\,dx - \frac{\theta_D}{T}(e^{\theta_D/T} - 1)^{-1}\right]. \tag{9.49}$$

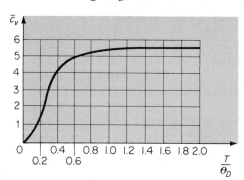

Fig. 9.5. Debye's prediction of specific heats of solids as function of T/θ_D.

Equation (9.49) is the Debye equation for the specific heat of a solid. Fig. 9.5 shows a plot of $\bar{c}_v$ versus T/θ_D based on Eq. (9.49).

At low temperatures, x is large and the second term in the brackets in Eq. (9.49) may be neglected. The specific heat at constant volume is then

$$\bar{c}_v = 36N_0 k\left(\frac{T}{\theta_D}\right)^3 \int_0^{\theta_D/T} \frac{x^3}{e^x - 1}\,dx$$

$$\approx 36N_0 k\left[\frac{\pi^4}{15}\left(\frac{T}{\theta_D}\right)^3 - e^{-\theta_D/T}\right] \approx 234\mathscr{R}\left(\frac{T}{\theta_D}\right)^3. \tag{9.50}$$

Equation (9.50) is called the *Debye T³ law*. It predicts that at low temperature the constant volume specific heat of a crystal varies as the third power of the absolute temperature. It further predicts that the specific heat is zero at the absolute zero of temperature. Note in Eq. (9.50) that the molal specific heat of the crystal is a function of only the normalized temperature, (T/θ_D).

Debye's formula yields results for simple isotropic monatomic lattices, which are in excellent agreement with the experimental data at the low temperatures. At intermediate temperatures, the Debye and Einstein formulas do not differ appreciably, and at high normalized temperatures both equations yield the expected classical result.

The close agreement between measured data and results calculated by the Debye formula does not necessarily prove the Debye model is correct. In 1937, Blackman made detailed calculations of the frequency distribution for specific crystals and showed that the actual frequency distribution differs significantly from that assumed by Debye. But, the statistical averaging process fortuitously led to fair agreement between results.

EXAMPLE 9.5: (a) Calculate the constant-volume specific heat of silver at 28.56°K; the Debye characteristic temperature of silver is 209°K. (b) If the calculated Einstein $\bar{c}_v$ at 28.56°K is 0.579 cal/gm-mole°K, estimate the fundamental frequency of oscillation of the atoms according to Einstein analysis.

Solution: (a) $\dfrac{\theta_D}{T} = \dfrac{209}{28.56} = 7.34$, and $\dfrac{T}{\theta_D} = \dfrac{1}{7.34} = 0.1363$.

Since $T \ll \theta_D$,

$$\bar{c}_v = 234\,\mathscr{R}\left(\frac{T}{\theta_D}\right)^3 = 1.18 \text{ cal/gm-mole°K.}$$

(b) The Einstein constant-volume specific heat is given by

$$(\bar{c}_v)_E = 3\,\mathscr{R}\left[\frac{\theta_E/T}{e^{\theta_E/T} - 1}\right]^2 e^{\theta_E/T}.$$

Values of $(\bar{c}_v)_E$ corresponding to different values of θ_E/T are calculated in the following table:

$\dfrac{\theta_E}{T}$	$e^{\theta_E/T}$	$e^{\theta_E/T}-1$	$\dfrac{\theta_E/T}{e^{\theta_E/T}-1}$	$\left[\dfrac{\theta_E/T}{e^{\theta_E/T}-1}\right]^2$	$(e^{\theta_E/T})\left[\dfrac{\theta_E/T}{e^{\theta_E/T}-1}\right]^2$	$(\bar{c}_v)_E$
7	1097	1096	$\dfrac{7}{1096} = 0.00639$	40.8×10^{-6}	0.0447	0.2682
6	403	402	$\dfrac{6}{402} = 0.0149$	0.000223	0.090	0.540
5.9	365	364	$\dfrac{5.9}{364} = 0.0162$	0.000263	0.0960	0.576

From the foregoing table, at $(c_v)_E = 0.579$, $\theta_E/T \approx 5.9$. From which,

$$\theta_E = (5.9)(28.56) = 168.3°\text{K}.$$

But

$$\theta_E = \frac{h\nu_E}{k},$$

therefore,

$$\nu_E = \frac{(168.3)(1.38049 \times 10^{-16})}{(6.6254 \times 10^{-27})} = 35.1 \times 10^{11}\ \text{sec}^{-1}.$$

Similarly, if the specific-heat value, $\bar{c}_v$, were 1.18 cal/gm-mole°K, the fundamental frequency would be calculated as follows:

$\dfrac{\theta_E}{T}$	$e^{\theta_E/T}$	$e^{\theta_E/T}-1$	$\dfrac{\theta_E/T}{e^{\theta_E/T}-1}$	$\left[\dfrac{\theta_E/T}{e^{\theta_E/T}-1}\right]^2$	$(e^{\theta_E/T})\left[\dfrac{\theta_E/T}{e^{\theta_E/T}-1}\right]^2$	$(\bar{c}_v)_E$
5	148.4	147.4	0.0339	0.00115	0.171	1.026
4.9	134.3	133.3	0.0367	0.00135	0.1813	1.088
4.80	121.5	120.5	0.0398	0.001585	0.1925	1.155

from which

$$\frac{\theta_E}{T} \approx 4.79 \quad \text{or} \quad \theta_E = 136.8°\text{K},$$

and

$$\nu_E = 2.85 \times 10^{12}\ \text{sec}^{-1}.$$

The fundamental frequency of oscillation of the Debye model is 4.33×10^{12} sec^{-1} corresponding to a $\bar{c}_v$ value of 1.18 cal/gm-mole°K. On the other hand, the Einstein equation indicates that, at this $\bar{c}_v$ value, the fundamental frequency is only 2.85×10^{12} sec^{-1}. At frequencies larger than this, the Einstein equation leads to specific-heat values that are considerably below those of the Debye equation.

9-8
The Third Law of Thermodynamics

Boltzmann's equation defines the entropy of a macrostate of a system in terms of thermodynamic probability: $S \equiv k \ln W$. In order to evaluate entropy by means of this relationship, it is necessary to enumerate the microstates corresponding to a certain macrostate. When a system of indistinguishable particles is at its minimum value of energy, each particle is in its lowest quantum state, and there is only one possible microstate. This microstate corresponds to the minimum possible value of W, which is $W = 1$. Therefore, the minimum value of S is zero. Since the entropy of a system is determined by the mechanical properties of its particles, a system in which the particles contribute nothing to entropy is arbitrarily assigned a zero value of entropy. At low temperatures, perfect crystals tend to form very orderly structures and their lattice vibrations are at their lowest energies. Therefore, at 0°K, the entropy of such crystals is conceivably zero. Since a temperature of absolute zero is unattainable, measurements cannot be made to prove that the entropy value is zero at zero degrees absolute. It can merely be assumed, on the basis of extrapolation, that this is true.

Nernst postulated in 1906 that the Gibbs free-energy function and the enthalpy of a system approach each other asymptotically as absolute zero temperature is approached. Also, he indicated that their variation becomes independent of temperature as T approaches zero. This variation is shown in Fig. 9.6 and may be expressed mathematically as

$$\lim_{T \to 0} \left(\frac{\partial \, \Delta G}{\partial T} \right)_p = \lim_{T \to 0} \left(\frac{\partial \, \Delta H}{\partial T} \right)_p = 0. \tag{9.51}$$

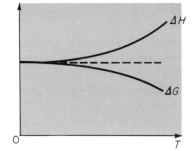

Fig. 9.6. $\lim\limits_{T \to 0} \left(\frac{\partial \Delta G}{\partial T} \right)_p = \lim\limits_{T \to 0} \left(\frac{\partial \Delta H}{\partial T} \right)_p = 0.$

According to Eq. (5.68), the change in free energy of a constant composition system as a result of temperature changes is related to entropy:

$$-\Delta S = \left(\frac{\partial \, \Delta G)}{\partial T} \right)_p.$$

From this information, Eq. (9.51) becomes

$$\lim_{T \to 0} \Delta S = 0. \tag{9.52}$$

The foregoing equation is called the *third law of thermodynamics*. It indicates that the entropy of a one-component substance in thermodynamic equilibrium approaches zero as the temperature approaches zero. This conclusion is also implicit in the expression relating entropy to the partition function:

$$S = k \left[\ln Z + T \left(\frac{\partial \ln Z}{\partial T} \right)_r \right].$$

The determination of the change in entropy of a system is accomplished by evaluating the integral $\int \left(\frac{dQ}{T}\right)_{rev}$ as heat interaction takes place reversibly between the system and its environment. Experimental data is extrapolated to zero absolute temperature, and the third law is assumed to be valid. The entropy of a closed system is

$$S = S_0 + \int_0^T \left(\frac{dQ}{T}\right)_{rev},$$

(9.53)

where S_0 is the entropy of the given system at $0°K$ and dQ is the reversible heat transfer to the system. If the third law does hold, then S_0 equals zero, and Eq. (9.53) can be rewritten as:

$$S = \int_0^{T^*} \left(\frac{dQ}{T}\right)_{rev} + \int_{T^*}^T \left(\frac{dQ}{T}\right)_{rev},$$

(9.54)

where T^* is the lowest temperature attainable in the calorimetric measurements, which is down to about 1 degree above $0°K$. The last term of Eq. (9.54) is evaluated completely from experimental measurements (of specific heat, heat of crystalline transition, heat of fusion, and heat of vaporization, as appropriate). Measurements of specific heat above T^* are made in conjunction with an appropriate theoretical equation, usually the Debye equation. On the other hand, the first term on the right side of Eq. (9.54) is evaluated by extrapolating from T^* to $0°K$.

Above the lowest temperature of measurement, T^*, the molecules of the given substance are distributed among the available quantum states in accordance with the appropriate distribution law. As the temperature is lowered, the distribution of molecules among the available levels of energy changes progressively in such a way that in the limit (at $T = 0$) the molecules have available only one possible state. If at the lowest temperature of measurement, T^*, a crystal of identical atoms, can exist in only a single quantum state of energy, its entropy at $0°K$ is assigned a value of zero, provided that the internal energy corresponding to T^* can be accounted for by the extrapolation from T^* to $0°K$.

Note that the third law does not limit the substance to any given crystalline forms. The substance may, at the lowest temperature of measurement, be in any of the several possible crystalline forms and each one of the different crystalline forms can conform to the requirements of the third law.

In order to confirm the validity of calculations based on the third law, some method of comparison and a criterion for appraisal are required. Both requirements are met by using statistical thermodynamics to determine the

TABLE 9.5 COMPARISON BETWEEN CLASSICAL AND STATISTICAL VALUES OF
ENTROPIES FOR SEVERAL SUBSTANCES (25°C AND 1 ATM)

Substance	Entropy, cal/gm-mole°K	
	Classical (calorimetric)	Statistical (spectroscopic)
HCl	44.5	44.64
HBr	47.6	47.48
HI	49.5	49.4
N_2	45.9	45.78
O_2	49.1	49.03
H_2	29.74	31.23
CO	46.2	47.31
H_2O	44.28	45.10
H_2S	49.15	49.10
CO_2	51.11	51.07
NH_3	45.91	45.94
CH_4	44.30	44.35
SO_2	59.24	59.18
C_2H_4	52.48	52.47

absolute entropy of a perfect gas and by comparing this entropy value with the value obtained through calorimetric measurements based on the third law. In the statistical approach, the Sackur-Tetrode equation is used to determine the translational entropy for monatomic gases. In the case of polyatomic gases, the energy levels of allowed particle quantum states are determined spectroscopically, from which the partition function and then the entropy are calculated.

In Table 9.5, values of molal entropy calculated by the third law are compared with values determined by statistical methods.

In general any substance obtainable in pure crystalline form at equilibrium is likely to conform to the requirements of the third law, and the absolute value of entropy can be calculated. Nonconformity with the third law occurs because the substance is not in a single quantum state at 0°K, owing to factors such as (a) the presence of two, or more, isotopes; (b) randomness in the structure of the crystal, (c) nonequilibrium distribution of molecules among the quantum states of energy, (d) presence of different molecules in solution or in a mixture, (e) existence of subcooled (metastable) state rather than crystalline form.

The third law of thermodynamics, as will be shown in Chapter 11, is useful in calculating thermodynamic properties and in analyzing chemical and phase equilibria. It is also used to explain the behavior of solids at very low temperatures.

EXAMPLE 9.6: Verify the value of entropy of N_2 as given in Table 9.5. The interatomic distance between the atoms of a nitrogen molecule is 1.094 Å.

Solution: The entropy is given by

$$S = k\left[\ln Z + T\left(\frac{\partial \ln Z}{\partial T}\right)_V\right].$$

For translation:

$$Z_{\text{trans}} = \frac{V(2\pi mkT)^{3/2}}{h^3}$$

$$\ln Z_{\text{trans}} = \frac{3}{2}\ln\frac{2\pi mk}{h^2} + \frac{3}{2}\ln T + \ln V.$$

But

$$\mathcal{Z}_{\text{trans}} = \frac{Z^N}{N!}.$$

Therefore,

$$\ln \mathcal{Z}_{\text{trans}} = N\ln Z - N\ln N + N.$$

Also,

$$\left(\frac{\partial \ln Z_{\text{trans}}}{\partial T}\right)_V = \frac{3}{2}\frac{1}{T}.$$

Therefore,

$$\bar{s}_{\text{trans}} = \mathcal{R}\left[\frac{3}{2}\ln\frac{2\pi mk}{h^2} + \frac{3}{2}\ln T + \ln\bar{v} - \ln N_0 + 1 + \frac{3}{2}\right]$$

For 1 mole,

$$\bar{v} = \frac{82.06\,T}{p}\,\text{cc/gm-mole} \quad (p \text{ in atm})$$

$$m = \frac{M}{6.025 \times 10^{23}} \quad (M \text{ in gm/gm-mole}).$$

Therefore,

$$\bar{s}_{\text{trans}} = \mathcal{R}\left[\frac{3}{2}\ln M + \frac{5}{2}\ln T - \ln p - 1.155\right].$$

The preceding equation is listed in Table 9.2. At 25°C and 1 atm,

$$\bar{s}_{\text{trans}} = 35.93 \text{ cal/gm-mole°K}.$$

For rotation,

$$Z_{\text{rot}} = \frac{8\pi^2 IkT}{\sigma h^2}$$

$$\ln Z_{\text{rot}} = \ln \frac{8\pi^2 k}{h} + \ln I + \ln T - \ln \sigma.$$

Substituting in Eq. (8.16) and considering 1 mole gives (see also Table 9.2)

$$\bar{s}_{\text{rot}} = \mathscr{R}\left[\ln \frac{8\pi^2 k}{h^2} + \ln I - \ln T - \ln \sigma + 1 \right].$$

Since

$$I_{N_2} = 1.39 \times 10^{-23} \, \text{gm-cm}^2/\text{molecule},$$

therefore,

$$\bar{s}_{\text{rot}} = 1.987\left[\ln \frac{8\pi^2(1.3804 \times 10^{-16})}{(6.624 \times 10^{-27})^2} + \ln 1.39 \times 10^{-23} - \ln 298.15 - \ln 2 + 1 \right]$$

$$= 9.78 \, \text{cal/gm-mole}^\circ\text{K}.$$

For vibration,

$$Z_{\text{vib}} = \frac{1}{1 - e^{-\theta_v/T}}$$

$$\ln Z_{\text{vib}} = -\ln(1 - e^{-\theta_v/T})$$

and

$$\partial\left(\frac{\ln Z_{\text{vib}}}{T} \right)_V = \frac{\theta_v}{T^2} \frac{1}{e^{\theta_v/T} - 1}.$$

Therefore,

$$\bar{s}_{\text{vib}} = \mathscr{R}\left[-\ln(1 - e^{-\theta_v/T}) + \frac{\theta_v}{T} \frac{1}{e^{\theta_v/T} - 1} \right].$$

For N_2, $\theta_v = 3340^\circ\text{K}$ so that $\theta_v/T = 11.2$ and $\bar{s}_{\text{vib}} \approx 0$. Thus the total entropy is

$$\bar{s} = 35.93 + 9.78 = 45.71 \, \text{cal/gm-mole}^\circ\text{K},$$

which compares well with the value of Table 9.5.

REFERENCES

9.1 Howerton, M. T., *Engineering Thermodynamics*. Princeton, N.J.: D. Van Nostrand Co., Inc., 1962, chap. 3, 4.

9.2 Lee, J. F., F. W. Sears, and D. L. Turcotte, *Statistical Thermodynamics*. Reading Mass.: Addison-Wesley Publishing Company, Inc., 1963, chap. 5, 7–10, 12.

PROBLEMS

9.1 Calculate the molecular translational partition function per cu cm for H_2 at 0°C and N_2 at 100°C. (Assume standard atmospheric pressure.)

9.2 Find the partition function per molecule of He at standard pressure and 25°C. Calculate the internal energy and entropy based on 1 cu cm under the same conditions.

9.3 Calculate the rotational and vibrational partition functions per molecule of O_2 and H_2 at 200°K.

9.4 Calculate the total energy of the first 8 energy levels of He molecules in a box of dimensions $1 \times 1 \times 2$ cm. What will be your answer if the box had dimensions $1 \times 1 \times 1$ cm?

9.5 Repeat the Problem 9.4 for the translational energy levels of H_2.

9.6 Find the number of the quantized translational energy states of H_2 molecules confined in a box of dimensions $1 \times 1 \times 1$ cm at 300°K, the maximum energy being $\frac{3}{2}kT$.

9.7 Calculate the difference between the third and fourth translational energy levels of H_2 molecules confined in a box of dimensions $0.1 \times 0.2 \times 0.3$ cm.

9.8 Determine the most probable rotational energy distribution for a system of unsymmetrical diatomic rigid rotators in which $8\pi^2 IkT/h^2 = 100$. Note that

$$\frac{N_i}{N} = \frac{g_i e^{-\epsilon_i/kT}}{\sum_i g_i e^{-\epsilon_i/kT}}, \qquad g_i = (2j + 1).$$

Plot a curve of N_i/N versus $j(j + 1)$.

9.9 Plot the relative number of H_2 molecules at 1000°K in the first few rotational and vibrational energy states.

$I_{H_2} = 4.64 \times 10^{-48}$ kg-m^2

$\nu_{H_2} = 1.32 \times 10^{14}$ cycles/sec and $\epsilon_i = h\nu(n)$ for vibration.

9.10 The quantized vibrational energies of each particle in a system of N particles is given by the expression

$$\epsilon_{vib} = nh\nu,$$

where $n = 0, 1, 2, 3 \ldots, \infty$.

If the particles occupy only the first four energy levels ($n = 0, 1, 2, 3$), find the partition function and the number of particles in each vibrational energy level. Assume the fundamental frequency of vibration $\nu = 10^{12}$ cycles/sec and $T = 25°C$.

9.11 Plot the rotational energy distribution for O_2 at 300°K.

9.12 Plot the vibrational energy distribution for O_2 at 300°K and 2260°K and show the quantized energy levels. ($\nu_{O_2} = 4.65 \times 10^{13}$ sec^{-1})

9.13 Compare the rotational energy distributions for N_2 at 60°K and 572°K. Plot your results as percentage of total molecules versus the quantum number j.

9.14 Calculate the vibrational constant volume specific heat in cal/gm-mole°K for N_2 and O_2 at 300, 800, and 3000°K. The frequencies are:
$$\nu_{N_2} = 6.96 \times 10^{13} \text{ sec}^{-1}$$
and
$$\nu_{O_2} = 4.65 \times 10^{13} \text{ sec}^{-1}.$$

9.15 Calculate the molal constant pressure specific heat for O_2 and N_2 at 500, 1000, 1500, and 2000°K. Compare your results with those found in gas tables.

9.16 Calculate the specific heat at constant volume of aluminum at 10°K and 900°K. $\theta_D = 398$°K.

9.17 Calculate the moment of inertia of HI (hydrogen iodide) in gm-cm² and the equilibrium interatomic separation in Å. $\theta_r = 9$°K for HI.

9.18 The following table gives properties of CO and N_2

	Molecular Weight	Interatomic Distance	Classical Value $\bar{c}_v$ (1 atm and 300°K)	Entropy at 298°K (cal/gm mole °K)
CO	28	1.128 Å	$\frac{5}{2}\mathcal{R}$	47.31
N_2	28	1.094 Å	$\frac{5}{2}\mathcal{R}$	45.78

Explain quantitatively the difference in the entropies of the two gases.

NOMENCLATURE

c_p Specific heat at constant pressure

c_v Specific heat at constant volume

G Gibbs function

g Gibbs function per unit mass

g Degeneracy

H Enthalpy

h Enthalpy per unit mass

h_{fg} Enthalpy of vaporization per unit mass

k Boltzmann's constant

M Molecular weight

m Mass

m_f Mass fraction

N Number of molecules

n Number of moles

p Pressure

Q Heat

q Heat per unit mass

R Gas constant

$\mathscr{R}$ Universal gas constant

S Entropy

s Entropy per unit mass

T Absolute temperature

t Temperature

U Internal energy

u Internal energy per unit mass

V Volume

v Specific volume

W Thermodynamic probability

x Mole fraction

Z Partition function

ϕ Relative humidity

α, β Lagrange's multipliers

ψ Saturation ratio

μ Chemical potential

ω Specific humidity

ρ Density

ϵ Energy per molecule

Subscripts:

i Refers to component i

j Refers to all i components except one

Superscripts:

$(^-)$ Refers to property per mole

10

NONREACTIVE GAS MIXTURES

10.1
Introduction
The thermodynamic behavior of a mixture of gases depends upon the individual properties of its constituent gases. Because substances in the gaseous phase are so miscible with each other, there is no limit to the number of different gaseous mixtures possible; therefore wide variation is possible in the properties of gaseous mixtures. Furthermore, individual constituents of gaseous mixtures often react chemically with each other, and these reactions introduce another factor that exerts a strong influence on the properties of a gas. This chapter deals only with mixtures of inert gases, in which changes in phase of constituents may take place. Properties of reactive gaseous mixtures are discussed in Chapter 11.

A gas mixture is frequently treated as if it consisted of a single component rather than many. Properties of the individual constituents of an inert gas tend to be submerged, so that the gas behaves, in certain ways, as though it were a single, pure substance. The main constituents of air, for example, are oxygen, nitrogen, argon, and water vapor. But air is commonly said to have a molecular weight of 28.97 lbm/lb-mole, even though this figure represents a composite value based on the molecular weights and the proportions of the constituent species.

The first part of this chapter treats mixtures of perfect gases. Equations are derived which express the properties of mixtures in terms of the properties of the constituents. Mixtures are treated in which no chemical reaction, condensation, or evaporation takes place. The derived expressions apply, in general, to gas mixtures over a wide range of temperatures and pressures. Although the study centers about perfect gases, mixtures containing nonperfect gases often show only negligible deviation from perfect gas behavior. In the latter part of the chapter, gaseous mixtures in which changes of phase occur are discussed.

10.2
Mixtures of
Perfect Gases
Consider a mixture of perfect gases $a, b, c, \ldots$, existing in equilibrium at a pressure p, and occupying a volume V, as shown in Fig. 10.1(a).
Each constituent occupies the same volume V that the entire mixture occupies, and each constituent is at the same temperature as the mixture. The total mass of the mixture is equal to the sum of the masses of the individual gases, or

$$m = m_a + m_b + m_c + \cdots = \sum_i m_i.$$

Similarly, the number of moles of the mixture is the sum of the moles of the individual components:

$$n = n_a + n_b + n_c + \cdots = \sum_i n_i.$$

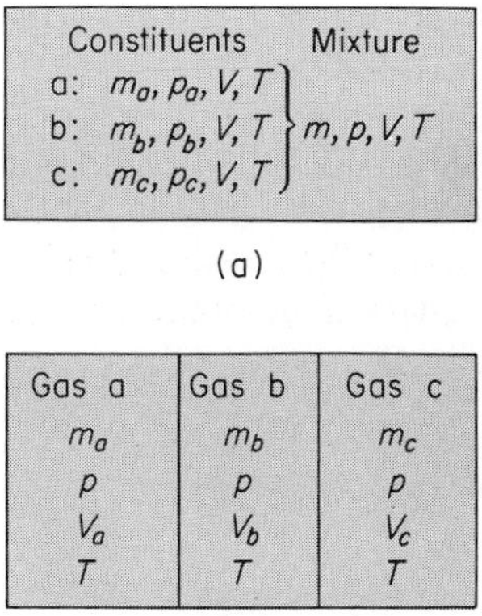

Fig. 10.1. *Dalton's and Amagat's laws.*

According to *Dalton's law*, the total pressure of a mixture of perfect gases is the sum of the partial pressures of the constituents. The partial pressure of a gas in a mixture is the pressure that it would exert if it alone occupied the whole volume of the mixture at the same temperature. Dalton's law can be written as

$$p = p_a + p_b + p_c + \cdots = \sum_i p_i \big|_{V,T}. \tag{10.1}$$

Suppose it were possible to separate gases a, b, c, ..., and to have each constituent at the pressure and temperature of the mixture, as shown in Fig. 10.1(b). According to *Amagat's law*, the sum of the partial volumes of the constituents would be equal to the total volume, or

$$V = V_a + V_b + V_c + \cdots = \sum_i V_i \big|_{p,T}. \tag{10.2}$$

It may be remarked that Dalton's law and Amagat's law are consistent with the kinetic theory of gases, which was discussed in Chapter 7. These laws assume that no intermolecular forces exist in a mixture of gases and that each constituent acts as if no other constituents were present.

When the mixture is analyzed from the standpoint of Dalton's law, the perfect gas equation can be applied individually to each constituent:

$$p_a V = n_a \mathcal{R} T,$$
$$p_b V = n_b \mathcal{R} T,$$
$$p_c V = n_c \mathcal{R} T,$$

etc. Adding the preceding equations gives

$$(p_a + p_b + p_c + \cdots)V = (n_a + n_b + n_c + \cdots)\mathcal{R} T$$

or

$$pV = n\mathscr{R}T.$$

This equation of state has the same form as the equation of state of a single-component perfect gas, so that a mixture of perfect gases also acts like a perfect gas. When each individual equation of state is divided by the mixture's equation of state, the following expressions for partial pressures are obtained

$$p_a = \frac{n_a}{n}p = x_a p,$$

$$p_b = \frac{n_b}{n}p = x_b p,$$

etc. Therefore, in general, for the ith component, the partial pressure p_i is

$$p_i = x_i p, \tag{10.3}$$

where x_i is the mole fraction (or molal concentration) of constituent i, and is defined as the ratio of the number of moles of that constituent to the total number of moles in the mixture:

$$x_i = \frac{n_i}{\sum_i n_i}. \tag{10.4}$$

The mole fractions of a gas mixture then must add up to unity:

$$x_a + x_b + \cdots = \sum_i x_i = 1. \tag{10.5}$$

According to Eq. (10.3), the ratio of the partial pressure of any constituent to the total pressure is equal to the mole fraction of that constituent. Since each constituent occupies the same volume and has the same temperature as the mixture, it follows that

$$\frac{p_a}{n_a} = \frac{p_b}{n_b} = \frac{p_c}{n_c} = \cdots = \frac{p_i}{n_i} = \frac{p}{n}. \tag{10.6}$$

When the mixture is analyzed from the standpoint of Amagat's law, the perfect gas law leads to

$$pV_a = n_a\mathscr{R}T,$$

$$pV_b = n_b\mathscr{R}T,$$

$$pV_c = n_c\mathscr{R}T,$$

etc. Adding the preceding equations gives

$$p(V_a + V_b + V_c + \cdots) = (n_a + n_b + n_c + \cdots)\mathscr{R}T,$$

or

$$pV = n\mathscr{R}T.$$

By dividing the perfect gas equation for each constituent by the equation for the entire mixture, one obtains the following:

$$\frac{V_a}{V} = \frac{n_a}{n} \quad \text{or} \quad V_a = x_a V,$$

and, in general, for the ith component, the partial volume V_i is

$$V_i = x_i V. \tag{10.7}$$

The ratio of the partial volume of any constituent to the total volume, then, is equal to the mole fraction of that constituent. Since the partial volumes of the constituents are at the same temperature and total pressure, it follows that

$$\frac{V_a}{n_a} = \frac{V_b}{n_b} = \frac{V_c}{n_c} = \cdots = \frac{V_i}{n_i} = \frac{V}{n}. \tag{10.8}$$

It can therefore be concluded, from Eq. (10.6) and (10.8), that the mole fraction of each constituent in a mixture of perfect gases is the same as its volume fraction and, also, the ratio of its partial pressure to the total pressure:

$$x_i = \frac{n_i}{n} = \frac{V_i}{V} = \frac{p_i}{p}. \tag{10.9}$$

In the equation of state of a gas mixture, a gas constant involving molecular weight appears. The value of this gas constant is determined as follows:

The perfect gas law for the mixture is

$$pV = mRT, \tag{10.10}$$

whereas for each constituent it is

$$p_a V = m_a R_a T,$$
$$p_b V = m_b R_b T,$$
$$p_c V = m_c R_c T,$$

etc. Since $p = p_a + p_b + p_c + \cdots$, therefore,

$$pV = (m_a R_a + m_b R_b + m_c R_c + \cdots)T.$$

By combining this equation with Eq. (10.10), one obtains the following:

$$R = \frac{m_a}{m} R_a + \frac{m_b}{m} R_b + \frac{m_c}{m} R_c + \cdots = \sum_i \frac{m_i R_i}{m},$$

or

$$R = m_{f_a} R_a + m_{f_b} R_b + m_{f_c} R_c + \cdots = \sum_i m_{f_i} R_i, \tag{10.11}$$

where m_f, the mass fraction, is the ratio of the mass of a constituent to the total mass of the mixture, or

$$m_{f_i} = \frac{m_i}{\sum\limits_i m_i}, \tag{10.12}$$

and

$$m_{f_a} + m_{f_b} + \cdots = 1. \tag{10.13}$$

To determine the molecular weight of the mixture, the mass of the mixture is divided by the total number of moles present in the mixture:

$$M = \frac{\sum\limits_i m_i}{\sum\limits_i n_i} = \frac{\sum\limits_i m_i}{\sum\limits_i (m_i/M_i)} = \frac{\sum\limits_i (nM)_i}{\sum\limits_i n_i}. \tag{10.14}$$

The mass of a constituent is equal to the number of moles of that constituent multiplied by its molecular weight. Therefore the masses of the individual components of the mixture are

$$m_a = n_a M_a,$$
$$m_b = n_b M_b,$$
$$m_c = n_c M_c,$$

etc. Adding the preceding equations yields

$$m_a + m_b + m_c + \cdots = m = n_a M_a + n_b M_b + n_c M_c + \cdots.$$

But the total mass of the mixture, m, is equal to

$$m = m_a + m_b + m_c + \cdots = nM,$$

where n and M are the total number of moles and the molecular weight of the mixture. By combining these two equations, the molecular weight of the mixture is obtained

$$M = \frac{n_a}{n} M_a + \frac{n_b}{n} M_b + \frac{n_c}{n} M_c + \cdots,$$

or

$$M = x_a M_a + x_b M_b + x_c M_c + \cdots = \sum_i x_i M_i, \tag{10.15}$$

which expresses M in terms of the mole fraction. By substituting the relation $R_i = \mathscr{R}/M_i$ in Eq. (10.11), M can be expressed in terms of mass fractions:

$$\frac{\mathscr{R}}{M} = m_{f_a} \frac{\mathscr{R}}{M_a} + m_{f_b} \frac{\mathscr{R}}{M_b} + m_{f_c} \frac{\mathscr{R}}{M_c} + \cdots,$$

from which

$$M = \frac{1}{(m_{f_a}/M_a) + (m_{f_b}/M_b) + (m_{f_c}/M_c) + \cdots} = \frac{1}{\sum_i (m_{f_i}/M_i)}. \tag{10.16}$$

Also, since $\mathscr{R} = MR$, then

$$M = \frac{\mathscr{R}}{R}. \tag{10.17}$$

EXAMPLE 10.1: A perfect gas mixture consists of 3 lbm of nitrogen and 5 lbm of carbon dioxide at a pressure of 40 psia and a temperature of 70°F. Find (a) the mole fraction of each constituent; (b) the equivalent molecular weight of the mixture; (c) the equivalent gas constant of the mixture; (d) the partial pressures and the partial volumes; (e) the volume and density of the mixture.

Solution: (a) Since $x = \dfrac{n_i}{\sum_i n_i}$,

then $x_{N_2} = \dfrac{(3/28.016)}{(3/28.016) + (5/44.01)} = 0.485.$

Similarly,

$$x_{CO_2} = \frac{(5/44.01)}{(3/28.016) + (5/44.01)} = 0.515.$$

(b) Using Eq. (10.15),

$$M = 0.485 \times 28.016 + 0.515 \times 44.01 = 36.25 \text{ lbm/lb-mole.}$$

(c) Using Eq. (10.11),

$$R = \frac{3}{8}\left(\frac{1545}{28.016}\right) + \frac{5}{8}\left(\frac{1545}{44.01}\right) = 42.55 \text{ ft-lbf/lbm } °R.$$

(d) Since the partial pressures are proportional to mole fractions, then

$$p_{N_2} = 0.485 \times 40 = 19.4 \text{ psia,}$$

$$p_{CO_2} = 0.515 \times 40 = 20.6 \text{ psia.}$$

Also,

$$V_{N_2} = \frac{m_{N_2} R_{N_2} T}{p} = \frac{3 \times (1545/28.016) \times 530}{40 \times 144} = 15.23 \text{ ft}^3,$$

$$V_{CO_2} = \frac{5 \times (1545/44.01) \times 530}{40 \times 144} = 16.12 \text{ ft}^3.$$

(e) The volume of the mixture can be obtained by several methods. Noting that each constituent occupies the same volume as the mixture, then

$$V = \frac{mRT}{p} = \frac{m_{N_2} R_{N_2} T}{p_{N_2}} = \frac{m_{CO_2} R_{CO_2} T}{p_{CO_2}}$$

$$= \frac{8 \times 42.55 \times 530}{40 \times 144} = \frac{3 \times (1545/28.016) \times 530}{19.4 \times 144} = \frac{5 \times (1545/44.01) \times 530}{20.6 \times 144}$$

$$= 31.4 \text{ ft}^3.$$

The density of the mixture is

$$\rho = \rho_{N_2} + \rho_{CO_2} = \frac{3}{31.4} + \frac{5}{31.4} = 0.2545 \text{ lbm/ft}^3,$$

or

$$\rho = \frac{m}{V} = \frac{8}{31.4} = 0.2545 \text{ lbm/ft}^3.$$

10.3
Internal
Energy,
Enthalpy,
Specific Heats,
and Entropy

According to the Gibbs-Dalton law, an extensive property of a mixture of perfect gases is the sum of the contributions of the individual constituents. Properties of a mixture can be expressed on either a mass or a mole basis and are referred to as per lbm or per lb-mole, respectively. Expressions for some of the extensive properties are presented here on a mass basis. The internal energy per unit mass of a mixture is given by

$$u = \frac{m_a}{\sum_i m_i} u_a + \frac{m_b}{\sum_i m_i} u_b + \frac{m_c}{\sum_i m_i} u_c + \cdots$$

$$= \sum_i m_{f_i} u_i = \frac{\sum_i m_i u_i}{\sum_i m_i}.$$

(10.18)

It was shown previously that

$$pV = m_a R_a T + m_b R_b T + m_c R_c T + \cdots.$$

Dividing both sides by $\sum_i m_i$ and substituting $p_i v_i$ for $R_i T$, gives

$$pv = \frac{m_a}{\sum_i m_i} (p_a v_a) + \frac{m_b}{\sum_i m_i} p_b v_b + \frac{m_c}{\sum_i m_i} p_c v_c + \cdots.$$

By adding the foregoing equation to Eq. (10.18), the expression for enthalpy is obtained:

$$h = \frac{m_a}{\sum_i m_i} h_a + \frac{m_b}{\sum_i m_i} h_b + \frac{m_c}{\sum_i m_i} h_c + \cdots$$

$$= \sum_i m_{f_i} h_i = \frac{\sum_i m_i h_i}{\sum_i m_i}.$$

(10.19)

By dividing the internal energy, Eq. (10.18), and the enthalpy, Eq. (10.19), by T, specific-heat values are obtained for the mixture:

$$c_v = \frac{m_a}{\sum_i m_i} c_{v_a} + \frac{m_b}{\sum_i m_i} c_{v_b} + \frac{m_c}{\sum_i m_i} c_{v_c} + \cdots$$

$$= \sum_i m_{f_i} c_{v_i} = \frac{\sum_i m_i c_{v_i}}{\sum_i m_i},$$

(10.20)

$$c_p = \frac{m_a}{\sum_i m_i} c_{p_a} + \frac{m_b}{\sum_i m_i} c_{p_b} = \frac{m_c}{\sum_i m_i} c_{p_c} + \cdots$$

$$= \sum_i m_{f_i} c_{p_i} = \frac{\sum_i m_i c_{p_i}}{\sum_i m_i}.$$

(10.21)

Similarly, the entropy of the mixture is

$$s = \frac{m_a}{\sum_i m_i} s_a + \frac{m_b}{\sum_i m_i} s_b + \frac{m_c}{\sum_i m_i} s_c + \cdots$$

$$= \sum_i m_{f_i} s_i = \frac{\sum_i m_i s_i}{\sum_i m_i}. \tag{10.22}$$

Changes in the internal energy and enthalpy of mixtures of perfect gases are

$$u_2 - u_1 = \sum_i m_{f_i}(u_2 - u_1)_i = \int_{T_1}^{T_2} c_v \, dT, \tag{10.23}$$

$$h_2 - h_1 = \sum_i m_{f_i}(h_2 - h_1)_i = \int_{T_1}^{T_2} c_p \, dT, \tag{10.24}$$

and

$$c_p - c_v = R. \tag{10.25}$$

The entropy change of a perfect gas mixture, expressed in terms of temperature and pressure, is

$$s_2 - s_1 = \sum_i m_{f_i}(s_2 - s_1)_i = \sum_i m_{f_i}\left[\int_{T_1}^{T_2} c_{p_i} \, d(\ln T) - R_i \ln \frac{p_{i,2}}{p_{i,1}}\right]$$

$$= \sum_i m_{f_i} \int_{T_1}^{T_2} c_{p_i} \, d(\ln T) - \sum_i m_{f_i} R_i \ln \frac{p_{i,2}}{p_{i,1}}.$$

By substituting values obtained from Eqs. (10.11), (10.21), and (10.9), the change of entropy of the mixture becomes

$$s_2 - s_1 = \int_{T_1}^{T_2} c_p \frac{dT}{T} - R \ln \frac{p_2}{p_1}. \tag{10.26}$$

The foregoing properties can also be expressed on a mole basis. If a superscript ($^-$) is used to indicate property that is given on a mole basis, the resultant equations are

$$\bar{u} = \frac{n_a}{\sum_i n_i} \bar{u}_a + \frac{n_b}{\sum_i n_i} \bar{u}_b + \frac{n_c}{\sum_i n_i} \bar{u}_c + \cdots = \sum_i x_i \bar{u}_i = \frac{\sum_i n_i \bar{u}_i}{\sum_i n_i}, \tag{10.27}$$

$$\bar{h} = \frac{n_a}{\sum_i n_i} \bar{h}_a + \frac{n_b}{\sum_i n_i} \bar{h}_b + \frac{n_c}{\sum_i n_i} \bar{h}_c + \cdots = \sum_i x_i \bar{h}_i = \frac{\sum_i n_i \bar{h}_i}{\sum_i n_i}, \tag{10.28}$$

$$\bar{c}_v = \frac{n_a}{\sum_i n_i} \bar{c}_{v_a} + \frac{n_b}{\sum_i n_i} \bar{c}_{v_b} + \frac{n_c}{\sum_i n_i} \bar{c}_{v_c} + \cdots = \sum_i x_i \bar{c}_{v_i} = \frac{\sum_i n_i \bar{c}_{v_i}}{\sum_i n_i}, \tag{10.29}$$

$$\bar{c}_p = \frac{n_a}{\sum\limits_i n_i}\bar{c}_{p_a} + \frac{n_b}{\sum\limits_i n_i}\bar{c}_{p_b} + \frac{n_c}{\sum\limits_i n_i}\bar{c}_{p_c} + \cdots = \sum_i x_i \bar{c}_{p_i} = \frac{\sum\limits_i n_i \bar{c}_{p_i}}{\sum\limits_i n_i}, \quad (10.30)$$

$$\bar{s} = \frac{n_a}{\sum\limits_i n_i}\bar{s}_a + \frac{n_b}{\sum\limits_i n_i}\bar{s}_b + \frac{n_c}{\sum\limits_i n_i}\bar{s}_c + \cdots = \sum_i x_i \bar{s}_i = \frac{\sum\limits_i n_i \bar{s}_i}{\sum\limits_i n_i}. \quad (10.31)$$

For perfect gases, changes in the foregoing properties are

$$\bar{u}_2 - \bar{u}_1 = \sum_i x_i(\bar{u}_2 - \bar{u}_1)_i = \int_{T_1}^{T_2} \bar{c}_v \, dT, \quad (10.32)$$

$$\bar{h}_2 - \bar{h}_1 = \sum_i x_i(\bar{h}_2 - \bar{h}_1)_i = \int_{T_1}^{T_2} \bar{c}_p \, dT, \quad (10.33)$$

$$\bar{c}_p - \bar{c}_v = \mathscr{R}, \quad (10.34)$$

$$\bar{s}_2 - \bar{s}_1 = \sum_i x_i(\bar{s}_2 - \bar{s}_1)_i$$

$$= \sum_i x_i \int_{T_1}^{T_2} \bar{c}_{p_i} \, d(\ln T) - \sum_i x_i \mathscr{R} \ln \frac{p_{i,2}}{p_{i,1}} \quad (10.35)$$

$$= \int_{T_1}^{T_2} \bar{c}_p \frac{dT}{T} - \sum_i x_i \mathscr{R} \ln \frac{p_2}{p_1}.$$

EXAMPLE 10.2: For the mixture of Example 10.1, calculate the constant-volume and constant-pressure specific heats. If the mixture is heated at constant volume to 100°F, find the change in internal energy, enthalpy, and entropy of the mixture. Assume the specific heats remain constant, and the perfect gas law applies.

Also, find the foregoing changes, if the heating process is performed at constant pressure.

Solution: For the constant-volume process:

$$c_v = \sum_i m_{f_i} c_{v_i} = \tfrac{3}{8} \times 0.177 + \tfrac{5}{8} \times 0.158$$

$$= 0.1651 \text{ Btu/lbm°F.}$$

$$c_p = \sum_i m_{f_i} c_{p_i} = \tfrac{3}{8} \times 0.248 + \tfrac{5}{8} \times 0.203$$

$$= 0.220 \text{ Btu/lbm°F.}$$

The change in internal energy is

$$\Delta u = \int_{T_1}^{T_2} c_v \, dT = 0.1651 \times (100 - 70) = 4.953 \text{ Btu/lbm of mixture,}$$

and

$$\Delta U = 8 \times 4.953 = 39.624 \text{ Btu.}$$

The change in enthalpy is

$$\Delta h = \int_{T_1}^{T_2} c_p \, dT = 0.22 \times 30 = 6.6 \text{ Btu/lbm of mixture,}$$

and

$$\Delta H = 8 \times 6.6 = 52.8 \text{ Btu.}$$

The change in entropy of the mixture, in terms of changes of temperature and volume is

$$\Delta s = \int_{T_1}^{T_2} c_v \frac{dT}{T} + R \ln \frac{v_2}{v_1}.$$

But since the volume is constant in this problem,

$$\Delta s = 0.1651 \ln \frac{560}{530} = 0.1651 \, (0.0535) = 0.00883 \text{ Btu/lbm}°\text{R,}$$

and

$$\Delta S = 8 \times 0.00883 = 0.07064 \text{ Btu/}°\text{R.}$$

For the constant-pressure process, the internal energy and enthalpy values are the same as the values calculated in the constant-volume process, since they are functions of temperature alone (perfect gas). The change of entropy, as given by Eq. (10.26), is

$$\Delta s = \int_{T_1}^{T_2} c_p \frac{dT}{T} - R \ln \frac{p_2}{p_1},$$

and for a constant-pressure process,

$$\Delta s = 0.22 \ln \frac{560}{530} = 0.22 \, (0.0535) = 0.01176 \text{ Btu/lbm}°\text{R,}$$

and

$$\Delta S = 8 \times 0.01176 = 0.094 \text{ Btu/}°\text{R.}$$

10.4 Entropy Change Due to Mixing of Perfect Gases

When perfect gases are mixed, a change of entropy occurs as a result of the increase in the disorder of the system. If the initial temperatures of all the constituents are the same, and if the mixing process is adiabatic, then the temperature does not change, but the entropy increases. Let the initial pressure and temperature of the individual gases before mixing be p and T, the same as the total pressure and temperature of the mixture. In the mixing process, each gas may be considered to undergo a free expansion from its initial pressure to its partial pressure in the mixture, with no work interaction. Mixing is an irreversible process, and according to the second law of thermodynamics, the increase in entropy corresponds to

$$ds = \sum_i (m_f \, ds)_i \geqslant 0.$$

Since the gases are perfect and the temperature remains constant, both internal energy and enthalpy are unchanged by the mixing process. Applying Eq. (10.26), the change of entropy is

$$\Delta S = -\left(m_a R_a \ln \frac{p_a}{p} + m_b R_b \ln \frac{p_b}{p} + \cdots \right) = -\sum_i m_i R_i \ln \frac{p_i}{p},$$

which becomes on a unit mass basis:

$$\Delta s = -\sum_i m_{f_i} R_i \ln \frac{p_{i,2}}{p_{i,1}}, \tag{10.36}$$

where subscripts 1 and 2 refer to the initial and final states of each component in the mixture. Since each partial pressure is less than the total pressure, the change of entropy calculated from Eq. (10.36) is always a positive number. Even though two gases may be in complete thermal equilibrium and pressure equilibrium, they are not necessarily in complete thermodynamic equilibrium. When gases are brought into contact with each other, they diffuse into each other, tending to establish a uniform distribution. As shown in Chapter 6, the thermodynamic characteristics of a system depend not only on two properties of the system, such as V and T, but also on the proportions of the constituents. The effect of composition is discussed in Section 10.6.

EXAMPLE 10.3: Find the increase in entropy when 2 lbm of oxygen at 150°F are mixed with 6 lbm of nitrogen at the same temperature. The initial pressure of each constituent is 14.7 psia and is the same as that of the mixture. (Assume perfect gases.)

Solution: Since the mixing process is isothermal, the change of entropy of the mixture is

$$\Delta S = - m_{O_2} R_{O_2} \ln \frac{p_{O_2}}{p} - m_{N_2} R_{N_2} \ln \frac{p_{N_2}}{p},$$

where

$$\frac{p_{O_2}}{p} = \frac{2/32}{2/32 + (6/28.016)} = 0.225$$

$$\frac{p_{N_2}}{p} = 1.000 - 0.225 = 0.775.$$

Therefore,

$$\Delta S = -2 \left(\frac{1545}{32} \right) \ln 0.225 - 6 \left(\frac{1545}{28.016} \right) \ln 0.775$$

$$= 143.7 + 84.3 = 288 \text{ ft-lbf/°R}$$

$$= 0.293 \text{ Btu/°R.}$$

**10.5
Mixtures of
Perfect Gases
at Different
Initial Pres-
sures and
Temperatures**

Three insulated vessels, each containing a perfect gas of mass m_i at temperature T_i and pressure p_i, are shown in Fig. 10.2. The three gases are different from each other, and subscripts a, b, and c identify the particular gas. For simplicity, the procedure is applied to three gases only but it can be extended to any number of gases. If the interconnecting valves are opened, so that the gases are allowed

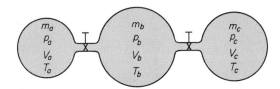

Fig. 10.2. *Mixing of perfect gases with different initial properties.*

to diffuse into one another, the final temperature and pressure of the mixture will be at some intermediate value. If no heat or work interactions take place at the boundary of the system, the internal energy of the system, as the first law dictates, is not affected by the mixing. The internal energy of the mixture per unit mass is

$$u = \frac{m_a}{m}u_a + \frac{m_b}{m}u_b + \frac{m_c}{m}u_c \,.$$

Since u is a function of temperature only for perfect gas and is given by $c_v T$, this equation becomes

$$c_v T = \frac{m_a}{m}c_{v_a}T_a + \frac{m_b}{m}c_{v_b}T_b + \frac{m_c}{m}c_{v_c}T_c = \sum_i \frac{m_i}{m}(c_v)_i T_i \,.$$

If the gases are all monatomic, then $c_v = \frac{3}{2}R$; if they are all diatomic, then $c_v = \frac{5}{2}R$; and in either case, the preceding equation becomes

$$mRT = m_a R_a T_a + m_b R_b T_b + m_c R_c T_c \,,$$

from which the temperature of the mixture is calculated:

$$T = \frac{m_a R_a T_a + m_b R_b T_b + m_c R_c T_c}{mR} \,. \tag{10.37}$$

Since $mR = m_a R_a + m_b R_b + m_c R_c$, Eq. (10.37) can be expressed as

$$T = \frac{m_a R_a T_a + m_b R_b T_b + m_c R_b T_c}{m_a R_a + m_b R_b + m_c R_c}.$$

From the perfect gas law, this equation can also be expressed in terms of the pressures, temperatures, and volumes of the individual gases before mixing:

$$T = \frac{p_a V_a + p_b V_b + p_c V_c}{(p_a V_a/T_a) + (p_b V_b/T_b) + (p_c V_c/T_c)}. \tag{10.38}$$

In Eq. (10.37), if $n_i \mathcal{R} T_i$ is substituted for $m_i R_i T_i$, then,

$$n \mathcal{R} T = n_a \mathcal{R} T_a + n_b \mathcal{R} T_b + n_c \mathcal{R} T_c ,$$

so that the temperature of the mixture can be calculated from the mole fractions of the constituents and their initial temperatures:

$$T = \frac{n_a}{n} T_a + \frac{n_b}{n} T_b + \frac{n_c}{n} T_c = \sum_i x_i T_i . \tag{10.39}$$

From Eq. (10.37), and by applying the perfect gas law, an expression for the pressure of the mixture can be obtained:

$$pV = p_a V_a + p_b V_b + p_c V_c ,$$

which leads to the following:

$$p = \frac{p_a V_a + p_b V_b + p_c V_c}{V}. \tag{10.40}$$

Note that the total volume V of the mixture is the sum of the initial volumes V_a, V_b, and V_c. These latter volumes are not the partial volumes of the components of the mixture; they are, instead, the volumes of the vessels which the component gases initially occupied.

EXAMPLE 10.4: The number of moles, the pressures, and the temperatures of gases a, b, and c, of Fig. 10.2 are given in the following table:

Gas	Number of Moles	Pressure (psia)	Temperature (°F)
N_2	1	50	200
CO	3	60	400
O_2	2	100	600

If the containers are connected, allowing the gases to mix freely, find (a) the pressure and temperature of the resulting mixture at equilibrium; (b) the change of entropy of each constituent and that of the mixture.

Solution: (a) According to Eq. (10.39),

$$T = \frac{1 \times 660 + 3 \times 860 + 2 \times 1060}{6} = 893°R.$$

Also,

$$V_{N_2} = \frac{n_{N_2} \mathcal{R} T_{N_2}}{p_{N_2}} = \frac{1 \times 1545 \times 660}{50 \times 144} = 141.6 \, ft^3,$$

$$V_{CO} = \frac{3 \times 1545 \times 860}{60 \times 144} = 461.5 \, ft^3,$$

$$V_{O_2} = \frac{2 \times 1545 \times 1060}{100 \times 144} = 227.5 \, ft^3.$$

Total

$$V = 141.6 + 461.5 + 227.5 = 830.6 \, ft^3.$$

The pressure of the mixture according to the perfect gas law is

$$p = \frac{n \mathcal{R} T}{V} = \frac{6 \times 1545 \times 893}{830.6 \times 144} = 69.1 \, psia.$$

The same result can also be obtained using Eq. (10.40).

(b) The partial pressures are

$$p_{N_2} = \tfrac{1}{6} \times 69.1 = 11.52 \, psia$$

$$p_{CO} = \tfrac{3}{6} \times 69.1 = 34.55 \, psia$$

$$p_{O_2} = \tfrac{2}{6} \times 69.1 = 23.03 \, psia.$$

Therefore,

$$\Delta s_{N_2} = \left(\int_{T_1}^{T_2} c_p \frac{dT}{T} - R \ln \frac{p_2}{p_1} \right)_{N_2}$$

$$= 0.248 \ln \frac{893}{660} - \frac{1545}{28.016 \times 778} \ln \frac{11.52}{50}$$

$$= 0.1787 \, Btu/lbm°R = 4.84 \, Btu/°R.$$

$$\Delta s_{CO} = 0.248 \ln \frac{893}{860} - \frac{1545}{28.010 \times 778} \ln \frac{34.55}{60}$$

$$= 0.049 \, Btu/lbm°R = 4.11 \, Btu/°R.$$

$$\Delta s_{O_2} = 0.219 \ln \frac{893}{1060} - \frac{1545}{32 \times 778} \ln \frac{23.03}{100}$$

$$= 0.0545 \, Btu/lbm°R = 3.48 \, Btu/°R.$$

$$\Delta S_{mixt} = 4.84 + 4.11 + 3.48 = 12.43 \, Btu/°R.$$

**10.6
Heterogeneous
System of
Several Phases**
In this section, equilibrium conditions in a system consisting of several multicomponent phases are described. Consider a heterogeneous system of volume V, in which several homogeneous phases $(f = a, b, \ldots r)$ exist in equilibrium. Suppose, also, that each phase consists of $k(i = 1, 2, \ldots k)$ components, and that the number of components in any phase is different from the others.

Within each phase, a change in internal energy is accompanied by a change in entropy, volume, and composition, according to Eq. (5.54).

$$dU_f = T_f \, dS_f - p_f \, dV_f + \sum_{i=1}^{i=k} (\bar{\mu}_i \, dn_i)_f . \tag{10.41}$$

A change in the internal energy of the entire system can therefore be expressed as

$$\sum_{f=a}^{f=r} dU_f = \sum_{f=a}^{f=r} T_f \, dS_f - \sum_{f=a}^{f=r} p_f \, dV_f + \sum_{f=a}^{f=r} \sum_{i=1}^{i=k} (\bar{\mu}_i \, dn_i)_f . \tag{10.42}$$

Furthermore, a change in the internal energy of the entire system involves changes in internal energy of the constituent phases:

$$dU = dU_a + dU_b + \cdots + dU_r = \sum_{f=a}^{f=r} dU_f .$$

Likewise, changes in volume, entropy, or chemical composition of the entire system result from contributions from each of the constituent phases:

$$dV = dV_a + dV_b + \cdots + dV_r = \sum_{f=a}^{f=r} dV_f$$

$$dS = dS_a + dS_b + \cdots + dS_r = \sum_{f=a}^{f=r} dS_f$$

$$dn = dn_a + dn_b + \cdots + dn_r = \sum_{f=a}^{f=r} dn_f .$$

In a closed system in equilibrium, however, the internal energy, volume, entropy, and mass* are constant, so that

---

*In a chemical reaction, the number of moles may change but the total mass of the system remains constant. Therefore the law of conservation of mass $dm = dm_a + dm_b + \cdots + dm_r = 0$ replaces the equation $dn = dn_a + dn_b + \cdots + dn_r$ in the derivation of conditions of equilibrium. It can be shown, however, that the final result remains unchanged.

$$dU = dV = dS = dn = 0.$$

The changes that occur in a heterogeneous, closed system, when the system deviates slightly from the equilibrium state, involve changes in the internal energy, entropy, volume, and mass in each of the phases. Changes in properties of one phase can be expressed in terms of the changes in properties of the remaining phases:

$$dU_a = -(dU_b + \cdots + dU_r) = -\sum_j dU_j,$$

$$dV_a = -\sum_j dV_j,$$

$$dS_a = -\sum_j dS_j, \qquad\qquad\qquad \textbf{(10.43)}$$

and

$$(dn_i)_a = -\sum_j (dn_i)_j.$$

Subscript j in these equations includes all phases except phase a.

In each of these expressions there are j independent variables and one dependent variable. Equation (10.42) can be rewritten in terms of the dependent variable and the j independent variables:

$$(T_a \, dS_a + \sum_j T_j \, dS_j) - (p_a \, dV_a + \sum_j p_j \, dV_j)$$
$$+ [\sum_i (\bar{\mu}_i \, dn_i)_a + \sum_j \sum_i (\bar{\mu}_i \, dn_i)_j] = 0.$$

Substituting from Eq. (10.43) into the foregoing equation gives

$$(-T_a \sum_j dS_j + \sum_j T_j \, dS_j) - (-p_a \sum_j dV_j + \sum_j p_j \, dV_j)$$
$$+ [-\sum_i \sum_j \bar{\mu}_{i_a} \, dn_{i_j} + \sum_j \sum_i (\bar{\mu}_i \, dn_i)_j] = 0,$$

where subscript ia refers to component i of phase a. Rearranging and combining the coefficients of the independent variables dS_j, dV_j, and dn_{i_j} yields

$$\sum_j (T_j - T_a) \, dS_j - \sum_j (p_j - p_a) \, dV_j + \sum_j \sum_i (\bar{\mu}_{i_j} - \bar{\mu}_{i_a}) \, dn_{i_j} = 0.$$

But since dS_j, dV_j, and dn_{i_j} are independent, their coefficients must vanish. Consequently,

$$T_j = T_a, \quad p_j = p_a, \quad \text{and} \quad \bar{\mu}_{i_j} = \bar{\mu}_{i_a}.$$

These equations represent conditions that exist when the system is in thermal, mechanical, and chemical equilibrium. Evidently, phases of several components must have the same temperature and pressure. In addition, the chemical potential of each of the components *i* within one phase is equal to the chemical potential of the component in each of the remaining phases. For example, when the liquid phase of a one-component substance is in equilibrium with its vapor, the following is true:

$$T_f = T_g, \quad p_f = p_g, \quad \text{and} \quad \bar{\mu}_f = \bar{\mu}_g,$$

where subscripts f and g refer to liquid and vapor respectively. Expressing the chemical potential according to Eq. (5.64) gives

$$\left(\frac{\partial U}{\partial n_f}\right)_{S,V} = \left(\frac{\partial U}{\partial n_g}\right)_{S,V},$$

and

$$\left(\frac{\partial G}{\partial n_f}\right)_{p,T} = \left(\frac{\partial G}{\partial n_g}\right)_{p,T}, \quad \text{or} \quad \bar{g}_f = \bar{g}_g.$$

10.7 Chemical Potential and the Perfect Gas Mixture

The volume and the chemical potential according to Eq. (5.67) and (5.64) are

$$V = \left(\frac{\partial G}{\partial p}\right)_{T,n_i} \quad \text{and} \quad \bar{\mu}_i = \left(\frac{\partial G}{\partial n_i}\right)_{p,T,n_j}.$$

Since the Gibbs function G is a point function, the following is true,

$$\left(\frac{\partial^2 G}{\partial p\, \partial n_i}\right)_{T,n_j} = \left(\frac{\partial^2 G}{\partial n_i\, \partial p}\right)_{T,n_j},$$

and, therefore,

$$\left(\frac{\partial \bar{\mu}_i}{\partial p}\right)_{T,n_i} = \left(\frac{\partial V}{\partial n_i}\right)_{T,p,n_j}. \tag{10.44}$$

But it can be shown, when the perfect gas law is applied to the gas mixture, that $(\partial V/\partial n_i)_{T,p,n_j} = \mathscr{R}T/p = \bar{v}$. The volume V of the gas mixture is also the volume occupied by each component of the mixture, according to Avogadro's law, so that $(\partial V/\partial n_i)_{T,p,n_j} = \bar{v}_i$. Similarly, when the perfect gas law is applied to component i,

$$\left(\frac{\partial V}{\partial n_i}\right)_{T,p,n_j} = \frac{\mathscr{R}T}{p_i}.$$

This equation can then be substituted in Eq. (10.44), to give

$$\left(\frac{\partial \bar{\mu}_i}{\partial p}\right)_{T, n_i} = \frac{\mathscr{R}T}{p_i} = \bar{v}_i .$$

(10.45)

Integration of this relationship, based on total derivatives, yields

$$\bar{\mu}_i = \bar{\mu}_i^\circ + \mathscr{R}T \ln p_i ,$$

(10.46)

where $\bar{\mu}_i^\circ$ is the constant of integration and is a function of temperature only. Note that the pressure at the lower limit in the above integration is unity.

Thus the chemical potential of a component i is a function of the partial pressure of the component and of the temperature of the mixture, which can be expressed as

$$\bar{\mu}_i = \bar{\mu}_i(p_i, T).$$

(10.47)

From Dalton's law, the partial pressure, p_i, can be expressed in terms of the mole fraction, x_i, and total pressure p:

$$p_i = x_i p.$$

Therefore, at constant temperature, the chemical potential, $\bar{\mu}_i$, is a function of the total pressure and the mole fraction:

$$\bar{\mu}_i = \bar{\mu}_i^\circ + \mathscr{R}T \ln (x_i p).$$

(10.48)

The entropy change during the mixing of perfect gases whose original pressure and temperature equals that of the final mixture, may be calculated as follows: It will be shown* that chemical potential is related to the Gibbs free energy of a mixture in the following way:

$$G = \sum_{i=1}^{i=k} \bar{\mu}_i n_i.$$

(10.49)

By substituting for $\bar{\mu}_i$ from Eq. (10.48), the Gibbs function of the mixture becomes

$$G = \sum_{i=1}^{i=k} n_i \bar{\mu}_i^\circ + \mathscr{R}T \sum_{i=1}^{i=k} n_i \ln (x_i p).$$

The total change in free energy of a gaseous mixture, in a process going from state 1 to state 2, then, is

*See Section 10.8 for the derivation of this equation.

$$\Delta G = G_2 - G_1 = \mathscr{R}T \sum_{i=1}^{i=k} n_i \ln x_i.$$

In a constant-pressure process, the free energy change and the entropy change are related as follows:

$$\Delta S = -\frac{\Delta G}{T}.$$

Therefore the entropy change, in terms of composition, is

$$\Delta S = -\mathscr{R} \sum_{i=1}^{i=k} n_i \ln x_i. \tag{10.50}$$

This expression is equivalent to Eq. (10.36) which was derived directly from the combined first and second laws. The change of chemical potential with respect to temperature may be derived from the relations

$$S = -\left(\frac{\partial G}{\partial T}\right)_{p,\,n_i} \quad \text{and} \quad \bar{\mu}_i = \left(\frac{\partial G}{\partial n_i}\right)_{p,\,T,\,n_j}$$

to give

$$\left(\frac{\partial \bar{\mu}_i}{\partial T}\right)_{p,\,n_i} = -\left(\frac{\partial S}{\partial n_i}\right)_{T,\,p,\,n_j} = -\bar{s}_i. \tag{10.51}$$

10.8
The Clausius-Clapeyron and the Gibbs-Duhem Equations

In this section, we derive two important equations governing phase equilibria: the Clausius-Clapeyron equation applies to a single-component system; the Gibbs-Duhem equation applies to a multicomponent system.

Consider the phase equilibrium between a liquid and its vapor in a single-component system. The chemical potentials of the liquid phase and the vapor phase are equal:

$$\bar{\mu}_f = \bar{\mu}_g.$$

In a single-component system, the chemical potential is a function of only pressure and temperature. The change in chemical potential of the liquid and vapor phases can be expressed in partial differential form:

$$d\bar{\mu}_f = \left(\frac{\partial \bar{\mu}_f}{\partial p}\right)_T dp + \left(\frac{\partial \bar{\mu}_f}{\partial T}\right)_p dT,$$

and

$$d\bar{\mu}_g = \left(\frac{\partial \bar{\mu}_g}{\partial p}\right)_T dp + \left(\frac{\partial \bar{\mu}_g}{\partial T}\right)_p dT.$$

Substituting for the coefficients of dp and dT from Eq. (10.45) and (10.51) and noting that $d\bar{\mu}_f = d\bar{\mu}_g$, then

$$\bar{v}_f \, dp - \bar{s}_f \, dT = \bar{v}_g \, dp - \bar{s}_g \, dT.$$

Hence,

$$\frac{dp}{dT} = \frac{\bar{s}_g - \bar{s}_f}{\bar{v}_g - \bar{v}_f} = \frac{\bar{s}_{fg}}{\bar{v}_{fg}}. \tag{10.52}$$

When equilibrium is established,

$$\bar{s}_g - \bar{s}_f = \frac{\bar{h}_g - \bar{h}_f}{T} = \frac{\bar{h}_{fg}}{T}.$$

Equation (10.52) can then be written

$$\frac{dp}{dT} = \frac{\bar{h}_{fg}}{T(\bar{v}_g - \bar{v}_f)}. \tag{10.53}$$

This equation, which was also derived in Chapter 6, is the *Clausius-Clapeyron equation*. It relates the pressure and temperature changes required to maintain equilibrium in a single-component system. The same procedure can be followed to derive equations applicable to phase equilibrium between vapor and solid phases or between solid and liquid phases. In the case of solid-vapor and liquid-vapor equilibria, the volume of the solid or the liquid can be neglected, since the volume of the vapor is relatively large. As an additional simplification, the perfect gas law can be assumed to apply to the vapor, so that Eq. (10.53) then becomes:

$$\frac{d \ln p}{dT} = \frac{\bar{h}_{fg}}{\mathscr{R}T^2} = \frac{h_{fg}}{RT^2}. \tag{10.54}$$

Next the equilibrium in a multicomponent system will be examined. At constant temperature and pressure, the Gibbs function depends on the chemical potential and the composition:

$$dG = \sum_{i=1}^{i=k} \bar{\mu}_i \, dn_i.$$

The mole fraction of each component is

$$x_i = \frac{n_i}{\sum\limits_{i} n_i}.$$

If the quantity, but not proportions, of the constituents changes; then

$$dn_i = x_i \, d \sum_i n_i.$$

The differential of the Gibbs function then is

$$dG = \sum_{i=1}^{i=k} \bar{\mu}_i x_i \, d \sum_{i=1}^{i=k} n_i.$$

Since $\bar{\mu}$ remains constant if the temperature, pressure, and mole fraction do not change, integration leads to

$$G = \sum_{i=1}^{i=k} \bar{\mu}_i x_i \int d\left(\sum_{i=1}^{i=k} n_i \right) = \sum_{i=1}^{i=k} \bar{\mu}_i x_i \sum_{i=1}^{i=k} n_i.$$

Therefore,

$$G = \sum_{i=1}^{i=k} \bar{\mu}_i n_i. \tag{10.55}$$

The differential of Eq. (10.55) is

$$dG = \sum_{i=1}^{i=k} \bar{\mu}_i \, dn_i + \sum_{i=1}^{i=k} n_i \, d\bar{\mu}_i.$$

But

$$dG = -S \, dT + V \, dp + \sum_{i=1}^{i=k} \bar{\mu}_i \, dn_i.$$

When these two equations are combined, the following results:

$$-S \, dT + V \, dp = \sum_{i=1}^{i=k} n_i \, d\bar{\mu}_i. \tag{10.56}$$

This equation, called the *Gibbs-Duhem equation*, shows the relationship between variations in temperature, pressure, and chemical potential of phases of a multicomponent system. Note that, according to the Gibbs-Duhem equation, there are $(k+2)$ variables in a system consisting of k

constituents, but only $(k+1)$ of them can vary independently. The Gibbs-Duhem equation is applied extensively in analyzing equilibrium systems. At constant temperature and pressure, the Gibbs-Duhem equation reduces to

$$\left[\sum_{i=1}^{i=k} n_i \, d\bar{\mu}_i\right]_{T, p} = 0, \qquad (10.57)$$

which can also be expressed in mole fractions:

$$\left[\sum_{i=1}^{i=k} x_i \, d\bar{\mu}_i\right]_{T, p} = 0. \qquad (10.58)$$

EXAMPLE 10.5: From Eq. (10.54) calculate the average latent heat of evaporation of water at pressures between 5 psia and 10 psia. Compare the results with values listed in the steam tables.

Solution: From the Clausius-Clapeyron equation,

$$\int_{p_1}^{p_2} d\ln p = \int_{T_1}^{T_2} \frac{h_{fg}}{RT^2} \, dT .$$

Integration gives

$$\left[\ln p\right]_{p_1}^{p_2} = \left(\frac{h_{fg}}{R}\right)\left[-\frac{1}{T}\right]_{T_1}^{T_2}$$

$$\ln \frac{p_2}{p_1} = \frac{h_{fg}}{R}\left(\frac{1}{T_1} - \frac{1}{T_2}\right),$$

from which

$$h_{fg} = \frac{(1545/18) \times \ln(10/5)}{(1/622.24) - (1/653.21)} \times \frac{1}{778} = 1005 \text{ Btu/lbm.}$$

The corresponding value from steam tables is 991 Btu/lbm.

**10.9
Effect of an
Inert Gas on
Vapor
Pressure**

Consider a liquid-vapor mixture of a one-component substance in a constant-volume container. If the mixture is in thermodynamic equilibrium; then

$$T_{l_1} = T_{v_1}, \quad p_{l_1} = p_{v_1}, \quad \text{and} \quad \bar{\mu}_{l_1} = \bar{\mu}_{v_1},$$

where subscript 1 refers to the original state of the one-component system. Now consider the addition of an inert gas to the system, keeping the temperature constant. At equilibrium, the following relations must be satisfied

$$T_{l_2} = T_{v_2} = T_g, \quad p_{l_2} = p_{v_2} + p_g \quad \text{and} \quad \bar{\mu}_{l_2} = \bar{\mu}_{v_2},$$

where subscript 2 refers to the final state of the two-component system. The chemical potentials change when the inert gas is added to the system. Furthermore, the change in chemical potential of the liquid phase must be equal in value to the change in the vapor phase, or

$$d\bar{\mu}_{l_1} = d\bar{\mu}_{v_1}. \qquad (10.59)$$

Since, however,

$$\bar{\mu} = \left(\frac{\partial G}{\partial n}\right)_{p,T} = \bar{g}(p, T),$$

therefore,

$$d\bar{g}_l = d\bar{g}_v. \qquad (10.60)$$

The total differential of $\bar{g}$ is

$$d\bar{g} = \bar{v} \, dp - \bar{s} \, dT,$$

which reduces at constant temperature to

$$d\bar{g} = \bar{v} \, dp.$$

Substitution into Eq. (10.60) gives

$$\bar{v}_l \, dp_l = \bar{v}_v \, dp_v.$$

The volume of the liquid phase can be assumed to remain unchanged. Also, the vapor phase follows the perfect gas law, so that

$$\bar{v}_l \, dp_l = \frac{\mathscr{R}T}{p_v} \, dp_v.$$

Integration gives

$$\frac{p_{v_2}}{p_{v_1}} = e^{(\bar{v}_l/\mathscr{R}T)(p_{l_2} - p_{l_1})}. \qquad (10.61)$$

Eq. (10.61) gives the ratio of the pressures of the vapor phase for states 1 and 2 in terms of the pressure of the liquid in the two states. The exponent in the foregoing equation is very small. As a result, the vapor pressure remains essentially constant, irrespective of the presence of the inert gas. For practical purposes, values of vapor pressure of a one-component substance can be used even when an inert gas is also present.

10.10 **The Statistical Approach to Properties of a Perfect Gas Mixture**

Methods of determining thermodynamic properties of a mixture of perfect gases can be developed not only by the classical approach which has been presented here, but also by application of concepts based on statistical techniques. Dalton's law, for example, may be interpreted either at the macroscopic level or at the microscopic level. Dalton's law states that the partial pressure of a constituent is proportional to its mole fraction:

$$p_i = n_i \frac{\mathscr{R}T}{V}.$$

Molecules of one constituent of a perfect gas mixture may be considered to be unaffected by the presence of molecules of other constituents, so that each constituent exerts a pressure independent of the presence of other gases.

Consider a chemically inert system containing gases $a, b, c, \ldots$ in thermodynamic equilibrium. The molecules of each constituent gas may be considered indistinguishable from each other; on the other hand, molecules of one constituent may be distinguished from those of the other constituents. If N_a, N_b, N_c, $\ldots$ represent the number of molecules corresponding to each constituent gas, the numbers of microstates corresponding to the most probable arrangements, according to Section 8.10, are

$$W_a = \prod_i \frac{g_{a_i}^{N_{a_i}}}{N_{a_i}!}, \quad W_b = \prod_i \frac{g_{b_i}^{N_{b_i}}}{N_{b_i}!}, \quad W_c = \prod_i \frac{g_{c_i}^{N_{c_i}}}{N_{c_i}!},$$

where g is the degeneracy of the energy levels, and N_{a_i}, N_{b_i}, and N_{c_i} are the numbers of particles of gases a, b, and c in the ith energy level.

The thermodynamic probability of the mixture is the product of the thermodynamic probabilities of the individual gases, or

$$W = W_a W_b W_c \cdots = \prod_i \frac{g_{a_i}^{N_{a_i}}}{N_{a_i}!} \prod_i \frac{g_{b_i}^{N_{b_i}}}{N_{b_i}!} \prod_i \frac{g_{c_i}^{N_{c_i}}}{N_{c_i}!} \cdots.$$

The logarithm of this equation is

$$\ln W = \sum_i (N_{a_i} \ln g_{a_i} - \ln N_{a_i}!) + \sum_i (N_{b_i} \ln g_{b_i} - \ln N_{b_i}!)$$
$$+ \sum_i (N_{c_i} \ln g_{c_i} - \ln N_{c_i}!) + \cdots.$$

Applying Stirling's formula ($\ln N_i! \approx N_i \ln N_i - N_i$) gives

$$\ln W = \sum_i (N_{a_i} \ln g_{a_i} - N_{a_i} \ln N_{a_i} + N_{a_i})$$

$$+ \sum_i (N_{b_i} \ln g_{b_i} - N_{b_i} \ln N_{b_i} + N_{b_i})$$

$$+ \sum_i (N_{c_i} \ln g_{c_i} - N_{c_i} \ln N_{c_i} + N_{c_i}) + \cdots.$$

Taking first derivatives in order to maximize the value of W gives

$$\delta \ln W = \sum_i (\ln g_{a_i} \, \delta N_{a_i} - \ln N_{a_i} \, \delta N_{a_i}) + \cdots,$$

so that

$$\sum_i \left(\ln \frac{N_{a_i}}{g_{a_i}} \, \delta N_{a_i} \right) + \sum_i \left(\ln \frac{N_{b_i}}{g_{b_i}} \, \delta N_{b_i} \right)$$

$$+ \sum_i \left(\ln \frac{N_{c_i}}{g_{c_i}} \, \delta N_{c_i} \right) + \cdots = 0. \tag{10.62}$$

The following constraints also exist:

(a) The number of molecules of each gas remains the same, so that the net change in the number of molecules of each gas is zero,

$$N_a = \sum_i N_{a_i} \quad \text{or} \quad \sum_i \delta N_{a_i} = 0, \tag{10.63a}$$

$$N_b = \sum_i N_{b_i} \quad \text{or} \quad \sum_i \delta N_{b_i} = 0, \tag{10.63b}$$

$$N_c = \sum_i N_{c_i} \quad \text{or} \quad \sum_i \delta N_{c_i} = 0. \tag{10.63c}$$

(b) The total internal energy of the mixture is constant,

$$U = \sum_i \epsilon_{a_i} N_{a_i} + \sum_i \epsilon_{b_i} N_{b_i} + \sum_i \epsilon_{c_i} N_{c_i} + \cdots$$

or

$$dU = \sum_i (\epsilon_{a_i} \, \delta N_{a_i} + \epsilon_{b_i} \, \delta N_{b_i} + \epsilon_{c_i} \, \delta N_{c_i} + \cdots) = 0. \tag{10.64}$$

Lagrange's method of undetermined multipliers is applied by multiplying Eq. (10.63a), (10.63b), (10.63c), and (10.64) respectively by $-\ln \alpha_a$, $-\ln \alpha_b$, $-\ln \alpha_c$, and β, and adding the result to Eq. (10.62) yields

$$\sum_i \left(\ln \frac{N_{a_i}}{g_{a_i}} - \ln \alpha_a + \epsilon_{a_i} \beta \right) \delta N_{a_i}$$

$$+ \sum_i \left(\ln \frac{N_{b_i}}{g_{b_i}} - \ln \alpha_b + \epsilon_{b_i} \beta \right) \delta N_{b_i}$$

$$+ \sum_i \left(\ln \frac{N_{c_i}}{g_{c_i}} - \ln \alpha_c + \epsilon_{c_i} \beta \right) \delta N_{c_i} + \cdots = 0.$$

Since the values of δN_{a_i}, δN_{b_i}, δN_{c_i}, ... may be considered independent, their coefficients in the foregoing equation must vanish separately, or

$$\left(\ln \frac{N_{a_i}}{g_{a_i}} - \ln \alpha_a + \epsilon_{a_i} \beta\right) = 0, \quad \text{or} \quad N_{a_i} = \alpha_a g_{a_i} e^{-\epsilon_{a_i}\beta}.$$

Similarly,

$$N_{b_i} = \alpha_b g_{b_i} e^{-\epsilon_{b_i}\beta} \quad \text{and} \quad N_{c_i} = \alpha_c g_{c_i} e^{-\epsilon_{c_i}\beta}.$$

In Section 8.5 it was shown that the value of β is $1/kT$, while α is N/Z, where $Z = \sum_i g_i e^{-\epsilon_i/kT}$. Substituting these values gives the distribution of the number of molecules as

$$N_{a_i} = \frac{N_a}{Z_a} g_{a_i} e^{-\epsilon_{a_i}/kT},$$

$$N_{b_i} = \frac{N_b}{Z_a} g_{b_i} e^{-\epsilon_{b_i}/kT},$$

etc. The properties of the mixture can now be evaluated by means of expressions outlined in Chapter 8 and by means of the partition function

$$Z = Z_a Z_b Z_c \cdots = \sum_i g_{a_i} e^{-\epsilon_{a_i}/kT} \sum_i g_{b_i} e^{-\epsilon_{b_i}/kT} \sum_i g_{c_i} e^{-\epsilon_{c_i}/kT} \cdots.$$

The internal energy U of the mixture is determined by adding the internal energies of each of the components:

$$U = \sum_i \epsilon_{a_i} N_{a_i} + \sum_i \epsilon_{b_i} N_{b_i} + \sum_i \epsilon_{c_i} N_{c_i} + \cdots$$

$$= \sum_i \epsilon_{a_i} \frac{N_a}{Z_a} g_{a_i} e^{-\epsilon_{a_i}/kT} + \sum_i \epsilon_{b_i} \frac{N_b}{Z_b} g_{b_i} e^{-\epsilon_{b_i}/kT} + \cdots$$

$$= \frac{N_a \sum_i \epsilon_{a_i} g_{a_i} e^{-\epsilon_{a_i}/kT}}{Z_a} + \frac{N_b \sum_i \epsilon_{a_i} g_{b_i} e^{-\epsilon_{b_i}/kT}}{Z_b} + \cdots.$$

Or

$$U = N_a kT^2 \frac{d(\ln Z_a)}{dT} + N_b kT^2 \frac{d(\ln Z_b)}{dT} + \cdots$$

$$= \sum_{x=a,b,c,\ldots} N_x kT^2 \frac{d(\ln Z_x)}{dT}. \tag{10.65}$$

The entropy of the mixture is determined by the maximum probability according to Boltzmann's treatment:

$$S = k \ln W$$

$$= k \left[\sum_i (N_{a_i} \ln g_{a_i} - N_{a_i} \ln N_{a_i} + N_{a_i}) \right.$$

$$\left. + \sum_i (N_{b_i} \ln g_{b_i} - N_{b_i} \ln N_{b_i} + N_{b_i}) + \cdots \right]$$

$$= k(N_a + N_b + N_c \cdots) + k \left[\sum_i N_{a_i} \ln \frac{g_{a_i}}{N_{a_i}} + N_{b_i} \ln \frac{g_{b_i}}{N_{b_i}} + \cdots \right]$$

$$= kN + k \left[\sum_i N_{a_i} \left(\ln \frac{Z_a}{N_a} + \frac{\epsilon_{a_i}}{kT} \right) + \sum_i N_{b_i} \left(\ln \frac{Z_b}{N_b} + \frac{\epsilon_{b_i}}{kT} \right) + \cdots \right].$$

Thus,

$$S = kN + \frac{U}{T} + k \left[\ln \left(\frac{Z_a}{N_a} \right)^{N_a} + \ln \left(\frac{Z_b}{N_b} \right)^{N_b} + \cdots \right]$$

$$= kN + \frac{U}{T} + k \sum_{x=a,b,c,\ldots} \ln \left(\frac{Z_x}{N_x} \right)^{N_x}. \qquad \textbf{(10.66)}$$

When gases are mixed, a change in entropy occurs, and this can be determined from Eq. (10.66):

$$\Delta S = k \left[\left\{ \ln \left(\frac{Z}{N_a} \right)^{N_a} - \ln \left(\frac{Z_a}{N_a} \right)^{N_a} \right\} + \left\{ \ln \left(\frac{Z}{N_b} \right)^{N_b} - \ln \left(\frac{Z_b}{N_b} \right)^{N_b} \right\} + \cdots \right]$$

$$= k \left[\ln \left(\frac{Z}{Z_a} \right)^{N_a} + \ln \left(\frac{Z}{Z_b} \right)^{N_b} + \ln \left(\frac{Z}{Z_c} \right)^{N_c} + \cdots \right],$$

where Z is the partition function after mixing. The partition function of monatomic gases is $Z = V \left(\frac{2\pi mkT}{h^2} \right)^{3/2}$, therefore the partition function is proportional to volume, at constant temperature:

$$\frac{Z}{Z_a} = \frac{V}{V_a}.$$

The entropy of mixing then becomes

$$\Delta S = k \left[\ln \left(\frac{V}{V_a} \right)^{N_a} + \ln \left(\frac{V}{V_b} \right)^{N_b} + \ln \left(\frac{V}{V_c} \right)^{N_c} + \cdots \right].$$

At constant temperature, the pressure of each constituent is inversely proportional to its volume so that:

$$\Delta S = -kN_a \ln \frac{p_a}{p} - kN_b \ln \frac{p_b}{p} - kN_c \ln \frac{p_c}{p} - \cdots$$

$$= -k \sum_{x=a,b,c,\ldots} N_x \ln \frac{p_x}{p}.$$

Since $kN_x = n_x \mathcal{R} = n_x M_x R_x = m_x R_x$, therefore the entropy change due to mixing is

$$\Delta S = -\sum_{x=a,b,c,\ldots} m_x R_x \ln \frac{p_x}{p} \quad \text{and} \quad \Delta s = -\sum_{x=a,b,c,\ldots} m_{f_x} R_x \ln \frac{p_x}{p}. \qquad (10.67)$$

These equations are equivalent to Eq. (10.36) and (10.50) which were obtained by classical means.

The Helmholtz function is

$$\begin{aligned} F &= U - TS \\ &= -kNT - kT\left[\ln\left(\frac{Z_a}{N_a}\right)^{N_a} + \ln\left(\frac{Z_b}{N_b}\right)^{N_b} + \ln\left(\frac{Z_c}{N_c}\right)^{N_c} + \cdots\right] \\ &= -kNT - kT \sum_{x=a,b,c,\ldots} \ln\left(\frac{Z_x}{N_x}\right)^{N_x}. \end{aligned} \qquad (10.68)$$

The Gibbs function is

$$\begin{aligned} G &= H - TS = F + pV \\ &= -kT \sum_{x=a,b,c,\ldots} \ln\left(\frac{Z_x}{N_x}\right)^{N_x}. \end{aligned} \qquad (10.69)$$

The chemical potential μ of each component per molecule can therefore be expressed as

$$\begin{aligned} \mu_x &= \left(\frac{\partial G}{\partial N_x}\right)_{p,T,n_j} \\ &= -kT\left[N_x \, d\ln\frac{Z_x}{N_x} + \ln\frac{Z_x}{N_x}\right] \\ &= -kT\left[\ln\frac{Z_x}{N_x}\right]. \end{aligned} \qquad (10.70)$$

From the cases listed in this section, it is evident that thermodynamic functions indicating properties of nonreactive gas mixtures can be derived by both classical and statistical approaches. The statistical approach usually yields expressions in terms of partition functions instead of in terms of mole fractions or partial pressures; on the other hand, in some cases identical expressions are obtained. Evidently information regarding molecular energies must generally be available if the statistical approach is to be applied. In many current problems, information regarding distribution of molecular energies is often experimentally determined.

**10.11
Air-Water
Vapor
Mixtures—
Psychrometry**

One common application of thermodynamics centers about control of both temperature and humidity. Atmospheric air is generally the fluid used in these applications. The composition of dry air, which is a mixture of oxygen, nitrogen, argon, carbon dioxide, hydrogen, and inert gases is shown in Table 10.1 in terms of proportions by mass and proportions by volume. Atmospheric air is a mixture of dry air and water vapor in equilibrium.

TABLE 10.1 COMPOSITION OF DRY AIR ($M = 28.97$ lbm/lb-mole; $R = 53.34$ ft-lbf/lbm°R; $c_p = 0.2417$ Btu/lbm°F at 212°F)

Constituent	Mass Fraction	Molal (Volumetric) Fraction or Partial Pressure
Oxygen, O_2	0.23188	0.2099
Nitrogen, N_2	0.75468	0.7803
Argon, A	0.01296	0.0094
Carbon dioxide, CO_2	0.00046	0.0003
Hydrogen, H_2	0.00001	0.0001
Inert gases, such as xenon, krypton	0.00001	—
	1.00000	1.0000

The mixture of N_2, A, CO_2, H_2, and the inert gases which normally are present in air is usually called *atmospheric nitrogen*. With this definition, the composition of dry air may be written as

	Mass Fraction	Molal Fraction
Oxygen	0.23188	0.2099
Atmospheric Nitrogen	0.76812	0.7901
	1.00000	1.0000

The air-water vapor mixture is a homogeneous two-component system and can be considered to follow the laws of perfect gases for mixtures; both dry air and water vapor individually also tend to behave according to the perfect gas law. In common applications, air containing water vapor behaves like perfect gas because the temperature of the dry air is usually very high compared to its critical temperature and because the partial pressure of water is relatively low compared to its critical pressure. Although this section deals with air-water vapor mixtures, the principles and formulas involved can be applied to any mixture of a gas and a condensable vapor. The study of the properties of air and water vapor pertaining to air conditioning problems is called *psychrometry*. Certain terms used in psychrometry are defined below.

A *saturated air mixture* is a mixture of dry air and water vapor in which the partial pressure of the vapor is equal to the saturation pressure of water at the temperature of the mixture. The mixture in this case is said to be *saturated* with vapor. An *unsaturated air mixture* (humid) is a mixture of dry air and superheated water vapor, the partial pressure of the vapor being less than the saturation pressure of water at the temperature of the mixture. A *supersaturated air mixture* is a mixture of dry air and water vapor in which the partial pressure of the water vapor is greater than the saturation pressure of water at the temperature of the mixture.

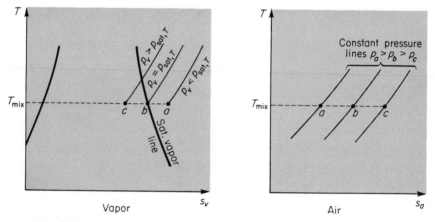

Fig. 10.3. *Temperature-entropy diagrams for water-vapor and air. (a) superheated; (b) saturated; (c) supersaturated.*

The three states are indicated on temperature-entropy graphs for water and dry air in Fig. 10.3, where points *a*, *b*, and *c* represent unsaturated, saturated, and supersaturated mixtures, respectively, at constant temperature. Note that as the partial pressure of water in a mixture increases, at constant temperature, the partial pressure of air decreases accordingly.

Absolute humidity, which is also called *specific humidity* or *humidity ratio*, is the mass of vapor per unit mass of dry air and is given the symbol ω:

$$\omega = \frac{m_v}{m_a}, \tag{10.71}$$

where ω is expressed in lbm or grains of water vapor per lbm of dry air (1 lbm = 7000 grains). Absolute humidity can be expressed in terms of pressures, rather than masses, by applying the perfect gas law:

$$\omega = \frac{m_v}{m_a} = \frac{p_v V / R_v T}{p_a V / R_a T} = \frac{p_v R_a}{p_a R_v}$$

$$= \frac{p_v M_v}{p_a M_a} = \frac{p_v}{p - p_v} \frac{M_v}{M_a} \tag{10.72}$$

$$= 0.622 \frac{p_v}{p - p_v} \quad \text{(for air–water vapor mixture)}.$$

Relative humidity, which is expressed on a percentage basis, is the ratio of the vapor pressure in the mixture at a given temperature to the saturation pressure of the vapor at that temperature. The relative humidity indicates the degree to which an air-vapor mixture is saturated. An alternate definition is the ratio of the moisture content in the mixture to the moisture content of an equal quantity of saturated air at the same temperature and total pressure.

Assuming that the perfect-gas equation of state applies to water vapor, relative humidity, ϕ, can be written as

$$\phi = \left(\frac{p_v}{p_{v,\text{sat}}}\right)_T = \frac{R_v T / v_v}{R_v T / v_{v,\text{sat}}} = \left(\frac{v_{v,\text{sat}}}{v_v}\right)_T = \left(\frac{\rho_v}{\rho_{v,\text{sat}}}\right)_T. \tag{10.73}$$

From this equation, then, the relative humidity can also be expressed as the ratio of the density of the water vapor at the given temperature to the density of saturated water vapor at the same temperature.

A relationship between absolute humidity and relative humidity in an air-water vapor mixture can be derived from Eq. (10.72) and (10.73):

$$\omega = 0.622 \frac{p_v}{p_a} = 0.622 \frac{p_v}{p_{v,\text{sat}}} \frac{p_{v,\text{sat}}}{p_a} = 0.622\phi \left(\frac{p_{v,\text{sat}}}{p_a}\right). \tag{10.74}$$

The *saturation ratio* indicates the degree of saturation and is the ratio of absolute humidity of the air to the absolute humidity of saturated air at the same temperature and total pressure. The saturation ratio, ψ, can be expressed as

$$\psi = \left(\frac{\omega}{\omega_{\text{sat}}}\right)_T. \tag{10.75}$$

The saturation ratio ψ can be shown to be related to the relative humidity ϕ. By substituting for ω and ω_{sat} in Eq. (10.75) one obtains

$$\psi = \left[\frac{p_v}{p_a} \frac{p_{a,\text{sat}}}{p_{v,\text{sat}}}\right]_T = \left[\frac{p_v}{p_{v,\text{sat}}} \frac{p - p_{v,\text{sat}}}{p - p_v}\right]_T = \phi\left(\frac{p - p_{v,\text{sat}}}{p - p_v}\right)_T. \tag{10.76}$$

At room temperature or lower, the vapor pressure of water is small, so that the saturation ratio tends to become identical with the relative humidity, ϕ. For a saturated air mixture the absolute humidity can be written as

$$\omega = 0.622 \, \frac{f(t)}{p - f(t)}, \tag{10.77}$$

where the saturation pressure of water vapor is expressed as a function of temperature $f(t)$, as indicated in steam tables. At 100 per cent relative humidity, values of the absolute humidity at various temperatures and at a constant total pressure can be calculated according to Eq. (10.77). The

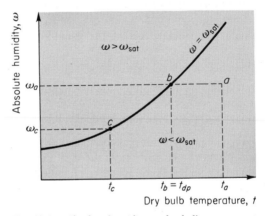

Fig. 10.4. *Absolute humidity vs dry-bulb temperature.*

result is shown in Fig. 10.4. In the region below the saturation curve, $\omega < \omega_{sat}$ so that the air is unsaturated and the water vapor is superheated. In the region above the saturated curve, $\omega > \omega_{sat}$ and the air is supersaturated with water vapor. The existing pressure of the vapor in this case is larger than the saturation pressure of water at that temperature, so that sudden and irreversible condensation of water tends to occur, accompanied by a sharp increase in entropy and reestablishment of equilibrium conditions. The resulting mixture of air and water is saturated with water vapor.

If an unsaturated mixture at state a of Fig. 10.4 is cooled at constant pressure, its absolute humidity remains constant until saturation is reached, which corresponds to point b. Any further cooling causes condensation. During the first phase of the cooling process, the partial pressure of the water vapor remains constant provided that the total pressure is kept constant. Temperature t_b, which is called the *dew point*, is the temperature at which an unsaturated gas-vapor mixture becomes saturated as a result of isobaric cooling at constant absolute humidity. The dew point is also the saturation temperature corresponding to the initial partial pressure of the vapor. If cooling proceeds further, both the temperature and the absolute humidity decrease, until point c on the saturation curve is reached. The amount of water condensed per pound mass of air is the difference in absolute humidity between point a and point c. The same cooling process is represented in Fig. 10.5 on the T-s diagram. Point a represents the unsatu-

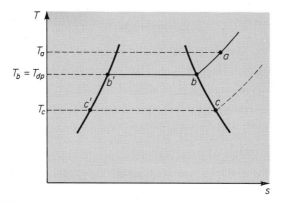

Fig. 10.5. *Cooling of a gas-vapor mixture at constant pressure.*

rated state of a mixture. The partial pressure of the vapor remains constant until the dew point temperature, point b, is reached, and condensation begins. Further cooling causes more condensation, so that both the temperature of the mixture and the partial pressure of the vapor are decreased. When a temperature such as T_c is reached, the saturated vapor at state c is in equilibrium with its condensate at state c'.

In a plot of absolute humidity versus temperature, it is possible to indicate points of constant relative humidity. This is shown in Fig. 10.6.

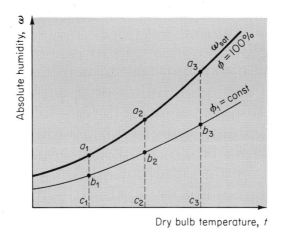

Dry bulb temperature, t

Fig. 10.6. *Plot of constant relative humidity lines.*

At a selected total pressure, values of absolute humidity are calculated according to Eq. (10.77), corresponding to saturation conditions ($\phi = 100$ per cent), at various temperatures. At other selected values of ϕ, absolute humidity is calculated from Eq. (10.74). Since at room temperature (or lower), the relative humidity can be assumed equal to the saturation ratio and since the saturation ratio is a ratio of two values of absolute humidity at constant temperature, points of constant ϕ can be determined from

$$\psi_1 = \phi_1 = \frac{b_1 c_1}{a_1 c_1} = \frac{b_2 c_2}{a_2 c_2} = \frac{b_3 c_3}{a_3 c_3} = \cdots,$$

In establishing constant relative humidity lines, the ordinates of the saturation curve are first divided into 10 equal parts and points at 10 per cent increments in relative humidity are established from them.

The enthalpy of an air–water vapor mixture is the sum of the enthalpies of the dry air and the accompanying water vapor, both taken at the temperature of the mixture. It is common practice in humidity calculations to express the enthalpy of the mixture per pound mass of dry air. The enthalpy of dry air is based on a zero value at $0°F$, whereas enthalpy of water vapor, as found in steam tables, is based on a zero value for the saturated liquid at $32°F$. Although the points of zero enthalpy for air and water vapor are not at the same temperature, the discrepancy can be ignored since interest lies in differences in enthalpy rather than in absolute values of enthalpy. Both the dry air and the water vapor are assumed to follow the perfect gas law so that their enthalpies are functions of temperature alone. In atmospheric air, the partial pressure of the water vapor is low, so that this assumption is valid. The enthalpy of a mixture of dry air and water vapor per lbm of dry air is

$$h = h_a + \omega h_v \simeq h_a + \omega h_g, \tag{10.78}$$

where h_a = enthalpy of dry air per lbm = $c_{p_a} T_a$,
$\quad \omega$ = specific humidity,
$\quad h_v$ = enthalpy of superheated vapor in the mixture,
$\quad h_v = c_{p_f}(t_{dp} - 32) + (h_{fg})_{t_{dp}} + c_{p_v}(t - t_{dp})$,
$\quad h_g$ = enthalpy of saturated steam per lbm at the temperature of the mixture.

Because enthalpy is primarily a function of temperature, and not pressure, the enthalpy of saturated steam, h_g, at a given temperature is virtually identical to the enthalpy of superheated steam, h_v, at that temperature. Note also that the enthalpy given by Eq. (10.78) expresses the enthalpy of the mixture per lbm of dry air rather than per lbm of mixture. The specific volume of a mixture of air and water vapor is given by

$$v = \frac{1}{\rho} = \frac{RT}{p} = \frac{T}{p} \left(\frac{m_a R_a + m_v R_v}{m_a + m_v} \right) = \frac{T}{p} \left(\frac{R_a + \omega R_v}{1 + \omega} \right). \tag{10.79}$$

Since the specific humidity $\omega = \rho_v/\rho_a$, the density of the water vapor is

$$\rho_v = \omega \rho_a = \frac{\omega p_a}{R_a T}. \tag{10.80}$$

In the case of a gaseous mixture, the density of the mixture is the sum of the densities of the air and water vapor, so that

$$\rho = \rho_a + \rho_v = \rho_a + \omega \rho_a = \rho_a(1 + \omega), \tag{10.81}$$

and the specific volume of the mixture is

$$v = \frac{1}{\rho} = \frac{v_a}{1 + \omega}. \tag{10.82}$$

EXAMPLE 10.6:   An air-water vapor mixture at 70°F and 14.7 psia has a relative humidity 80 per cent. Determine
(a) The partial pressures of the vapor and the air
(b) The specific humidity
(c) The saturation ratio
(d) The dew point
(e) The density of the mixture
(f) If the mixture is cooled at constant pressure to a temperature of 50°F, find the amount of water vapor condensed per lbm of dry air.

Solution: From steam tables at 70°F, $p_{v,\,\text{sat}} = 0.3631$ psia.

But, $\phi = 0.8 = \left(\dfrac{p_v}{p_{v,\,\text{sat}}} \right)_{70°\text{F}}$. Therefore,

(a) $p_v = 0.8 \times 0.3631 = 0.29$ psia

$\qquad p_a = p - p_v = 14.7 - 0.29 = 14.41$ psia.

(b) $\omega_1 = 0.622 \dfrac{p_v}{p_a} = 0.622 \dfrac{0.29}{14.41} = 0.0125$ lbm/lbm.

(c) $\psi = \left(\dfrac{\omega}{\omega_{\text{sat}}} \right)_{70°} = \phi \dfrac{p - p_{v,\,\text{sat}}}{p - p_v} = 0.8 \dfrac{14.3369}{14.41} = 0.797.$

(d) From steam tables, at $p_v = 0.29$ psia,

$\qquad t_{dp} = 63.5°\text{F}.$

(e) $\rho = \rho_a(1 + \omega)$

$\qquad = \dfrac{14.41 \times 144}{53.34 \times 530} (1 + 0.0125) = 0.0744$ lbm/ft³.

Since 50°F is below the dew point, some of the vapor will condense, leaving a mixture of 100 per cent relative humidity.

At 50°F $p_v = p_{v,\,sat} = 0.17811$ psia,

$$\omega_2 = 0.622 \frac{0.17811}{14.7 - 0.17811} = 0.00763 \text{ lbm/lbm.}$$

The amount of vapor condensed per lbm of dry air is
$$\omega_1 - \omega_2 = 0.0125 - 0.00763 = 0.00487 \text{ lbm/lbm.}$$

10-12
Adiabatic
Saturation
Process

Consider a stream of air and water vapor flowing through an insulated chamber, as shown in Fig. 10.7. Assume that the mixture entering the chamber at section 1 is at a relative humidity less than 100 per cent. At the same time, a stream of water is sprayed into the chamber. As the mixture flows through the chamber some of the

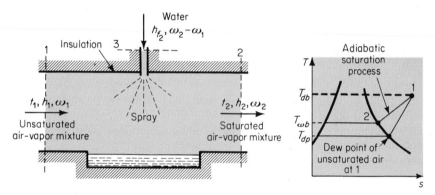

Fig. 10.7. *Adiabatic saturation process.*

liquid water evaporates, and is carried by the air stream. Energy is needed for evaporation; this is reflected in a lowering of the temperature of the air stream. By the time the air reaches section 2, it is assumed that equilibrium between the two streams is established and the air stream is saturated with water vapor. At this point, the chemical potentials of the water in the liquid and vapor states are equal. If the water stream is added adiabatically and the temperature of the water stream does not change during the process, the mixture at section 2 attains a temperature called the *adiabatic saturation temperature*. To maintain steady state, make-up water must be added at a rate equal to that of evaporation, and its temperature is assumed to be equal to the adiabatic saturation temperature. The reduction in temperature of the air mixture is a measure of the degree of saturation of the entering mixture.

In this adiabatic cooling process, there is no heat interaction and also no work interaction. The first law of thermodynamics for a steady flow process may then be applied; assuming no changes in kinetic energy or potential energy:

$$h_{a_1} + \omega_1 h_{v_1} + (\omega_2 - \omega_1) h_{f_2} = h_{a_2} + \omega_2 h_{v_2} . \qquad \text{(10.83)}$$

$$\underset{\substack{\text{unsaturated} \\ \text{air-vapor mixture}}}{} \qquad \underset{\text{water}}{} \qquad \underset{\substack{\text{saturated air-} \\ \text{vapor mixture}}}{}$$

From this equation, ω_1 can be determined if temperatures and pressures at sections 1 and 2 are known. Equation (10.83) can be arranged to take any one of the following forms:

$$h_{a_1} + \omega_1 h_{v_1} - \omega_1 h_{f_2} = h_{a_2} + \omega_2 h_{v_2} - \omega_2 h_{f_2} , \qquad \text{(10.84)}$$

$$(h_{a_1} + \omega_1 h_{fg_1}) + \omega_1 (h_{f_1} - h_{f_2}) \approx (h_{a_2} + \omega_2 h_{fg_2}) , \qquad \text{(10.85)}$$

$$\omega_1 (h_{v_1} - h_{f_2}) \approx (h_{a_2} - h_{a_1}) + \omega_2 h_{fg_2} . \qquad \text{(10.86)}$$

10-13 Wet-Bulb Temperature

A simple method of determining the relative humidity of an air–water vapor mixture is by use of dry-bulb and wet-bulb thermometers. The dry-bulb temperature is indicated by a conventional thermometer placed in the mixture. The wet-bulb temperature is measured by a thermometer whose bulb is covered with a wick saturated with water and placed in the air-water vapor stream. If the air surrounding the wet-bulb thermometer is unsaturated, the pressure of the water vapor at the surface of the wick exceeds the partial pressure of the water vapor in the mixture. Evaporation of water from the wick then occurs, because of the difference in chemical potential between the liquid and the vapor phases. This evaporation is accompanied by a drop in the temperature of the wick, which is reflected in a lowering of the temperature of the wet-bulb thermometer since heat is transferred from both the wick and the thermometer to sustain the evaporation process. Equilibrium is attained when the chemical potentials of the liquid and vapor phases are identical, and at this point the wick is at the so-called wet-bulb temperature. The wet-bulb temperature is ordinarily less than the dry-bulb temperature; when the dry-bulb thermometer is surrounded by saturated air, both temperatures are equal.

The temperature indicated by a wet-bulb thermometer is very nearly equal to the adiabatic saturation temperature. But some difference does exist. The wet-bulb temperature depends on both mass transfer and heat transfer from the liquid phase; on the other hand, the adiabatic saturation temperature (also called the *thermodynamic wet-bulb temperature*) involves an equilibrium temperature in which no transfer of heat occurs from the liquid phase to the gas phase. Because the rate of exchange of heat and mass affects the readings shown by wet-bulb thermometers, the wet-bulb temperature is not a property of the mixture. In practice, however, the wet-bulb temperature is easily determined; on the other hand, the thermodynamic wet-bulb temperature is difficult to measure because it is difficult to attain equilibrium between the unsaturated air-water vapor mixture and water under adiabatic conditions. Since the difference between the two temperatures is negligible, the wet-bulb temperature is ordinarily used in place of the thermodynamic wet-bulb temperature in humidity calculations.

10-14
Psychrometric
Chart

The wet-bulb and dry-bulb temperatures of air are used in determining the relative humidity of air. A psychrometric chart is shown in Fig. 10.8 in skeleton form, to illustrate how properties of air–water vapor

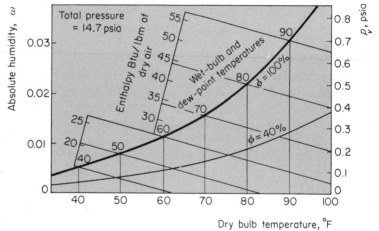

Fig. 10.8.   *Skeleton psychrometric chart.*

mixtures can be presented graphically. (A complete chart is found in the Appendix.) The psychrometric chart is essentially a composition-temperature chart. The specific humidity (identifying composition) and the partial pressure are ordinates; the dry-bulb temperature is the abscissa. On the chart shown in Fig. 10.9, lines of constant relative humidity, volume, wet-bulb temperature, and enthalpy are indicated. Most psychrometric charts are constructed for a constant total pressure of 29.92 in. Hg. Some charts give correction curves for pressures other than atmospheric pressure.

Since the wet-bulb temperature is almost the same as the adiabatic saturation temperature, it is reasonable to expect that the constant enthalpy lines will run parallel to the wet-bulb temperatures on the psychrometric chart. Thus the process of adiabatic humidification (or dehumidification) of

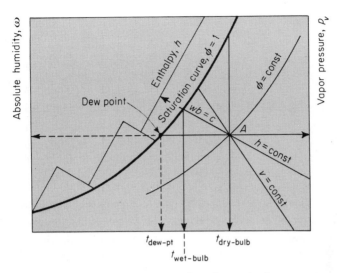

Fig. 10.9. *Components of psychrometric chart.*

air can be considered to be a constant-enthalpy process. Application of the first law of thermodynamics to an adiabatic saturation process shows that

$$h_1 + (\omega_2 - \omega_1)h_f = h_2, \qquad (10.87)$$

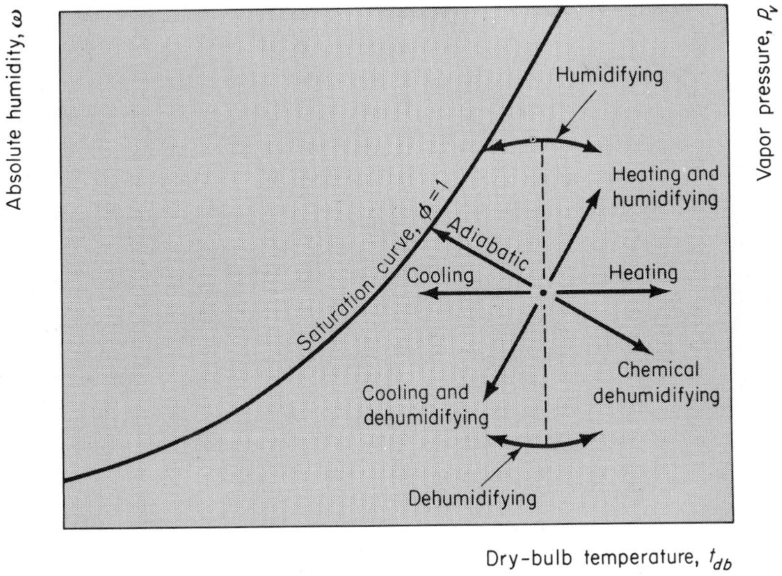

Fig. 10.10. *Air-conditioning processes.*

where h_f is the enthalpy of the injected water. But clearly, since $h_1 \neq h_2$, the process cannot be considered a constant enthalpy process. The term $(\omega_2 - \omega_1) h_f$ is, however, small when compared with h_1 or h_2 so that the deviation from a constant-enthalpy process is minor. Some psychrometric charts account for this deviation by including lines of constant "enthalpy-deviation."

Air conditioning processes, such as cooling, heating, humidifying, and dehumidifying, can be represented on the psychrometric chart shown in Fig. 10.10. With this chart, processes can be more readily visualized and the changes in properties can be determined easily. The use of the chart will be illustrated in Section 10.15.

10-15 Processes Involving Air-Water Vapor Mixtures

Some of the most common processes in air-conditioning involving air-water vapor mixtures are (a) mixing, (b) heating or cooling, (c) humidifying, (d) dehumidifying.

(a) *Mixing process:* This process can be illustrated by considering the mixing of two streams of humid air. As shown in Fig. 10.11, the original streams are at states 1 and 2, and the final stream is at state 3. If the flow is steady, the energy balance leads to the following equation:

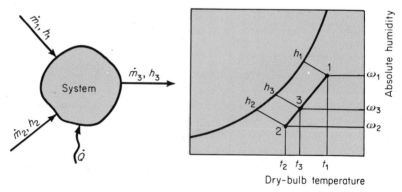

Fig. 10.11. *Adiabatic mixing process.*

$$(\dot{m}_{a_1} h_{a_1} + \dot{m}_{v_1} h_{v_1}) + (\dot{m}_{a_2} h_{a_2} + \dot{m}_{v_2} h_{v_2}) + \dot{Q} = (\dot{m}_{a_3} h_{a_3} + \dot{m}_{v_3} h_{v_3}).$$

Since $\omega = m_v/m_a$, therefore,

$$\dot{m}_{a_1}(h_{a_1} + \omega_1 h_{v_1}) + \dot{m}_{a_2}(h_{a_2} + \omega_2 h_{v_2}) + \dot{Q} = \dot{m}_{a_3}(h_{a_3} + \omega_3 h_{v_3}).$$

Denoting $h_a + \omega h_v = h$, the enthalpy of the mixture per lbm of dry air, the preceding equation becomes

$$\dot{m}_{a_1} h_1 + \dot{m}_{a_2} h_2 + \dot{Q} = \dot{m}_{a_3} h_3. \tag{10.88}$$

The continuity equations are

$$\dot{m}_{a_1} + \dot{m}_{a_2} = \dot{m}_{a_3} \quad \text{(for air)},$$
$$\dot{m}_{v_1} + \dot{m}_{v_2} = \dot{m}_{v_3} \quad \text{(for water vapor)}.$$

The continuity equation for water vapor can also be expressed as

$$\omega_1 \dot{m}_{a_1} + \omega_2 \dot{m}_{a_2} = \omega_3 \dot{m}_{a_3}.$$

Assuming that mixing occurs adiabatically and substituting for $\dot{m}_{a_3}$, the energy equation becomes

$$\dot{m}_{a_1} h_1 + \dot{m}_{a_2} h_2 = (\dot{m}_{a_1} + \dot{m}_{a_2}) h_3 ,$$

or

$$\frac{\dot{m}_{a_1}}{\dot{m}_{a_2}} = \frac{h_3 - h_2}{h_1 - h_3}. \tag{10.89}$$

Similarly, the continuity equation for water vapor is

$$\omega_1 \dot{m}_{a_1} + \omega_2 \dot{m}_{a_2} = \omega_3 (\dot{m}_{a_1} + \dot{m}_{a_2}) ,$$

or

$$\frac{\dot{m}_{a_1}}{\dot{m}_{a_2}} = \frac{\omega_3 - \omega_2}{\omega_1 - \omega_3}. \tag{10.90}$$

It is obvious from Eq. (10.89) and (10.90) that changes in enthalpy of the mixture per lbm of dry air are paralleled by changes in the specific humidity. This is an extremely convenient relationship. As shown in Fig. 10.11, if the initial states 1 and 2 are located on the chart, the state of the resulting mixture lies on the line connecting the two states 1 and 2. Point 3 divides the distance 1–2 into two parts, such that the ratio of the lengths 1–3 and 3–2 is equal to the ratio of the masses of dry air in the two streams before they mix.

EXAMPLE 10.7: The properties of two streams of air are as follows:

	Temperature (°F)	Pressure (psia)	Relative Humidity (%)	Flow Rate (ft³/min)
Stream (1)	55	14.7	20	650
Stream (2)	75	14.7	80	900

If these two streams are mixed adiabatically, and the pressure is maintained at

14.7 psia, evaluate the following properties of the mixed stream: (a) relative humidity and specific humidity; (b) specific volume. (Assume steady state.)

Solution

(a) $\omega_1 = 0.622 \dfrac{0.2 \times 0.2141}{14.7 - 0.2 \times 0.2141} = 0.00182 \text{ lbm/lbm.}$

$\omega_2 = 0.622 \dfrac{0.8 \times 0.4298}{14.7 - 0.8 \times 0.4298} = 0.0149 \text{ lbm/lbm.}$

$m_{a_1} = \dfrac{p_{a_1} V_1}{R_a T_1} = \dfrac{(14.7 - 0.2 \times 0.2141) \times 144 \times 650}{53.34 \times 515}$

$= 49.9 \text{ lbm of air per minute.}$

$m_{a_2} = \dfrac{p_{a_2} V_2}{R_a T_2} = \dfrac{(14.7 - 0.8 \times 0.4298) \times 144 \times 900}{53.34 \times 535}$

$= 65.5 \text{ lbm of air per minute.}$

The continuity equation for the water vapor is

$$\omega_1 \dot{m}_{a_1} + \omega_2 \dot{m}_{a_2} = \omega_3 (\dot{m}_{a_1} + \dot{m}_{a_2});$$

from this equation

$$\omega_3 = \frac{49.9}{115.4} \times 0.00182 + \frac{65.5}{115.4} \times 0.0149 = 0.00924 \text{ lbm/lbm.}$$

The equivalent values from the psychrometric chart are

$$\omega_1 = 0.0018, \quad \omega_2 = 0.015, \quad \omega_3 = 0.0093.$$

The vapor pressure, according to Eq. (10.72), is

$$p_{v_3} = \frac{\omega_3 p}{\omega_3 + 0.622} = \frac{0.00924 \times 14.7}{0.63124} = 0.215 \text{ psia.}$$

An energy balance gives

$$\dot{m}_{a_1}(c_{p_a} + \omega_1 c_{p_v})t_1 + \dot{m}_{a_2}(c_{p_a} + \omega_2 c_{p_v})t_2 = \dot{m}_{a_3}(c_{p_a} + \omega_3 c_{p_v})t_3 .$$

Therefore,

$$49.5(0.24 + 0.00182 \times 0.44)55 + 65.5(0.24 + 0.0149 \times 0.44)75$$
$$= 115.4(0.24 + 0.00924 \times 0.49)t_3 ,$$

from which $t_3 = 67°F$. From the steam tables, at $t_3 = 67°F$,

$$p_{v,\text{sat}} = 0.3276 \text{ psia.}$$

Therefore,

$$\phi_3 = \left[\frac{p_v}{p_{v,\text{sat}}}\right]_{67°F} = \frac{0.215}{0.3276} = 65.7 \text{ per cent.}$$

(b) $v_3 = \dfrac{v_{a_3}}{1 + \omega_3} = \dfrac{[(53.34 \times 527)/(14.7 - 0.215) \times 144]}{1.00924} = 13.38 \text{ ft}^3/\text{lbm.}$

Values obtained directly from the chart are

$$t_3 = 66.5°F, \quad \phi_3 = 67 \text{ per cent}, \quad v_3 = 13.45 \text{ ft}^3/\text{lbm.}$$

(b) *Heating and cooling processes:* Both the constant-volume process and the constant-pressure process will be considered. In the case of the constant-volume process, the specific volume of each component of the mixture remains constant; also, the heat transfer equals the change in internal energy of the mixture. In the case of the constant-pressure process, the vapor pressure and the specific humidity of the mixture remain constant, provided that no condensation takes place. This process is represented by a horizontal line on the psychrometric chart. If, however, condensation occurs as a result of cooling below the dew point, the specific humidity decreases and the partial pressure of the water vapor becomes equal to the saturation pressure of water at the temperature of the mixture. The following two examples illustrate the constant-volume and the constant-pressure processes.

EXAMPLE 10.8: A rigid vessel, which has a volume of 8 ft^3, contains dry air at 80°F. If 0.8 lbm of water, also at 80°F, is injected into the vessel so that the pressure becomes 15 psia, find
   (a) The relative humidity of the mixture
   (b) The minimum amount of heat that must be transferred to evaporate all the water; also, the resulting temperature and pressure
   (c) The relative humidity if the vessel is heated further to 700°F.

Solution: (a) at 80°F, $p_{v,\text{sat}} = 0.5069$ psia.
If all the injected water were in the vapor state, then its partial pressure would be

$$p_v = \frac{m_v R_v T}{V} = \frac{0.8 \times 85.68 \times 540}{8 \times 144} = 32.1 \text{ psia.}$$

But the partial pressure of water cannot exceed its saturation vapor pressure. Therefore the vessel contains air at 100 per cent relative humidity and some water in the liquid state.

$$p_a = 15 - 0.5069 = 14.4931 \text{ psia}$$

and

$$m_a = \frac{14.4931 \times 144 \times 8}{53.34 \times 540} = 0.579 \text{ lbm.}$$

(b) The specific volume of vapor $= 8/0.8 = 10$ ft³/lbm and by steam tables this corresponds to a temperature of 270.4°F and a p_v of 42.137 psia.

$$p_a = \frac{0.579 \times 53.34(460 + 270.4)}{8 \times 144} = 19.55 \text{ psia.}$$

The pressure of the mixture $= p_v + p_a = 42.137 + 19.55 = 61.687$ psia. The heat transfer is

$$Q = \Delta U$$
$$= m_v(\Delta u)_v + m_a(c_v)_a(\Delta T)$$
$$= 0.8(1092.7 - 48) + 0.579 \times 0.173(270.4 - 80)$$
$$= 854.83 \text{ Btu.}$$

(c) at 700°F and specific volume of 10 ft³/lbm, the partial pressure of water is

$$p_v = \frac{85.68 \times 1160}{10 \times 144} = 69 \text{ psia.}$$

The vapor pressure p_v can also be obtained from superheated steam tables corresponding to a specific volume of 10 and 700°F.

The value from the steam tables is $p_v = 69.5$ psia.

$$\phi = \left(\frac{p_v}{p_{v,\text{sat}}}\right)_{700°F} = \frac{69.5}{3093.7} = 2.25 \text{ per cent.}$$

Note that this example assumes no temperature change. But there is a slight change due to absorption or release of energy incurred in phase change.

EXAMPLE 10.9: An air-water vapor mixture at 57°F and 60 per cent relative humidity at a pressure of 14.7 psia is heated at constant pressure to a temperature of 90°F. Determine
  (a) The initial and final specific humidities of the mixture
  (b) The final relative humidity, the dew point, and the amount of heat transfer per lbm of dry air
  (c) If the initial mixture is cooled isobarically to 35°F, determine the amount of water vapor condensed and the heat transfer per lbm of dry air.

Solution: (a) At 57°F, $p_{v,\text{sat}} = 0.2302$ psia.

Hence, $p_v = 0.6 \times 0.2302 = 0.138$ psia.

The specific humidity and the vapor pressure are unchanged by heating.

$$\omega_1 = \frac{m_v}{m_a} = 0.622 \frac{p_v}{p - p_v} = 0.622 \frac{0.138}{14.7 - 0.138} = 0.00591.$$

(b) At 90°F, $p_{v,\text{sat}} = 0.6982$ psia.

$$\phi = \frac{0.138}{0.6982} = 19.76 \text{ per cent.}$$

From steam tables at $p_v = 0.138$ psia, $t_{dp} = 43.3°F$.

$$Q_{1-2} = h_2 - h_1 = (c_{p_a} + \omega c_{p_v})(t_2 - t_1)$$
$$= (0.24 + 0.00591 \times 0.44)(90 - 57)$$
$$= 8 \text{ Btu/lbm of dry air.}$$

(c) Since 35°F is below the dew point of the mixture, condensation will occur.

At 35°F, $p_v = p_{v,\,sat} = 0.09995$ psia.

$$\omega_3 = 0.622 \frac{0.09995}{14.7 - 0.09995} = 0.00426 \text{ lbm/lbm of air.}$$

$$\text{Mass of vapor condensed} = \omega_1 - \omega_3 = 0.00591 - 0.00426$$
$$= 0.00165 \text{ lbm/lbm of air.}$$

Heat transfer per lbm of dry air

$$Q_{1-3} = c_{p_a}(t_3 - t_1) - \omega_1 h_{g_1} + \omega_3 h_{g_3} + (\omega_1 - \omega_3)h_{f_3}$$
$$= 0.24(35 - 57) - 0.00591 \times 1086.7 + 0.00426 \times 1077.1$$
$$+ 0.00165 \times 3.02 = -7.1 \text{ Btu.}$$

For comparison, Fig. 10.12 shows the processes of the preceding example on the psychrometric chart.

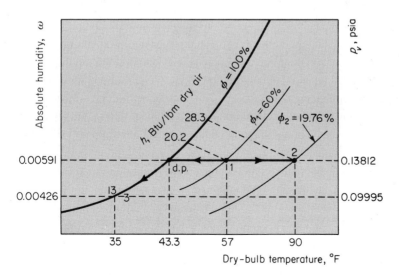

Fig. 10.12.   Example 10.9.

(d) *Humidifying processes:* Two methods are commonly used to increase the specific humidity of air: one involves adiabatic evaporation; the other involves evaporation with heat interaction. These processes are shown

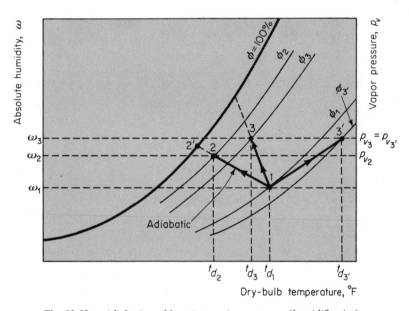

Fig. 10.13.   *Adiabatic and heat interaction processes (humidification).*

schematically in Fig. 10.13. In the adiabatic evaporation process, air at state 1 is passed through a spray of water. Some of this water evaporates, so that the specific humidity of the air increases, while, at the same time, the air mixture is cooled. The wet air tends to maintain a constant wet-bulb temperature, and the evaporation process stops when the air becomes saturated (state 2'). In evaporation accompanied by heating, air is passed through a spray of water while, at the same time, heat is transferred to the system. The cooling due to evaporation opposes the rise in temperature due to heat interaction. The resultant effect may be either a net reduction in temperature, as shown by process 1–3 of Fig. 10.13, or a net increase in temperature, as shown by 1–3'. In process 1–3 the relative humidity increases; on the other hand, in process 1–3' the relative humidity decreases.

EXAMPLE 10.10: Atmospheric air at a temperature of 60°F, pressure 14.7 psia, and relative humidity 20 per cent is to be humidified under steady-state conditions to a specific humidity of 0.005 lbm of vapor/lbm of dry air. Utilizing the psychrometric chart, compare the following processes with regard to the final relative humidity, final temperature, and amount of heat transfer per lbm of dry air: (a) adiabatic evaporative; (b) constant dry-bulb temperature, (c) constant relative humidity. Assume that the humidifying water is at 60°F.

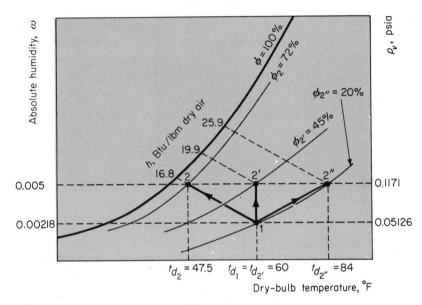

Fig. 10.14. *Example 10.10.*

Solution: The solution is shown in Fig. 10.14. The heat interactions are
(a) $Q_{1-2} = 0$.
(b) $Q_{1-2'} = 19.9 - 16.8 = 3.1$ Btu/lbm of dry air.
(c) $Q_{1-2''} = 25.9 - 16.8 = 9.1$ Btu/lbm of dry air.
The results are tabulated in the following table:

	$\phi(\%)$	$T_{db}(°F)$	Q(Btu)
Initial conditions	20	60	—
Adiabatic process	72	47.5	0
Constant-T_{db} process	45	60	3.1
Constant-ϕ process	20	84	9.1

A cooling tower tends to operate on an adiabatic isobaric evaporative cooling process. As shown in Fig. 10.15, warm water at the top of the tower is sprayed through nozzles or over baffles to form a large water surface. Unsaturated air is drawn upward by a fan through the tower and leaves almost saturated. The evaporation process cools the water at constant pressure with negligible heat losses.

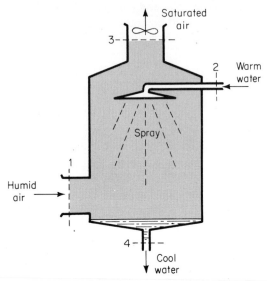

Fig. 10.15. *Cooling tower.*

EXAMPLE 10.11:   It is required to cool 10,000 lbm of water per hour from 100°F to 80°F in a cooling tower. The unsaturated air mixture enters the tower at 70°F and 40 per cent relative humidity and leaves at 85°F and 90 per cent relative humidity. Assuming the steady-state process to be isobaric-adiabatic, calculate the rate of air flow and the rate at which water is evaporated.

Solution: At 70°F $p_{v,\,\mathrm{sat_1}} = 0.3631$ psia, therefore

$$p_{v_1} = 0.4 \times 0.3631 = 0.1452 \text{ psia.}$$

$$\omega_1 = 0.622 \frac{p_v}{p - p_v} = 0.622 \times \frac{0.1452}{14.7 - 0.1452} = 0.0062 \text{ lbm/lbm.}$$

At 85°F $p_{v,\,\mathrm{sat_3}} = 0.5050$ psia, therefore

$$p_{v_3} = 0.9 \times 0.5959 = 0.5363 \text{ psia.}$$

$$\omega_3 = 0.622 \frac{0.5363}{14.7 - 0.5363} = 0.622 \times \frac{0.5363}{14.1637} = 0.0236 \text{ lbm/lbm.}$$

Mass of water evaporated $= \omega_3 - \omega_1 = 0.0236 - 0.0062$
$$= 0.0174 \text{ lbm/lbm of dry air.}$$

The energy balance, from the first law and the continuity equation, is

$$(h_{a_1} + \omega_1 h_{v_1}) + m_{f_2} h_{f_2} = (h_{a_3} + \omega_3 h_{v_3}) + m_{f_4} h_{f_4},$$

where m_f is the mass of liquid/lbm of dry air. The energy equation can be arranged as

$$c_{p_a}(t_1 - t_3) + \omega_1 h_{g_1} + m_{f_2} h_{f_2} = \omega_3 h_{g_3} + [m_{f_2} - (\omega_3 - \omega_1)]h_{f_4}.$$

Substituting values gives

$$0.24(70 - 85) + 0.0062 \times 1092.3 + m_{f_2} \times 67.97$$
$$= 0.0236 \times 1098.8 + (m_{f_2} - 0.0174)(48.02),$$

from which

$$m_{f_2} = 1.1 \text{ lbm/lbm of dry air.}$$

Mass of air-water vapor mixture introduced

$$m_1 = \frac{10,000(1 + \omega_1)}{m_{f_2}}$$

$$= 10,000 \times \frac{1.0062}{1.1} = 9140 \text{ lbm/hr.}$$

Rate of evaporation of water $= (\omega_3 - \omega_1) \times \dfrac{10,000}{m_{f_2}}$

$$= 0.0174 \times \frac{10,000}{1.1} = 158 \text{ lbm/hr.}$$

(d) *Dehumidifying processes:* Air is often subject to dehumidification processes, in which water vapor is removed from the air. This may be accomplished chemically by the use of hygroscopic materials which absorb water vapor. It may also be accomplished by cooling the mixture below its dew point. The water that condenses out is then removed; the remaining mixture may then be heated to the desired temperature.

REFERENCES

10.1 Denbigh, K. G., *The Principles of Chemical Equilibrium*. Cambridge: Cambridge University Press, 1957, chap. 2, 3, 6.

10.2 Gilmont, R., *Thermodynamic Principles for Chemical Engineers*. Englewood Cliffs, N.J., Prentice-Hall, Inc., 1959, chap. 13.

10.3 Kiefer, P. J., G. F. Kinney, and M. C. Stuart, *Principles of Engineering Thermodynamics*. New York: John Wiley & Sons, Inc., 1954, chap. 10.

10.4 Lee, J. F., and F. W. Sears, *Thermodynamics*. Reading, Mass.: Addison Wesley Publishing Company, Inc., 1955, chap. 10.

10.5 Van Wylen, G. J., *Thermodynamics*. New York: John Wiley & Sons, Inc., 1959, chap. 9.

10.6 Jennings, B. H., *Heating and Air Conditioning*. New York: International Text Book Co., 1956, chap. 3.

10.7 Stoecher, W. F., *Refrigeration and Air Conditioning*. New York: McGraw-Hill Book Company, 1958, chap. 16.

PROBLEMS

10.1 A mixture of perfect gases at 70°F has the following composition by volume:

$$N_2 = 55 \text{ per cent}, \quad O_2 = 20 \text{ per cent}, \quad CH_4 = 25 \text{ per cent}.$$

If the partial pressure of CH_4 is 7.5 psia, determine
(a) The partial pressures of N_2 and O_2
(b) The mass proportions of the mixture
(c) R_{mixt} and the volume per mole of the mixture.

10.2 Five moles of a perfect gas mixture has the following mass analysis:

$$N_2 = 45 \text{ per cent}, He = 27 \text{ per cent}, \quad \text{and } C_6H_6 = 28 \text{ per cent}.$$

Find
(a) The analysis by volume and the number of moles of each constituent
(b) The molecular weight of the mixture
(c) The volume of the mixture at 50 psia and 70°F.

10.3 The analysis by weight of a perfect gas mixture at 70°F and 20 psia is 10 per cent oxygen, 70 per cent nitrogen, 15 per cent carbon dioxide, and 5 per cent carbon monoxide. Determine
(a) Partial pressures of the constituents (at 70°F and 20 psia)
(b) Gas constant of the mixture
(c) Enthalpy and internal energy of the mixture
(d) Constant pressure specific heat of the mixture
(e) Entropy of the mixture.
Use a reference state of 0°F and 1 atm for property calculations.

10.4 A rigid vessel has a volume of 1 ft³ and contains air at 14.7 psia and 70°F. Helium at 70°F is added to the vessel until the pressure is rasied to 20 psia. Compute
(a) The partial pressures of the final components of the mixture composed of oxygen, nitrogen, and helium
(b) The masses of the components of the mixture
(c) The gas constant of the mixture.

10.5 Prove that, for a reversible adiabatic process of a mixture of two gases a and b, the individual entropy change of a and b is zero subject to the condition that

$$\bar{c}_{p_a} = \bar{c}_{p_b} = \bar{c}_p .$$

Explain.

10.6 Two perfect gases initially have the following properties:

	Volume (ft³)	Pressure (psia)	Temperature (°F)
Gas A	2	15	60
Gas B	8	5	60

If these two gases are combined in a single vessel of 10 ft³ volume at a temperature of 60°F, what will be the pressure of the mixture?

10.7 Three perfect gases initially have the following properties:

	Volume (ft³)	Pressure (psia)	Temperature (°F)
N_2	2.5	35	60
O_2	6.0	10	120
H_2	10.0	100	20

If the foregoing gases are mixed adiabatically and equilibrium is attained, find
(a) The final temperature and pressure of the mixture
(b) The analysis by volume and mass
(c) The partial pressures and partial volumes of the constituents
(d) The change of entropy.

10.8 One lbm of O_2 at 10 psia and 100°F is mixed with 3 lbm of He at 10 psia and 200°F. If the volume of the mixture is equal to the sum of the volumes of the O_2 and He before mixing, compute
(a) The amount of heat necessary to raise the temperature of the mixture to 200°F at constant volume
(b) The entropy increase due to the mixing process only
(c) The entropy increase due to the heating process.

10.9 Compare the values of dp/dT for saturated water vapor at atmospheric pressure as obtained from the steam tables and the Clausius-Clapeyron equation.

10.10 Determine the pressure of water vapor at 200°F if h_{fg} is 977.9 Btu/lbm at this temperature. Compare your result with the steam tables.

10.11 The vapor pressure of a pure substance UDMH is given by the following equation. Assuming that the vapor behaves like a perfect gas, derive an expression of the enthalpy of vaporization. What is the value of h_{fg} at 70°F?

$$\log_{10} p = -\frac{2717.132}{T} - 6.745741 \log_{10} T + 28.000194$$

$$T \text{ in } °K, \quad p \text{ in mm Hg}, \quad R = 26 \text{ ft-lbf/lbm } °R.$$

10.12 Determine the enthalpy of vaporization for ammonia if the boiling point at 14.7 psia is −27°F and its vapor pressure at 0°F is 30.42 psia.

10.13 A constant-volume vessel of 10 ft³ capacity contains an air-water vapor mixture at 80°F and 60 per cent relative humidity.
(a) If the total pressure is 10 psia, calculate, without using charts, the specific humidity, R_{mix} and M_{mix}.
(b) Calculate, without using charts, the amount of water that should be injected into the vessel to obtain a relative humidity (RH) of 100 per cent at a temperature of 100°F.

10.14 A room with a capacity of 2000 ft³, contains atmospheric air at 80°F and 14.7 psia. If the specific humidity of the air is 0.01 of vapor per lbm of dry air, calculate

(a) The mass of water vapor in the room
(b) The relative humidity
(c) The vapor pressure
(d) The dew point.
Check the results by the psychrometric chart.

10.15 A 100 ft³ vessel contains a mixture of air and water vapor at 70°F and 14.7 psia. If the RH of the mixture is 70 per cent, find
(a) The specific humidity ω
(b) The vapor pressure
(c) The dew point and wet-bulb temperature
(d) The mass of vapor and air
(e) The equivalent gas constant
(f) The equivalent molecular weight
(g) If the mixture is cooled to 50°F in a constant-pressure process, find the amount of water condensed.

10.16 A water vapor-air mixture at 70°F db and 50 per cent RH is contained in a piston-cylinder device at a pressure of 29.92 in. Hg abs. It is desired to add steam to the cylinder by throttling from a 20 psia supply main until the mixture in the cylinder shows a dew point temperature of 75°F and a RH of 70 per cent, still maintaining the pressure of 29.92 in. Hg abs.
(a) How much steam must be added per lbm of dry air?
(b) What should be the quality of the steam that is supplied from the main?

10.17 A piston-cylinder container is filled with an air-vapor mixture under the following initial conditions:

Initial pressure   = 10 psia
Initial volume   = 8 cu ft
Initial temperature   = 50°F
Initial relative humidity = 60 per cent.

If this mixture is compressed adiabatically and reversibly ($pv^\gamma = C$) until the temperature reaches 120°F, determine
(a) Mass ratio of vapor to air
(b) Total pressure of mixture in final state
(c) Relative humidity in final state
(d) Dew point of mixture at final state.

$$c_p = 0.24 \text{ Btu/lbm°F} \quad \text{(air)}, \qquad c_p = 0.44 \text{ Btu/lbm°F} \quad \text{(vapor)}.$$

10.18 A mixture of air and water vapor is contained in a piston-cylinder arrangement under the following initial conditions:

Initial volume of the cylinder = 8 cu ft
Initial pressure   = 10 psia
Initial temperature   = 120°F
Initial relative humidity   = 20 per cent.

(a) Heat is transferred from the mixture at constant volume until the mixture temperature is reduced to 80°F. Calculate the amount of heat interaction during the process, and also the final pressure in the tank.

(b) Starting with the initial conditions just given, water vapor at 120°F is added adiabatically to the cylinder while maintaining a constant cylinder pressure of 10 psia until a final relative humidity of 50 per cent is obtained. What is the mass of water vapor added to the cylinder?

10.19 In a steady flow humidification process, water enters the humidifier at 70°F and air enters at 16.0 psia, 70°F, and a specific humidity of 0.01 lbm of vapor per lbm of dry air. The stream leaving the apparatus has a pressure of 15 psia, a temperature of 100°F, and a RH of 90 per cent. Calculate the amount of heat transfer to the humidifier per lbm of water evaporated.

10.20 Air at 130°F *db* and 80°F dew point, at 30 psia, is used in a drying process. Under steady-flow equilibrium conditions, the air enters the dryer at the rate of 10,000 lbm/hr and leaves at 80 per cent RH with no change in total pressure.
(a) How much moisture is picked up by the air in lbm/hr?
(b) What is the dry-bulb temperature of the leaving air?

10.21 Water flowing at rate of 5000 gallons per hour is to be cooled from 160°F to 90°F in a cooling tower. Atmospheric air at 100°F and 25 per cent RH is available for the cooling process. Assuming that the air leaves the cooling tower saturated with water vapor at 90°F, find the minimum air circulation rate and the make-up water per hour.

10.22 Air enters a cooling tower at 14.7 psia, 95°F, 55 per cent RH; the air leaves the tower at 90°F, and 95 per cent RH. Water is cooled from 100°F to 85°F in the tower. The water flow rate to the tower is 13.9 lbm/sec.
(a) What air flow rate (lbm/sec) is necessary?
(b) What fraction of the water evaporates?
(c) Could the desired cooling have been accomplished by simple heat transfer to the air in a heat exchanger? Explain.

NOMENCLATURE

a	Activity	T	Absolute temperature
c_p	Specific heat at constant pressure	V	Volume
c_v	Specific heat at constant volume	v	Specific volume
F	Helmholz function (free energy)	W	Thermodynamic probability
f	Fugacity	X	Property
G	Gibbs function (free energy)	ϵ	Energy per molecule
g	Gibbs function per unit mass	Z	Partition function
g	Degeneracy	z	Affinity
H_f	Enthalpy of formation	ϕ	Function
ΔH	Enthalpy of reaction	λ	Degree of advance of reaction
H	Enthalpy	ν	Stoichiometric coefficient
h	Enthalpy per unit mass	μ	Chemical potential
K	Equilibrium constant	α	Molal fraction dissociated
k	Boltzmann's constant	α, β	Lagrange's multipliers
M	Molecular weight	*Subscripts*	
m	Mass	a	Air
N	Number of molocules or atoms	f	Fuel
n	Number of moles or atoms	p	Products
p	Pressure	r	Reactants
Q	Heat	i, j	Refer to components i and j
q	Heat per unit mass	*Superscripts*	
ΔU	Internal energy of reaction	$(°)$	Denotes initial or standard value (77°F and 1 atm)
U	Internal energy		
u	Internal energy per unit mass	$(^-)$	Means per mole
$\mathscr{R}$	Universal gas constant	e	Denotes equilibrium
S	Entropy		

11

REACTIVE MIXTURES

11-1
Introduction
Thermodynamic relationships determine the equilibrium composition of product mixtures resulting from chemical reaction. The nature of the product species, their proportions, their temperature, and their pressure depend upon three major controlling factors. For one thing, the composition of the products of reaction is affected by material balance considerations. This requires that the total quantity of each chemical element in the product mixture be the same as that in the reactants.* We shall therefore consider the calculation of elemental composition of various mixtures and examine the laws of stoichiometry which apply in chemical reactions. Second, the resultant temperature and pressure of product mixtures depend upon the first law of thermodynamics. This dictates that the total energy be conserved, just as the total mass is. Hence this chapter gives attention to calculation of flame temperatures of combustible mixtures. Third, equilibrium composition is determined by relationships that arise indirectly from the second law of thermodynamics. The second law dictates that the composition of the products depends on temperature and pressure, whereas the first law indicates that the temperature and pressure of the products depend on their composition. Clearly, then, complex interactions are involved, and problems of calculation of product composition can be handled only by considering both laws simultaneously.

Although the principles outlined in this chapter apply to any chemical reaction, particular attention will be given to an important class of chemical reactions, the combustion processes. *Combustion* may be defined as a rapid exothermic reaction between a fuel and an oxidizer in which chemical energy is liberated.

11-2
Stoichiometry and the Chemical Equation
Chemical reactions are indicated in a compact form by means of chemical equations. The reaction of carbon monoxide and oxygen, for example, may be written as

$$CO(g) + \tfrac{1}{2} O_2(g) \rightleftharpoons CO_2(g). \qquad (11.1)$$

The substances at the beginning of the reaction are called *reactants*, whereas those resulting from the reaction are called *products*. The arrows indicate the direction of the reaction. At low temperatures, the preceding reaction proceeds from left to right; at high temperatures, the direction is reversed so that CO_2 tends to dissociate into CO and O_2. The letters in parentheses following each species in Eq. (11.1) identify the phases of the various substances, whether solid, liquid, or gas.

The proportions in which molecules of the reactants combine to form

*This discussion excludes nuclear reactions.

474

the products are also indicated in the chemical equation. In the preceding equation, 1 mole of CO combines with $\frac{1}{2}$ a mole of O_2 to form 1 mole of CO_2. In abbreviated form, the chemical equation may be written

$$\sum_{i=1}^{f} a_i A_i \rightleftharpoons \sum_{j=1}^{k} c_j C_j , \qquad (11.2)$$

where a_i and c_j are the relative molal proportions in which the various species A_i and C_j interact. The reactants and products in Eq. (11.2) are identified by subscripts $i = 1, 2 \ldots f$ and $j = 1, 2 \ldots k$ respectively. In a chemical reaction the total mass is conserved, although the total number of moles does not necessarily remain unchanged. Mass proportions are readily obtained from molal proportions by multiplying each component by its molecular weight.

In most combustion processes, air serves as the oxidizer. The ratio on a molal basis of nitrogen to oxygen in the atmosphere is approximately $0.7901/0.2099 = 3.76$; that is, every mole of oxygen is accompanied by 3.76 moles of nitrogen. On a mass basis, each lbm of oxygen is accompanied by 3.31 lbm ($= 0.768/0.232$) of atmospheric nitrogen. Although the nitrogen of the air does not contribute to the oxidation reactions, it leaves the reacting system at the same temperature as the products; consequently, its energy, on leaving as a product, is different from the energy it had at the entrance. This factor is taken into consideration in the energy balance of the combustion process.

The minimum amount of air required for the complete oxidation of a fuel is called the *theoretical* or *stoichiometric* air. The mass ratio of the fuel to the stoichiometric air is called the stoichiometric fuel-air ratio. The stoichiometric form of Eq. (11.2) is

$$\sum_{i=1}^{f} \nu_i A_i \rightleftharpoons \sum_{j=1}^{k} \nu_j C_j, \qquad (11.3)$$

where ν_i and ν_j are called *stoichiometric coefficients* of the species A_i and C_j. As an example, consider the chemical equation for the stoichiometric reaction of benzene with oxygen:

$$C_6H_6(l) + 7.5\ O_2(g) \longrightarrow 6\ CO_2(g) + 3\ H_2O(g).$$

Since each mole of oxygen, in air, is accompanied by 3.76 moles of nitrogen, the complete equation is

$$C_6H_6(l) + 7.5\ O_2(g) + 7.5(3.76)\ N_2(g) \longrightarrow$$
$$6\ CO_2(g) + 3\ H_2O(g) + 7.5(3.76)\ N_2(g),$$

or

$$C_6H_6(l) + 7.5\ O_2(g) + 28.2\ N_2(g) \longrightarrow$$

$$6\ CO_2(g) + 3\ H_2O(g) + 28.2\ N_2(g).$$

The preceding equation indicates that a minimum of 7.5 moles of O_2 accompanied by 28.2 moles of N_2 are necessary to oxidize completely 1 mole of C_6H_6 to form 6 moles of CO_2 and 3 moles of H_2O.

The amount of air actually supplied may exceed or be less than the theoretical amount required. If excess air is used, oxygen (gaseous) will appear in the products of combustion; if insufficient air is used, the combustion is incomplete and products, such as CO, CH_4, H_2, and unburned fuel, may also appear. In the previous example, if 20 per cent by volume excess air is supplied, the foregoing equation is written

$$C_6H_6(l) + 1.2(7.5)\ O_2(g) + 1.2(28.2)\ N_2(g) \longrightarrow$$

$$6\ CO_2(g) + 3\ H_2O(g) + 0.2(7.5)\ O_2(g) + 1.2(28.2)\ N_2(g).$$

In practice, some excess air is generally supplied in order to insure that no unburned fuel is contained in the products. On the other hand, a large amount of excess air is also avoided, because the additional oxygen and nitrogen absorb energy from the system, thus lowering the temperature of the combustion products, and consequently lowering the rate of heat transfer from the combustion products.

The fuel used in combustion may be solid, liquid, or gas. Oil and natural gas fuels in common use consist primarily of hydrocarbons. Liquid fuels are often classified in terms of the hydrogen-carbon mass ratio m_H/m_C, whereas natural gas fuels are specified in terms of the mole fractions of their constituents. A fuel often consists of many hydrocarbons, but it is convenient in many cases to express its formula in terms of an equivalent

TABLE 11.1 HYDROGEN-CARBON RATIOS BY ATOMS FOR SOME FUELS

Methane	CH_4	4.00	Natural gas	3.5
Ethene	C_2H_4	2.00	Gasoline	2.1
Ethane	C_2H_6	3.00	Kerosene	2.1
Propane	C_3H_8	2.67	Diesel fuel	1.8
Butane	C_4H_{10}	2.50	Heavy fuel oil	1.5
Benzene	C_6H_6	1.00	Bituminous coal	0.6
Hexane	C_6H_{14}	2.33	Crude oils	$1.6 \to 1.9$
Heptane	C_7H_{16}	2.28		
Octane	C_8H_{18}	2.25		
Decane	$C_{10}H_{22}$	2.20		
Cetane	$C_{16}H_{34}$	2.12		
Ethyl alcohol	C_2H_6O	3.00		

hydrogen-carbon ratio based on atomic quantities. Table 11.1 lists some fuels and their corresponding hydrogen-carbon ratios.

EXAMPLE 11.1: A natural gas has the following composition by volume:

Gas	Per Cent
Methane (CH₄)	67.4
Ethane (C₂H₆)	16.8
Propane (C₃H₈)	15.8

Calculate the equivalent hydrogen-carbon ratio for this gas by atoms and mass.

Solution

Constituent	Mole Fraction	Composition by Atoms	
		Carbon	Hydrogen
CH₄	0.674	0.674	2.696
C₂H₆	0.168	0.336	1.008
C₃H₈	0.158	0.474	1.264
Totals	1.000	1.484	4.968

The hydrogen-carbon ratio by atoms is $4.968/1.484 = 3.35$ atoms of hydrogen per atom of carbon. The combustion calculations can therefore be based on a hydrocarbon fuel with the chemical formula $C_{1.484} H_{4.968}$. The molal mass of the fuel is

$$1.484 \times 12 + 4.968 \times 1 = 22.788 \text{ lbm/lb-mole.}$$

The hydrogen-carbon ratio by mass is

$$\frac{m_H}{m_C} = \frac{4.968 \times 1}{1.484 \times 12} = 0.279 \text{ lbm of hydrogen/lbm of carbon.}$$

11-3
Typical
Problems

Problems in stoichiometry are divided into two main categories, depending on whether the composition of the fuel or the composition of the reaction products is known.

EXAMPLE 11.2: Determine the stoichiometric air required for the complete combustion of 1 lbm of normal heptane C_7H_{16}. What is the percentage analysis of the products on a mass and a molal basis?

Solution: The chemical equation is

$$C_7H_{16}(l) + 11 \, O_2(g) + 11(3.76) \, N_2(g) \rightarrow 7 \, CO_2(g) + 8 \, H_2O(g)$$
$$+ 11(3.76) \, N_2(g).$$

The air-fuel ratio on a mass basis is

$$\frac{(11 \times 32) + (11 \times 3.76 \times 28)}{(7 \times 12) + (16 \times 1.008)} = 15.12 \text{ lbm air/lbm fuel.}$$

Alternately, since there are $(11 + 11 \times 3.76)$ moles of air, the air-fuel ratio is

$$\frac{(11 + 11 \times 3.76)(28.97)}{(100.205)} = 15.12 \text{ lbm air/lbm fuel.}$$

The air-fuel ratio on a mole basis is

$$\frac{11 + 11 \times 3.76}{1} = 52.3 \text{ moles air/mole fuel.}$$

The analyses of the products on a mass and molal basis are as follows:

	By Mole			By Mass	
CO_2	7	12.42%	$7 \times 44 =$ 308	19.11%
H_2O	8	14.20%	$8 \times 18 =$ 144	8.94%
N_2	41.36	73.38%	$41.36 \times 28 =$ 1160	71.95%
Totals	56.36	100.00%	1612	100.00%

EXAMPLE 11.3:   Five moles of propane C_3H_8 are completely burned at atmospheric pressure in the theoretical amount of air. Determine

(a) The volume of air used in the combustion process measured at 14.7 psia and 77°F.

(b) The partial pressure of each constituent of the products.

(c) The volumetric analysis of the dry products.

Solution: (a) The chemical equation is

$$5 \, C_3H_8(g) + 25 \, O_2(g) + 25 \, (3.76) \, N_2(g) \rightarrow 15 \, CO_2(g) + 20 \, H_2O(g)$$
$$+ \, 25 \, (3.76) \, N_2(g),$$

or

$$5 \, C_3H_8(g) + 25 \, O_2(g) + 94.0 \, N_2(g) \rightarrow 15 \, CO_2(g) + 20 \, H_2O(g)$$
$$+ \, 94.0 \, N_2(g).$$

Thus, 25 moles of O_2 are required or $25 \, (1/0.2099) = 119$ moles of air, (25 moles of O_2 plus 94 moles of N_2).
If air is assumed a perfect gas, then

$$V = \frac{n \mathscr{R} T}{p} = \frac{119 \times 1545(77 + 460)}{14.7 \times 144} = 46700 \text{ ft}^3.$$

(b) The partial pressures of the product constituents are proportional to the mole fractions. Therefore,

$$p_{CO_2} = \frac{15}{15 + 20 + 94} \times 14.7 = 1.71 \text{ psia,}$$

$$p_{H_2O} = \frac{20}{129} \times 14.7 = 2.28 \text{ psia,}$$

$$p_{N_2} = \frac{94}{129} \times 14.7 = \underline{10.71 \text{ psia.}}$$

Total pressure $= 14.7$ psia.

(c) $\dfrac{V_{CO_2}}{V_{CO_2} + V_{N_2}} = \dfrac{15}{15 + 94} = 13.75$ per cent

$\dfrac{V_{N_2}}{V_{CO_2} + V_N} = 1 - 0.1375 = 86.25$ per cent.

EXAMPLE 11.4: The analysis of a sample of coal gives the following values by weight (the remainder is ash).

Carbon	80.7%
Hydrogen	4.9%
Sulfur	1.8%
Oxygen	5.3%
Nitrogen	1.1%

What is the air-fuel ratio by weight if 20 per cent excess air is used in the combustion process?

Solution: For 1 lbm of fuel, the following table can be formulated

	Number of Moles per lbm of Fuel	Moles of O_2 Required for Complete Combustion of 1 lbm of Fuel	Reaction Equation
C	$\dfrac{0.807}{12} = 0.0673$	0.0673	$0.0673 \text{ C}(s) + 0.0673 \text{ O}_2(g) \to 0.0673 \text{ CO}_2(g)$
H$_2$	$\dfrac{0.049}{2} = 0.0245$	0.01225	$0.0245 \text{ H}_2(g) + 0.01225 \text{ O}_2(g) \to 0.0245 \text{ H}_2\text{O}(g)$
S	$\dfrac{0.018}{32} = 0.000563$	0.000563	$0.000563 \text{ S}(s) + 0.000563 \text{ O}_2(g) \to 0.000563 \text{ SO}_2(g)$
O$_2$	$\dfrac{0.053}{32} = 0.001655$	0	
N$_2$	$\dfrac{0.011}{28} = 0.000393$	0	

O_2 required $= 0.080113$ mole
O_2 in fuel $\ \ = 0.001655$ mole
Difference $\ \ = 0.078458$ mole O_2 per lbm of fuel

Stoichiometric air-fuel ratio $= 0.078458(100/20.99) \times 28.97 = 10.83$ lbm air/lbm fuel.

With 20 per cent excess air, the air-fuel ratio is

$10.83 \times 1.2 = 13$ lbm air/lbm fuel.

EXAMPLE 11.5: The composition of a hydrocarbon fuel by mass is 85 per cent carbon, 13 per cent hydrogen, and 2 per cent oxygen. Determine

(a) The chemically correct mass of air required for the complete combustion of 1 lbm of fuel.

(b) The volumetric analysis of the products of combustion and the dew point if the total pressure is 14.7 psia.

(c) If the products of combustion are cooled to 60°F, what is the mass of the water vapor that condensed?

Solution: (a) Consider the combustion of 1 lbm of fuel composed of 0.85 lbm of carbon, 0.13 lbm of hydrogen, and 0.02 lbm of oxygen. In the complete combustion process the carbon oxidizes to CO_2 and the hydrogen to H_2O according to the equations

$$C(s) + O_2(g) \rightarrow CO_2(g)$$

$$H_2(g) + \tfrac{1}{2} O_2(g) \rightarrow H_2O(g).$$

The oxygen requirement as dictated by these two equations is, however, reduced by the amount of oxygen already existing in the fuel. The number of moles of

$$O_2 \text{ required} = \frac{0.85}{12.01} + \frac{0.13}{2.016 \times 2} - \frac{0.02}{32} = 0.07075 + 0.03225 - 0.000625$$

$$= 0.102375 \text{ mole of } O_2/\text{lbm of fuel,}$$

$$\text{mass of air} = \frac{0.102375}{0.2099} \times 28.97 = 14.1 \text{ lbm air/lbm fuel.}$$

(b) The analysis of the products of combustion by mass and volume is given in the accompanying table:

	Moles per lbm Fuel	lbm per lbm Fuel	Molal Analysis
CO_2	$\frac{0.85}{12.01} = 0.07075$	3.12	0.136
H_2O	$\frac{0.13}{2.016} = 0.0645$	1.16	0.124
N_2	$(3.76 \times 0.102375) = 0.385$	10.82	0.740
Totals	0.52025	15.1	1.000

The dew point temperature may be found from steam tables corresponding to the pressure of the water vapor in the combustion products:

Pressure of $H_2O = 0.124 \times 14.7 = 1.82$ psia.

Dew point $= 122.5°F.$

(c) Since 60°F is below the dew point temperature, some water vapor will condense. The vapor pressure is then equal to the saturation vapor pressure corresponding to 60°F.

From steam tables, $p_{v,\text{sat}}$ at 60°F $= 0.2563$ psia and $v_g = 1206.7$ ft^3/lbm. The volume occupied by the water vapor is equal to the volume occupied by the CO_2

and the N_2 at their partial pressure of $14.7 - 0.2563 = 14.4437$ psia. The volume according to the perfect gas law is

$$V = \frac{n\mathscr{R}T}{p} = \frac{(0.07075 + 0.385)1545 \times 520}{14.4437 \times 144} = 176.3 \text{ ft}^3.$$

Mass of vapor in products $= \dfrac{V}{v_g} = \dfrac{176.3}{1206.7} = 0.1462$ lbm.

Mass of vapor that condensed $= 1.16 - 0.1462 = 1.0138$ lbm.

EXAMPLE 11.6:   A hydrocarbon fuel in the vapor state is burned with atmospheric air at 14.7 psia, 80°F, and 60 per cent relative humidity. The volumetric analysis of the dry products of combustion is

Product	Percentage	
CO_2	10.00	
O_2	2.37	
CO	0.53	
N_2	87.10	(by difference from 100)
	100.00	

Calculate
   (a) Ratio of hydrogen to carbon by mass for the fuel
   (b) Air-fuel ratio by mass
   (c) Air used as percentage of the stoichiometric value
   (d) Volume of the humid air supplied per lbm of fuel.

Solution: (a) The following table gives the number of atoms of carbon, oxygen, and nitrogen per mole of dry products:

	Moles (per Mole of Dry Products)	Carbon	Oxygen	Nitrogen
CO_2	0.10	0.10	0.20	—
O_2	0.0237	—	0.0474	—
CO	0.0053	0.0053	0.0053	—
N_2	0.871	—	—	1.742
Totals	1.0000	0.1053	0.2527	1.742

Assuming that H_2O is the only remaining product of combustion, the amount of hydrogen in the fuel may be determined by finding the amount of oxygen used to form the H_2O.

Total moles of O_2 supplied with 0.871 mole of $N_2 = \dfrac{0.871}{3.76} = 0.231.$

Moles of O_2 accounted for in the reactions considered $= 0.12635.$
   Hence the difference used in formation of H_2O $= 0.10465$ moles
   of O_2.

The formation of H_2O can thus be expressed as

$$0.2093 \text{ H}_2(g) + 0.10465 \text{ O}_2(g) \rightarrow 0.2093 \text{ H}_2O(g),$$

which indicates that 0.2093 mole of H_2O is formed per mole of dry products. The hydrogen-carbon ratio in the fuel is

$$\frac{H}{C} = \frac{2 \times 0.2093}{0.1053} = 3.97 \quad \text{(by atoms)}$$

$$= \frac{(2 \times 0.2093) \times 1.008}{(0.1053) \times 12.01} = 0.333 \quad \text{(by weight)}.$$

(b) The air-fuel ratio $= \dfrac{[0.871 \times (1.0/0.79)]28.97}{(0.1053 \times 12.01) + (0.2093) \times 2.016}$

$$= \frac{31.95}{1.687} = 18.9 \text{ lbm air/lbm fuel}.$$

(c) The number of moles of oxygen required for stoichiometric combustion is

$$0.1053 \text{ C}(s) \ + 0.1053 \ \text{O}_2(g) \rightarrow 0.1053 \text{ CO}_2(g)$$

$$0.2093 \text{ H}_2(g) + 0.10465 \text{ O}_2(g) \rightarrow 0.2093 \text{ H}_2\text{O}(g)$$

$$\overline{ 0.20995 \text{ moles of O}_2 \text{ per mole of dry products.}}$$

Since the oxygen-air ratio is constant in atmospheric air, the percentage of the air supplied is the same as that of the oxygen. Hence the percentage of the stoichiometric air used is

$$\frac{0.231}{0.20995} = 1.1 \quad \text{or} \quad 110 \text{ per cent.}$$

(d) The number of moles of dry air is

$$0.87 \left(\frac{1}{0.79} \right) = 1.102 \text{ moles air/mole dry products, but the mass of fuel} = 1.687$$

lbm fuel/mole dry products. Therefore, the number of moles of air per lbm of fuel $= 1.102/1.687 = 0.653$.

At 80°F

$$p_{v,\text{sat}} = 0.5069 \text{ psia}$$

and

$$p_v = 0.6 \times 0.5069 = 0.30414 \text{ psia}.$$

Hence

$$V = \frac{n\mathscr{R}T}{p} = \frac{0.653 \times 1545.33 \times 540}{(14.7 - 0.30414) \times 144} = 263 \text{ ft}^3/\text{lbm of fuel}.$$

11-4
The Chemical
System and
Conservation
of Mass

The number of independent properties which define an equilibrium state of a chemical system depends on the number of parameters necessary to define the ambient medium of the system. Two independent properties, such as temperature and pressure, in addition to parameters indicative of the degree of the reaction are sufficient to define the state of a chemical system. The degree of chemical reaction may be indicated by the number of moles of each component, the chemical potential, or by a parameter λ called the *degree of advance of the chemical reaction*. If the latter is used, an equation defining the state of a chemical system may be written

$$\phi(p, T, \lambda) = 0. \tag{11.4}$$

The advance of the reaction varies from $0(\lambda = 0)$ at the beginning of a stoichiometric reaction to unity ($\lambda = 1.0$) upon termination of the reaction. Thus the advance of the reaction may be defined according to the following equations:

$$n_1 = n_1^\circ + \nu_1 \lambda$$
$$n_2 = n_2^\circ + \nu_2 \lambda$$
$$\cdot \qquad \cdot \qquad \cdot$$
$$n_r = n_r^\circ + \nu_r \lambda,$$

or, in terms of the ith component ($i = 1, 2 \ldots r$),

$$n_i = n_i^\circ + \nu_i \lambda, \tag{11.5}$$

where n_i is the number of moles of component i in the system when the advance of the reaction is λ, n_i° is the number of moles of component i at the beginning of the reaction, and ν_i is the number of moles of component i in the stoichiometric reaction.* Summation over all components of the reaction gives

$$\sum_{i=1}^{i=r} n_i = \sum_{i=1}^{i=r} n_i^\circ + \lambda \sum_{i=1}^{i=r} \nu_i,$$

or

$$n = n^\circ + \lambda \, \Delta\nu, \tag{11.6}$$

where

$$n = \sum_{i=1}^{i=r} n_i, \quad n^\circ = \sum_{i=1}^{i=r} n_i^\circ \quad \text{and} \quad \Delta\nu = \sum_{i=1}^{i=r} \nu_i.$$

At the beginning of the reaction, $\lambda = 0$ and $n_i = n_i^\circ$. As the reaction progresses, λ increases continuously until one of the reactants disappears and

*The value of ν_i, as expressed in Eq. (11.5), is positive for products and negative for reactants.

no further reaction takes place. Thus if component 1 disappears first, the maximum value of λ of the reaction is given by

$$\lambda_{\max} = -\frac{n_1^\circ}{\nu_1}. \tag{11.7}$$

The relation between the number of moles of the reactants can be obtained by differentiating Eq. (11.5). Thus the change in the number of moles of any component is given by

$$dn_i = \nu_i \, d\lambda, \tag{11.8}$$

and accordingly, the proportions of the species created or destroyed have the following relation

$$\frac{dn_1}{\nu_1} = \frac{dn_2}{\nu_2} = \frac{dn_3}{\nu_3} = \cdots = d\lambda. \tag{11.9}$$

The degree of advance of the reaction λ is a function of composition which may be expressed in terms of the number of moles $n_1, n_2, \ldots, n_r$ of the components of the system. Therefore at constant temperature and pressure, the differential of a property $X = X(p, T, \lambda)$ with respect to λ is

$$\left(\frac{\partial X}{\partial \lambda}\right)_{p,T} = \left(\frac{\partial X}{\partial n_1}\right)_{p,T} \frac{dn_1}{d\lambda} + \left(\frac{\partial X}{\partial n_2}\right)_{p,T} \frac{dn_2}{d\lambda} + \cdots + \left(\frac{\partial X}{\partial n_r}\right)_{p,T} \frac{dn_r}{d\lambda}.$$

But

$$\left(\frac{\partial X}{\partial n_i}\right)_{p,T} = \bar{x}_i \quad \text{and} \quad \frac{dn_i}{d\lambda} = \nu_i,$$

hence

$$\left(\frac{\partial X}{\partial \lambda}\right)_{p,T} = \bar{x}_1 \nu_1 + \bar{x}_2 \nu_2 + \cdots + \bar{x}_r \nu_r = \sum_{i=1}^{r} \bar{x}_i \nu_i. \tag{11.10}$$

Equation (11.10) expresses the change of a property X with respect to λ at constant p and T in terms of the molal properties and the stoichiometric number of moles of the components.

Equation (11.5), when multiplied by the molecular weight and summed up for all the components, gives the following equation in terms of the masses of the components:

$$\sum_{i=1}^{i=r} n_i M_i = \sum_{i=1}^{i=r} n_i^\circ M_i + \sum_{i=1}^{i=r} \nu_i M_i \lambda,$$

or

$$m = m^\circ + \sum_{i=1}^{i=r} \nu_i M_i \lambda. \tag{11.11}$$

Since the mass of the system is conserved during the chemical reaction, that is, $m = m^\circ$, it follows that

$$\sum_{i=1}^{i=r} \nu_i M_i \lambda = 0.$$

The foregoing equation is also independent of the value of λ, hence

$$\sum_{i=1}^{i=r} \nu_i M_i = 0, \tag{11.12}$$

which is a mass balance of the stoichiometric equation (11.3). Note that Eq. (11.12) substantiates the law of conservation of mass applicable to chemical reactions.

The foregoing relations were derived for a single reaction of one phase. For several reactions and phases, the procedure is to apply the preceding relations to each reaction and to every phase and to sum up the equations over all the reactions and phases. When phase change occurs as part of the reaction, the energy transfer due to phase change must be taken into consideration.

11-5
Enthalpy of
Formation

To establish an enthalpy scale for elements and compounds, it is first necessary to choose an arbitrary datum for zero enthalpy. It was conventionally agreed to assign a zero value to the enthalpy of elements in their most stable forms at a standard reference state of 1 standard atmospheric pressure and 25°C (77°F). If an element has two or more stable forms, that form which is stable at 25°C is chosen as reference. With this standard reference state established, enthalpies of all species have a common base. The *enthalpy of formation** of a compound is defined as the enthalpy change that accompanies the formation of 1 mole of the compound at the standard reference state from elements at the same state. The enthalpy of formation is given the symbol $\bar{h}_f^\circ$, where the subscript f refers to the formation of the compound from its elements, and superscript ($^\circ$) indicates that all reactants and products are at the standard state. Thus, if elements A, B, and C at atmospheric pressure and a temperature of 77°F combine to form compound $A_a B_b C_c$ at the same reference state, then the chemical equation can be written

*The term *heat of formation* is often used instead of enthalpy of formation.

$$aA(g) + bB(g) + cC(g) \rightarrow A_aB_bC_c(g).$$

An energy balance gives

$$a\bar{h}_A^\circ + b\bar{h}_B^\circ + c\bar{h}_C^\circ + \Delta\bar{h}_{p_o, T_o} \rightarrow \bar{h}_{A_aB_bC_c}^\circ,$$

TABLE 11.2   Enthalpy of Formation, Absolute Entropy,
and Gibbs Free Energy of Formation
(25°C (77°F) and 1 atm)

Substance	Symbol	State	$\bar{h}_f^\circ$ kcal* gm-mole	$\bar{s}^\circ$ cal gm-mole °K	$\bar{g}_f^\circ$ kcal gm-mole
Acetylene	C_2H_2	Gas	54.194	47.997	50.000
Ammonia	NH_3	Gas	−11.04	46.01	−3.976
Argon	A	Gas	0	36.983	0
Benzene	C_6H_6	Gas	19.820	64.34	30.989
n-Butane	C_4H_{10}	Gas	−30.15	74.12	−4.10
l-Butene	C_4H_8	Gas	−0.03	73.04	17.09
Carbon	C	Graphite	0	1.3609	0
		Gas	171.698	37.7611	160.845
Carbon dioxide	CO_2	Gas	−94.0518	51.061	−94.2598
Carbon monoxide	CO	Gas	−26.4157	47.300	−32.8077
Carbon tetrachloride	CCl_4	Gas	−25.5	73.95	−15.3
n-Dodecane	$C_{12}H_{26}$	Gas	−69.52	148.79	11.98
Ethane	C_2H_6	Gas	−20.236	54.85	−7.860
Ethylene	C_2H_4	Gas	12.496	52.45	16.282
Helium	He	Gas	0	30.126	0
n-Heptane	C_7H_{16}	Gas	−44.89	102.24	1.94
n-Hexane	C_6H_{14}	Gas	−39.96	92.83	−0.07
Hydrogen	H_2	Gas	0	31.211	0
Hydrogen sulfide	H_2S	Gas	−4.815	49.15	−7.892
Krypton	Kr	Gas	0	39.19	0
Mercury	Hg	Gas	14.54	41.80	7.59
Methane	CH_4	Gas	−17.889	44.50	−12.140
Neon	Ne	Gas	0	34.948	0
Nitric oxide	NO	Gas	21.600	50.339	20.719
Nitrogen	N_2	Gas	0	45.767	0
n-Octane	C_8H_{18}	Gas	−49.82	111.55	3.95
		Liquid	−59.74	86.23	1.58
Oxygen	O_2	Gas	0	49.003	0
n-Pentane	C_5H_{12}	Gas	−35.00	83.40	−2.00
Propane	C_3H_8	Gas	−24.820	64.51	−5.614
Sulfur dioxide	SO_2	Gas	−70.96	59.40	−71.79
Water	H_2O	Gas	−57.7979	45.106	−54.6351
		Liquid	−68.3174	16.716	−56.6899
Xenon	Xe	Gas	0	40.53	0

*1 cal/gm-mole = 1.8 Btu/lb-mole; 1 cal/gm-mole °K = 1 Btu/lb-mole °R.
SOURCE: Data from National Bureau of Standards Circ. 500, February, 1952,
and from API Research Project 44, National Bureau of Standards, Washington,
December, 1952, as adapted by E. F. Obert, *Concepts of Thermodynamics,*
McGraw-Hill Book Company, 1960.

where $\Delta \bar{h}_{p_o, T_o}$ is the enthalpy change at the standard reference state per mole of products. By definition, $\bar{h}_A^\circ$, $\bar{h}_B^\circ$, and $\bar{h}_C^\circ$ are zero, and therefore, the enthalpy of formation is equal to the enthalpy of the compound at the standard reference state, or

$$\bar{h}_f^\circ = \bar{h}_{A_a B_b C_c}^\circ = \Delta \bar{h}_{p_o, T_o}.$$

A positive value of $\bar{h}_f^\circ$ means that the enthalpy of formation of the compound is more than the enthalpy of its elements at the reference state. Such compounds are often unstable.

A compound at a temperature T above 77°F will then have an enthalpy equal to the sum of its enthalpy of formation plus the sensible enthalpy above the standard state, or

$$\bar{h} = \bar{h}_f^\circ + (\bar{h}_T - \bar{h}_{537}). \tag{11.13}$$

Table 11.2 gives enthalpies of formation for a number of substances. The table also shows values of absolute entropy and Gibbs function of formation discussed in Section 11.12.

**11-6
Enthalpy and
Internal
Energy of
Reaction**

Chemical energy is part of the internal energy of a system and is attributed to the binding energy between the atoms of the substance. In previous chapters, chemical reactions were not considered, and consequently, chemical energy was excluded. In this chapter, however, chemical energy constitutes the major part of the internal energy term in the first law.

In chemical reactions, one important concern is the amount of heat transfer due to the reaction. Two cases will be considered: (1) when the reaction takes place at constant pressure, (2) when it takes place at constant volume. Consider first, the constant-pressure process.

If no work other than reversible work is done, the first law of thermodynamics applied to a closed system is

$$dQ = dH - V\,dp.$$

The differential of the enthalpy $H = H(p, T, \lambda)$ is

$$dH = \left(\frac{\partial H}{\partial p}\right)_{T,\lambda} dp + \left(\frac{\partial H}{\partial T}\right)_{p,\lambda} dT + \left(\frac{\partial H}{\partial \lambda}\right)_{p,T} d\lambda.$$

Substituting in the first law and letting $dp = 0$ for a constant-pressure process, yields

$$dQ_p = \left(\frac{\partial H}{\partial T}\right)_{p,\lambda} dT + \left(\frac{\partial H}{\partial \lambda}\right)_{p,T} d\lambda.$$

The coefficient of dT,

$$\left(\frac{\partial H}{\partial T}\right)_{p,\lambda} = (n\bar{c}_p)_\lambda,$$

where $\bar{c}_p$ is the specific heat per mole at constant pressure. The coefficient of $d\lambda$, $(\partial H/\partial \lambda)_{p,T}$ is called the *enthalpy of reaction* and is given the symbol $\Delta H_{p,T}$. It is equal to the amount of heat interaction when the reaction is carried out at constant pressure with no change in temperature. Therefore,

$$dQ_p = (n\bar{c}_p)_\lambda \, dT + \Delta H_{p,T} \, d\lambda.$$

Integrating the foregoing equation between a reference state (o) and any other state, gives

$$Q_p = \int_{T_o}^{T} (n\bar{c}_p)_\lambda \, dT + \int_{\lambda_o}^{\lambda} \Delta H_{p,T} \, d\lambda. \tag{11.14}$$

If the reaction is stoichiometric where λ changes from 0 to 1, and if, further, the temperature at the end of the reaction is equal to the temperature at the beginning of the reaction, then

$$Q_p = \int_0^1 \Delta H_{p,T} \, d\lambda = \Delta H_{p,T}, \tag{11.15}$$

which means that the heat interaction is equal to the enthalpy of reaction subject to the conditions previously stated. According to Eq. (11.10),

$$\Delta H_{p,T} = \left(\frac{\partial H}{\partial \lambda}\right)_{p,T} = \sum_i \nu_i \bar{h}_i = (\sum_i \nu_i \bar{h}_i)_p - (\sum_i \nu_i \bar{h}_i)_r, \tag{11.16}$$

where subscripts r and p on the right-hand side of Eq. (11.16) refer to reactants and products, respectively. In the case of *exothermic** reaction, $\Delta H_{p,T}$ is negative and

$$(\sum_i \nu_i \bar{h}_i)_p < (\sum_i \nu_i \bar{h}_i)_r.$$

Similarly, if $H_{p,T}$ is positive, the reaction is *endothermic* and

$$(\sum_i \nu_i \bar{h}_i)_p > (\sum_i \nu_i \bar{h}_i)_r.$$

---

*A reaction in which heat interaction is negative is called *exothermic*; a reaction in which heat interaction is positive is called *endothermic*.

The second case to be considered is the constant-volume process. The procedure is analogous to the constant-pressure case. The first law applied to a closed system when only reversible work is involved is

$$dQ = dU + p\,dV.$$

The differential of $U = U(V, T, \lambda)$ is

$$dU = \left(\frac{\partial U}{\partial V}\right)_{T,\lambda} dV + \left(\frac{\partial U}{\partial T}\right)_{V,\lambda} dT + \left(\frac{\partial U}{\partial \lambda}\right)_{V,T} d\lambda.$$

Substituting for dU in the first law and considering constant volume, then

$$dQ_V = \left(\frac{\partial U}{\partial T}\right)_{V,\lambda} dT + \left(\frac{\partial U}{\partial \lambda}\right)_{V,T} d\lambda,$$

where $(\partial U/\partial T)_{V,\lambda} = (n\bar{c}_v)_\lambda$, $\bar{c}_v$ being the specific heat per mole at constant volume, and $(\partial U/\partial \lambda)_{V,T} = \Delta U_{V,T}$ is called the *internal energy of the reaction*.

Therefore,

$$dQ_V = (n\bar{c}_v)_\lambda\, dT + \Delta U_{V,T}\, d\lambda, \tag{11.17}$$

where $\Delta U_{V,T}$, according to Eq. (11.10), is given by

$$\Delta U_{V,T} = \left(\frac{\partial U}{\partial \lambda}\right)_{V,T} = \sum_i \nu_i \bar{u}_i = \left(\sum_i \nu_i \bar{u}_i\right)_p - \left(\sum_i \nu_i \bar{u}_i\right)_r. \tag{11.18}$$

The relation between $\Delta H_{p,T}$ and $\Delta U_{V,T}$ is obtained as follows:

$$\Delta H_{p,T} = \left[\sum_i \nu_i(\bar{u}_i + p_i \bar{v}_i)\right]_p - \left[\sum_i \nu_i(\bar{u}_i + p_i \bar{v}_i)\right]_r$$

$$= \left[\left(\sum_i \nu_i \bar{u}_i\right)_p - \left(\sum_i \nu_i \bar{u}_i\right)_r\right] + \left[\sum_i \nu_i p_i \bar{v}_i\right]_p - \left[\sum_i \nu_i p_i \bar{v}_i\right]_r$$

$$= \Delta U_{V,T} + \left[\sum_i \nu_i p_i \bar{v}_i\right]_p - \left[\sum_i \nu_i p_i \bar{v}_i\right]_r.$$

In the case of reactions involving liquids and solids, the changes in volume are small and can be neglected in comparison to gaseous substances in the reaction. If, further, the gaseous reactants and products are considered perfect gases, then $p_i \bar{v}_i = \mathcal{R}T$. Therefore,

$$\Delta H_{p,T} = \Delta U_{V,T} + \mathcal{R}T \sum_i (\nu_{i_p} - \nu_{i_r}). \tag{11.19}$$

Note that the term in parentheses is the change in the number of moles due to the reaction. Therefore, $\Delta H_{p,T} = \Delta U_{V,T}$ if there is no change in the number of moles of the gaseous substances due to the reaction.

EXAMPLE 11.7: The chemical equation for n-octane when burned with oxygen at 77°F is

$$C_8H_{18} \, (l) + 12.5 \, O_2(g) \rightarrow 8 \, CO_2 \, (g) + 9 \, H_2O(g).$$

If the enthalpy of reaction at constant pressure $\Delta H_{p,T} = -19{,}256$ Btu/lbm, calculate the internal energy of reaction. Assume all gases to be perfect.

Solution: Neglecting the volume occupied by liquid octane, the change of number of moles is

$$\sum_i \nu_i = (9 + 8) - 12.5 = 4.5 \text{ moles}.$$

Using Eq. (11.19),

$$\Delta U_{V,T} = \Delta H_{p,T} - \mathcal{R}T(4.5)$$

$$= -19256 - \frac{1.986 \times 537 \times 4.5}{114}$$

$$= -19256 - 43 = -19299 \text{ Btu/lbm}.$$

**11-7
Enthalpy of
Reaction at the
Standard State** The change of enthalpy in a chemical reaction depends only on the initial and final states of the system. The difference between the energy of the reactants and products is equal to the energy released during the reaction. As mentioned in Section 11-5, a standard state ($p_o = 1$ atm, $T_o = 537°$R) is chosen as a basis for comparison. A more appropriate standard state would be at $0°$R, but difficulties in measurement at or near such temperature have excluded this possibility. The enthalpy of the reaction at the standard state is equal to the difference between the enthalpies of the reactants and products measured at the standard state, or

$$\Delta H° = (\sum_i \nu_i \bar{h}_i°)_p - (\sum_i \nu_i \bar{h}_i°)_r. \tag{11.20}$$

Thus $\Delta H°$ is in effect a comparison between the enthalpies of the reactants and products at the standard state. A negative sign in front of $\Delta H°$ means that the enthalpy of the products is less than that of the reactants (exothermic reaction) which is typical in combustion processes. Table 11.3 gives enthalpies of combustion of some hydrocarbon fuels.

The enthalpy of reaction can, in many cases, be measured by direct calorimetry. It may also be calculated from the enthalpies of formation according to the equation

$$\Delta H° = \sum (H_f°)_p - \sum (H_f°)_r, \tag{11.21}$$

which states that the enthalpy of reaction $\Delta H°$ is equal to the difference between the enthalpies of formation of all the products and all the reactants.

TABLE 11.3 Enthalpy of combustion $(-\Delta H^\circ$ at 77°F)

Substance	Symbol	Enthalpy of Vaporization h_{fg}, (Btu/lbm)	$H_2O(l)$ and $CO_2(g)$		$H_2O(g)$ and $CO_2(g)$	
			$\dfrac{kcal}{gm\text{-}mole}$	$\dfrac{Btu}{lbm}$	$\dfrac{kcal}{gm\text{-}mole}$	$\dfrac{Btu}{lbm}$
Acetylene	$C_2H_2(g)$	—	310.62	21,460	300.10	20,734
Benzene	$C_6H_6(g)$	186	789.08	18,172	757.52	17,446
n-Butane	$C_4H_{10}(g)$	156	687.65	21,283	635.05	19,655
Isobutane	$C_4H_{10}(g)$	141	685.65	21,221	633.05	19,593
l-Butene	$C_4H_8(g)$	156	649.45	20,824	607.37	19,475
Carbon	C(graphite)	—	94.0518	14,086		
Carbon monoxide	$CO(g)$	—	67.6361	4,343.6		
n-Decane	$C_{10}H_{22}(g)$	155	1632.34	20,638	1516.63	10,175
n-Dodecane	$C_{12}H_{26}(g)$	155	1947.23	20,564	1810.48	19,120
Ethane	$C_2H_6(g)$	—	372.82	22,304	341.26	20,416
Ethylene	$C_2H_4(g)$	—	337.23	21,625	316.20	20,276
n-Heptane	$C_7H_{16}(g)$	157	1160.01	20,825	1075.85	19,314
n-Hexane	$C_6H_{14}(g)$	157	1002.57	20,928	928.93	19,391
Hydrogen	$H_2(g)$	—	68.3174	60,957	57.7979	51,571
Methane	$CH_4(g)$	—	212.80	23,861	191.76	21,502
n-Nonane	$C_9H_{20}(g)$	156	1474.90	20,687	1369.70	19,211
n-Octane	$C_8H_{18}(g)$	156	1317.45	20,747	1222.77	19,256
n-Pentane	$C_5H_{12}(g)$	157	845.16	21,072	782.04	19,499
Isopentane	$C_5H_{12}(g)$	147	843.24	21,025	780.12	19,451
Propane	$C_3H_8(g)$	147	530.6	21,646	488.53	19,929
Propylane	$C_3H_6(g)$	—	491.99	21,032	460.43	19,683

SOURCE: Data from API Research Project 44, National Bureau of Standards, Washington, December, 1952, as adapted by E. F. Obert, *Concepts of Thermodynamics,* McGraw-Hill Book Company, 1960.

At any temperature T, other than the standard temperature $(T_o = 537°R)$, the enthalpy of reaction ΔH_T depends on the temperature of the reaction. Consider the change of state of a chemical system at atmospheric pressure from state 1 to state 2; first along path a and second along paths b, c, and d as shown in Fig. 11.1. States 1 and 2 are at $T_o = 537°R$ and 3

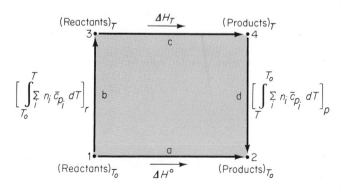

Fig. 11.1. *Evaluation of ΔH_T at a temperature other than T.*

and 4 are at temperature T. The process along path a is the conversion of the reactants to products at a temperature $537°R$. The enthalpy of reaction is $\Delta H°$ and may be computed from Eq. (11.21). Since the change of enthalpy is independent of the path, the same result may be obtained by changing the state of the system from state 1 to state 2 along paths b, c, and d. The changes of enthalpies along these processes are given by

$$\left(\int_{T_o}^{T} \sum_i n_i \bar{c}_{p_i} \, dT \right)_r, \quad \Delta H_T \quad \text{and} \quad \left(\int_{T}^{T_o} \sum_i n_i \bar{c}_{p_i} \, dT \right)_p.$$

Hence

$$\Delta H_T = [\sum_i (n_i \bar{h}°_{f_i})_p - \sum_i (n_i \bar{h}°_{f_i})_r]$$

$$- \left(\int_{T_o}^{T} \sum_i n_i \bar{c}_{p_i} \, dT \right)_r - \left(\int_{T}^{T_o} \sum_i n_i \bar{c}_{p_i} \, dT \right)_p$$

$$= \sum_i \left(n_i \bar{h}°_{f_i} + \int_{T_o}^{T} n_i \bar{c}_{p_i} \, dT \right)_p - \sum_i \left(n_i \bar{h}°_{f_i} + \int_{T_o}^{T} n_i \bar{c}_{p_i} \, dT \right)_r.$$

$$(11.22)$$

A term in common usage in combustion processes is the *heating value* of a fuel. It is equal to the enthalpy of combustion but of opposite sign. The heating value is a positive number. There are two types of heating values, depending on the phase of the water formed in the products of combustion. The *higher heating* value (HHV) is measured when all the water vapor is condensed at the reference temperature T_o. If the water is in the vapor state, the *lower heating value* (LHV) is measured. The relation between these two values is

$$LHV = HHV - m_{H_2O} h°_{fg} = HHV - (1050.4)_{77°F} m_{H_2O}, \qquad (11.23)$$

where m_{H_2O} is the mass of the water vapor in the products per lbm of fuel and the heating values are in Btu/lbm of fuel.

EXAMPLE 11.8:   Find the heat interaction when propane $C_3H_8(g)$ is burned according to the chemical equation

$$C_3H_8(g) + 5 O_2(g) \rightarrow 3 CO_2(g) + 4 H_2O(l).$$

Assume both reactants and products are at a pressure of 1 atm and 77°F. All gaseous components follow the perfect gas law.

Solution: The enthalpies of formation for the reactants and products are

$$(H°_f)_r = (\bar{h}°_f)_{C_3H_8} + 5 (\bar{h}°_f)_{O_2} = -44,676 + 0 = -44,676 \text{ Btu},$$

$$(H_f^\circ)_p = 3\,(\bar{h}_f^\circ)_{CO_2} + 4\,(\bar{h}_f^\circ)_{H_2O} = 3(-169,293) + 4(-122,971) = -999,762 \text{ Btu.}$$

The heat interaction in this case is equal to the difference between the enthalpy of formation of the products and reactants, and is given by

$$\Delta H^\circ = Q_{p_0,\,T_0} = (H_f^\circ)_p - (H_f^\circ)_r = -999,762 - (-44,676)$$
$$= -955,087 \text{ Btu/lb-mole of propane.}$$

EXAMPLE 11.9: Calculate the enthalpy of reaction at the standard state of benzene C_6H_6 when it reacts with oxygen at $77°F$ to form carbon dioxide and liquid water.

Solution: $C_6H_6(l) + 7.5\,O_2(g) \rightarrow 6\,CO_2(g) + 3\,H_2O(l).$

The enthalpies of formation of the different species, according to Table 11.2, are

$(H_f^\circ)_{C_6H_6} = 35,630 \text{ Btu/lb-mole}$

$(H_f^\circ)_{O_2} = 0$

$(H_f^\circ)_{CO_2} = -169,293 \text{ Btu/lb-mole}$

$(H_f^\circ)_{H_2O} = -122,971 \text{ Btu/lb-mole.}$

Therefore,

$$\Delta H^\circ = \sum (H_f^\circ)_p - \sum(H_f^\circ)_r$$
$$= [6(-169,293) + 3(-122,971)] - [35,630]$$
$$= -1,420,291 \text{ Btu/lb-mole of } C_6H_6.$$

EXAMPLE 11.10: Calculate the enthalpy of formation of n-heptane if the enthalpy of combustion is $\Delta H^\circ = -1160.01$ kcal/gm-mole.

Solution: The combustion equation is

$$C_7H_{16}(g) + 11\,O_2(g) \rightarrow 7\,CO_2(g) + 8\,H_2O(l) \qquad \Delta H^\circ = -1160.01$$
$$\text{kcal/gm-mole.}$$

$$\Delta H^\circ = -1160.01 = 7\bar{h}_{f_{CO_2}}^\circ + 8\bar{h}_{f_{H_2O}}^\circ - \bar{h}_{f_{C_7H_{16}}}^\circ$$
$$= 7(-94.0518) + 8(-68.3174) - \bar{h}_{f_{C_7H_{16}}}^\circ \,.$$

From which $\bar{h}_{f_{C_7H_{16}}}^\circ = -44.8918$ kcal/gm-mole,

which agrees with the value given in Table 11.2.

EXAMPLE 11.11: The enthalpy of combustion of n-octane when the water formed in the products is in the liquid phase is $-20,747$ Btu/lbm (Table 11.3).

What is the value of the enthalpy of combustion if the water in the products remains in the vapor phase?

Solution: The combustion equation is

$$C_8H_{18}(g) + 12.5\,O_2(g) \to 8\,CO_2(g) + 9\,H_2O(l) \quad \Delta H^\circ = -20{,}747 \text{ Btu/lbm}.$$

The difference between the two values of enthalpies of combustion per lbm of fuel is equal to the amount of H_2O formed per lbm of fuel multiplied by its enthalpy of vaporization.

$$\text{mass of } H_2O = \frac{9(18)}{8 \times 12 + 18(1)} = \frac{162}{114} = 1.42 \text{ lbm/lbm of fuel}$$

Therefore,

$$-\Delta H^\circ \text{ with } H_2O(g) = 20{,}747 - 1.42\,(1050.4)_{77^\circ F}$$
$$= 20{,}747 - 1{,}490 = 19{,}257 \text{ Btu/lbm}.$$

This checks with the value given in Table 11.3.

11-8
First Law
Applied to
Chemical
Reactions

With the preceding definition of the standard state, the enthalpy of formation, and enthalpy of reaction, the first law may be expressed in the form of Eq. (3.49) as

$$\left[\sum_i \nu_i(\bar{h}_i - \bar{h}_i^\circ)\right]_r + Q + W + (-\Delta H^\circ) = \left[\sum_i \nu_i(\bar{h}_i - \bar{h}_i^\circ)\right]_p, \tag{11.24}$$

and on a mass basis

$$\left[\sum_i m_i(h_i - h_i^\circ)\right]_r + Q + W + (-\Delta H^\circ) = \left[\sum_i m_i(h_i - h_i^\circ)\right]_p. \tag{11.25}$$

Gas tables* which take variations of specific heats into consideration may be conveniently used to determine the enthalpies of the species, as the following example illustrates.

EXAMPLE 11.12: One lbm of $C_7H_{16}(g)$ at 77°F is burned with 100 per cent excess air at 120°F in a constant-pressure steady-flow process. If the products of combustion leave at 700°F, determine the amount of heat transferred.

Solution: The chemical equation of the reaction is

$$C_7H_{16}(g) + 2(11)\,O_2(g) + 2(11 \times 3.76)\,N_2(g) \to 7\,CO_2(g) + 8\,H_2O(g)$$
$$+ 2(11 \times 3.76)\,N_2(g) + 11\,O_2(g),$$

*J. H. Keenan and J. Kaye, *Gas Tables*, New York: John Wiley & Sons, Inc., 1948.

or

$$C_7H_{16}(g) + 22\,O_2(g) + 82.72\,N_2(g) \rightarrow 7\,CO_2(g) + 8\,H_2O(g)$$
$$+ 82.72\,N_2(g) + 11\,O_2(g).$$

Neglecting changes in kinetic and potential energy, the amount of heat transferred to the chemical system is given by the first law, according to the relation $Q = H_p - H_r$.

$$H_r = (\bar{h}_f^\circ)_{C_7H_{16}(g)} + 22(\bar{h}_{120} - \bar{h}_{77})_{O_2} + 82.72(\bar{h}_{120} - \bar{h}_{77})_{N_2}$$
$$= -80,900 + 22(4027 - 3725)_{O_2} + 82.72(4028 - 3730)_{N_2}$$
$$= -80,900 + 6640 + 24,650 = -49,610 \text{ Btu/lb-mole of fuel.}$$

$$H_p = 7(\bar{h}_f^\circ + \bar{h}_{700} - \bar{h}_{77})_{CO_2} + 8(\bar{h}_f^\circ + \bar{h}_{700} - \bar{h}_{77})_{H_2O}$$
$$+ 82.72(\bar{h}_{700} - \bar{h}_{77})_{N_2} + 11(\bar{h}_{700} - \bar{h}_{77})_{O_2}$$
$$= 7(-169,293 + 10,490 - 4030) + 8(-104,071 + 9467 - 4258)$$
$$+ 82.72(8129 - 3725) + 11(8314 - 3730)$$
$$= -1,516,303 \text{ Btu/lb-mole of fuel.}$$

H_p can also be calculated from Keenan and Kaye, *Gas Tables* (Table 7) as

$$H_p = 7(-169,293) + 8(-104,071) + (7 + 8 + 82.72 + 11)(\bar{h}_{700} - \bar{h}_{77})_p$$
$$= -1,185,051 - 832,568 + 108.72(8375 - 3774)$$
$$= -1,517,619 \text{ Btu/lb-mole of fuel.}$$

Therefore,

$$Q = -1,516,303 + 49,610 = -1,466,693 \text{ Btu/lb-mole of fuel.}$$

11-9
Adiabatic
Reaction
Temperature

Under adiabatic conditions, the temperature attained in a reaction is called the *adiabatic reaction* (or *flame*) *temperature*. In actual processes the combustion temperature is considerably less, owing to the inevitable heat interaction with the environment. Also, some of the reactants may fail to react, or may decompose only partially. Dissociation of the products of combustion also results in a further reduction of the combustion temperature. The adiabatic reaction temperature is an upper limit of temperature and therefore is a useful parameter in the design of combustion chambers.

The adiabatic reaction temperature may be determined from the first law which reduces to

$$\Sigma\,H_r = \Sigma\,H_p. \tag{11.26}$$

The following example illustrates the use of Eq. (11.26).

EXAMPLE 11.13: Calculate the adiabatic reaction temperature of $C_7H_{16}(g)$ when burned with 100 per cent excess air at atmospheric pressure. Assume no dissociation and the reactants to be at 77°F.

Solution: The chemical equation is

$$C_7H_{16}(g) + 22\ O_2(g) + 82.72\ N_2(g) \rightarrow 7\ CO_2(g) + 8\ H_2O(g)$$
$$+ 82.72\ N_2(g) + 11\ O_2(g).$$

Several methods of solving this problem will be presented. The adiabatic reaction temperature will be computed, making use of (a) gas tables for 200 per cent theoretical air; (b) enthalpy of formation; (c) enthalpy of combustion; (d) specific heat equations.

(a) $\sum H_r = -\Delta H° = 19,314$ Btu/lbm of fuel

$$= 19,314 \times 100 = 1,931,400 \text{ Btu/lb-mole of fuel}$$

$$\sum H_p = [\sum_i (n_i h_i)_T - \sum_i (n_i h_i)_{77}]_p.$$

Therefore,

$$1,931,400 = (7 + 8 + 82.72 + 11)(\bar{h}_T - \bar{h}_{77})_p.$$

But from Table 7 of the gas tables, at 77°F, $\bar{h}_{77} = 3774$ Btu/lb-mole of products.

Therefore,

$$\bar{h}_T = 3774 + \frac{1.931.400}{108.72} = 3774 + 17,770$$

$$= 21,544 \text{ Btu/lb-mole of fuel.}$$

From gas tables, the temperature corresponding to this value of $\bar{h}_T$ is

$$T_{\text{products}} = 2728°R.$$

(b) If enthalpies of formation are used, then

$$\sum H_r = (\bar{h}_f°)_{C_7H_{16}(g)} = -80,900 \text{ Btu/lb-mole of fuel}$$
$$H_p = 7(\bar{h}_f° + \bar{h}_T - \bar{h}_{77})_{CO_2} + 8(\bar{h}_f° + \bar{h}_T - \bar{h}_{77})_{H_2O}$$
$$+ 82.72(\bar{h}_T - \bar{h}_{77})_{N_2} + 11(\bar{h}_T - \bar{h}_{77})_{O_2}$$
$$= 7(-169,293 + \bar{h}_{T_{CO_2}} - 4030) + 8(-104,071 + \bar{h}_{T_{H_2O}} - 4258)$$
$$+ 82.72(\bar{h}_{T_{N_2}} - 3736) + 11(\bar{h}_{T_{O_2}} - 3725).$$

Assuming $T = 2728°R$ as found in part (a), gives

$$\sum H_p = 7(30,973 - 173,323) + 8(25,272 - 108,329)$$
$$+ 82.72(20,480 - 3,736) + 11(21,428 - 3,725)$$
$$= 2827 \text{ Btu/lb-mole of fuel as compared to } -80,900.$$

Assume $T = 2700°R$

$$\sum H_p = 7(30,581 - 173,323) + 8(24,957 - 108,329)$$
$$+ 82.72(20,246 - 3,736) + 11(21,183 - 3,725)$$
$$= -108,132 \text{ as compared to } -80,900.$$

Assume $T = 2710°R$

$$\sum H_p = 7(30,721 - 173,323) + 8(25,070 - 108,329)$$
$$+ 82.72(20,430 - 3,736) + 11(21,270 - 3,725)$$
$$= -91,281 \text{ Btu/lb-mole of fuel.}$$

From the preceding trials, a good approximation of T is $2712°R$.

(c) If the enthalpy of combustion is used, then

$$\sum H_r = -\Delta H° = 19,314 \text{ Btu/lbm of fuel}$$
$$= 19,314 \times 100 = 1,931,400 \text{ Btu/lb-mole of fuel.}$$
$$\sum H_p = 7(\bar{h}_T - \bar{h}_{77})_{CO_2} + 8(\bar{h}_T - \bar{h}_{77})_{H_2O} + 82.72(\bar{h}_T - \bar{h}_{77})_{N_2}$$
$$+ 11(\bar{h}_T - \bar{h}_{77})_{O_2}.$$

Assuming a temperature $T = 2710°R$ gives

$$\sum H_p = 7(30,721 - 4,030) + 8(25,070 - 4,258)$$
$$+ 82.72(20,430 - 3,736) + 11(21,270 - 3,736)$$
$$= 186,837 + 166,496 + 1,380,000 + 192,995$$
$$= 1,906,328 \text{ Btu/lb-mole of fuel as compared to } 1,931,400.$$

Note that this method utilizes the enthalpy of combustion as compared to method (b) where the enthalpies of formation are used. The relation between these enthalpies, according to Eq. (11.21), is clearly

$$\Delta H° = \sum (\Delta H°_f)_p - \sum (\Delta H°_f)_r$$

or

$$-1,931,400 = [7(-169,293) + 8(-104,071)] - [-80,900].$$

The slight difference between the two sides of the previous equation is due to different sources of enthalpies of combustion and of formation. Method (c), therefore, should give the same result as method (b), that is, $T = 2712°R$.

(d) If the constant-pressure specific heat equations are used, then

$$\sum H_r = -\Delta H° = 1,931,400 \text{ Btu/lb-mole of fuel.}$$

$$\sum H_p = 7 \int_{537}^{T} \bar{c}_{p_{CO_2}} \, dT + 8 \int_{537}^{T} \bar{c}_{p_{H_2O}} \, dT + 82.72 \int_{537}^{T} \bar{c}_{p_{N_2}} \, dT$$
$$+ 11 \int_{537}^{T} \bar{c}_{p_{O_2}} \, dT.$$

Substituting for the values of $\bar{c}_p$ (Table A.3, Appendix) gives

$$\sum H_p = 7 \int_{537}^{T} \left(16.2 - \frac{6.53 \times 10^3}{T} + \frac{1.41 \times 10^6}{T^2}\right) dT$$

$$+ 8 \int_{537}^{T} \left(19.86 - \frac{597}{\sqrt{T}} + \frac{7500}{T}\right) dT$$

$$+ 82.72 \int_{537}^{T} \left(9.47 - \frac{3.47 \times 10^3}{T} + \frac{1.16 \times 10^6}{T^2}\right) dT$$

$$+ 11 \int_{537}^{T} \left(11.515 - \frac{172}{\sqrt{T}} + \frac{1530}{T}\right) dT.$$

Assuming values of T, $\sum H_p$ can be evaluated and should be equal to $\sum H_r$ at the correct T. This calculation leads to a value of T not much different from those determined by the previous methods. (The check is left to the student as an exercise.)

11-10 Second Law Applied to Chemical Reactions

The second law of thermodynamics dictates that the entropy of an isolated system can never decrease; it may increase or remain unchanged. The equilibrium composition of an isolated system corresponds to the state of maximum entropy subject to the imposed constraints on the variation of the system. Therefore, as explained in Chapter 5, entropy can be used as a criterion of equilibrium for an isolated system.

Chemical reactions generally take place while the system is in contact with an enivronment at constant pressure and temperature. Furthermore, chemical reactions are not restricted to isolated systems. Therefore, entropy is not a readily applicable criterion to determine equilibrium compositions under these conditions. The Gibbs function (free energy) fills this gap and may be used to predict the spontaneity of chemical processes as well as their equilibrium compositions. As explained in Chapter 5, the spontaneity of a chemical reaction at constant temperature and pressure is associated with a decrease in the Gibbs function such that

$$(\Delta G)_{p,T} = (G_2 - G_1)_{p,T} < 0. \tag{11.27}$$

The equilibrium state corresponds to a minimum value of Gibbs function, so that

$$(dG)_{p,T} = 0. \tag{11.28}$$

Another criterion of equilibrium in a chemical system is given in terms of the chemical potential. At constant temperature and pressure, the differential of the Gibbs function according to Eq. (5.57) is

$$dG_{p,T} = \sum_i \bar{\mu}_i \, dn_i,$$

where $\bar{\mu}_i$ represents the chemical potential and n_i represents the number of moles of the ith species. But from Eq. (11.9)

$$dn_i = \frac{\nu_i}{\nu_1} \, dn_1,$$

where subscript 1 refers to component 1.

Therefore

$$dG_{p,T} = \sum_i \bar{\mu}_i \frac{\nu_i}{\nu_1} \, dn_1.$$

At equilibrium, since $dG_{p,T} = 0$, and since ν_1 and dn_1 are not zero, therefore

$$\sum_i \nu_i \bar{\mu}_i = 0. \qquad \qquad \textbf{(11.29)}$$

Equation (11.29) presents the criterion for chemical equilibrium in terms of the chemical potential and the number of moles of the species in the system. The negative of $\sum_i \nu_i \bar{\mu}_i$ is called the *affinity* of the reaction. Affinity is discussed in more detail in the following section.

11-11
Chemical
Affinity
are as follows:

In a reversible process in which p-V work is the only work involved, the energy relationships, according to the first law of thermodynamics,

$$dQ = dH - V \, dp.$$

Since enthalpy is a function of temperature, pressure, and the extent of the reaction λ, enthalpy may be expressed in the form:

$$dH = \left(\frac{\partial H}{\partial T}\right)_{p,\lambda} dT + \left(\frac{\partial H}{\partial p}\right)_{T,\lambda} dp + \left(\frac{\partial H}{\partial \lambda}\right)_{p,T} d\lambda.$$

Each of the three coefficients of this equation can be described with equivalent terms:

$$\left(\frac{\partial H}{\partial T}\right)_{p,\lambda} = (n\bar{c}_p)_\lambda = (mc_p)_\lambda,$$

$$\left(\frac{\partial H}{\partial p}\right)_{T,\lambda} = V - T\left(\frac{\partial V}{\partial T}\right)_{p,\lambda},^*$$

$$\left(\frac{\partial H}{\partial \lambda}\right)_{p,T} = \Delta H_{p,T}.$$

Therefore enthalpy can be expressed as

$$dH = (n\bar{c}_p)_\lambda \, dT + \left[V - T\left(\frac{\partial V}{\partial T}\right)_{p,\lambda}\right] dp + \Delta H_{p,T} \, d\lambda.$$

By using this expression for enthalpy, the first law then becomes

$$đQ = (n\bar{c}_p)_\lambda \, dT - T\left(\frac{\partial V}{\partial T}\right)_{p,\lambda} dp + \Delta H_{p,T} \, d\lambda. \tag{11.30}$$

The rate at which a reaction proceeds depends upon the concentration of the reactants. During the course of a reaction, the concentration of reactants ordinarily decreases, so that the rate of reaction constantly diminishes. Finally, when equilibrium is reached the affinity of the reaction is zero and the reaction stops completely. In an irreversible process, the entropy change and the heat transfer are related through the inequality

$$Td \, S > đQ.$$

If $đQ'$ represents the heat required in excess of that used if the process were reversible, then the preceding inequality can be replaced by an equality,

---

*To obtain this equivalent expression, the first and second laws are first combined in the form

$$dH = T \, dS + V \, dp.$$

The change of enthalpy as a function of pressure, at constant temperature, is as follows:

$$\left(\frac{\partial H}{\partial p}\right)_{T,\lambda} = T\left(\frac{\partial S}{\partial p}\right)_{T,\lambda} + V.$$

But according to the Maxwell relation

$$\left(\frac{\partial S}{\partial p}\right)_{T,\lambda} = -\left(\frac{\partial V}{\partial T}\right)_{p,\lambda}.$$

Consequently

$$\left(\frac{\partial H}{\partial p}\right)_{T,\lambda} = V - T\left(\frac{\partial V}{\partial T}\right)_{p,\lambda}.$$

$$T\,dS = dQ + dQ'. \tag{11.31}$$

Thus if dQ/T represents the entropy increase due to the reversible portions of a process, then dQ'/T represents the entropy increase due to the irreversibilities of the process.

The amount of heat dQ' in an irreversible reaction is associated with the extent of the reaction. The ratio of the differentials of these terms expresses the affinity of a system,

$$z \equiv \frac{dQ'}{d\lambda}. \tag{11.32}$$

The entropy change can now be expressed, through Eq. (11.31), in terms of affinity:

$$T\,dS = dQ + z\,d\lambda.$$

In Eq. (11.30) the heat interaction is expressed as a function of temperature, pressure, and extent of reaction. Entropy and affinity can therefore be introduced into this equation so that

$$dS = \frac{(n\bar{c}_p)_\lambda\,dT}{T} - \left(\frac{\partial V}{\partial T}\right)_{p,\lambda} dp + \left(\frac{\Delta H_{p,T} + z}{T}\right) d\lambda.$$

Since entropy is a property which can be determined by temperature, pressure, and λ, it can be expressed as

$$dS = \left(\frac{\partial S}{\partial T}\right)_{p,\lambda} dT + \left(\frac{\partial S}{\partial p}\right)_{T,\lambda} dp + \left(\frac{\partial S}{\partial \lambda}\right)_{p,T} d\lambda.$$

The coefficients associated with the extent of the reaction in the preceding two equations can be equated:

$$\left(\frac{\partial S}{\partial \lambda}\right)_{p,T} = \frac{\Delta H_{p,T} + z}{T}.$$

From which

$$z = -\Delta H_{p,T} + T\left(\frac{\partial S}{\partial \lambda}\right)_{p,T}. \tag{11.33}$$

But it was shown previously in Eq. (11.10) that entropy and λ are related as follows:

$$\left(\frac{\partial S}{\partial \lambda}\right)_{p,T} = \sum_{i=1}^{i=r} \nu_i \bar{s}_i = (S_p - S_r)_{p,T} = \Delta S_{p,T}.$$

Therefore affinity can be described by

$$z = -\Delta H_{p,T} + T\,\Delta S_{p,T} = -\Delta G_{p,T} = -\sum_i \nu_i \bar{\mu}_i,$$ (11.34)

where $\Delta S_{p,T}$ is the difference in entropy between the products and the reactants when they are at the same pressure and temperature. Evidently affinity indicates the decrease in Gibbs function that occurs during chemical reaction. When a system is in equilibrium the Gibbs function is zero, and so there is no chemical affinity.

11-12
Free Energy
and Chemical
Equilibrium
During the course of a chemical reaction, many intermediate compositions are formed before equilibrium is reached and the final composition is attained. In a chemical reaction, the products can react in the reverse direction, forming reactants, just as the reactants form products in the forward direction. At equilibrium, the rates of the forward reaction and the reverse reaction are equal. In this section the factors governing the final composition of a chemical system are considered. The Gibbs function is the main criterion for equilibrium.

The reference state for the Gibbs free energy of formation is 77°F and 1 standard atm. The stable form of each element at the standard reference state is arbitrarily assigned a value of zero free energy of formation. The free energy change of any reaction is given by

$$\Delta G° = \sum (G_f°)_p - \sum (G_f°)_r.$$ (11.35)

When a compound is formed from its elements, the resultant free-energy change at the standard state represents the standard free energy of formation $G_f°$ of the compound. A negative value of $\Delta G°$ indicates that reactants at the standard state proceed spontaneously to products at the standard state. Conversely a positive value of $\Delta G°$ indicates the reaction does not take place spontaneously. Table 11.2 gives the free energy of formation of several substances.

The free energy change of a chemical reaction under isothermal standard-state conditions may be determined according to the equation

$$\Delta G° = \Delta H° - T_o\,\Delta S°.$$ (11.36)

The change of entropy $\Delta S°$ is determined from the absolute entropies of the reactants and products at the standard state according to the equation

$$\Delta S° = \sum S_p° - \sum S_r°.$$ (11.37)

Absolute values of entropy of several pure substances at the standard state

(77°F and 1 atm pressure) are listed in the Table 11.2. According to the third law of thermodynamics, the entropy of a pure substance in equilibrium approaches zero as the temperature approaches zero. Thus a datum point for entropy is established at zero absolute temperature. Note that elements as well as compounds have entropies greater than zero at 77°F and 1 atm pressure. At other temperatures and pressures, the absolute entropy of a perfect gas can be calculated from the Sackur-Tetrode equation which developed from statistical mechanics. When the entropy of a perfect gas is known at one pressure and temperature, its entropy at another set of temperature and pressure conditions can be calculated from

$$\bar{s} = \bar{s}^\circ + \bar{c}_p \ln \frac{T}{T_o} - \mathscr{R} \ln \frac{p}{p_o}. \tag{11.38}$$

As in the case of enthalpy of formation, the difference between the entropy of a compound at the standard state and the entropy of its elements at the standard state is the entropy of formation:

$$\Delta S_f^\circ = S_{\text{compound}}^\circ - \Sigma \, S_{\text{elements}}^\circ. \tag{11.39}$$

The standard state is 77°F and 1 atm pressure. The Gibbs function can be expressed as

$$dG = dH - T \, dS - S \, dT.$$

But it was shown that entropy could be expressed in terms of reversible heat interaction and affinity:

$$T \, dS = \bar{d}Q + z \, d\lambda.$$

From the first law of thermodynamics, this becomes

$$T \, dS = dH - V \, dp + z \, d\lambda.$$

Therefore the Gibbs function becomes

$$dG = -S \, dT + V \, dp - z \, d\lambda. \tag{11.40}$$

Since the Gibbs function is a property determined by temperature, pressure, and extent of reaction,

$$\left(\frac{dG}{d\lambda}\right)_{p,T} = -z. \tag{11.41}$$

But it was shown that the Gibbs function could be described by Eq. (11.10):

$$\left(\frac{dG}{d\lambda}\right)_{p,T} = \sum_{i=1}^{i=r} \nu_i \bar{\mu}_i = \Delta G_p - \Delta G_r .$$

These two equations, when combined, lead to

$$z = -\Delta G_{p,T} = (\Delta G_r - \Delta G_p)_{p,T} ,$$

which is the same as Eq. (11.34).

A relationship can be shown to exist between affinity and enthalpy of reaction. Equation (11.34) can be written as

$$z = -\Delta H_{p,T} + T \Delta S_{p,T} .$$

But

$$z = -\Delta G_{p,T} ,$$

also, since

$$S = -\left(\frac{\partial G}{\partial T}\right)_{p,\lambda} ;$$

therefore,

$$\Delta S_{p,T} = -\left(\frac{\partial \Delta G}{\partial T}\right)_{p,\lambda} .$$

These substitutions therefore lead to

$$\Delta G_{p,T} = \Delta H_{p,T} + T\left(\frac{\partial \Delta G}{\partial T}\right)_{p,\lambda} , \tag{11.42}$$

which is called the *Gibbs-Helmholtz* relation. It shows the effect of changes in temperature on the Gibbs function.

Now Eq. (11.42) may be transformed into an integrable form. First, Eq. (11.34) is expressed as

$$\frac{z}{T} = -\frac{\Delta H_{p,T}}{T} + \Delta S_{p,T} .$$

Differentiation with respect to temperature alone leads to

$$\frac{\partial}{\partial T}\left(\frac{z}{T}\right)_{p,\lambda} = \left(\frac{\Delta H_{p,T}}{T^2}\right)_{p,\lambda} - \frac{1}{T}\left(\frac{\partial \Delta H_{p,T}}{\partial T}\right)_{p,\lambda} + \left(\frac{\partial \Delta S_{p,T}}{\partial T}\right)_{p,\lambda} .$$

But from the first and second laws of thermodynamics, it can be shown that

$$\left(\frac{\partial \Delta S_{p,T}}{\partial T}\right)_{p,\lambda} = \frac{1}{T}\left(\frac{\partial \Delta H_{p,T}}{\partial T}\right)_{p,\lambda}.$$

Therefore,

$$\frac{\partial}{\partial T}\left(\frac{z}{T}\right)_{p,\lambda} = \left(\frac{\Delta H_{p,T}}{T^2}\right)_{p,\lambda},$$

which, when integrated, gives

$$\frac{z}{T} = \int \frac{\Delta H_{p,T}}{T^2}\,dT + C \quad (dp = 0 \quad \text{and} \quad d\lambda = 0), \tag{11.43}$$

where C is a constant of integration.

11-13
Equilibrium
Constant

This section investigates the condition of equilibrium for a reaction given by the equation

$$\nu_a A + \nu_b B + \ldots \longrightarrow \nu_c C + \nu_d D + \ldots.$$

The differential of the Gibbs function is

$$dG = V\,dp - S\,dT.$$

Two conditions are now imposed on the preceding expression. The first is that either the reaction is isothermal; that is, the temperature during the reaction remains unchanged, or, alternatively, the temperature is the same at only the beginning and end of the reaction. The second condition is that only perfect gases are involved. The differential of the Gibbs function then becomes

$$dG = V\,dp = \frac{n\mathscr{R}T}{p}\,dp.$$

Integrating the foregoing equation from the standard state to any other state at the same temperature gives

$$G - G^\circ = n\mathscr{R}T \ln \frac{p}{p_0}, \tag{11.44}$$

where G° is the free energy at the standard state and p_0 is the reference pressure of 1 atm. Equation (11.44) on a mole basis may be written

$$\bar{g} = \bar{g}^\circ + \mathscr{R}T \ln p, \tag{11.45}$$

where p is the pressure in atmospheres.

The change of the Gibbs function, when reactants A, B, ..., are transformed to products C, D, ..., is

$$\Delta G = \Sigma\, G_p - \Sigma\, G_r$$
$$= (\nu_c \bar{g}_c + \nu_d \bar{g}_d + \ldots) - (\nu_a \bar{g}_a + \nu_b \bar{g}_b + \ldots).$$

Substituting from Eq. (11.45) gives

$$\Delta G = (\nu_c \bar{g}_c^\circ + \nu_d \bar{g}_d^\circ + \ldots) - (\nu_a \bar{g}_a^\circ + \nu_b \bar{g}_b^\circ + \ldots)$$
$$+ (\nu_c \mathscr{R}T \ln p_c + \nu_d \mathscr{R}T \ln p_d + \ldots)$$
$$- (\nu_a \mathscr{R}T \ln p_a + \nu_b \mathscr{R}T \ln p_b + \ldots).$$

But $\quad \Delta G^\circ = (\nu_c \bar{g}_c^\circ + \nu_d \bar{g}_d^\circ + \ldots) - (\nu_a \bar{g}_a^\circ + \nu_b \bar{g}_b^\circ + \ldots),$

then $\quad \Delta G = \Delta G^\circ + \mathscr{R}T \ln \dfrac{p_C^{\nu_c} p_D^{\nu_d} \cdots}{p_A^{\nu_a} p_B^{\nu_b} \cdots}. \tag{11.46}$

At equilibrium $dG = 0$ and the Gibbs function at the reference state may then be expressed as

$$-\Delta G^\circ = z^\circ = \mathscr{R}T \ln \frac{p_C^{\nu_c} p_D^{\nu_d} \cdots}{p_A^{\nu_a} p_B^{\nu_b} \cdots} = \mathscr{R}T \ln K_p. \tag{11.47}$$

K_p is called the *equilibrium constant* defined by the equation

$$K_p = e^{-\Delta G^\circ / \mathscr{R}T} = e^{z^\circ / \mathscr{R}T} = \frac{p_C^{\nu_c} p_D^{\nu_d} \cdots}{p_A^{\nu_a} p_B^{\nu_b} \cdots}. \tag{11.48}$$

The subscript p is to emphasize that K_p is defined in terms of the partial pressure of reactants and products. Note that ΔG° and K_p are independent of the total pressure. They depend only on temperature and the nature of the reactants and products of the reaction. Recall also that in choosing the reference state, the unit of pressures for the components was expressed in atmospheres. Therefore, the value of K_p is based on this unit of pressure. In the preceding definition of K_p the partial pressures of the products are placed in the numerator and the partial pressures of the reactants are placed in the denominator. When the reaction is reversed, the value of the equilibrium constant becomes the reciprocal of that of the forward reaction. Values of K_p as a function of temperature are usually given in the form of an equation, table, or graph. Figure 11.2 shows K_p plotted versus absolute temperature for several reactions.

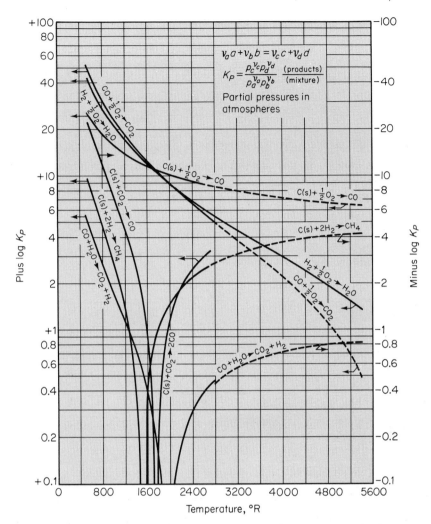

Fig. 11.2. *Equilibrium constants. (Solid lines, API Research Project 44, Tables 1y, 0y, National Bureau of Standards, Washington, Aug. 31, 1944, and Aug. 31, 1946. Dashed lines, B. Lewis and G. von Elbe, "Combustion Flames and Explosions of Gases," Table II, New York: Cambridge University Press, 1938.)*

The equilibrium constant may also be expressed in terms of mole fractions. Noting that the mole fraction of a component in a perfect gas mixture is equal to the ratio of the partial pressure of the component to the total pressure, the equilibrium constant, according to Eq. (11.48), becomes

$$K_p = \frac{n_C^{v_c} n_D^{v_d} \cdots}{n_A^{v_a} n_B^{v_b} \cdots} \left(\frac{p}{\sum_i n_i} \right)^{v_c + v_d + \cdots - v_a - v_b - \cdots}, \tag{11.49}$$

or in terms of the mole fraction,

$$K_p = \frac{x_C^{\nu_c} x_D^{\nu_d} \cdots}{x_A^{\nu_a} x_B^{\nu_b} \cdots} \, p^{\nu_c + \nu_d + \cdots - \nu_a - \nu_b - \cdots} \, . \tag{11.50}$$

Note that the equilibrium constant is equal to $\frac{x_C^{\nu_c} x_D^{\nu_d} \cdots}{x_A^{\nu_a} x_B^{\nu_b} \cdots}$ if $\nu_c + \nu_d + \cdots$ $= \nu_a + \nu_b + \cdots$ that is, if the number of moles remain unchanged during the reaction. This means further that at constant temperature and pressure the volume of the gaseous components remains constant. It will be shown in Section 11-15 that the equilibrium composition of a reacting system at a given temperature and pressure can be determined if the equilibrium constant is known.

The affinity z can be expressed in terms of K_p as

$$z = \mathscr{R}T \ln K_p - \mathscr{R}T \sum_i \nu_i \ln p_i. \tag{11.51}$$

But

$$z^\circ = \mathscr{R}T \ln K_p,$$

then

$$z = z^\circ - \mathscr{R}T \sum_i \nu_i \ln p_i. \tag{11.52}$$

At equilibrium $z = 0$, so that

$$\ln K_p = \sum_i \ln p_i^{\nu_i},$$

or

$$K_p = p_1^{\nu_1} + p_2^{\nu_2} + \cdots + p_r^{\nu_r} = \sum_{i=1}^{i=r} p_i^{\nu_i}. \tag{11.53}$$

A relation between the equilibrium constant and the enthalpy of reaction may be derived as follows: The equilibrium constant as given by Eq. (11.48) is written

$$\ln K_p = \frac{-\Delta G^\circ}{\mathscr{R}T}.$$

But the free energy change in an isothermal process when both reactants and products are at the standard state is

$$\Delta G^\circ = \Delta H^\circ - T \Delta S^\circ;$$

therefore,

$$\ln K_p = \frac{-(\Delta H^\circ - T\,\Delta S^\circ)}{\mathscr{R}T} = -\frac{\Delta H^\circ}{\mathscr{R}T} + \frac{\Delta S^\circ}{\mathscr{R}}.$$

Differentiation of the preceding equation with respect to T and noting that ΔH° and ΔS° are constants gives

$$\frac{d\ln K_p}{dT} = \frac{\Delta H^\circ}{\mathscr{R}T^2}$$

or

$$\frac{d\ln K_p}{d(1/T)} = -\frac{\Delta H^\circ}{\mathscr{R}}. \tag{11.54}$$

If ΔH° is positive (endothermic reaction), K_p increases with increasing temperature, and if ΔH° is negative (exothermic reaction), K_p decreases with increasing temperature. Equation (11.54) is called the *Van't Hoff*

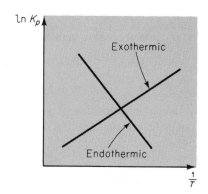

Fig. 11.3. *ln K_p vs 1/T.*

equation. Figure 11.3 shows a plot of $\ln K_p$ versus $1/T$ which is a straight line with a slope of $-\Delta H^\circ/\mathscr{R}$. The sign of the slope depends on the sign of ΔH°, whether positive or negative, corresponding to exothermic or endothermic reactions respectively. Equation (11.54) may be used to determine the value of ΔH° as a function of temperature, provided that the variation of K_p with temperature is known.

11-14
Fugacity and
Activity

In order to determine the equilibrium constant when the gaseous species of a chemical reaction do not follow the perfect gas law a new function, fugacity, is introduced. When this function is substituted for pressure, the equations for the equilibrium constant become applicable to real gases.

The differential of the Gibbs function of a perfect gas undergoing an isothermal process is

$$dG = V \, dp = \frac{n\mathscr{R}T}{p} \, dp = n\mathscr{R}T \, d(\ln p). \tag{11.55}$$

Analogously, the differential of the Gibbs function for a real gas is

$$dG = n\mathscr{R} \, T \, d(\ln f), \tag{11.56}$$

where f is called the *fugacity* and has the dimensions of pressure. Equation (11.56) may be considered as a definition of fugacity. It has the same form as Eq. (11.55) but applies to real gases. The value of fugacity approaches the value of pressure as the latter tends to zero; that is, where perfect gas conditions apply. Integrating Eq. (11.56) between a reference state (°) and any other state, gives,

$$G - G° = n\mathscr{R}T \ln \frac{f}{f°} = n\mathscr{R}T \ln a, \tag{11.57}$$

where a is called the *activity* and is defined as

$$a \equiv \frac{f}{f°}. \tag{11.58}$$

Following the same procedure as in Section 11-13, the following expression for a constant-pressure equilibrium constant K_a for a real gas may be obtained:

$$K_a = e^{-\Delta G°/\mathscr{R}T} = \frac{a_C^{v_c} a_D^{v_d} \ldots}{a_A^{v_a} a_B^{v_b} \ldots}, \tag{11.59}$$

and

$$\Delta G° = -\mathscr{R}T \ln K_a. \tag{11.60}$$

Note that activities replace partial pressure in the expression for the equilibrium constant.

11-15
Equilibrium
Constant and
Dissociation

The equilibrium composition of a chemical system at high temperatures can be quite different from that at low temperature owing to dissociation and interactions of the constituents. Although the degree of dissociation increases with temperature, dissociation, in many cases, can be neglected at room temperature and atmospheric pressure. The degree of dissociation of carbon dioxide at atmospheric pressure, for example, is negligible at room temperature but increases to 34.4 per cent at 5200°R.

Consider the equilibrium composition of a mixture of oxygen and hydrogen at high temperature. The following reactions are possible:

$$H_2(g) + \tfrac{1}{2} O_2(g) \rightleftharpoons H_2O(g)$$
$$\tfrac{1}{2} H_2(g) + \tfrac{1}{2} O_2(g) \rightleftharpoons OH(g)$$
$$H_2(g) \rightleftharpoons 2 H(g)$$
$$O_2(g) \rightleftharpoons 2 O(g).$$

A chemical system in which the preceding reactions occur contains six species, H_2, O_2, H_2O, OH, H, and O, and therefore six equations are required for the solution. Two are provided by the conservation of atoms of hydrogen and oxygen such that

for hydrogen: $2n_{H_2} + 2n_{H_2O} + n_{OH} + n_H = N_H$,

for oxygen: $n_{HO} + 2n_{O_2} + n_{OH} + n_O = N_O$,

where N_H and N_O are the total number of atoms of hydrogen and oxygen respectively. The other four equations can be written in terms of the equilibrium constants, as the following example illustrates.

EXAMPLE 11.14: Compare the degree of dissociation of H_2O and CO_2 at 5200°R. The total pressure in each case is 1.25 atm and 2.25 atm.

Solution: The chemical equation for the dissociation of H_2O is

$$H_2O(g) \rightleftharpoons H_2(g) + \tfrac{1}{2}O_2(g).$$

Consider 1 mole of H_2O of which a fraction α dissociates to form H_2 and O_2, thus producing α moles of H_2 and $\alpha/2$ moles of O_2 according to the preceding equation. The number of moles in the products at equilibrium is, therefore;

$$1 - \alpha \quad \text{moles of } H_2O \quad \text{(undissociated)}$$
$$\alpha \qquad \text{moles of } H_2$$
$$\underline{\alpha/2 \qquad \text{moles of } O_2}$$
$$\text{Total} = 1 + (\alpha/2).$$

The partial pressures of the products are

$$p_{H_2O} = \left[\frac{1 - \alpha}{1 + (\alpha/2)}\right] p_{\text{total}},$$

$$p_{H_2} = \left[\frac{\alpha}{1 + (\alpha/2)}\right] p_{total},$$

$$p_{O_2} = \left[\frac{\alpha/2}{1 + (\alpha/2)}\right] p_{total} = \left(\frac{\alpha}{2 + \alpha}\right) p_{total}.$$

The equilibrium constant for the preceding reaction is

$$K_p = \frac{p_{H_2O}}{p_{H_2} p_{O_2}^{1/2}} = \frac{\left[\dfrac{1 - \alpha}{1 + (\alpha/2)}\right] p_{total}}{\left[\dfrac{\alpha}{1 + (\alpha/2)}\right] p_{total} \left(\dfrac{\alpha}{2 + \alpha}\right)^{1/2} p_{total}^{1/2}} = \frac{(1 - \alpha)(2 + \alpha)^{1/2}}{\alpha^{3/2} p_{total}^{1/2}},$$

where p_{total} is measured in atmospheres. A plot of K_p versus α according to the foregoing equation is shown in Fig. 11.4. At 5200°R, Fig. 11.2 gives

$$\log K_p = 1.52 \quad \text{or} \quad K_p = 33.$$

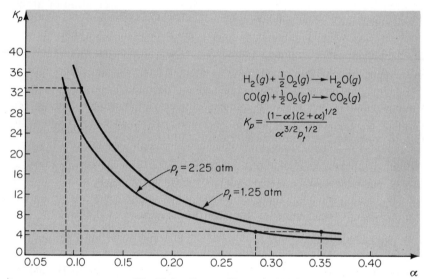

Fig. 11.4. K_p vs α (Example 11.14).

For the dissociation of CO_2, the chemical equation is

$$CO_2(g) \rightleftharpoons CO(g) + \tfrac{1}{2}O_2(g),$$

and for a mole fraction α of CO_2 dissociated, the numbers of moles of the products are

$\quad 1 - \alpha \quad$ moles of CO_2 (undissociated)

$\quad \alpha \quad\quad$ moles of CO

$\quad \alpha/2 \quad$ moles of O_2

Total $= 1 + (\alpha/2)$.

The expression for K_p is the same as in the case of H_2O. At $5200°R$

$$\log K_p = 0.68 \quad \text{or} \quad K_p = 4.78.$$

From Fig. 11.4, at 1.25 atm,

$$(K_p)_{H_2O} = 33 \quad \text{and} \quad \alpha_{H_2O} = 0.1065 = 10.65 \text{ per cent,}$$
$$(K_p)_{CO_2} = 4.78 \quad \text{and} \quad \alpha_{CO_2} = 0.35 = 35.0 \text{ per cent.}$$

At 2.25 atm,

$$\alpha_{H_2O} = 0.092 = 9.2 \text{ per cent,}$$
$$\alpha_{CO_2} = 0.284 = 28.4 \text{ per cent.}$$

If the temperature of the reaction is unknown, the procedure to determine the composition of the products involves a double trial-and-error solution. At the adiabatic reaction temperature, the reactants and the products are identical in enthalpy value; furthermore, the properties of the product constituents fulfill the equilibrium requirements appropriate for that temperature and pressure. For non-adiabatic conditions, a reaction temperature is first assumed and the corresponding equilibrium composition is determined using the equations resulting from the assumed dissociation reactions and the balance of the atoms of the elements in the reactants and products. The assumed temperature is ascertained by calculating the enthalpy of both the reactants and products and equating the difference to the amount of heat transfer in the reaction. If the result does not agree, another reaction temperature is assumed and the procedure is repeated.

**11-16
Statistical
Analysis of the
Chemical
System**
The expression for the equilibrium constant, as well as for other thermodynamic parameters pertaining to chemical systems, can be deduced from molecular properties. Analogous to the classical approach, the statistical approach leads to the law of mass action (conservation of mass), to the conditions of equilibrium and to the equilibrium composition in a chemical reaction.

Although the statistical approach applies to any chemical reaction, a simple reaction will be considered. The procedure, however, is analogous. Consider the reaction

$$A + B \rightleftharpoons AB,$$

in which N_A and N_B molecules of elements A and B react to form N_{AB} molecules of product AB. The molecules of each species in the reactive mixture are considered indistinguishable among themselves but they are

TABLE 11.4 Number and Energy of Molecules of the System

$$A + B \rightleftarrows AB$$

Constituent	Number of Molecules at Different Energy Levels	Total Number of Molecules	Energy Levels	Degeneracy of Energy Levels	Energy of Constituents
A	$N_{a_1}, N_{a_2}, \ldots N_{a_i}$	$N_a = \sum_i N_{a_i}$	$\epsilon_{a_1}, \epsilon_{a_2}, \ldots \epsilon_{a_i}$	$g_{a_1}, g_{a_2}, \ldots g_{a_i}$	$U_a = \sum_i N_{a_i} \epsilon_{a_i}$
B	$N_{b_1}, N_{b_2}, \ldots N_{b_i}$	$N_b = \sum_i N_{b_i}$	$\epsilon_{b_1}, \epsilon_{b_2}, \ldots \epsilon_{b_i}$	$g_{b_1}, g_{b_2}, \ldots g_{b_i}$	$U_b = \sum_i N_{b_i} \epsilon_{b_i}$
AB	$N_{ab_1}, N_{ab_2}, \ldots N_{ab_i}$	$N_{ab} = \sum_i N_{ab_i}$	$\epsilon_{ab_1}, \epsilon_{ab_2}, \ldots \epsilon_{ab_i}$	$g_{ab_1}, g_{ab_2}, \ldots g_{ab_i}$	$U_{ab} = \sum_i N_{ab_i} \epsilon_{ab_i}$

distinguishable from other species. Both reactants and products are assumed to be perfect gases.

Let the energy associated with each molecule be denoted by ϵ_{a_i}, ϵ_{b_i}, ..., where the subscript $i = 1, 2, 3, \ldots$ denotes the energy level of the molecule. The energies of the reactants and product may be measured relative to any arbitrarily chosen datum. The energy of the product AB relative to this datum includes its energy of formation. Table 11.4 indicates nomenclature describing the distribution of molecules of different species and energies in a chemical system composed of reactants A and B and product AB.

Several constraints are imposed on the behavior of the chemical system. First, the total number of molecules (or atoms) of each constituent must not change, or

$$\sum_i \delta N_{a_i} = 0 \tag{11.61a}$$

$$\sum_i \delta N_{b_i} = 0 \tag{11.61b}$$

$$\sum_i \delta N_{ab_i} = 0. \tag{11.61c}$$

The number of any elemental constituent must fulfill the following:

$$N_A = N_a + N_{ab}, \tag{11.62}$$

$$N_B = N_b + N_{ab}. \tag{11.63}$$

Second, the total energy of the system at equilibrium, which is the sum of the energies of its constituents, must not change, or

$$\sum_i \epsilon_{a_i} \delta N_{a_i} + \sum_i \epsilon_{b_i} \delta N_{b_i} + \sum_i \epsilon_{ab} \delta N_{ab_i} = 0. \tag{11.64}$$

The total energy is equal to

$$U = U_a + U_b + U_{ab} = \sum_i N_{a_i} \epsilon_{a_i} + \sum_i N_{b_i} \epsilon_{b_i} + \sum_i N_{ab_i} \epsilon_{ab_i}.$$

Based on the assumption that the molecules of a species are indistinguishable from each other, the number of different microstates into which each constituent can be arranged is given by the expressions:

$$W_a = \prod_i \frac{g_{a_i}^{N_{a_i}}}{N_{a_i}!}, \quad W_b = \prod_i \frac{g_{b_i}^{N_{b_i}}}{N_{b_i}!}, \quad \text{and} \quad W_{ab} = \prod_i \frac{g_{ab_i}^{N_{ab_i}}}{N_{ab_i}!}.$$

The total number of microstates for a given macrostate is equal to the product of the preceding expressions of probabilities, or

$$W = W_a W_b W_{ab} = \prod_i \frac{g_{a_i}^{N_{a_i}}}{N_{a_i}!} \prod_i \frac{g_{b_i}^{N_{b_i}}}{N_{b_i}!} \prod_i \frac{g_{ab_i}^{N_{ab_i}}}{N_{ab_i}!}. \tag{11.65}$$

The process of finding the equilibrium distribution of the chemical reaction is performed in two steps: First, the maximum number of microstates for given values of N_a, N_b, and N_{ab} is determined. A second maximization of the probability of this state leads to the identification of those values of N_a, N_b, and N_{ab} which constitute the chemical equilibrium composition. The logarithm of the number of microstates is

$$\ln W = \left[\sum_i N_{a_i} \ln g_{a_i} - \sum_i \ln N_{a_i}! \right]$$

$$+ \left[\sum_i N_{b_i} \ln g_{b_i} - \sum_i \ln N_{b_i}! \right]$$

$$+ \left[\sum_i N_{ab_i} \ln g_{ab_i} - \sum_i \ln N_{ab_i}! \right].$$

Applying Stirling's approximation formula to the last term of each bracket, the preceding equation becomes

$$\ln W = \left[\sum_i N_{a_i} \ln \frac{g_{a_i}}{N_{a_i}} + N_a \right] + \left[\sum_i N_{b_i} \ln \frac{g_{b_i}}{N_{b_i}} + N_b \right]$$

$$+ \left[\sum_i N_{ab_i} \ln \frac{g_{ab_i}}{N_{ab_i}} + N_{ab} \right]. \tag{11.66}$$

The maximum value of the probability is obtained by equating the differential of Eq. (11.66) to zero.

$$\delta(\ln W) = 0 = -\sum_i \ln \left(\frac{N_{a_i}}{g_{a_i}} \right) \delta N_{a_i} - \sum_i \ln \left(\frac{N_{b_i}}{g_{b_i}} \right) \delta N_{b_i}$$

$$- \sum_i \ln \left(\frac{N_{ab_i}}{g_{ab_i}} \right) \delta N_{ab_i}. \tag{11.67}$$

Lagrange's method of undetermined multipliers can now be applied to Eq. (11.67), when combined, by the use of multipliers $\ln \alpha$ and β, with Eq. (11.61) and (11.64):

$$\sum_i \left(-\ln \frac{N_{a_i}}{g_{a_i}} + \ln \alpha_a - \beta \epsilon_{a_i} \right) \delta N_{a_i} + \sum_i \left(-\ln \frac{N_{b_i}}{g_{b_i}} + \ln \alpha_b - \beta \epsilon_{b_i} \right) \delta N_{b_i}$$

$$+ \sum_i \left(-\ln \frac{N_{ab_i}}{g_{ab_i}} + \ln \alpha_{ab} - \beta \epsilon_{ab_i} \right) \delta N_{ab_i} = 0.$$

Since δN_{a_i}, δN_{b_i}, and δN_{ab_i} can be treated as independent, their coefficients in the preceding equation must vanish separately. This leads to the following expression for the distribution numbers:

$$-\ln\frac{N_{a_i}}{g_{a_i}} + \ln\alpha_a - \beta\epsilon_{a_i} = 0, \quad \text{or} \quad N_{a_i} = \alpha_a g_{a_i} e^{-\beta\epsilon_{a_i}}.$$

Similarly,

$$-\ln\frac{N_{b_i}}{g_{b_i}} + \ln\alpha_b - \beta\epsilon_{b_i} = 0, \quad \text{or} \quad N_{b_i} = \alpha_b g_{b_i} e^{-\beta\epsilon_{b_i}}$$

and

$$-\ln\frac{N_{ab_i}}{g_{ab_i}} + \ln\alpha_{ab} - \beta\epsilon_{ab_i} = 0, \quad \text{or} \quad N_{ab_i} = \alpha_{ab} g_{ab_i} e^{-\beta\epsilon_{ab_i}}.$$

It can be shown, by methods similar to those outlined in Chapter 8, that the Lagrange multipliers can be expressed as

$$\beta = \frac{1}{kT}, \quad \alpha_a = \frac{N_a}{Z_a}, \quad \text{and} \quad \alpha_{ab} = \frac{N_{ab}}{Z_{ab}},$$

where Z is the partition function defined by

$$Z_a = \sum_i g_{a_i} e^{-\epsilon_i/kT}, \text{ etc.}$$

Substituting these expressions for α and β, and the distribution numbers $(N_{a_i}, N_{b_i}, \text{ and } N_{ab_i})$ into Eq. (11.66) gives

$$\ln W = \left\{ \sum_i N_{a_i} \ln\left[\frac{g_{a_i}}{(N_a/Z_a)g_{a_i}e^{-\epsilon_{a_i}/kT}}\right] + N_a \right\}$$

$$+ \left\{ \sum_i N_{b_i} \ln\left[\frac{g_{b_i}}{(N_b/Z_b)g_{a_i}e^{-\epsilon_{b_i}/kT}}\right] + N_b \right\}$$

$$+ \left\{ \sum_i N_{ab_i} \ln\left[\frac{g_{ab_i}}{(N_{ab}/Z_{ab})g_{ab_i}e^{-\epsilon_{ab_i}/kT}}\right] + N_{ab} \right\}$$

$$= \left\{ \left[\sum_i N_{a_i}\frac{\epsilon_{a_i}}{kT} + \sum_i N_{a_i}\ln Z_a - \sum_i N_{a_i}\ln N_a + N_a \right] + \cdots \right\}.$$

Thus

$$\ln W = \frac{U}{kT} + (N_a \ln Z_a - N_a \ln N_a + N_a)$$

$$+ (N_b \ln Z_b - N_b \ln N_b + N_b)$$

$$+ (N_{ab} \ln Z_{ab} - N_{ab} \ln N_{ab} + N_{ab}), \qquad \textbf{(11.68)}$$

where U is the internal energy of all the species.

The next step is to determine the numbers of molecules N_a, N_b, and N_{ab} which exist in the equilibrium mixture. This is accomplished by finding the maximum value of W in the Eq. (11.68). Denoting the maximum probability by W^e, the differential of Eq. (11.68) at its maximum value is

$$
\begin{aligned}
\delta(\ln W^e) = 0 &= \left(\ln Z_a\, \delta N_a - N_a \frac{\delta N_a}{N_a} - \ln N_a\, \delta N_a + \delta N_a \right) \\
&+ \left(\ln Z_b\, \delta N_b - N_b \frac{\delta N_b}{N_b} - \ln N_b\, \delta N_b + \delta N_b \right) \\
&+ \left(\ln Z_{ab}\, \delta N_{ab} - N_{ab} \frac{\delta N_{ab}}{N_{ab}} - \ln N_{ab}\, \delta N_{ab} + \delta N_{ab} \right) \\
&= (\ln Z_a - \ln N_a)\delta N_a + (\ln Z_b - \ln N_b)\delta N_b \\
&+ (\ln Z_{ab} - \ln N_{ab})\delta N_{ab}.
\end{aligned}
$$

(11.69)

The conditions of constraint imposed on Eq. (11.69), according to Eq. (11.62) and (11.63), are

$$
\delta N_a + \delta N_{ab} = 0,
\tag{11.70}
$$

and

$$
\delta N_b + \delta N_{ab} = 0.
\tag{11.71}
$$

Applying Lagrange's method of undetermined multipliers, multiply Eq. (11.70) by α' and (11.71) by α'' and combine these with Eq. (11.69):

$$
\begin{aligned}
(\ln Z_a - \ln N_a + \alpha')\, \delta N_a + (\ln Z_b - \ln N_b + \alpha'')\, \delta N_b \\
+ (\ln Z_{ab} - \ln N_{ab} + \alpha' + \alpha'')\, \delta N_{ab} = 0.
\end{aligned}
$$

Since N_a, N_b, and N_{ab} can be treated as independent, then

$$
\ln Z_a - \ln N_a + \alpha' = 0
$$
$$
\ln Z_b - \ln N_b + \alpha'' = 0
$$

and

$$
\ln Z_{ab} - \ln N_{ab} + \alpha' + \alpha'' = 0.
$$

Eliminating α' and α'' from the preceding three equations and denoting the equilibrium distribution numbers by superscript (e), the relation between the species concentration at the equilibrium condition is

$$
\ln Z_a Z_b - \ln N_a^e N_b^e - \ln Z_{ab} + \ln N_{ab}^e = 0
$$

or

$$K_N = \frac{N_{ab}^e}{N_a^e N_b^e} = \frac{Z_{ab}^e}{Z_a^e Z_b^e},$$ (11.72)

where K_N is called the *equilibrium distribution constant*. Therefore, a knowledge of the partition functions of the species of the reaction is sufficient to determine the equilibrium distribution of the different species involved in a chemical reaction. Equation (11.72) is the law of mass action.

The equilibrium constant K_p may be shown to be related to K_N in the following way. The equilibrium constant K_p is

$$K_p = \frac{p_{ab}^e}{p_a^e p_b^e},$$

where p_{ab}^e, p_a^e, and p_b^e are the equilibrium partial pressures of the species AB, A, and B. Their values, according to the perfect gas law, are given by

$$p_{ab}^e V = N_{ab}^e kT, \quad p_a^e V = N_a^e kT, \quad \text{and} \quad p_b^e V = N_b^e kT.$$

Therefore,

$$K_p = \frac{(N_{ab}^e kT/V)}{(N_a^e kT/V)(N_b^e kT/V)} = \left(\frac{N_{ab}^e}{N_a^e N_b^e}\right) \frac{V}{kT} = \left(\frac{N_{ab}^e}{N_a^e N_b^e}\right) \frac{N}{p},$$ (11.73)

and in terms of the partition function,

$$K_p = \frac{N}{p} \left(\frac{Z_{ab}^e}{Z_a^e Z_b^e}\right) = \frac{N}{p} K_N.$$ (11.74)

Expressions for other properties which apply to chemical reaction may similarly be obtained. Of these, entropy, Helmholtz and Gibbs functions, and chemical potential will be considered.

At equilibrium, Boltzmann's law, $S = k \ln W^e$ may be used to obtain the following expression for entropy. Using Eq. (11.68), then

$$S = \frac{U}{T} + kN_a \left(\ln \frac{Z_a}{N_a} + 1\right) + kN_b \left(\ln \frac{Z_b}{N_b} + 1\right) + kN_{ab} \left(\ln \frac{Z_{ab}}{N_{ab}} + 1\right)$$

$$= \frac{U}{T} + k \ln \left[\left(\frac{Z_a}{N_a}\right)^{N_a} \left(\frac{Z_b}{N_b}\right)^{N_b} \left(\frac{Z_{ab}}{N_{ab}}\right)^{N_{ab}}\right] + k(N_a + N_b + N_{ab}).$$ (11.75)

An expression for the Helmholtz function $F = U - TS$ is

$$F = -kT \ln \left[\left(\frac{Z_a}{N_a}\right)^{N_a} \left(\frac{Z_b}{N_b}\right)^{N_b} \left(\frac{Z_{ab}}{N_{ab}}\right)^{N_{ab}}\right] - kT(N_a + N_b + N_{ab}).$$ (11.76)

The Gibbs function $G = H - TS = F + pV$, is given by

$$G = -kT \ln \left[\left(\frac{Z_a}{N_a} \right)^{N_a} \left(\frac{Z_b}{N_b} \right)^{N_b} \left(\frac{Z_{ab}}{N_{ab}} \right)^{N_{ab}} \right]. \tag{11.77}$$

The expressions for the chemical potentials for the species A, B, and AB are

$$\mu_a = \left(\frac{\partial F}{\partial N_a} \right)_{N_b, V, T} = -kT \left[N_a \left(\frac{-Z_a}{N_a^2} \right) \frac{N_a}{Z_a} + \ln \frac{Z_a}{N_a} \right] - kT$$

$$= -kT \ln \frac{Z_a}{N_a}.$$

Similarly,

$$\mu_b = \left(\frac{\partial F}{\partial N_b} \right)_{N_a, V, T} = -kT \ln \frac{Z_b}{N_b},$$

$$\mu_{ab} = \left(\frac{\partial F}{\partial N_{ab}} \right)_{V, T} = -kT \ln \frac{Z_{ab}}{N_{ab}}.$$

Adding the first two equations,

$$\mu_a + \mu_b = -kT \ln \frac{Z_a Z_b}{N_a N_b}.$$

But at chemical equilibrium, according to Eq. (11.72),

$$\frac{N_a^e N_b^e}{N_{ab}^e} = \frac{Z_a^e Z_b^e}{Z_{ab}^e}.$$

Therefore,

$$\mu_a^e + \mu_b^e = \mu_{ab}^e. \tag{11.78}$$

Note that Eq. (11.78) satisfies Eq. (11.29), necessary for chemical equilibrium.

The foregoing expressions for the Helmholtz and Gibbs functions can be written in terms of the chemical potential as follows:

$$F = N_a \mu_a + N_b \mu_b + N_{ab} \mu_{ab} - pV, \tag{11.79}$$

$$G = \mu_a (N_a + N_{ab}) + \mu_b (N_b + N_{ab}) = \mu_a N_A + \mu_b N_B. \tag{11.80}$$

(The proof of Eq. (11.79) (11.80) is left to the student as an exercise.)

The present section, comparable to Section 10-10, indicates that both classical and statistical approaches may be used to derive expressions describing equilibrium conditions in a reactive mixture. In particular, this analogy is illustrated by comparing the equilibrium constant equation (11.73), derived from a statistical approach, with Eq. (11.49), derived from a classical approach. For the three-component system consisting of species a, b, and ab:

$$\frac{N_{ab}N}{N_a N_b p} = \frac{n_{ab}n}{n_a n_b p},$$

and the two equations are equivalent.

REFERENCES

11.1 Denbigh, K. G., *The Principles of Chemical Equilibrium.* Cambridge: Cambridge University Press, 1957, chaps. 2, 3, and 4.

11.2 De Estrada, A., *Thermodinamica Technica.* Buenos Aires: Libreria y Editorial Alsina, 1955, chap. 5, 16.

11.3 Hougen, O. A., K. M. Watson, R. A. Ragatz, *Chemical Process Principles.* New York: John Wiley & Sons, Inc., 1954, chap. 20.

11.4 Keenan, J. H., *Thermodynamics.* New York: John Wiley & Sons, Inc., 1952, chap. 17.

11.5 Kiefer, P. J., G. F. Kinney and M. C. Stuart, *Principles of Engineering Thermodynamics.* New York: John Wiley & Sons, Inc., 1954, chap. 12.

11.6 Rushbrooke, G. S., *Introduction to Statistical Mechanics.* London: Oxford University Press, 1962, chap. 6, 7.

11.7 Van Wylen, G. J., *Thermodynamics.* New York: John Wiley & Sons, Inc., 1958, chap. 15.

PROBLEMS

11.1 The analysis of a sample of coal is carbon 80.1 per cent; hydrogen 4.3 per cent; oxygen 4.2 per cent; nitrogen 1.7 per cent; sulfur 1.0 per cent, and the rest is ash. What would be the air-fuel ratio on a mass basis if this coal is burned with 20 per cent excess air?

11.2 Calculate the molal analysis of the products of combustion when normal heptane (C_7H_{16}) is burned with 150 per cent excess air. What is the dew point of the products if combustion takes place at a pressure of 16 psia?

11.3 Octane, C_8H_{18}, is burned with air.
(a) Determine the minimum mass of air required for complete combustion per lbm of octane.
(b) What is the volume of combustion products per lbm of fuel at 15 psia and 900°F?
(c) If the products of combustion are cooled isobarically to a temperature of 70°F, what is the volume per lbm of fuel?

(d) If 25 per cent excess air is used, determine the preceding volumes (at 900°F and 70°F) at 15 psia.

11.4 The volumetric analysis of natural gas is 21.2 per cent C_2H_6 and 78.8 per cent CH_4. Find
(a) The stoichiometric air-fuel ratio
(b) The percentage by mass of the hydrogen and carbon in the fuel
(c) The mass of CO_2 and H_2O formed per lbm of fuel.

11.5 The volumetric analysis of the products of combustion of a hydrocarbon fuel is as follows:

$$CO_2 = 12 \text{ per cent}$$

$$O_2 = 0 \text{ per cent}$$

$$CO = 0.8 \text{ per cent.}$$

If the relative humidity of the atmospheric air at 100°F used for combustion is 50 per cent, calculate
(a) The air-fuel ratio
(b) The hydrogen-carbon ratio by atoms
(c) The volume of the dry air supplied per mole of dry products.

11.6 Calculate the enthalpy of formation per lbm of propane $C_3H_8(g)$ if the enthalpy of combustion is $\Delta H° = -19,929$ Btu/lbm. The enthalpies of formation of H_2O and CO_2 are

$$\bar{h}°_{f_{H_2O}} = -57,797.9 \text{ cal/gm-mole}$$

$$\bar{h}°_{f_{CO_2}} = -94,051.8 \text{ cal/gm-mole.}$$

11.7 Using values of enthalpies of formation from Table 11.2, calculate the enthalpy of combustion of liquid octane at 77°F. (Assume liquid H_2O in the products of combustion.)

11.8 (a) Using values of enthalpies of formation for substances other than methane $CH_4(g)$, calculate the enthalpy of formation per lbm of methane if its enthalpy of combustion $\Delta H° = -21,502$ Btu/lbm. (b) Using values of enthalpies of formation, calculate the enthalpy of combustion of propane $C_3H_8(g)$ at the standard state. (Assume gaseous H_2O in the products.)

11.9 Calculate the enthalpy of reaction at 77°F when 1 mole of propane C_3H_8 is burned according to the following equation:

$$C_3H_8(g) + 5 O_2(g) \longrightarrow 3 CO_2(g) + 4 H_2O(l).$$

Assume steady-flow combustion process.

11.10 Calculate the adiabatic reaction temperature of methane at 77°F when burned with 200 per cent stoichiometric air at 340°F.

11.11 If the temperature of the products in the previous problem is reduced by 100°F, what is the amount of heat transfer to the environment?

11.12 Find the percentage of theoretical oxygen used in burning propane $C_3H_8(g)$ if the adiabatic reaction temperature is 2540°F. (Assume complete combustion, gaseous products, and the reactants to be at 77°F.)

11.13 The adiabatic reaction temperature when liquid heptane is burned in a steady-flow process is 2200°R. The initial temperature of the fuel is 77°F and the initial temperature of the air is 440°F. If the combustion process is complete, what is the percentage of excess air used? ($h_{fg} = 15,750$ Btu/lb mole)

11.14 Determine the change of entropy and the Gibbs free energy at the standard state for the reaction

$$CO(g) + \tfrac{1}{2} O_2(g) \longrightarrow CO_2(g).$$

Assume steady flow and reactants and products both at the standard state.

11.15 Determine the Gibbs free energy of formation of CO using the reaction

$$C(s) + \tfrac{1}{2} O_2(g) \longrightarrow CO(g).$$

Assume all reactants and products are at the standard state.

11.16 Calculate the Gibbs free energy change when propane C_3H_8 at 77°F and 1 atm is burned with 400 per cent theoretical air. Assume the products are at 77°F and 1 atm.

11.17 Noting that $dG = 0$ at equilibrium, compare the spontaniety of the vaporization and condensation of water at atmospheric pressure near its boiling point.

11.18 Determine the enthalpy of reaction and the entropy change when CO is burned at 5 atm and 500°F according to the reaction

$$CO(g) + \tfrac{1}{2} O_2(g) \longrightarrow CO_2(g).$$

Assume steady-flow process.

11.19 Using values of free energies from Table 11.2, calculate the equilibrium constant at 77°F and 1 atm for the reaction

$$CO_2(g) \rightleftharpoons CO(g) + \tfrac{1}{2} O_2(g).$$

11.20 Compute the equilibrium constant for the reaction

$$CH_4(g) + 2 O_2(g) \rightleftharpoons CO_2(g) + 2 H_2O(g),$$

at 77°F and 1 atm.

11.21 What will be the value of the equilibrium constant in the previous problem if the reaction takes place at 800°R?

11.22 What percentage of OH is formed when H_2O is heated to 5000°K at a pressure of 14.7 psia? ($K_p = 6.03$)

11.23 Nitrogen tetroxide N_2O_4 dissociates to nitrogen dioxide NO_2 at relatively low temperatures according to the equation $N_2O_4 \longrightarrow 2 NO_2$. If the degree of dissociation $\alpha = 18.46$ per cent at 25°C and 1 atm, what will be the degree of dissociation at 0.5 atm?

11.24   Octane (C_8H_{18}) is burned with the stoichiometric amount of air at atmospheric pressure. Determine the equilibrium composition of the products of combustion if the combustion temperature is 2500°R.

11.25   Compute the value of the equilibrium constant for the reaction

$$CO(g) + \tfrac{1}{2} O_2(g) \rightleftharpoons CO_2(g),$$

at a temperature 1000°K.

NOMENCLATURE

A	Constant	S	Entropy or Seebeck coefficient
B	Magnetic field strength	s	Entropy per unit mass
b	Darrieus function per unit mass	U	Internal energy
c	Velocity of sound	u	Internal energy per unit mass
c_p	Specific heat at constant pressure	r_c	Cut-off ratio
c_v	Specific heat at constant volume	r_v	Compression ratio
E	Electric field strength	r_p	Pressure ratio
e	Effectiveness	T	Absolute temperature
F	Thrust or force	t	Temperature
h	Enthalpy per unit mass	V	Volume or voltage
I	Irreversibility or electric current	V	Velocity
j	Current density	v	Specific volume or velocity
K	Thermal conductivity	W	Work
k	Boltzmann's constant	w	Work per unit mass
m	Mass	x	Quality
P	Power	Z	Figure of merit
p	Pressure	α	Ratio of specific heats $= \dfrac{c_p}{c_v}$
Q	Heat	ϕ	Electric potential
q	Heat per unit mass or electric charge	π	Peltier coefficient
		ψ	Availability function
R	Gas constant	ρ	Density or electrical resistivity
R	Electric resistance	η	Efficiency
$\mathscr{R}$	Universal gas constant	τ	Thomson coefficient

12

ANALYSIS OF THERMODYNAMIC CYCLES

12-1   In Chapter 4 it was shown that the Carnot cycle
Introduction   yields the best possible performance of all cycles
operating between a high-temperature source and a low-temperature heat
sink. In addition to being reversible, the Carnot cycle imposes no limitations
on the behavior of the working substance.

This chapter is concerned with the analysis of actual cycles. The Carnot
cycle serves as the starting point of an analysis, but then models are devised
to take into consideration the behavior of the working substances. Actual
cycles may approach standard or idealized cycles as an upper limit of
performance; however, the performance of the idealized cycle is still inferior
to that of the Carnot cycle.

Four basic types of idealized cycles will be considered: (a) the Rankine
vapor-power cycle; (b) the reciprocating internal combustion engine cycle;
(c) the Brayton gas turbine cycle; (d) the Rankine vapor-compression cycle.
These cycles will be discussed from the standpoint of both the thermodynamic analysis and the principles of operation. The treatment will not
extend to a discussion of physical equipment. Direct-energy conversion
systems are presented in the latter part of this chapter.

12-2   Idealized cycles employ ideal processes, such as
Ideal   the reversible adiabatic process, the reversible
Processes   isothermal process, the constant pressure process, etc. The performance obtained in many actual processes is almost
the same as that of ideal processes. An actual process becomes essentially an
adiabatic process when the system is thermally insulated or when the actual
process is so rapid that heat interaction between the system and its environment is negligible. Similarly, reversible isothermal processes may almost be
attained when the system is in contact with a thermal reservoir that allows
heat interaction to take place with very small temperature differences.

An important process encountered in ideal model cycles is the reversible adiabatic (isentropic) process. The compression of water in a pump or
the expansion of steam in a turbine is idealized by an isentropic process.
Actual processes deviate from isentropic processes because irreversibilities,
such as fluid or mechanical friction, inevitably occur during compression
or expansion. A real adiabatic process, therefore, is accompanied by an
increase in entropy. In a preliminary analysis, the pressure drop due to fluid
flow is usually neglected and emphasis is placed on the deviation of a
compression process or an expansion process from the ideal process.

In a compression process, the actual work done on a system is more
than the ideal work done on the system. The difference represents work
done to overcome irreversibilities in the actual process. For similar reasons,
the actual work done by a system in an expansion process is less than the
ideal work. The deviation of an actual process from the isentropic process

is indicated by *isentropic efficiency*. For a pump or a compressor the isentropic compression efficiency is defined by

$$\eta_{\text{isentropic}} = \frac{W_{\text{isentropic}}}{W_{\text{actual}}}.$$

Similarly, the isentropic expansion efficiency of a turbine or an engine is

$$\eta_{\text{isentropic}} = \frac{W_{\text{actual}}}{W_{\text{isentropic}}}.$$

**12-3
The Rankine
Vapor-power
Cycle**

In the Rankine cycle, a fluid is recirculated in a reversible closed cycle. The components of the Rankine cycle, also called the *standard vapor-power cycle*, are shown in Fig. 12.1. A steam power plant is a typical system which employs a steady-flow vapor-power

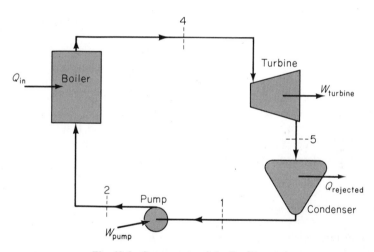

Fig. 12.1. *Components of the Rankine cycle.*

cycle. Although the present analysis deals with water as a working substance, it is equally applicable to any fluid. In the vapor-power cycle, water at low pressure and low temperature is compressed reversibly and adiabatically to the boiler pressure by the feed pump. Heat is then transferred to the water in the boiler at constant pressure. The heat interaction raises the temperature of the water to the saturation temperature. After evaporation, further transfer of heat superheats the vapor to a higher temperature. The superheated vapor then is allowed to expand reversibly and adiabatically in a steam engine or turbine to the condenser pressure. Condensation occurs at constant pressure in the condenser as heat is rejected from the hot vapors by cold water. The condensed steam then enters the boiler feed pump and the cycle is repeated. The *T-s* and *h-s* diagrams of the Rankine cycle are shown in Fig. 12.2. In cycle 1–2–3–4–5–1, there is no superheating of the vapor, whereas in cycle 1–2–3–4–6–7–1 superheating does occur. In both the

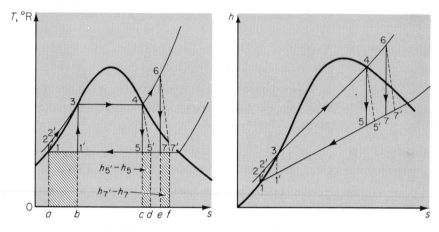

Fig. 12.2. *T-s and h-s diagrams of the Rankine cycle.*

steam generator and the condenser, heat is transferred at constant pressure; in both the pump and the turbine the flow is isentropic. Since constant-pressure and constant-temperature lines are identical in the liquid-vapor region, a Carnot cycle occurs if all four processes of the Rankine cycle are located in that region. Thus cycle 1′–3–4–5–1′ is a Carnot cycle.

The first law of thermodynamics may be applied in an analysis of the Rankine cycle 1–2–3–4–5–1. Neglecting changes in kinetic and potential energies, the following information is obtained, based on one lbm of fluid flowing under steady-state conditions:

Heat interaction in the boiler, $q_{2-4} = h_4 - h_2$.

Work done by the turbine, $w_{4-5} = h_4 - h_5$.

Heat rejected in the condenser, $q_{5-1} = h_5 - h_1$.

Work done on the pump, $w_{1-2} = h_2 - h_1$.

The thermal efficiency of the Rankine cycle is expressed as

$$\eta_{th} = \frac{w_{net,out}}{q_{in}} = \frac{w_{4-5} - w_{1-2}}{q_{2-4}} = \frac{(h_4 - h_5) - (h_2 - h_1)}{h_4 - h_2}$$

or

$$= 1 - \frac{q_{out}}{q_{in}} = 1 - \frac{h_5 - h_1}{h_4 - h_1}. \tag{12.1}$$

An expression for thermal efficiency may be obtained in terms of the average temperatures during the heat interaction processes. Noting that all processes in the Rankine cycle are reversible, the areas underneath these processes on the T-s diagram represent heat. The efficiency can then be written as

$$\eta_{th} = \frac{q_{in} - q_{out}}{q_{in}} = 1 - \frac{q_{5-1}}{q_{2-4}} = 1 - \frac{-\int_5^1 T\, ds}{\int_2^4 T\, ds}$$

$$= 1 - \frac{T_{avg,5-1}(s_5 - s_1)}{T_{avg,2-4}(s_4 - s_2)} = 1 - \frac{T_{avg,5-1}}{T_{avg,2-4}}. \tag{12.2}$$

Equation (12.2) provides a basis for comparing the thermal efficiencies of the Rankine and Carnot cycles. In the Carnot cycle $1'$–3–4–5–$1'$ shown on the T-s diagram of Fig. 12.2, the ratio of the heat rejected to the heat supplied is equal to the ratio of area $1'$–5–c–b to area 3–4–c–b. The corresponding ratio, for the Rankine cycle 1–2–3–4–5–1, is the ratio of area a–1–5–c to area a–2–3–4–c. Noting that a small value of this ratio means a higher value of efficiency, it becomes evident that the efficiency of the Rankine cycle is less than that of the Carnot cycle operating between the same thermal reservoirs. Note also that the average temperature at which heat is supplied in the Rankine cycle is less than that of the Carnot cycle.

A high Carnot efficiency requires a greater range of temperature between the low- and high-temperature thermal reservoirs. The lowest temperature is fixed by the temperature of the environment and the highest temperature is limited to the critical temperature. The latter is equal to 705.6°F in the case of water. For a fixed $T_{avg,5-1}$, Eq. (12.2) indicates that an increase in the thermal efficiency can be attained by raising the average temperature at which heat is supplied. This can be accomplished by superheating the steam to a high temperature. The average temperature, on the other hand, does not increase appreciably because most of the heat interaction takes place during the constant-temperature vaporization process. Thus, in general, it may be stated that higher boiler temperatures (and pressures) and lower condenser pressures improve the thermal efficiency. Superheating has also the added advantage of limiting the moisture content at the exhaust of the turbine to its maximum allowable value of 10 per cent. Moisture contents in excess of this value may cause the turbine blades and casing to erode.

In Fig. 12.2 the actual expansion in the turbine is represented by the irreversible line 4–$5'$ instead of by the isentropic expansion 4–5. Area c–5–$5'$–d–c is the resulting increase in the unavailable energy. The same conclusion can be reached by noting that the change of availability per unit mass during the expansion process is

$$\Delta\psi = b_5 - b_4 = (h_5 - h_4) - T_5(s_5 - s_4) = h_5 - h_4,$$

and the irreversibility is

$$I = -\Delta\psi - (-w) = (h_4 - h_5) - (h_4 - h_{5'}) = h_{5'} - h_5 = T_5(s_{5'} - s_5),$$

which is equal to area c–5–$5'$–d–c.

Another way of expressing the performance of a vapor-power cycle is in terms of the *heat rate*, defined as the heat input divided by the net work output; choosing 1 hp-hr ($= 2545$ Btu) or 1 kwhr ($= 3413$ Btu) as a unit output, then

$$\text{heat rate} = \frac{2545}{\eta_{\text{th}}} \quad \text{Btu/hp-hr} \tag{12.3a}$$

$$= \frac{3413}{\eta_{\text{th}}} \quad \text{Btu/kwhr}. \tag{12.3b}$$

The *steam rate* is defined as the amount of steam required to produce 1 hp-hr or 1 kwhr,

$$\text{steam rate} = \frac{2545}{W_{\text{net, out}}} \quad \text{lbm/hp-hr} \tag{12.4a}$$

$$= \frac{3413}{W_{\text{net, out}}} \quad \text{lbm/kwhr}. \tag{12.4b}$$

A major impracticality in the Carnot cycles as applied to steam power plants is the state of the working substance at the pump inlet. That state is in the mixed phase region which has a high value of specific volume and therefore requires a large pump to handle the wet compression process. This difficulty is surmounted in the Rankine cycle, since condensation continues to the saturated liquid line, thus reducing the volume appreciably.

It is clear from the foregoing discussion that the Rankine cycle represents a realistic model for the actual vapor-power cycle.

EXAMPLE 12.1: Superheated steam at 400 psia and 600°F enters the turbine of a steam power plant and expands to a condenser pressure of 1 psia. Assuming the isentropic efficiencies of the turbine and pump are 85 per cent and 80 per cent respectively and steady state to prevail, calculate
  (a) The thermal efficiency of the cycle
  (b) The heat rate in Btu/kwhr
  (c) The steam supply in lbm/hr to deliver 1000 kw
  (d) What is the corresponding Rankine cycle efficiency?

Solution: (a) Referring to Fig. 12.2, the work input to an ideal pump is

$$\text{ideal } w_p = h_2 - h_1 = \int_{p_1}^{p_2} v \, dp \simeq v_{f_1}(p_2 - p_1)$$

$$= \frac{0.01614(400 - 1)144}{778} = 1.193 \text{ Btu/lbm}.$$

The actual work input is

$$\text{actual } w_p = h_{2'} - h_1 \simeq \frac{v_{f_1}(p_2 - p_1)}{\eta_p} = \frac{1.193}{0.8} = 1.49 \text{ Btu/lbm}.$$

From steam tables, $h_1 = 69.70$ Btu/lbm. The enthalpy at point 2 is

$$h_2 = 69.70 + 1.193 = 70.893 \text{ Btu/lbm}$$

and

$$h_{2'} = 69.70 + 1.49 = 71.19 \text{ Btu/lbm}.$$

To calculate h_7 it is first necessary to determine the quality at state 7. At 400 psia and 600°F, $s_6 = s_7 = 1.5894$ Btu/lbm °R.
But

$$s_7 = s_{f_7} + x \, s_{fg_7}$$

then

$$1.5894 = 0.1326 + x(1.8456) \quad \text{or} \quad x = \frac{1.5894 - 0.1326}{1.8456} = 79 \text{ per cent}.$$

Hence h_7 is

$$h_7 = h_{f_7} + x h_{fg_7} = 69.7 + 0.79(1036.3) = 887.7 \text{ Btu/lbm}.$$

The preceding value of h_7 can also be determined from the Mollier diagram. For the turbine,

$$\text{ideal } w_{\text{turbine}} = h_7 - h_6 = 887.7 - 1306.9 = -419.2 \text{ Btu/lbm}$$

$$\text{actual } w_{\text{turbine}} = (h_7 - h_6)\eta_{\text{tur}} = h_{7'} - h_6 = (-419.2) \times 0.85 = -356 \text{ Btu/lbm}.$$

The thermal efficiency of the cycle 1–2′–3–6–7′–1 is

$$\eta_{\text{th}} = \frac{(h_6 - h_{7'}) - (h_{2'} - h_1)}{h_6 - h_{2'}}$$

$$= \frac{356 - 1.49}{1306.9 - 71.19} = \frac{354.51}{1235.71} = 28.7 \text{ per cent}.$$

(b) Heat rate $= \dfrac{3413}{0.287} = 11900$ Btu/kwhr.

(c)   Steam flow $= 1000 \left(\dfrac{3413}{w_{net,\,out}} \right) = 1000 \left(\dfrac{3413}{354.51} \right) = 9620$ lbm/hr.

(d)   The Rankine efficiency is

$$\eta_{Rankine} = \frac{(h_6 - h_7) - (h_2 - h_1)}{h_6 - h_2}$$

$$= \frac{419.2 - 1.193}{1306.9 - 70.893} = \frac{418}{1236} = 33.8 \text{ per cent.}$$

EXAMPLE 12.2:   Using the data of Example. 12.1, compare the Carnot and Rankine efficiencies. Assume saturated vapor to enter the turbine.

Solution: Referring to Fig. 12.2, the Carnot and Rankine efficiencies are

$$\eta_{Carnot} = \frac{T_{3-4} - T_{5-1'}}{T_{3-4}} = \frac{904.59 - 561.74}{904.59} = \frac{342.85}{904.59} = 37.9 \text{ per cent.}$$

$$\eta_{Rankine} = \frac{(h_4 - h_5) - (h_2 - h_1)}{h_4 - h_2} = \frac{(1204.5 - 829) - 1.193}{1204.5 - 70.893} = \frac{374.307}{1133.603}$$

$$= 33 \text{ per cent.}$$

12-4

Reheat Cycle

Two modifications of the Rankine cycle which improve the performance of steam power plants are the *reheat* and *regenerative* cycles.

The components of the reheat cycle are shown in Fig. 12.3. Figure 12.4 shows this cycle on a *T-s* and an *h-s* diagram. The vapor, after expanding in the high-pressure turbine, is returned to the boiler for further reheating before expanding in the low-pressure turbine. Reheating occurs essentially

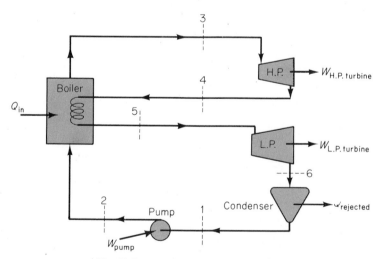

Fig. 12.3. *Components of the reheat cycle.*

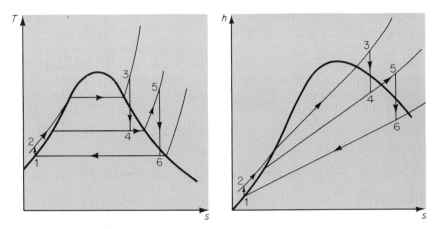

Fig. 12.4. *T-s and h-s diagrams of the reheat cycle.*

at constant pressure and raises the temperature of the steam to T_5 (usually equal to T_3), thus increasing the average effective temperature at which heat is supplied. Reheating has a twofold advantage. First, it avoids excessive moisture in the low-pressure end of the turbine. Low quality steam causes corrosion in the turbine blades. Second, although more energy is expended in the reheat cycle than in the Rankine cycle, a larger percentage of work is usually obtained. The net result is an improvement in the thermal efficiency. An increase in efficiency may thus be attained without an increase in the maximum pressure or temperature of the cycle. Note that the availability of energy is improved by reheating since a higher percentage of heat is supplied at a high temperature. Referring to Fig. 12.4, the efficiency of the reheat cycle is

$$\eta = \frac{(h_3 - h_4) + (h_5 - h_6) - (h_2 - h_1)}{(h_3 - h_2) + (h_5 - h_4)}. \tag{12.5}$$

EXAMPLE 12.3: Determine the enthalpy and entropy of the successive states of steam in a reheat cycle. The steam is supplied at 1100 psia and 740°F to the high-pressure turbine. After expansion to 200 psia it is reheated at constant pressure to 720°F before expanding in the the low-pressure turbine to 2 in. Hg. Determine: (a) the work output for the high- and low-pressure turbines; (b) the thermal efficiency and the steam rate of the cycle. Assume isentropic expansion and compression for the turbines and pump.

Solution: (a) From steam tables at 2 in. Hg, $h_f = 69.1$ Btu/lbm. The pump work is

$$w_p \simeq \frac{(1100 - 2 \times 0.491) \times 144 \times 0.01614}{778} = 3.29 \text{ Btu/lbm.}$$

The enthalpy at state 2 is

$$h_2 = 69.1 + 3.29 = 72.39 \text{ Btu/lbm.}$$

Using the steam tables or Mollier chart and the foregoing value of h_2, the values of the enthalpy and entropy at the successive states of the cycle may be determined. These are shown in Fig. 12.5. The work interactions in the high- and low-pressure turbines are

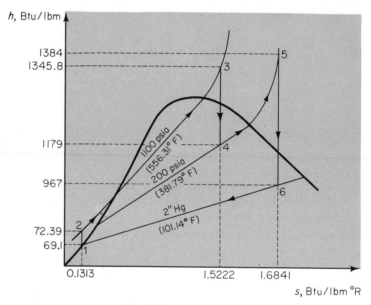

Fig. 12.5. *Example 12.3.*

$$w_{hp} = h_4 - h_3 = 1179 - 1345.8 = -166.8 \text{ Btu/lbm}$$
$$w_{lp} = h_6 - h_5 = 967 - 1384 \quad = -417 \text{ Btu/lbm.}$$

(b) The efficiency of the cycle, according to Eq. (12.5), is

$$\eta_{th} = \frac{166.8 + 417 - 3.29}{(1345.8 - 72.39) + (1384 - 1179)} = \frac{580.51}{1478.41} = 39.3 \text{ per cent.}$$

The steam rate $= \dfrac{2545}{580.51} = 4.39 \text{ lbm/hp-hr.}$

**12-5
Regenerative
Cycle**

The regenerative cycle is another modification of the Rankine cycle which results in an improvement in thermal efficiency. In actual cycles, the feed water enters the boiler at a temperature well below the saturation temperature corresponding to the boiler pressure (subcooled state). Upon heat interaction, the temperature rises first to the saturated liquid state before vaporization begins. This initial heating process constitutes a major irreversibility in the cycle because of the wide range of thermal potential between the combustion products and the water in the boiler. In the regenerative cycle, the degree of irreversibility is reduced by decreasing the temperature difference during this heat interaction process.

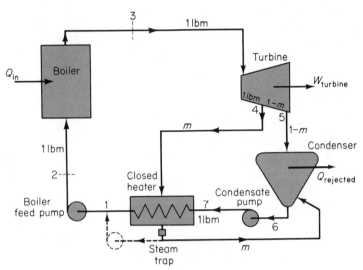

Fig. 12.6. *Components of the regenerative cycle.*

Figure 12.6 shows an ideal regenerative cycle. Part of the steam is extracted from the boiler at different stages and utilized to heat the feed water before it enters the boiler. Several heaters may be used. In each one, water is heated to within a few degrees from the saturation temperature corresponding to the extraction pressure. Ideally, if an infinite number of heaters are used, each heating the feed water an infinitesimal amount, the temperature of the feed water reaches the saturation temperature corresponding to the boiler pressure. The heating process thus approaches a reversible isothermal heat interaction process. The boiler in this case supplies only the energy necessary for vaporization and superheat. In actual cycles with a finite number of heaters, heat interaction cannot be reversible because of the temperature difference between the extracted steam and the water entering the heater. Note, however, that as the number of heaters is increased the heat transfer process takes place with a smaller temperature difference and consequently the irreversibility incurred in the process is decreased.

Analysis of the regenerative cycle is accomplished by performing a

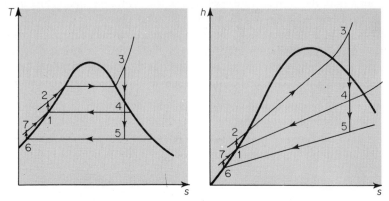

Fig. 12.7. *T-s and h-s diagrams of the regenerative cycle.*

mass balance and an energy balance on each component of the system. Referring to the *T-s* and *h-s* diagram of Fig. 12.7 consider 1 lbm of steam entering the turbine at state 3. Let *m* lbm be the mass (or mass fraction) extracted from the turbine at state 4 for feed water heating. The remaining mass (1 − *m*) continues to expand and perform work till the pressure drops to the condenser pressure. As the extracted steam of mass *m* condenses in the heater, it transfers its latent heat to the feed water flowing through the heater. The condensed steam then leaves the heater and flows to the condenser where it mixes with the (1 − *m*) lbm of steam entering the condenser from the turbine side. The total mass, 1 lbm, leaves the condenser and enters the heater as feed water. Under ideal and adiabatic conditions, the temperature of the condensed mass *m* and the feed water leaving the heater are the same and are represented by state 1. The feed water is then pumped to the boiler pressure and enters the boiler where it is heated to state 3 and the cycle is repeated.

Compared to the Rankine cycle operating between the same two extreme pressures, the regenerative cycle produces less work per lbm entering the turbine because less mass, (1 − *m*), is expanding between states 4 and 5. On the other hand, the amount of heat transfer from state 2 to state 3 is less than in the case of the Rankine cycle. When these two differences are taken into consideration and the two cycles analysed, the regenerative cycle shows an improvement in the thermal efficiency over the Rankine cycle. This increase in efficiency, as previously explained, is attributed to the decrease in irreversibility in the process of feed water heating. Referring to Fig. 12.7, the thermal efficiency of the regenerative cycle is

$$\eta_{th} = \frac{(1)(h_3 - h_4) + (1 - m)(h_4 - h_5) - w_{pump}}{(h_3 - h_2)} \qquad (12.6)$$

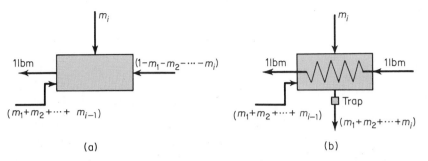

Fig. 12.8. *Open and closed heaters.*

Feed water heating takes place in either an *open* or a *closed* heater. In the open heater shown in Fig. 12.8(a), the extracted steam is allowed to mix with the incoming feed water. The mixture then proceeds to the boiler feed pump. In the closed heater shown in Fig. 12.8(b), the incoming feed water does not mix with the extracted steam and both streams flow separately through the heater. A steam trap, which allows only liquid to pass, is inserted in the condensed steam line leaving the heater to insure that all the extracted steam condenses before it leaves the heater. Most of the energy of the steam is thus released and delivered to the feed water. After passing through the steam trap, the condensate is either pumped into the feed water line leaving the heater or is connected to a lower pressure region, such as the condenser or a low-pressure heater. The choice of either scheme is a matter of economics in which the pumping cost is weighed against the cost of energy loss if the condensate goes to the condenser.

EXAMPLE 12.4: An ideal regenerative feed water heating cycle operates with steam supplied at 400 psia and 500°F, and condenser pressure of 2 in. Hg abs. Extraction points for two heaters (one closed and one open) are at 50 psia and 10 psia, respectively. Calculate the thermal efficiency of the plant, neglecting pump work.

Solution: Figure 12.9 shows the components of the cycle together with an *h-s* diagram. Assuming 1 lbm of steam enters the turbine, an energy balance on the closed heater gives

$$m_1 = \frac{h_8 - h_6}{h_2 - h_7} = \frac{250 - 161}{1078 - 250} = \frac{89}{828} = 0.1075 \text{ lbm/lbm.}$$

An energy balance on the open heater gives

$$m_1 h_7 + (1 - m_1 - m_2)h_5 + m_2 h_3 = (1)h_6$$

$$0.1075 \times 250 + (1 - 0.1075 - m_2) \times 69 + m_2 \times 974 = 161,$$

from which $m_2 = 0.0802$ lbm/lbm.

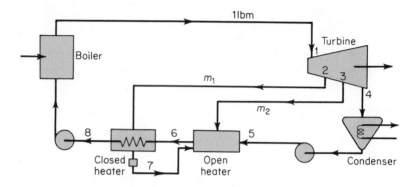

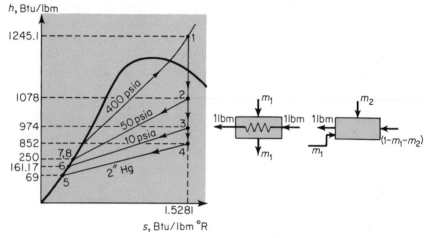

Fig. 12.9. Example 12.4.

The work done is

$$w = (1)(h_2 - h_1) + (1 - m_1)(h_3 - h_2) + (1 - m_1 - m_2)(h_4 - h_3)$$
$$= (1)(1078 - 1245) + (1 - 0.1075)(974 - 1078)$$
$$+ (1 - 0.1075 - 0.0802)(852 - 974) = -359 \text{ Btu/lbm.}$$

The thermal efficiency is

$$\eta_{th} = \frac{w_{net, out}}{h_1 - h_8} = \frac{359}{1245 - 250} = \frac{359}{995} = 36.1 \text{ per cent.}$$

EXAMPLE 12.5: From the data of Example 12.1, compare the efficiencies of the reheat and regenerative cycles. The reheat pressure in the reheat cycle is 40 psia, and the extraction pressure in the regenerative cycle is also 40 psia. Assume isentropic efficiencies for the turbines and boiler feed water pumps to be 100 per cent. (Neglect the power required for the condensate pump.)

Solution: (a) Regenerative cycle: Referring to Fig. 12.10(a), an energy balance on the feed water heater gives

$$m(h_4 - h_1) = (1 - m)(h_1 - h_6),$$

$$m(1106 - 236.03) = (1 - m)(236.03 - 69.7),$$

from which $m = 0.1605$ lbm/lbm. The work done on the boiler feed pump is

$$w_{1-2} = h_2 - h_1 \simeq v_1 \Delta p$$
$$= \frac{0.01715(400 - 40) \times 144}{778} = 1.142 \text{ Btu/lbm}.$$

The thermal efficiency, according to Eq. (12.6), is

$$\eta_{\text{th}} = \frac{(1306.9 - 1106) + (1 - 0.1605)(1106 - 887.7) - 1.142}{1306.9 - (236.03 + 1.142)}$$
$$= 35.8 \text{ per cent}.$$

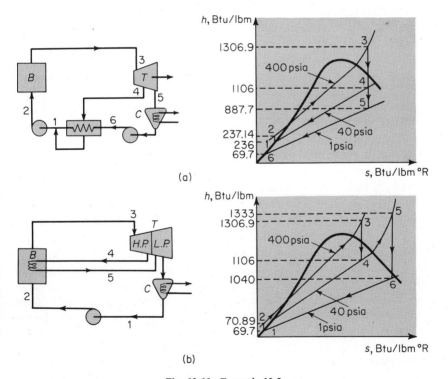

Fig. 12.10. Example 12.5.

(b) Reheat cycle: Referring to Fig. 12.10(b), the thermal efficiency, according to Eq. (12.5), is

$$\eta_{\text{th}} = \frac{(1306.9 - 1106) + (1333 - 1040) - 1.193}{(1306.9 - 70.89) - (1333 - 1106)} = 33.6 \text{ per cent}.$$

**12-6
Reciprocating
Internal Com-
bustion Engines** In internal combustion engines (referred to as I.C.E.), chemical energy is released within the engine cylinders as a result of the combustion of an air-fuel mixture. Reciprocating internal combustion engines operate on either a *four-stroke* cycle (suction, compression, expansion, and exhaust) or on a *two-stroke* cycle (compression and expansion). Some are ignited by a spark (spark-ignition engines), such as automotive engines; others are ignited by compression (compression-ignition engines), such as diesel engines.

Although the mechanical components of an engine go through complete cycles, the working fluid does not. When the air-fuel mixture is introduced into the cylinders of a spark-ignition engine, the vapors are compressed and ignited. The resulting combustion products are allowed to expand, and then they are discharged to the surrounding atmosphere. The cycle is then repeated with a fresh charge of an air-fuel mixture. This type of cycle is called an *open cycle* in contrast to the closed cycle in which the same fluid is constantly recirculated.

A *closed* standard cycle is based on the following conditions: (a) the working fluid is a perfect gas with constant specific heats; (b) all processes are reversible; (c) heat interaction occurs between the system and a high-temperature source (instead of combustion) and between the system and a low-temperature reservoir (in place of exhaust).

Even under ideal conditions the conversion of the chemical energy of the fuel into mechanical energy is incomplete. This is shown by the second law of thermodynamics. In actual engines the degree of conversion is less than in the ideal case because irreversible losses occur. These are associated with mechanical and fluid frictions. In addition, there is incomplete combustion; energy is also lost from the system as heat is transferred from the hot gases to the environment. An overall index of performance of I.C.E. is *thermal efficiency*, which is defined as the ratio of the net work output to the energy supplied to the engine. Other methods indicating certain aspects of engine performance include mechanical efficiency and volumetric efficiency.

The power developed by the cylinders of an engine as a result of the combustion process is measured by an engine indicator and is called *indicated horsepower* (Ihp). The power delivered by the engine shaft is called *brake horsepower* (bhp), and is less than the indicated horsepower. Some of the power is lost in mechanical friction and fluid friction during the transmission process; some of the power is consumed driving engine auxiliaries, such as fuel pump, generator, and water pump. The ratio of the bhp to the Ihp therefore indicates the *mechanical efficiency* of the engine:

$$\eta_{\text{mech}} = \frac{\text{bhp}}{\text{Ihp}}. \tag{12.7}$$

The performance of an engine also depends upon its aspirating capacity. During its suction stroke, the piston creates a partial vacuum in the cylinder, and air is therefore drawn into the cylinder. However, inertia of the air and the frictional resistance at the inlet ports tend to impede the flow of air and reduce the quantity of air that enters the cylinder. Insufficient air in the cylinders results in incomplete combustion, which means less engine power. A measure of this aspirating effect is given by the *volumetric efficiency*:

$$\eta_{vol} = \frac{m_{actual}}{m_{ideal}} = \frac{\dot{m}_{actual}}{\dot{m}_{ideal}}, \tag{12.8}$$

where m_{actual} = actual mass introduced in the cylinders,
m_{ideal} = ideal mass introduced in the cylinders.
In high-speed engines volumetric inefficiencies can represent large power losses. Improvement in volumetric efficiency can be achieved by a *supercharger*. The supercharger, which is essentially a low-pressure compressor, forces the air through the inlet ports into the cylinders at a pressure slightly higher than atmospheric. To justify the use of a supercharger, its power consumption must be less than the gain in power due to the increase in volumetric efficiency.

The Otto and Diesel standard cycles, used as ideal models for the spark-ignition and compression-ignition engines, will be discussed in the following sections.

12-7
Standard Otto Cycle

Figure 12.11 shows the standard Otto cycle on p-V and T-s diagrams. Considering a perfect gas with constant specific heats in a piston-cylinder arrangement, the Otto cycle is performed according to the following processes:

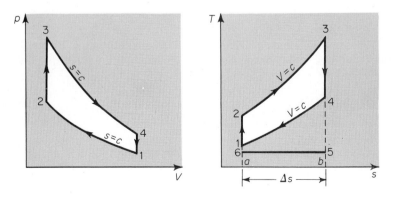

Fig. 12.11. Standard Otto cycle.

(a) Process 1–2 is a reversible adiabatic compression in which the perfect gas is compressed by the inward stroke of the piston. State 2 is at a higher temperature and pressure than state 1.

(b) During process 2–3 heat is transferred reversibly to the system at constant volume resulting in an increase in temperature, pressure, and entropy. The heat interaction is accomplished by allowing the system to come in contact with a high-temperature reservoir. The amount of heat transfer to the system is

$$Q_{2-3} = mc_v(T_3 - T_2).$$

(c) Process 3–4 is a reversible adiabatic expansion which takes place as the piston moves on its outward stroke. Both the temperature and pressure decrease.

(d) During process 4–1 heat is transferred reversibly from the system at a constant volume. The heat interaction between the system and a low-temperature reservoir (or environment) results in a decrease in temperature, pressure, and entropy. The amount of heat transferred from the system is

$$Q_{4-1} = mc_v(T_4 - T_1).$$

The thermal efficiency of the Otto cycle is

$$\eta_{th} = \frac{Q_{2-3} - Q_{4-1}}{Q_{2-3}} = 1 - \frac{Q_{4-1}}{Q_{2-3}} = 1 - \frac{mc_v(T_4 - T_1)}{mc_v(T_3 - T_2)}$$
$$= 1 - \frac{T_1}{T_2}\left[\frac{(T_4/T_1) - 1}{(T_3/T_2) - 1}\right].$$

The volumes and temperatures of the end states of the compression and expansion processes are given by the following isentropic relations:

$$\frac{T_2}{T_1} = \left(\frac{V_1}{V_2}\right)^{\gamma-1} = \left(\frac{V_4}{V_3}\right)^{\gamma-1} = \frac{T_3}{T_4}.$$

Thus

$$\frac{T_4}{T_1} = \frac{T_3}{T_2}.$$

The expression for efficiency then becomes

$$\eta_{th} = 1 - \frac{T_1}{T_2} = 1 - \frac{1}{r_v^{\gamma-1}}, \tag{12.9}$$

where r_v is called the *compression ratio* $= V_1/V_2 = V_4/V_3$. Note that the thermal efficiency is a function of the compression ratio r_v and specific heat ratio γ. For constant γ, an increase in the compression ratio results in an increase in thermal efficiency. A plot of η_{th} versus r_v of the air-standard cycle given by Eq. (12.9) is shown in Fig. 12.12. In spark-ignition engines

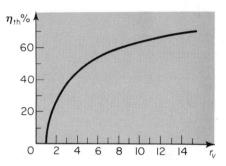

Fig. 12.12. *Thermal efficiency of the Otto cycle as a function of compression ratio ($\gamma = 1.4$).*

the upper limit of compression ratio is set by the ignition temperature of the fuel. The temperature of the air-fuel mixture at the end of the compression stroke must be below the fuel ignition temperature. If this limit is exceeded, a high-speed, high-pressure combustion wave (detonation wave) will propagate in the engine cylinder causing "engine knock."

Referring to the T-s diagram of Fig. 12.11, area a–2–3–b–a is equal to the amount of heat transferred to the system during the constant volume process 2–3. Since T_6 is the lowest temperature at which heat may be rejected, process 5–6 corresponds to the minimum possible heat rejection. The area above process 5–6 (area 6–2–3–5–6) is available energy; the area below it (area a–6–5–b–a) is unavailable energy. The rejection of heat along process 5–6 is however impractical, since it requires expansion to state 5 corresponding to a low pressure and to a temperature equal to that of the environment, followed by a constant temperature heat rejection along process 5–6. In the Otto cycle, rejection of heat is along process 4–1. This process divides the amount of heat input into available energy (area 1–2–3–4–1) and unavailable energy (area a–1–4–b–a). Note that area 6–1–4–5–6 represents the increase in unavailable energy due to heat rejection along 4–1 instead of along the constant temperature process 5–6.

EXAMPLE 12.6: An air-standard Otto cycle has a compression ratio of 8. At the start of the compression process, the temperature is 540°R and the pressure is 14 psia. If the maximum temperature of the cycle is 2000°F, determine: (a) the heat supplied per lbm of air; (b) the net work done per lbm of air; (c) the thermal efficiency of the cycle.

Solution: Referring to Fig. 12.11, the temperatures at states 2 and 4 are determined from isentropic process relations with $\gamma = 1.4$.

$$\frac{T_2}{T_1} = \left(\frac{V_1}{V_2}\right)^{\gamma-1} \quad \text{or} \quad T_2 = 540(8)^{0.4} = 1243°R$$

and

$$\frac{T_4}{T_3} = \left(\frac{V_3}{V_4}\right)^{\gamma-1} \quad \text{or} \quad T_4 = 2460(8)^{0.4} = 1070°R.$$

(a) Assuming air to be a perfect gas of $c_v = 0.1715$ Btu/lbm°R, the heat supplied per lbm of air is

$$q_{2-3} = c_v(T_3 - T_2) = 0.1715(2460 - 1243) = 209 \text{ Btu/lbm}.$$

(b) The work done per lbm of air is given by

$$w_{net} = -q_{4-1} - q_{2-3}$$

but

$$q_{4-1} = c_v(T_1 - T_4) = 0.1715(540 - 1070) = -91 \text{ Btu/lbm}$$

therefore,

$$w_{net} = 91 - 209 = -118 \text{ Btu/lbm}.$$

(c) The thermal efficiency is

$$\eta_{th} = \frac{w_{net,\,out}}{q_{2-3}} = \frac{118}{209} = 0.565 \quad \text{or} \quad 56.5 \text{ per cent}.$$

The preceding solution assumes constant specific heats throughout the wide temperature range of the cycle. More accurate answers may be obtained by considering the cycle as an open cycle and by taking the variation of the specific heats into account. Tables of isentropic relations given in Keenan and Kaye's *Gas Tables* may be used to give the following more accurate solution.

At $T_1 = 540°R$,

$$v_{r_1} = 144.32, \quad u_1 = 92.04 \text{ Btu/lbm}.$$

For the isentropic process 1–2,

$$v_{r_2} = v_{r_1}\left(\frac{V_2}{V_1}\right) = 144.32\left(\frac{1}{8}\right) = 18.04$$

at $v_{r_2} = 18.04$,

$$T_2 = 1211.5°R, \quad u_2 = 211.2 \text{ Btu/lbm}.$$

At 2000°F,

$$v_{r_3} = 2.327, \quad u_3 = 465.7 \text{ Btu/lbm}.$$

For the isentropic process 3–4,

$$v_{r_4} = v_{r_3}\left(\frac{V_3}{V_4}\right) = 2.237(8) = 17.896$$

at $v_{r_4} = 17.896$,

$u_4 = 211.86$ Btu/lbm.

(a) The heat supplied per lbm of air is

$q_{2-3} = u_3 - u_2 = 465.7 - 211.2 = 254.5$ Btu/lbm.

(b) The net work done per lbm of air is

$$w_{\text{net}} = -q_{4-1} - q_{2-3} = (211.86 - 92.04) - (465.7 - 211.2)$$
$$= -134.88 \text{ Btu/lbm.}$$

(c) The thermal efficiency is

$$\eta_{\text{th}} = \frac{w_{\text{net, out}}}{q_{\text{in}}} = \frac{134.88}{254.5} = 53 \text{ per cent.}$$

12-8
Standard Die-
sel Cycle
Compression-ignition reciprocating engines operate on the Diesel cycle. Figure 12.13 shows the standard Diesel cycle on p-V and T-s diagrams. During the compression stroke 1–2 a perfect gas with constant specific heats is compressed reversibly and adiabatically to a high temperature and pressure. Process 2–3 is a constant pressure heat interaction. The amount of heat transferred to the system is

$$Q_{2-3} = mc_p(T_3 - T_2).$$

In actual cycles the energy supplied to the engine is accomplished by

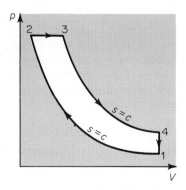
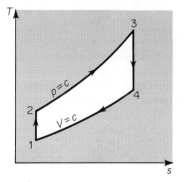

Fig. 12.13. *Standard Diesel cycle.*

fuel injection during process 2–3. The temperature after compression exceeds the fuel ignition temperature so that fuel ignites spontaneously upon injection into the combustion chamber.

The ratio V_3/V_2 is called the *cut-off ratio*. It is equal to the percentage of the stroke during which heat is supplied. Process 3–4 is a reversible adiabatic expansion in which the pressure and temperature decrease. Process 4–1 is a constant-volume heat rejection accompanied by a further decrease in temperature and pressure. The amount of heat rejected from the system is

$$Q_{4-1} = mc_v(T_4 - T_1).$$

The thermal efficiency of the Diesel cycle is

$$\eta_{th} = \frac{Q_{2-3} - Q_{4-1}}{Q_{2-3}} = 1 - \frac{Q_{4-1}}{Q_{2-3}} = 1 - \frac{mc_v(T_4 - T_1)}{mc_p(T_3 - T_2)}$$

$$= 1 - \frac{T_1[(T_4/T_1) - 1]}{\gamma T_2[(T_3/T_2) - 1]}.$$

Using isentropic relations between temperatures and volumes for processes 1–2 and 3–4, the foregoing expression becomes

$$\eta_{th} = 1 - \frac{1}{r_v^{\gamma-1}}\left[\frac{r_c^{\gamma} - 1}{\gamma(r_c - 1)}\right], \tag{12.10}$$

where r_c is the cut-off ratio $= V_3/V_2$.

Comparison of the expressions of the thermal efficiencies of the Otto and Diesel cycles, Eq. (12.9) and (12.10), shows that, for the same compression ratio, the Otto cycle is more efficient than the Diesel cycle. This conclusion may be verified by noting that when $r_c = 1$, Eq. (12.10) reduces to Eq. (12.9) and, when $r_c > 1$, the bracketed term of Eq. (12.10) is more than unity. Diesel cycles have, however, a higher compression ratio than Otto cycles, resulting in a higher efficiency.

EXAMPLE 12.7: A Diesel engine operates on the air-standard Diesel cycle. The engine has six cylinders of $4\frac{1}{8}$-in. bore and $4\frac{7}{8}$-in. stroke. The engine speed is 2000 rpm. At the beginning of compression the air is at 14 psia and 80°F. If the clearance volume is 12.5 per cent of the stroke volume, compute (a) compression ratio; (b) pressure and temperature of the air after compression; (c) thermal efficiency and power output if the air is heated to 2500°F.

Solution: (a) Referring to Fig. 12.13, V_2 is the clearance volume, thus

$$0.125 = \frac{V_2}{V_1 - V_2} = \frac{1}{(V_1/V_2) - 1} = \frac{1}{r_v - 1},$$

from which $r_v = 9$.

(b)   The specific volume at state 1 according to the perfect gas law is

$$v_1 = \frac{RT_1}{p_1} = \frac{53.3\,(540)}{14 \times 144} = 14.3 \text{ ft}^3/\text{lbm}.$$

Therefore,

$$v_2 = \frac{v_1}{r_v} = \frac{14.3}{9} = 1.59 \text{ ft}^3/\text{lbm}.$$

From gas tables at $T_1 = 540°\text{R}$,

$$v_{r_1} = 144.3, \quad p_{r_1} = 1.386, \quad u_1 = 92.04 \text{ Btu/lbm}.$$

Therefore,

$$v_{r_2} = v_{r_1}\left(\frac{v_2}{v_1}\right) = 144.3\left(\frac{1}{9}\right) = 16.05,$$

and from gas tables at $v_{r_2} = 16.05$,

$$T_2 = 1264°\text{R}, \quad p_{r_2} = 29.15, \quad h_2 = 307.7 \text{ Btu/lbm}.$$

The pressure at state 2 is

$$p_2 = p_1\left(\frac{p_{r_2}}{p_{r_1}}\right) = 14\left(\frac{29.15}{1.386}\right) = 294 \text{ psia},$$

or from the perfect gas law

$$p_2 = \frac{RT_2}{v_2} = \frac{53.3\,(1264)}{1.59 \times 144} = 294 \text{ psia}.$$

(c)   At $T_3 = 2960°\text{R}$,

$$h_3 = 778.97 \text{ BTU/lbm}, \quad v_{r_3} = 1.2332.$$

Therefore,

$$v_3 = \frac{RT_3}{p_3} = \frac{53.3\,(2960)}{294 \times 144} = 3.73 \text{ ft}^3/\text{lbm},$$

$$v_{r_4} = v_{r_3}\left(\frac{v_4}{v_3}\right) = 1.2332\left(\frac{14.3}{3.73}\right) = 4.72,$$

and from gas tables at $v_{r_4} = 4.72$,

$$T_4 = 1933°\text{R}, \quad u_4 = 353.67 \text{ Btu/lbm}.$$

The thermal efficiency of the cycle is

$$\eta_{\text{th}} = 1 - \frac{q_{\text{out}}}{q_{\text{in}}} = 1 - \frac{u_4 - u_1}{h_3 - h_2} \cdot$$

$$= 1 - \frac{353.67 - 92.04}{778.97 - 307.7} = 1 - \frac{261.63}{471.27} = 44.5 \text{ per cent}.$$

The volume V_1 of each cylinder is

$$V_1 = V_{\text{clearance}} + V_{\text{displacement}},$$

where

$$V_{\text{disp}} = \frac{(\pi/4)(4.125)^2 \times 4.875}{1728} = 0.038 \text{ ft}^3;$$

hence

$$V_1 = 0.125(0.038) + 0.038 = 0.0425 \text{ ft}^3.$$

The mass of the air for the six cylinders is

$$m = \frac{6V_1}{v_1} = \frac{6 \times 0.0425}{14.2} = 0.0179 \text{ lbm}.$$

The work output is

$$W = mw = 0.0179(471.27 - 261.63) = 3.75 \text{ Btu,}$$

and the power developed is

$$P = W \times \frac{rpm}{2} = \frac{3.75 \times 1000 \times 60}{2545} = 88.4 \text{ hp}.$$

12-9
Dual Cycle
Combustion in the Otto cycle is based on a constant-volume process; in the Diesel cycle it is based on a constant-pressure process. But combustion in actual spark-ignition engines requires an appreciable amount of time if the process is to go to completion. For this reason, combustion in Otto cycle engines does not actually occur under constant-volume conditions. Similarly, in compression-ignition engines, combustion does not occur under constant-pressure conditions because of the rapid, uncontrolled combustion process.

The operation of the reciprocating I.C.E. represents a compromise

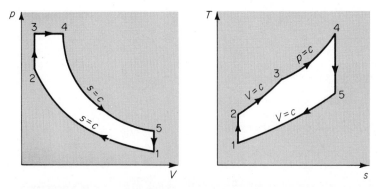

Fig. 12.14. *Standard dual cycle.*

between the Otto cycle and the Diesel cycle, and can be described as a dual-combustion or a limited-pressure standard cycle. Figure 12.14 shows the cycle on p-V and T-s diagrams. Heat transfer to the system may be considered to occur first at constant-volume and then at constant-pressure. In the actual system, injection of fuel is started during the compression stroke, and continues during part of the return stroke. The efficiency of the limited-pressure standard cycle may be shown to be

$$\eta_{\text{th}} = 1 - \frac{T_5 - T_1}{T_3 - T_2 + \gamma(T_4 - T_3)}. \tag{12.11}$$

12-10
The Gas Tur-
bine Cycle

The gas turbine is a rotary type of internal combustion engine. As shown in Fig. 12.15, the gas turbine plant consists of a compressor, a combustion chamber, and a turbine. After compression, air enters the combustion chamber into which fuel is injected. The mixture of fuel and air burns, and the combustion occurs at a fairly constant pressure. The resulting products of combustion then expand and drive the turbine wheel, before they are discharged into the atmosphere.

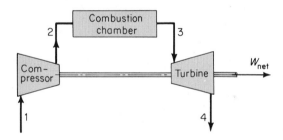

Fig. 12.15. *Simple gas turbine plant.*

The ideal cycle for the gas turbine is the *Brayton* or *Joule* cycle. This cycle is of the closed type utilizing a perfect gas with constant specific heats as a working fluid. The combustion and heat rejection processes of actual cycles are idealized by heat interactions between thermal reservoirs and the working fluid. The Brayton cycle is shown in Fig. 12.16 on p-V and T-s diagrams. It consists of the following processes:

(a) Process 1–2 is a reversible adiabatic compression in which both the temperature and the pressure of the system increase.

(b) During process 2–3 the system is brought in contact with a high-temperature thermal reservoir and reversible heat interaction takes place at constant pressure. The heat interaction process increases both the temperature and the entropy of the system. The amount of heat transferred to the system is

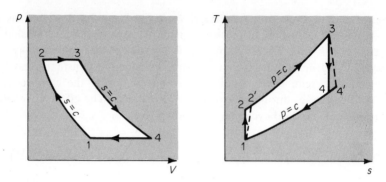

Fig. 12.16. *Brayton cycle.*

$$Q_{2-3} = mc_p(T_3 - T_2).$$

(c) Process 3–4 is a reversible adiabatic expansion in which the temperature and pressure decrease.

(d) Process 4–1 is a reversible constant-pressure heat rejection. The amount of heat rejected from the system is

$$Q_{4-1} = mc_p(T_4 - T_1).$$

The thermal efficiency of the Brayton cycle is

$$\eta_{\text{th}} = \frac{Q_{2-3} - Q_{4-1}}{Q_{2-3}} = 1 - \frac{Q_{4-1}}{Q_{2-3}} = 1 - \frac{mc_p(T_4 - T_1)}{mc_p(T_3 - T_2)}$$

$$= 1 - \frac{T_1(T_4/T_1 - 1)}{T_2(T_3/T_2 - 1)}.$$

The pressures and temperatures of the end states of the compression and expansion processes are given by the following isentropic relations:

$$\frac{T_2}{T_1} = \left(\frac{p_2}{p_1}\right)^{(\gamma-1)/\gamma} = \left(\frac{p_3}{p_4}\right)^{(\gamma-1)/\gamma} = \frac{T_3}{T_4}.$$

Hence

$$\frac{T_4}{T_1} = \frac{T_3}{T_2}.$$

The expression for the thermal efficiency of the Brayton cycle then becomes

$$\eta_{\text{th}} = 1 - \frac{T_1}{T_2} = 1 - \frac{1}{(p_2/p_1)^{(\gamma-1)/\gamma}} = 1 - \frac{1}{r_p^{(\gamma-1)/\gamma}}, \tag{12.12}$$

where r_p is called the *pressure ratio* $= p_2/p_1 = p_3/p_4$. Note that the efficiency of the Brayton cycle increases as the pressure ratio is increased. Equation (12.12) also indicates that, for the same pressure ratio and specific heat ratio, all Brayton cycles have the same thermal efficiency. An expression for the optimum pressure ratio corresponding to maximum work output (Problem 12.17) is given by

$$r_p = \left(\frac{T_3}{T_1}\right)^{\gamma/[2(\gamma-1)]}, \tag{12.13}$$

and the maximum work done per unit mass is

$$w = c_p T_1 [r_p^{(\gamma-1)/\gamma} - 1] + c_p T_3 \left[\frac{1}{r_p^{(\gamma-1)/\gamma}} - 1\right]. \tag{12.14}$$

Gas turbines may operate either on a closed or on an open cycle. Closed cycles are typical in power plants using nuclear reactors as an energy source. A suitable fluid transfers the energy from the reactor to the gas turbine either directly or by means of a secondary fluid through a heat exchanger. The majority of gas turbines currently in use operate on the open cycle in which the working fluid, after completing the cycle, is exhausted to the atmosphere. The air-fuel ratio used in these gas turbines is approximately 60: 1.

The compressor and turbine in gas-turbine plants are usually mounted on the same shaft and a large percentage of the power developed by the turbine is utilized to drive the compressor. The compressor power requirement varies from 40 per cent to 80 per cent of the power output of the turbine. The remainder is net power output. This high power requirement of the compressor is typical when a gas is compressed because of the large specific volume of gases in comparison to that of liquids. In the case of steam power plants, for example, the pump requirement is only a very small percentage of the turbine output. This is not true in gas-turbine power plants. Hence, careful design of the compressor is mandatory in order to minimize the power required for compression. Even with this drawback, the gas-turbine power plant has many advantages: It can operate with different fuels; it is simple in construction and easier to maintain; it has a small power-to-weight ratio; it can handle large volumes of gas compared to reciprocating engines. Gas turbines, on the other hand, cannot withstand high temperatures because of the continuous exposure of some of the components to a high unchanging temperature.

EXAMPLE 12.8: An open-cycle gas-turbine power plant receives air at 14 psia and 70°F. The air is compressed to 75 psia and reaches a maximum temperature of 1200°F in the combustion chamber. The hot air expands in the turbine back to 14 psia. Assuming an air-standard cycle, compute the thermal efficiency of the plant if the compressor and turbine are each 83 per cent efficient. What is the ratio of the work required to drive the compressor to the work developed by the turbine?

Solution: Figure 12.16 shows the different processes of the cycle. At $t_1 = 70°F$, the gas tables give

$$p_{r_1} = 1.2983, \quad h_1 = 126.66 \text{ Btu/lbm.}$$

Therefore,

$$p_{r_2} = p_{r_1}\left(\frac{p_2}{p_1}\right) = 1.2983\left(\frac{75}{14}\right) = 6.95.$$

From gas tables at $p_{r_2} = 6.95$,

$$h_2 = 204.8 \text{ Btu/lbm},$$

$$h_{2'} = h_1 + \frac{h_2 - h_1}{\eta_{\text{comp}}} = 126.7 + \left(\frac{204.8 - 126.7}{0.83}\right) = 220.9 \text{ Btu/lbm.}$$

At $t_3 = 1200°F$,

$$p_{r_3} = 82.83, \quad h_3 = 411.82 \text{ Btu/lbm},$$

$$p_{r_4} = p_{r_3}\left(\frac{p_4}{p_3}\right) = 82.83\left(\frac{14}{75}\right) = 15.47.$$

From gas tables at $p_{r_4} = 15.47$,

$$h_4 = 257.21 \text{ Btu/lbm}, \quad T_4 = 1065°R,$$

$$h_{4'} = h_3 - \eta_{\text{turb}}(h_3 - h_4) = 411.8 - 0.83(411.8 - 257.2) = 283.7 \text{ Btu/lbm.}$$

The thermal efficiency of the cycle is

$$\eta_{\text{th}} = \frac{(h_3 - h_{4'}) - (h_{2'} - h_1)}{h_3 - h_{2'}} = \frac{(411.8 - 283.7) - (220.9 - 126.7)}{411.8 - 220.9}$$

$$= \frac{128.1 - 94.2}{190.9} = 17.75 \text{ per cent.}$$

The compressor-turbine work ratio $= \dfrac{h_{2'} - h_1}{h_3 - h_{4'}} = \dfrac{220.9 - 126.66}{411.82 - 283.7} = 0.735$

12-11
Regenerative
Gas-Turbine
Cycle

In the simple gas-turbine cycle, the temperature of the exhaust gases leaving the turbine is higher than the temperature of air leaving the compressor. Utilization of any of the energy of the exhaust gases, which are otherwise discarded to the environment, results in an improvement in the thermal efficiency of the turbine. The exhaust gases can therefore heat the air entering the combustion chamber, thereby reducing

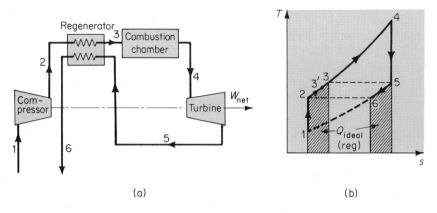

(a)   (b)

Fig. 12.17. *Regenerative Brayton cycle.*

the energy requirement of the fuel. Figure 12.17(a) shows a gas-turbine plant in which a regenerator is incorporated between the compressor and the combustion chamber. The hot gases, upon leaving the turbine, enter the regenerator where they transfer heat to the compressed air. Figure 12.17(b) shows the T-s diagram of a regenerative gas-turbine cycle. In a counterflow regenerator, the temperature difference between the exhaust gases and the air can be made very small, thus approaching reversible conditions. Under ideal conditions, the temperature of the air leaving the regenerator is then equal to the temperature of the exhaust gases entering the regenerator ($T_5 = T_3$). This condition forms the basis for calculating *regenerator effectiveness*, which is defined as

$$e_{reg} = \frac{h_{3'} - h_2}{h_5 - h_6},$$

where $h_{3'}$ is the enthalpy of the air leaving the regenerator. Note that an ideal situation exists if the air leaves at state 3; the effectiveness then would be unity.

Since $h_5 = h_3$ and $h_6 = h_2$, then

$$e_{reg} = \frac{h_{3'} - h_2}{h_3 - h_2}. \tag{12.15}$$

For a perfect gas with constant specific heats, the preceding equation becomes

$$e_{reg} = \frac{T_{3'} - T_2}{T_3 - T_2}. \tag{12.16}$$

An expression of the thermal efficiency for the ideal regenerative gas-turbine cycle is

$$\eta_{th} = 1 - \frac{Q_{out}}{Q_{in}} = 1 - \frac{h_6 - h_1}{h_4 - h_3}.$$

For a perfect gas with constant specific heats, this expression becomes

$$\eta_{th} = 1 - \frac{T_6 - T_1}{T_4 - T_3}$$

but $T_3 = T_5$ and $T_6 = T_2$, therefore

$$\eta_{th} = 1 - \frac{T_2 - T_1}{T_4 - T_5} = 1 - \frac{T_1[(T_2/T_1) - 1]}{T_4[1 - (T_5/T_4)]}.$$

Substituting for the temperature ratios from the isentropic relations

$$\frac{T_2}{T_1} = \left(\frac{p_2}{p_1}\right)^{(\gamma-1)/\gamma} \quad \text{and} \quad \frac{T_5}{T_4} = \left(\frac{p_1}{p_2}\right)^{(\gamma-1)/\gamma}$$

gives

$$\eta_{th} = 1 - \left(\frac{T_1}{T_4}\right)\left(\frac{p_2}{p_1}\right)^{(\gamma-1)/\gamma}. \tag{12.17}$$

According to Eq. (12.17), thermal efficiency in a regenerative cycle depends on the ratio of the two extreme temperatures T_1/T_4 as well as on the pressure ratio. Comparison of Eqs. (12.12) and (12.17) shows an improvement in thermal efficiency when a regenerator is used.

EXAMPLE 12.9: An ideal regenerative heater is added to the cycle of Example 12.8. If the air is heated to 635°F before it enters the combustor, what is the thermal efficiency and what is the effectiveness of the regenerator?

Solution: At $t = 635°F$, $h = 264.7$ Btu/lbm. From Example 12.8, the net work output is $= 33.9$ Btu/lbm. The heat transferred to the system is

$$q = 411.8 - 264.7 = 147.1 \text{ Btu/lbm.}$$

The thermal efficiency is

$$\eta_{th} = \frac{33.9}{147.1} = 23 \text{ per cent}$$

and

$$e_{reg} = \frac{264.7 - 220.9}{283.7 - 220.9} = \frac{43.8}{62.8} = 69.8 \text{ per cent.}$$

12-12
Turbo-jet

A turbo-jet operates on an open gas-turbine cycle, and generates a high-velocity gas stream. The turbo-jet engine consists of the same type of components as in the gas turbine plant, but in addition it contains an expansion nozzle. As shown

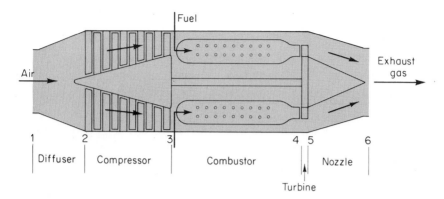

Fig. 12.18. *Turbo-jet engine.*

in Fig. 12.18, the components are an inlet diffuser, compressor, combustor, turbine, and exit nozzle. The cycle of an ideal turbo-jet engine appears on a *T-s* diagram in Fig. 12.19. Air entering the diffuser is decelerated and slightly compressed, changing from state 1 to state 2. The air entering the

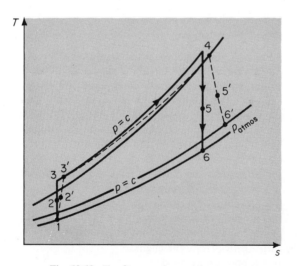

Fig. 12.19. *T-s diagram for a turbo-jet engine.*

compressor is further compressed proceeding from state 2 to state 3. The compressed air then enters the combustor where it is heated at constant pressure from state 3 to state 4. In the turbine, the air expands from state 4 to state 5, and further expansion takes place in the exit nozzle to state 6. As a result of the momentum of the exhaust gases flowing at high velocity from the nozzle, the engine exerts a forward thrust. In actual turbo-jets, a slight pressure drop occurs in the combustor. Also, the compression and expansion processes are not quite isentropic. These nonideal processes are shown as dotted lines in Fig. 12.19.

Since the entire power output of the turbine is directed toward driving the compressor, turbo-jets are usually rated in terms of *specific thrust*, which is defined as the thrust force divided by the air flow rate.*

$$F_{\text{specific}} = \frac{F}{\dot{m}_{\text{air}}}. \tag{12.18}$$

Assuming that atmospheric pressure acts on the turbo-jet and neglecting the momentum of the fuel at the entrance, the *thrust* of the turbo-jet, from the momentum equation, is

$$F = \left(\frac{\dot{m}_a + \dot{m}_f}{g_c}\right) V_6 - \frac{\dot{m}_a}{g_c} V_1 = \frac{\dot{m}_a}{g_c}\left[\left(1 + \frac{m_f}{m_a}\right) V_6 - V_1\right], \tag{12.19}$$

where V_1 and V_2 are the velocities of the flow entering and leaving the system, and subscripts a and f refer to air and fuel respectively. The *specific thrust* is

$$F_{\text{sp}} = \frac{1}{g_c}\left[\left(1 + \frac{m_f}{m_a}\right) V_6 - V_1\right]. \tag{12.20}$$

EXAMPLE 12.10:   A jet-propelled plane consuming air at the rate of 40 lbm/sec, is to fly at a Mach number† 0.6 at an altitude of 15,000 ft ($p = 8.0$ psia, $t = 0°F$). The diffuser, which has a pressure coefficient of 0.9, decelerates the flow to a negligible velocity. The compressor pressure ratio is 5 and the maximum temperature in the combustion chamber is 1840°F. After expanding in the turbine, the gases continue to expand in the nozzle to a pressure of 10 psia. The isentropic efficiencies of the compressor, turbine, and nozzle are, respectively, 0.81, 0.85, and 0.915. The enthalpy of combustion of the fuel $\Delta h° = -20,000$ Btu/lbm. Assuming that the products of combustion have the same properties as air, find

   (a)   The power input to the compressor
   (b)   The power output of the turbine
   (c)   The fuel-air ratio on a mass basis
   (d)   The exit Mach number
   (e)   The thrust provided by the engine
   (f)   The thrust power developed.

Solution: (a), (b) Referring to Figs. 12.18 and 12.20, the velocity at the inlet of the diffuser is

*The specific thrust may alternatively be defined as the thrust force divided by the flow rate of the fuel, rather than of the air.
†The *Mach number* is the ratio of local flow velocity to the local velocity of sound $\left(M = \dfrac{V}{c}\right)$. For a perfect gas, $M = \dfrac{V}{\sqrt{\gamma g_c RT}}$, and $c = 49\sqrt{T}$ for air.

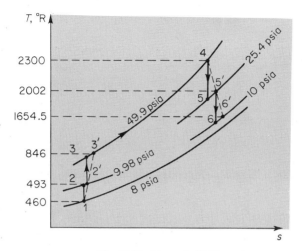

Fig. 12.20. *Example 12.10.*

$$V_1 = M_1 c_1 = 0.6 \,(49 \sqrt{460}) = 632 \text{ ft/sec.}$$

From gas tables at $T_1 = 460°R$, $h_1 = 109.9$ Btu/lbm. Since the velocity at point 2 is negligible, then

$$h_2 = h_{2'} = h_1 + \frac{V_1^2}{2g_c} = 109.9 + \frac{(632)^2}{64.35 \times 778} = 109.9 + 7.98$$

$$= 117.88 \text{ Btu/lbm of air.}$$

At $h_2 = 117.88$ Btu/lbm, $T_2 = 493°R$.

For isentropic flow in the diffuser

$$\frac{p_2}{p_1} = \left(\frac{T_2}{T_1}\right)^{\gamma/(\gamma-1)},$$

from which

$$p_2 = 8 \left(\frac{493}{460}\right)^{1.4/0.4} = 10.2 \text{ psia,}$$

$$p_{2'} = p_1 + \eta_{\text{diff}}(p_2 - p_1) = 8 + 0.9(10.2 - 8) = 9.98 \text{ psia.}$$

At state $2'$, $p_{r_{2'}} = 1.0081$. Therefore

$$p_{r_3} = \left(\frac{p_3}{p_{2'}}\right) p_{r_{2'}} = 5(1.0081) = 5.0405, \text{ giving } h_3 = 186.8 \text{ Btu/lbm of air.}$$

$$h_{3'} = h_{2'} + \frac{h_3 - h_{2'}}{\eta_{\text{comp}}} = 117.88 + \left(\frac{186.8 - 117.88}{0.81}\right) = 203 \text{ Btu/lbm of air.}$$

At $h_{3'} = 203$ Btu/lbm, $T_{3'} = 846°R$ and $p_3 = 5(9.98) = 49.9$ psia.

The work done on the compressor is $w = h_{3'} - h_2 = (203 - 117.88) = 85.12$ Btu/lbm of air. The power input to the compressor is

$$\dot{m}_{air}(h_{3'} - h_2) = \frac{40(203 - 117.88) \times 3600}{2545}$$

$$= 4820 \text{ hp,}$$

which is equal to the power output from the turbine.

(c) At $T_4 = 2300°R$, $h_4 = 588.82$ Btu/lbm, $p_{r_4} = 308.1$.

Neglecting changes in kinetic energies, the first law applied to the combustor gives

$$\dot{m}_a(h_{3'} - h°)_a + \dot{m}_f(h_3 - h°)_f + \dot{m}_f(-\Delta h°)_f = (\dot{m}_a + \dot{m}_f)(h_4 - h_4°)_p,$$

where superscript $(°)$ refers to the standard state at 77°F, and subscripts a, f, and p refer to air, fuel, and products respectively. Assuming that the fuel is introduced at 77°F, the preceding equation may be written

$$(h_{3'} - h°)_a + \frac{\dot{m}_f}{\dot{m}_a}(-\Delta h°)_f = \left(1 + \frac{\dot{m}_f}{\dot{m}_a}\right)(h_4 - h_4°)_p.$$

Assuming that the properties of the products are the same as those of air, then

$$(203 - 128.3) + \frac{\dot{m}_f}{\dot{m}_a}(20,000) = \left(1 + \frac{\dot{m}_f}{\dot{m}_a}\right)(588.82 - 128.3),$$

from which

$$\frac{\dot{m}_f}{\dot{m}_a} = 0.0197, \quad \text{and} \quad \frac{\dot{m}_a}{\dot{m}_p} = 0.98.$$

(d) The work done on the compressor $= 85.12 \times 0.98 = 83.5$ Btu/lbm of products. The enthalpy at the exit of the turbine is

$$h_{5'} = 588.82 - 83.5 = 505.32 \text{ Btu/lbm of products,}$$

corresponding to a temperature $T_{5'} = 2002°R$ and $p_{r_{5'}} = 174.7$. For the isentropic expansion

$$h_5 = h_4 - \frac{h_4 - h_{5'}}{\eta_{turbine}} = 588.82 - \left(\frac{83.5}{0.85}\right)$$

$$= 588.82 - 98.3 = 490.52 \text{ Btu/lbm of products.}$$

At $h_5 = 490.52$, $p_{r_5} = 156.7$,

$$p_5 = p_{5'} = p_4\left(\frac{p_{r_5}}{p_{r_4}}\right) = 49.9\left(\frac{156.7}{308.1}\right) = 25.4 \text{ psia.}$$

$$p_{r_6} = \left(\frac{p_6}{p_{5'}}\right)p_{r_{5'}} = \frac{10}{25.4}(174.7) = 68.8,$$

corresponding to $h_6 = 391.2$ Btu/lbm of products. The velocity at exit of the nozzle is

$$V_{6'} = \eta_{\text{nozzle}} \sqrt{2g_c(h_{5'} - h_6)}$$
$$= 0.915 \sqrt{64.35 \times 778(505.32 - 391.2)} = 2180 \text{ ft/sec.}$$
$$h_{6'} = h_{5'} - \frac{V_{6'}^2}{2g_c} = 505.32 - \frac{(2180)^2}{64.35 \times 778} = 505.32 - 95$$
$$= 410.32 \text{ Btu/lbm,}$$

corresponding to a temperature $T_{6'} = 1654.5°$R. The Mach number at the exit is

$$M_{6'} = \frac{V_{6'}}{49 \sqrt{T_{6'}}} = \frac{2180}{49 \sqrt{1654.5}} = 1.092$$

(e)   Neglecting the difference in pressure forces on the turbo-jet and assuming that the momentum of the fuel at entrance is small, the thrust force is

$$F = \frac{\dot{m}_a}{g_c}\left[\left(1 + \frac{\dot{m}_f}{\dot{m}_a}\right)V_{6'} - V_1\right] = \frac{40}{32.174}[(1 + 0.0197)2180 - 632] = 1974 \text{ lbf.}$$

(f)   The thrust power is

$$P = \frac{FV_1}{550} = \frac{1974 \times 632}{550} = 2265 \text{ hp.}$$

**12-13
Stage Com-
pression and
Expansion**   In Section 12–11 it was shown that the regenerative gas-turbine cycle reduces the amount of fuel consumed in the combustion chamber and consequently results in an improvement in thermal efficiency. Another improvement in thermal efficiency may be obtained by adhering to isothermal rather than to isentropic compression and expansion processes. As shown in Fig. 12.21 isothermal

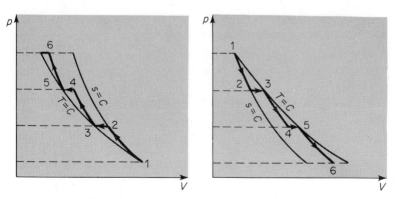

Fig. 12.21. *Stage compression and stage expansion.*

compression and expansion result, respectively, in minimum work input and maximum work output during a flow process. Hence by adhering to isothermal processes, the work input to the compressor is reduced while the work output from the turbine is increased resulting in an increase in the net work output. But the isothermal compression or expansion requires an infinite number of stages of intercoolers and reheaters, a situation similar to that encountered in regenerative feed water heating in vapor-compression power cycles. In practice, a finite number of stage compression with inter-cooling and stage expansion with heating is used as a substitute for the isothermal process. Figure 12.21 shows the sequence of processes (represented by 1–2–3–4–5–6) with three stages of compression or expansion. Cooling or heating takes place at constant pressure. A gas turbine regenerative cycle with a double-stage compression with intercooling, and a double-stage expansion with reheating is shown in Fig. 12.22. The thermal efficiency of this cycle is

$$\eta_{th} = 1 - \frac{(h_{10} - h_1) + (h_2 - h_3)}{(h_6 - h_5) + (h_8 - h_7)}. \tag{12.21}$$

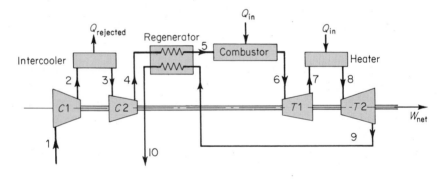

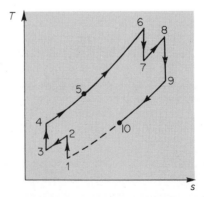

Fig. 12.22. *Regenerative Brayton cycle with stage compression and stage expansion.*

12-14 **Refrigeration** **Cycles** A refrigeration system removes heat from a low-temperature region and transfers heat to a high-temperature region. Refrigeration can be accomplished by noncyclic methods, such as by melting ice or by subliming carbon dioxide (dry ice), or by cyclic methods. Refrigeration cycles are analogous to power cycles and may be classified as gas-compression cycles or vapor-compression cycles. Of these two, the vapor-compression cycle is more commonly used and will be discussed in the following sections.

The Carnot cycle can serve as the model of the ideal refrigeration cycle. Considering all refrigerators operating between the same two thermal reservoirs, the maximum coefficient of performance is attained by the

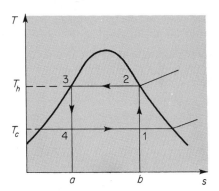

Fig. 12.23. *Carnot refrigeration cycle.*

Carnot refrigeration cycle. Figure 12.23 shows the Carnot refrigeration cycle on a T-S diagram. The working substance is a condensable vapor. Starting at state 1 and following the arrows, the four processes of the cycle are reversible adiabatic compression, reversible isothermal heat rejection, reversible adiabatic expansion, and reversible isothermal heat absorption. During the heat rejection (process 2-3), condensation takes place at a constant temperature T_h and the area a-3-2-b-a in the T-S diagram represents the heat removed Q_h. Similarly, during the heat absorption (process 4-1), evaporation takes place as heat is absorbed from the surrounding space at temperature T_c, and the area a-4-1-b-a in the T-S diagram represents the refrigeration effect Q_c. The coefficient of performance of the Carnot refrigeration cycle is described by

$$COP_{ref} = \frac{Q_c}{Q_h - Q_c} = \frac{T_c}{T_h - T_c}. \tag{12.22}$$

It is not practical, however, to operate a refrigeration unit according to the Carnot cycle requirements. The main difficulty lies in the isothermal heat interaction processes. These processes proceed at a very slow rate so that very large heat transfer surfaces are needed. Furthermore, the presence of the liquid phase of the working fluid in the compressor creates problems, for it causes severe erosion of the compressor. This difficulty is avoided in the Rankine refrigeration cycle. Refrigerant entering the compressor in the Rankine cycle consists of saturated vapor, and the subsequent compression process produces only superheated vapor. Another objection to the Carnot cycle arises from the reversible expansion (process 3–4). Only a work-producing machine, such as a turbine or an engine, can produce reversible expansion of a fluid. The work output of such a machine is too small to justify its expense. For this reason, an expansion or a throttling valve is used in the Rankine cycle, so that a lower cost is achieved, but the expansion is not reversible.

The ideal *gas refrigeration cycle* operates on a reversed Brayton cycle. An aircycle refrigeration system is shown in Fig. 12.24. The temperature of the air is lowered by removing energy in the form of work from the air. After an initial cooling in a heat exchanger, compressed air is allowed to expand in a turbine, causing a further reduction in temperature. The work developed by the turbine is used to circulate the cool air first through the heat exchanger and then into an enclosed area. Gas refrigeration systems are commonly used in aircraft applications.

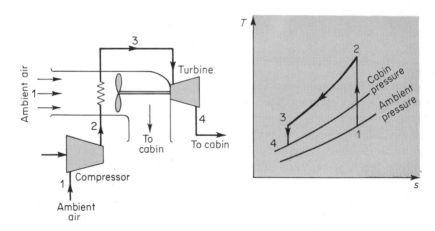

Fig. 12.24. *Air refrigeration cycle.*

A unit used in refrigeration systems is called the *ton*. It indicates rate of cooling. One ton of refrigeration is equivalent to 200 Btu/min or 12,000 Btu/hr. Another index of performance of refrigerators is the power input per ton of refrigeration. This may be expressed in terms of the *COP* as

$$\text{hp per ton} = \frac{W_{\text{net}}/2545}{Q_c/12,000} = \frac{4.713}{COP}, \tag{12.24}$$

or

$$\text{kw per ton} = \frac{W_{\text{net}}/3413}{Q_c/12{,}000} = \frac{3.514}{COP}. \tag{12.25}$$

**12-15
The Rankine
Vapor-com-
pression Re-
frigeration
Cycle**

Analogous to the Rankine vapor-power cycle, the Rankine vapor-compression refrigeration cycle is considered as the ideal model for actual cycles. As shown in Fig. 12.25, it is a closed cycle using a refrigerant*, such as ammonia, freon-12, methyl chloride, and carbon dioxide.

The cycle consists of the following sequence of processes taking place in the compressor, condensor, expansion valve, and evaporator, respectively:

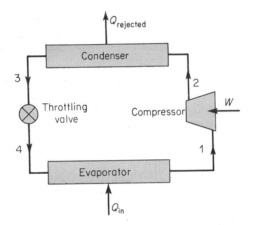

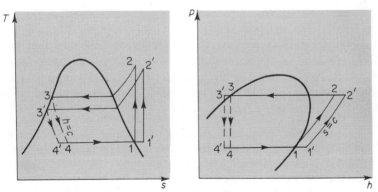

Fig. 12.25. *Vapor-compression refrigeration cycle.*

*Tables of properties of ammonia and freon-12 as well as a *p-h* chart for ammonia are given in the Appendix.

(a) Process 1–2 is a reversible adiabatic (isentropic) compression. The saturated vapor at state 1 is superheated to state 2. The amount of work done on the system (working substance) of mass m is

$$W_{1-2} = m(h_2 - h_1).$$

(b) Process 2–3 is a reversible constant-pressure heat rejection in which the working substance is first desuperheated and then condensed to the saturated liquid state 3. During this process the working substance rejects most of its energy to the condenser cooling water. The amount of heat rejected is

$$Q_{2-3} = m(h_2 - h_3).$$

(c) Process 3–4 is an irreversible throttling process in which the pressure drops at constant enthalpy ($h_3 = h_4$).

(d) Process 4–1 which completes the cycle is a reversible constant-pressure heat interaction in which the working substance is evaporated to the saturated vapor state 1. The latent heat necessary for evaporation is supplied by the refrigerated space surrounding the evaporator. The amount of heat transferred to the working substance (refrigeration effect) is

$$Q_{4-1} = m(h_1 - h_4).$$

The coefficient of performance of the Rankine refrigeration cycle is

$$COP = \frac{Q_{4-1}}{W_{1-2}} = \frac{h_1 - h_4}{h_2 - h_1}. \tag{12.26}$$

Actual refrigeration cycles have a lower value of COP than that given by Eq. (12.26) because of the inevitable irreversibilities and other heat interactions encountered in actual cycles. Also states 3 and 1 do not necessarily lie on the saturated liquid and vapor lines. The cycle identified by primes in Fig. 12.25 shows these deviations.

EXAMPLE 12.11: An ideal ammonia refrigerating machine is required to transfer 1000 Btu/min from a cold room. The evaporator pressure is 30 psia and the condenser pressure 180 psia. Compute
    (a) Evaporator temperature
    (b) Condenser temperature
    (c) COP
    (d) Power requirements
    (e) Volumetric flow rate of vapor entering compressor.

What is the coefficient of performance of a Carnot unit operating between the same temperature limits?

Solution: Referring to Fig. 12.25, the following temperatures may be obtained from ammonia tables.

(a) Evaporator temperature $t_1 = -0.57°F$.

(b) Condenser temperature $t_3 = 89.78°F$.

(c) The enthalpies at the key points are

$$h_1 = 611.6, \quad h_2 = 725.4, \quad h_3 = h_4 = 143.3 \text{ Btu/lbm}.$$

The refrigeration effect is

$$q_{4-1} = h_1 - h_4 = 611.6 - 143.3 = 468.3 \text{ Btu/lbm}.$$

The work input to the compressor is

$$w_{1-2} = h_2 - h_1 = 725.4 - 611.6 = 113.8 \text{ Btu/lbm}.$$

The coefficient of performance is

$$COP = \frac{468.3}{113.8} = 4.12.$$

(d) The rate of refrigerant flow $= \dfrac{1000 \text{ Btu/min}}{468.3 \text{ Btu/lbm}} = 2.14 \text{ lbm/min}.$

The power input $= \dfrac{(2.14 \text{ lbm/min})(113.8 \text{ Btu/lbm})}{42.42 \text{ Btu/hp-min}} = 5.74 \text{ hp}.$

(e) Volumetric flow rate $= \dot{m}v_1$
$$= (2.14 \text{ lbm/min})(9.24 \text{ ft}^3/\text{lbm}) = 19.7 \text{ ft}^3/\text{min}.$$

The coefficient of performance of a Carnot refrigerator operating between $-0.57°F$ and $89.78°F$ is

$$COP_{\text{Carnot}} = \frac{459.4}{549.8 - 459.4} = 5.08.$$

12-16
Modifications
of the Rankine
Refrigeration
Cycle

Particular applications dictate modifications of the Rankine refrigeration cycle and evidently result in an improvement of the COP. A multiple evaporator refrigeration system using a single compressor and a single condenser is shown in Fig. 12.26. This system is used for an application requiring two or more low-temperature regions. The valve at the exit of the high-pressure evaporator regulates the suction pressure of the compressor. Figure 12.27 shows a double-stage compression refrigeration system. Multiple compression

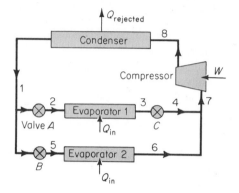

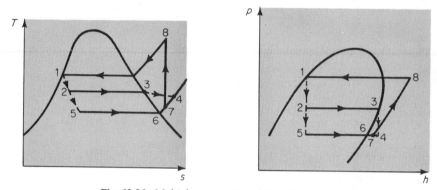

Fig. 12.26. *Multiple evaporator refrigeration system.*

systems are justified when the compression ratio is high and stage compression with intercooling reduces the work input to the compressor. The high-pressure receiver (or intercooler) desuperheats the incoming vapor from the low-pressure compressor and also serves to supply refrigerant in the liquid state only to the expansion valve. The low-pressure receiver serves as a by-pass of the vapor from the expansion valve to the inlet of the low-pressure compressor.

EXAMPLE 12.12: A multiple evaporator refrigeration system uses freon-12 as a refrigerant. Pressures in the condenser, evaporator 1, and evaporator 2 are 120, 45, and 30 psia, respectively. Saturated liquid leaves the condenser and saturated vapor leaves each evaporator. Valve C is an evaporator-pressure regulator which maintains the higher pressure in evaporator 1; while the compressor suction pressure is the pressure in evaporator 2. If the loads on evaporators 1 and 2 are respectively 10 and 5 tons, and the system is ideal, find (a) mass rate of flow of refrigerant passing through each evaporator; (b) the horsepower required to operate the compressor.

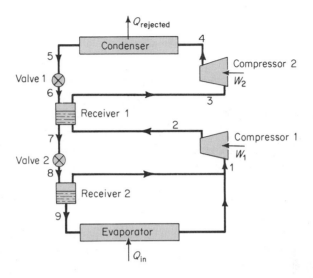

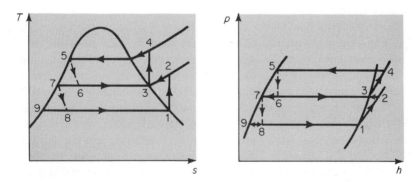

Fig. 12.27. *Multiple-stage compression and expansion refrigeration system.*

Solution: Referring to Fig. 12.26, the values of state 1 to 6 of the following table may be found in freon-12 tables:

state	1	2	3	4	5	6	7	8
p(psia)	120	45	45	30	30	30	30	120
$t(°F)$	93.4	32.3	32.3	27.9	11.1	11.1	21.9	118.3
h(Btu/lbm)	29.5	29.5	81.9	81.9	29.5	79.5	81.0	92.1
s(Btu/lbm°R)							0.17325	0.17375

The mass flow rates in evaporators 1 and 2 are

$$\dot{m}_3 = \frac{10(200)}{81.9 - 29.5} = 38.3 \text{ lbm/min.}$$

and

$$\dot{m}_6 = \frac{5(200)}{79.5 - 29.5} = 20 \text{ lbm/min.}$$

An energy balance gives the enthalpy at the compressor's inlet as

$$h_7 = \frac{\dot{m}_4 h_4 + \dot{m}_6 h_6}{\dot{m}_4 + \dot{m}_6} = \frac{38.3(81.9) + 20(79.5)}{58.3} = 81 \text{ Btu/lbm.}$$

The enthalpy of the refrigerant at the end of compression, $h_8 = 92.1$ Btu/lbm. The power input to the compressor is

$$P = \dot{m}_7(h_8 - h_7) = \frac{(58.3)(60)(92.1 - 81.0)}{2545} = 15.2 \text{ hp.}$$

12-17
Direct-Energy Conversion Systems

In conventional power plants, energy is transferred to a fluid, the fluid expands, producing mechanical work, and finally the mechanical work is converted into electrical energy. Several losses are incurred in these conversion steps, however; hence the availability of energy is reduced.

Direct-energy conversion systems eliminate some of the intermediate steps, converting the energy of the source directly into electrical energy. Direct-conversion systems for power generation are currently centered about five different approaches, involving thermoelectric converters, thermionic converters, magnetohydrodynamics (MHD), photovoltaic cells, and fuel cells. Thermoelectric converters have been employed in space vehicles, producing from a few watts to several kilowatts of power. As a source of large-scale power, only MHD offers the promise of being feasible. Although these systems are currently either low in efficiency or difficult to operate and control, experimental work continues to show that improved performance characteristics can be attained. We shall briefly describe some of these energy conversion methods in the following sections and discuss their characteristics from the standpoint of thermodynamics. Certain quantum-physical phenomena associated with the energy bands of solids are characteristic of these direct-energy conversion techniques.

12-18
Energy Bands

Because the distance between adjacent atoms in a solid is small, there is some interaction between an electron and the adjacent atoms. As a result of these interactions, the electrons differ among themselves, to some extent, in their allowed energy levels. Consequently, the atoms of a solid are not degenerate, and the electrons occupy energy bands rather than energy levels. Like the energy levels of the electrons of an isolated atom, these allowed energy bands are

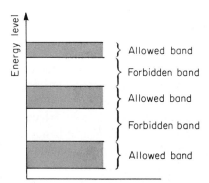

Fig. 12.28. *Energy bands in a solid.*

discrete, and as shown in Fig. 12.28, they are separated by "forbidden bands" which cannot be occupied by an electron.

The distinction between a conductor, an insulator, and a semiconductor may be explained by means of the band theory of solids. When electrons fill an allowed energy band completely, electrons (negative-charge carriers) cannot shift from one atom to another and so no conduction of electricity is possible. Likewise, if an energy band is completely unoccupied, no electrons are available for conduction. Therefore, only solids with partially occupied energy bands are capable of conducting electricity.

Two energy bands separated by a forbidden band constitute the element which determines the electrical properties of a solid. One energy band is called the *valence* band and the other is called the *conduction* band. When an electric field is applied to a solid, electrons in the valence band gain small amounts of energy. If this energy enables a large number of electrons to migrate to the conduction band, the solid acts as an electric conductor. Each electron leaving the valence band creates a void or an unfilled state, called a *hole*, which is equivalent to a positive charge. Both the holes and the electrons contribute to the flow of electric current. A *conductor* is a material in which electrons and holes are plentiful at all temperatures. If the width of the forbidden gap is large, electrons may not acquire enough energy to migrate to the conduction band, even if the valence band is filled. The solid then acts as an *insulator*. The valence band of diamond, for example, is filled but the forbidden gap is 6 ev wide, and so it is an insulator. A substance in which the valence band is filled, the conduction band is empty, and the forbidden gap is narrow, is a *semiconductor*. At high temperatures, large numbers of electrons in a semiconductor can jump across the forbidden gap to the conduction band; at low temperatures, on the other hand, only a small number of electrons can move from the valence band to the conduction band. A material is a semiconductor if the number of electrons in the conduction band depends upon temperatures. A semiconductor may act as a conductor or as an insulator, depending upon the energy supplied, thus the name "semiconductor." The forbidden gaps in silicon and germanium, which are semiconductors, are 1.1 ev and 0.7 ev respectively.

Two types of semiconductors exist; *intrinsic* semiconductors and *impurity* semiconductors. In intrinsic semiconductors, thermal excitation is sufficient to produce electrical conduction. In impurity semiconductors, impurity atoms are present which donate or accept electrons from the conduction and the valence bands of the main substance, thereby helping conduction due to thermal excitation. Impurity atoms are either donors or acceptors of electrons. The donors are called *n-type* (negative charges); the acceptors are called *p-type* (positive charges). The energy bands of semicon-

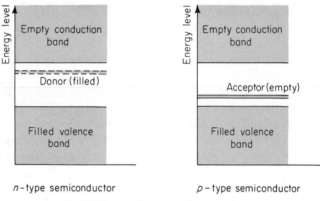

n-type semiconductor   *p*-type semiconductor

Fig. 12.29. *n and p types of semiconductors.*

ductors resulting from both types are shown in Fig. 12.29. The *n*-type impurity atoms introduce discrete energy levels just below the conduction band; the p-type impurity atoms provide energy levels just above the valence band.

12-19   Thermoelectric effects refer to phenomena in-
Thermoelectric   volving the interchange of heat and electrical
Effects   energy. One familiar example is the heating effect due to the flow of an electric current in a resistor. The electric power dissipation depends on the current flow I and the potential V according to the equation:

$$P = VI.$$

If the current flows through a material which obeys Ohm's law, then

$$P = VI = I^2 R,$$

where R is the electric resistance of the material. This dissipation of electrical energy as heat energy is called *ohmic loss* or *Joule heating*. Obviously, this type of energy conversion is irreversible, although some thermoelectric effects are reversible.

Three thermoelectric reversible effects, called the *Seebeck, Peltier,* and *Thomson* effects, are now defined.

(a) *The Seebeck effect:* In 1833 Seebeck held the junctions of two dissimilar electrical conductors at different temperatures and noted that an open-circuit voltage was generated that was proportional to the difference in temperature between the two junctions. In equation form, the Seebeck effect is

$$S_{AB} = \lim_{\Delta T \to 0} \frac{\Delta V}{\Delta T}, \tag{12.27}$$

where $\Delta V =$ open circuit potential difference

$\Delta T =$ temperature difference between the two junctions

$S_{AB} =$ a coefficient of proportionality dependent on temperature.

S_{AB} is called the *Seebeck coefficient* and is usually expressed in units of volts per degree centigrade. The subscript AB denotes that S depends on the materials constituting the junctions. A familiar example which illustrates the Seebeck effect is the thermocouple. Heat supplied at one of the junctions is converted into electrical energy, which is then measured.

Two main losses tend to reduce the useful electrical power output provided by the Seebeck effect: heat conduction and electric power loss in the leads. Because a good electrical conductor is also a good heat conductor, much of the heat transferred to a junction is conducted away by the wires, so that there are problems in the choice of circuit constants which will lead to optimum power production. At present, even the best metal combinations in a thermocouple achieve an efficiency of only 3 per cent in the conversion of heat into electrical energy.

(b) *The Peltier effect:* In the Peltier effect, which is the inverse of the Seebeck effect, an electric current is sent through a junction of two dissimilar materials A and B, and this results in either a heating or cooling of the junction. The rate of heating (or cooling) is proportional to the current flow, and is given by the equation

$$\dot{Q} = \pi_{AB} I, \tag{12.28}$$

where the coefficient π_{AB} is a function of temperature called the *Peltier coefficient*. The subscript AB indicates that the Peltier coefficient also depends on the two materials A and B. A typical unit of π_{AB} is the volt. If current flows in the direction of the potential drop characteristic of the junction, then the temperature of the junction decreases, and a refrigerating effect occurs in the space surrounding the junction. If current flows in the direction of the junction's potential rise, the temperature of the junction increases and heat must be transferred from the junction to maintain constant temperature at the junction.

(c) *The Thomson effect:* When an electric current flows through a homogeneous material, heat is exchanged between the environment and the material, and the rate of transfer of heat depends on both the quantity of current that flows through the material and the temperature gradient that exists in the material. The *Thomson coefficient* τ is defined as

$$\tau_A = \frac{d\dot{Q}/dx}{I(dT/dx)},\tag{12.29}$$

where $d\dot{Q}/dx$ is the rate of heat interaction per unit length of the conductor and dT/dx is the temperature gradient along the length of the conductor. Like the Seebeck and Peltier effects, the Thomson effect is reversible; on the other hand, it involves only a single substance.

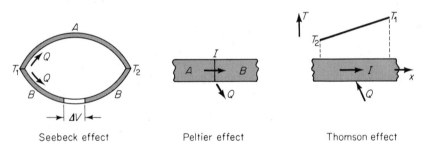

Seebeck effect   Peltier effect   Thomson effect

Fig. 12.30. *Thermoelectric effects.*

The Seebeck, Peltier, and Thomson effects occur in both metals and semiconductors, but these effects are more pronounced in semiconductors. The three effects are illustrated in Fig. 12.30.

12-20
Thermoelectric
Converter

The thermoelectric converter shown in Fig. 12.31 consists essentially of two semiconductor blocks connected by a conductor. The conductor receives heat from a thermal source at temperature T_h, whereas the open ends of the blocks reject heat to a low-temperature reservoir at temperature T_c. The sides of the semiconductors are insulated so that heat flow takes place unidimensionally through the semiconductors. When heat is transferred to the hot junction, electrons in n-type semiconductors, and holes in p-type semiconductors, tend to flow away from the hot junction. An electric

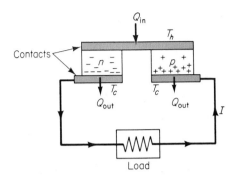

Fig. 12.31. *Thermoelectric generator.*

potential is therefore generated, and if the circuit is completed at the cold junction, an electric current flows through the load.

This system may be reversed by supplying electrical energy rather than heat. The current flow then serves to remove heat from one junction and to deliver heat to the other junction. The process of thermoelectric refrigeration represents an application of the Peltier effect.

An index used in rating thermoelectric converters is called the *figure of merit*, and is defined as

$$Z = \frac{S^2}{\rho K},\tag{12.30}$$

where Z is the figure of merit, S is the Seebeck coefficient, ρ is the electrical resistivity, and K is the thermal conductivity of the semiconductors. A high figure of merit is achieved by using substances of large Seebeck coefficient, small electrical resistivity, and small thermal conductivity. Maximum values of the figure of merit are obtained when the electric and conduction losses are at a minimum, and when the two losses are approximately equal.

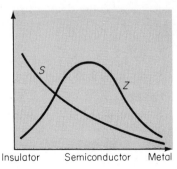

Fig. 12.32. *S and Z versus carrier concentration.*

Figure 12–32 shows the variations of S and Z as a function of electron density. The maximum value of Z is obtained with semiconductors having an electron density of the order of 10^{19} to 10^{20} electrons/cc. Typical values of Z are in the range of 1×10^{-3} °C^{-1} to 3×10^{-3} °C^{-1}.

The ideal thermal efficiency of a thermoelectric converter is

$$\text{ideal } \eta_{\text{th}} = \frac{P_{\text{out}}}{\dot{Q}_{\text{in}}} = \left(\frac{T_h - T_c}{T_h}\right)\left[\frac{M - 1}{M + (T_c/T_h)}\right] = \eta_{\text{Carnot}}\,\eta_{\text{rel}}, \qquad (12.31)$$

where

$$M = \sqrt{1 + \frac{Z}{2}(T_h + T_c)} \quad \text{and} \quad \eta_{\text{rel}} = \frac{M - 1}{M + (T_c/T_h)}.$$

The relative efficiency η_{rel} reflects the reduction in efficiency resulting from irreversible losses. The over-all efficiencies of actual thermoelectric converters lie between 2 per cent and 6 per cent which are considerably below the efficiencies of the conventional power plants. Special features, such as light weight, small size, and simplicity rather than thermodynamic efficiency make them suitable for space vehicles.

If the thermoelectric converter is operated as a refrigerator, then

$$\text{ideal } COP_{\text{ref}} = \frac{\dot{Q}_c}{P_{\text{in}}} = \left(\frac{T_c}{T_h - T_c}\right)\left[\frac{M - (T_c/T_h)}{M + 1}\right]$$
$$= (COP_{\text{ref}})_{\text{Carnot}}(COP_{\text{ref}})_{\text{rel}}, \qquad (12.32)$$

where

$$(COP_{\text{ref}})_{\text{rel}} = \frac{M - (T_c/T_h)}{M + 1}.$$

If it is used as a heat pump, its performance is described by

$$\text{ideal } COP_{\text{heat pump}} = \frac{\dot{Q}_h}{P_{\text{in}}} = \frac{T_c}{T_h - T_c}\left(1 - 2\frac{M - 1}{T_h^2}\right)$$
$$= (COP_{\text{ht.p}})_{\text{Carnot}}(COP_{\text{ht.p}})_{\text{rel}}, \qquad (12.33)$$

where

$$(COP_{\text{ht.p}})_{\text{rel}} = \frac{T_c}{T_h}\left(1 - 2\frac{M - 1}{T_h^2}\right).$$

12-21
Thermionic
Converter

A thermionic converter is a source of low-voltage, high-current electrical energy. The basic elements of the thermionic converter, which is classified as a diode, are shown in Fig. 12.33. The cathode and anode are separated by either an evacuated or a vapor-filled space. When heat is transferred to the cathode, electrons in the metal become energetic enough

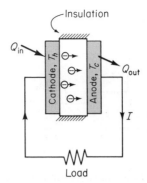

Fig. 12.33. *Thermionic converter.*

to leave the surface of the metal and to travel toward the anode. An abundance of holes then exists in the cathode, which becomes positive, whereas the anode becomes negative. If a resistive load is placed across the terminals of the electrodes, electric current can be drawn. Thus the thermionic converter is an engine in which heat transferred to the cathode is converted to electricity.

A major impediment to the flow of electrons is the space-charge barrier. The space charge is formed by electrons and tends to limit the current density.* Two solutions to this difficulty are possible. In one method, the space between the electrodes is reduced, thus limiting the emission current of the space charge. In the closed-spaced diode, interelectrode spacing is of the order of 0.001 cm (10 microns). Temperatures of $1500°K$ to $2000°K$ at the cathode and $1000°K$ at the anode are common, with a diode output of 2 to 10 watts/cm².

In the other method, the space charge is suppressed by the introduction of positive ions into the interelectrode space, thus neutralizing the negative space charge (plasma† diode). This neutralization is achieved through the presence of a vapor, such as cesium vapor, at low density in the space between electrodes. Cesium has a low ionization potential (3.88 volt) so that it ionizes readily. Ionization results when cesium atoms collide with the emitted electrons or with the hot cathode wall, according to the equation

$$Cs \rightleftharpoons Cs^+ + e^-.$$

In plasma diodes, the interelectrode spacing is of the order of 0.1 cm, and cathode temperatures lie in the range of $1600°K$ to $2600°K$. The electrostatic potential diagram of the circuit of a diode in thermodynamic equilibrium is shown in Fig. 12–34(a). The potential ϕ_E is called the *work function* of the

---

*Current density (amp/cm²) is the product of the velocity of each electron and its charge, summed up for all the electrons emitted by the cathode.

†A neutral mixture of ions and electrons is called a *plasma*.

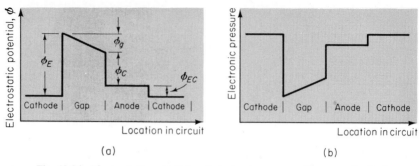

Fig. 12.34. *Electrostatic potential and electronic pressure diagrams of a diode.*

emitter (cathode) and is equal to the potential difference between a point in the interior of the cathode and a point on its surface. It represents the barrier potential of the emitter, which is the excess potential an electron must possess in order to be able to leave the surface of the cathode. Similarly, the potential ϕ_C represents the potential barrier of the collector (anode). The potential ϕ_g is called the *gap potential* or *contact potential* and is equal to the difference in potential between two points on the surfaces of the electrodes. The *junction potential* ϕ_{EC} is equal to the potential between the fused junctions of the metals of the emitter and collector.

Figure 12.34(b) shows the simultaneous electronic pressure diagram, which is a mirror image of the potential diagram. Note that the highest pressure occurs in the metals because of their high electron density. The pressure distribution completely balances the force created by the potential distribution at every point of the circuit except when the electrodes are at different temperatures. Any electrons that leave the cathode's surface are accelerated as a result of the potential of the cesium ions adjacent to the cathode surface. The potential of the electrons is thus raised to a value

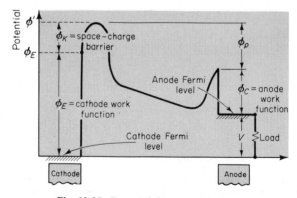

Fig. 12.35. *Potential diagram of a diode.*

ϕ' as shown in Fig. 12.35. The potential ϕ_p is the plasma potential drop, and ϕ_K is potential due to the kinetic energy of the electrons. $\phi_p - \phi_K$ represents the difference in potential between the emitter surface and the collector surface. The potential ϕ_C is the collector work function. The output voltage as seen from the diagram is therefore

$$V = \phi_E + \phi_K - \phi_p - \phi_C.$$

(12.34)

The diode current density (current per unit area) is given by the *Richardson-Dushman* equation* which applies to both the cathode and the anode:

$$j = AT^2 e^{\phi'/kT}$$

(12.35)

where j = current density
A = constant equal to 120.1 amp/cm²-°K²
T = absolute temperature
ϕ' = work function = $\phi_E + \phi_K$
k = Boltzmann's constant.

A small quantity of current flows in the reverse direction from the anode, so that the net diode current is the difference between the current emitted from the cathode and the "back current" from the anode, or

$$j = j_{\text{cathode}} - j_{\text{anode}}.$$

(12.36)

The current from the anode is small compared to that emitted from the cathode, because the anode is much lower in temperature than the cathode. If losses due to heat conduction are not considered, it may be shown that the thermal efficiency of the thermionic converter is

$$\eta_{\text{th}} = \frac{jV}{\dot{q}_e + \dot{q}_r} = \frac{jV}{(\phi' + 2V_T)j + \dot{q}_r},$$

(12.37)

where $\dot{q}_e$ is the amount of heat per unit area and unit time necessary to drive off the electrons from the emitter surface, $\dot{q}_r$ is the radiation heat loss per unit area and unit time from the cathode to the anode, V is the output voltage, V_T is the voltage equivalent of the cathode temperature (kT_{cath}/e), and j is the current density. If the collector work function is reduced, a higher thermal efficiency may be attained; on the other hand, if the work function is very small (~ 0.5 volt), the back current is large.

The thermoelectric converter and the thermionic converter are similar in many respects. As shown in Fig. 12.36, metal A in a thermocouple appears

*See reference 12.1 for derivation of this equation.

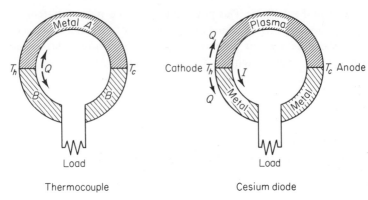

Thermocouple   Cesium diode

Fig. 12.36. *Analogy between thermoelectric and thermionic converters.*

as a plasma in a thermionic converter. The junction potential barrier in a thermocouple is the Peltier coefficient; in a thermionic converter it is the work function.

Thermionic converters are suited for applications which require a large power-to-weight ratio, although the maximum efficiency attained at present is 10 per cent.

12-22

Fuel Cell

A *fuel cell* is an electrochemical device which converts chemical energy directly into electrical energy. The basic components of a fuel cell which uses hydrogen (or hydrocarbon) as a fuel and oxygen (or air) as an oxidizer, are shown in Fig. 12.37. Each gas is introduced at high pressure into a chamber; the two chambers are separated from each other by an electrolyte, which may be solid or liquid. Porous ceramic (zirconia oxide), solid polymers, and alkaline solutions (potassium hydroxide) have been successfully used as electrolytes. At elevated temperatures, the electrolyte acts like a sieve, allowing hydrogen ions to migrate through the material. As a result, an ionic potential develops between the two sides of the electrolyte. When a solid electrolyte is used, its surface is first impregnated with a catalyst to facilitate the ion migration process. Impregnation also allows the two sides of the electrolyte to be used as electrodes. When a liquid electrolyte is used, separate electrodes are necessary. The electrical load is connected between the anode (hydrogen side) and the cathode (oxygen side).

The principle of operation of a fuel cell using hydrogen and oxygen is as follows: At the anode-electrolyte interface, hydrogen molecules dissociate, forming hydrogen ions and two free electrons per molecule. The reaction at the anode can be expressed as

$$2H_2(g) \longrightarrow 4H^+ + 4e^-.$$

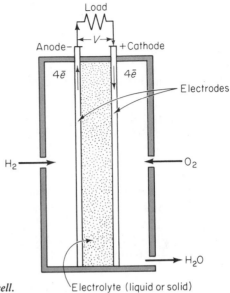

Fig. 12.37. *Hydrogen-oxygen fuel cell.*

These electrons flow through the external circuit and return to the fuel cell at the cathode, leaving a positive charge at the anode. At the same time, the hydrogen ions diffuse through the electrolyte. When the hydrogen ions reach the cathode, they combine with the electrons and with oxygen molecules to form water. The reaction at the cathode is

$$4e^- + 4H^+ + O_2(g) \longrightarrow 2\,H_2O(l).$$

The overall cell reaction is therefore

$$2H_2(g) + O_2(g) \longrightarrow 2\,H_2O(l).$$

A quantity of energy representing the enthalpy of combustion of the fuel, $\Delta H°$, is released by this chemical reaction. Part of this energy is available for conversion to electrical energy, the maximum amount being equal to the change of the Gibbs function $(-W_e \leqslant G_1 - G_2)$. The remaining energy that is released appears as heat. The electrical energy output per mole of O_2 (or per 2 moles of H_2) is

$$W_e = 4N_0 eV,$$

where N_0 is Avogadro's number, e is the electronic charge, and V is the voltage developed.

Under reversible steady-state conditions, the maximum value of W_e is equal to the change in the Gibbs free-energy:

$$W_e = G_2 - G_1. \tag{12.38}$$

Therefore the maximum voltage that can be developed by a fuel cell is

$$V = \frac{G_2 - G_1}{nN_0 e}, \tag{12.39}$$

where n is the number of electrons released per molecule of oxygen. In forming one gm-mole of liquid water from hydrogen and oxygen, the free-energy change is -56.6899 kcal/gm-mole. The maximum voltage attainable from the chemical reaction shown above is then:

$$V = \frac{(-2 \times 56.6899 \times 10^3)(4.182)}{4 \times 6.025 \times 10^{23}(-1.602 \times 10^{-19})} = 1.23 \text{ volt.}$$

If a potassium hydroxide solution is the electrolyte, the following reactions take place:

anode: $2\,H_2(g) + 4(OH)^- \longrightarrow 4\,H_2O(l) + 4e^-$

cathode: $O_2(g) + 2\,H_2O(l) + 4e^- \longrightarrow 4\,(OH)^-$

total reaction: $2\,H_2(g) + O_2(g) \longrightarrow 2\,H_2O(l).$

The maximum efficiency of a fuel cell is

$$\eta_{\text{th}} = \frac{W_e}{(-\Delta H^\circ)} = \frac{nN_0 eV}{(-\Delta H^\circ)}. \tag{12.40}$$

For the hydrogen-oxygen reaction in which liquid water is formed, the enthalpy of combustion is -68.3174 k cal/gm-mole, so that the efficiency is 83 per cent.

Unlike heat engines, fuel cells are not subject to limitation imposed by the Carnot cycle, and theoretical efficiencies as high as 90 per cent can be expected. However, high efficiencies are attained only at relatively light loads, and at voltages of about 1 volt. Some advantages of the fuel cell are its simplicity and its high power-to-weight ratio. Its disadvantages include high cost, need for equipment to control the flow of reactants to match reaction rates, problems in selection of component materials that are not attacked by the reactants, and relatively short life, especially at high temperatures.

12-23
MHD
Generator

According to Faraday's law of electromagnetic induction, a changing magnetic field induces an electric field in any conductor located in it. The electric field acts on the free charges in the conductor, causing a current to flow. In a conventional electric generator, copper conductors cross the lines of the magnetic field; in the magnetohydrodynamic generator, ionized gas, which acts like an electrical conductor, flows across the lines of a magnetic field. In either case, a voltage is induced. In the MHD generator, a portion of the energy of the ionized gas is transformed into electrical energy. Figure 12.38 shows the basic components of an MHD generator. Hot ionized gas at a high velocity passes between the poles of an electromagnet. This induces a potential difference between a pair of electrodes placed at right angles to the magnetic field. When the electrodes are connected by a resistive load, a current flows in the circuit.

The ionized gas needed for the MHD generator may be obtained by heating a gas to temperatures between 3500°F and 4500°F. A nuclear fuel may serve as the energy source. Alternately, the gas may be seeded with small quantities of a material which ionizes easily, such as cesium or

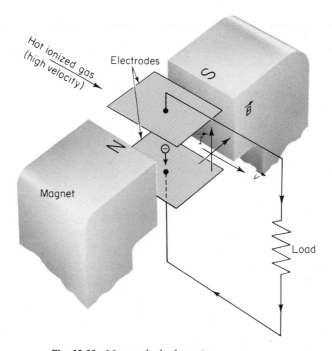

Fig. 12.38. *Magnetohydrodynamic generator.*

potassium, and the gas may then be used at temperatures as low as 2000°F. After passing through the MHD generator, the ionized gas is usually re-circulated through a regenerator where energy is added to the gas before it re-enters the MHD generator.

The electromagnetic force $\vec{F}$ acting on a moving charge is

$$\vec{F} = q(\vec{E} + \vec{v} \times \vec{B}), \tag{12.41}$$

where q = charge

$\vec{E}$ = electric field strength

$\vec{v}$ = velocity of the ionized gas

$\vec{B}$ = magnetic field strength

× indicates vector product.

The efficiency of the MHD generator, which is the electric energy produced divided by the energy input, is

$$\eta_{\text{th}} = \frac{VI}{\dot{h}_{o,\text{in}}} = \frac{\dot{h}_{o,\text{in}} - \dot{h}_{o,\text{out}}}{\dot{h}_{o,\text{in}}} = 1 - \frac{\dot{h}_{o,\text{out}}}{\dot{h}_{o,\text{in}}}, \tag{12.42}$$

where

V = voltage produced

I = current flow

$\dot{h}_{o,\text{in}}$ and $\dot{h}_{o,\text{out}}$ = total enthalpy* fluxes of the hot gas stream respectively entering and leaving the generator.

MHD generators are being considered as topping generators for conventional gas-turbine and steam-turbine cycles. The main problems encountered in MHD systems center about selection of materials that are capable of withstanding the high temperatures of the ionized gas.

REFERENCES

12.1 Chang, Sheldon, S. L., *Energy Conversion*. Englewood Cliffs, N.J.: Prentice-Hall, Inc., 1963.

12.2 Kiefer, P. J., G. F. Kinney, and M. C. Stuart, *Principles of Engineering Thermodynamics*. New York: John Wiley & Sons, Inc., 1954, chap. 13, 14, 15.

12.3 Lay, J. E., *Thermodynamics*. Columbus, Ohio: Charles E. Merrill Books, Inc., 1963, chap. 19.

*Total enthalpy h_o is defined as $h_o = h + V^2/2g_c$.

12.4 Lee, J. F., and F. W. Sears, *Thermodynamics*. Reading, Mass.: Addison-Wesley Publishing Company, Inc., 1963, chap. 11, 12, 13.

12.5 Pidd, R. W., *Heat to Electricity Conversion: Plasma Method*. (Unpublished.)

12.6 Weidner, R. T., R. L. and Sells, *Elementary Modern Physics*. New York: Allyn & Bacon, Inc., 1963, chap. 11.

PROBLEMS

12.1 Compare the thermal efficiencies of the Carnot and Rankine cycles operating between two thermal reservoirs at 400°F and 212°F. (Assume water to be the working fluid.)

12.2 Steam at 500 psia and 600°F is delivered to a turbine where it expands irreversibly and adiabatically to an exhaust pressure of 2 in. Hg abs. Assuming that the kinetic and potential energy changes are negligible and that the work realized is 70 per cent of the ideal work, find
(a) The entropy change in the actual turbine compared with an ideal turbine operating between the same initial temperature and pressure and the same exhaust pressure
(b) The steam rate in lbm/hp-hr
(c) The increase in unavailable energy due to the irreversible expansion.
Sketch the process on a *T-s* diagram.

12.3 A Rankine cycle operates with steam at 500 psia and 600°F and a condenser pressure of 2 in. Hg abs. Assuming steady-state and kinetic and potential energy changes are negligible, find
(a) The ideal work done by the turbine per lbm of steam
(b) The amount of steam required per net horsepower hour output (steam rate)
(c) The thermal efficiency of the cycle
(d) The amount of heat required per net horsepower hour output (heat rate)

12.4 Using Tables A.4, A.5 and A.6 of the Appendix, complete the following tabulation which pertains to a Rankine cycle:

ENTERING	p psia	T (°F)	h (Btu/lbm)	u (Btu/lbm)	pv (Btu/lbm)	v (ft³/lbm)	s (Btu/lbm°R)	x
Pump	1	101.7						
Boiler	600	101.7						
Superheater	600							0.98
Turbine	600	550						
Condenser	1						1.650	

Find (a) Heat rejected in the condenser
(b) Work required by the pump

(c) Heat interaction in the boiler
(d) Heat interaction in the superheater
(e) Work developed by the turbine
(f) Work developed by a reversible adiabatic turbine operating on the same cycle.
All answers to be on the basis of Btu/lbm. Sketch the cycle on *h-s* diagram.

12.5 The following data are for a steam power plant operating on the Rankine cycle:

Point		*p*(psia)	*T*(°F)	*x*(per cent)
1	Leaving boiler	400	600	
2	Entering turbine	380	560	
3	Leaving turbine (entering condenser)	2		93
4	Leaving condenser (entering pump)	1.9	115	
5	Leaving pump (entering boiler)	420		

Calculate the following per lbm of steam flowing through the plant:
(a) Pump work
(b) Turbine work
(c) Heat transfer in line between boiler and turbine
(d) Heat transfer in boiler
(e) Heat transfer in condenser.

12.6 In a steam power plant, steam is supplied to the high-pressure turbine at a pressure and temperature of 400 psia and 700°F. After expansion to 80 psia, the steam is returned to the boiler and reheated at 80 psia to 700°F, and is then further expanded in the low-pressure turbine to an exhaust pressure of 1 in. Hg abs. For the corresponding ideal cycle, find
(a) The cycle efficiency
(b) If the steam were not reheated, what would be the corresponding efficiency of the Rankine cycle?

12.7 A steam power plant operates on the theoretical reheat cycle. Steam is generated at 500 psia and 800°F and expands through the high-pressure turbine to the saturated vapor condition. It is reheated at constant pressure to 800°F and expands through the low-pressure turbine to a condenser at 1 psia. Neglecting pump work, find the thermal efficiency of the cycle. What is the reheat pressure?
If the efficiency of the turbines is 80 per cent and reheating takes place at the same reheat pressure, determine the thermal efficiency, heat rate, and steam rate (neglect pump work).

12.8 A steam power plant operates on a theoretical regenerative cycle. Steam enters the turbine at 500 psia and 800°F. Part of the steam is bled at a pressure of 30 psia into an open heater and the remainder is condensed at a pressure of 1 psia. Negelecting pump work, find the thermal efficiency.

12.9 Compare the thermal efficiency and the steam consumption in lbm/kwhr for the Rankine, regenerative, and reheat cycles under the following conditions:

Initial steam pressure	250 psia
Initial superheat	200°F
Extraction pressure for the open heater in the regenerative cycle	30 psia
Exhaust pressure	2 in. Hg abs.

Reheating in the reheat cycle takes place at 30 psia to the initial superheat before expanding in the low-pressure turbine to 2 in. Hg abs (neglect pump work).

12.10 In a two-heater (closed) regenerative cycle, steam is supplied to the turbine at 400 psia and 700°F. Condenser pressure is 1 in. Hg abs. If the extraction pressures are 100 and 12 psia, calculate the thermal efficiency of the cycle.

12.11 A steam turbine plant equipped with a single regenerative feed-water heater of the open type operates under the following conditions:

Initial steam pressure	250 psia
Initial superheat	200°F
Extraction pressure	30 psia
Exhaust pressure	2 in. Hg abs.

Neglecting work of the pump, compare the regenerative and Rankine cycles with respect to the following: (a) thermal efficiency; (b) steam consumption in lbm/kwhr; (c) condenser duty (steam condensed per kwhr).

12.12 Verify Eq. (12.10) and Eq. (12.11).

12.13 An ideal Otto cycle and an ideal Diesel cycle utilize the same quantity of the same working substance. The states of the working substance are identical in both cycles at the beginning of the compression stroke, at the end of heat supply, and at the end of the expansion stroke. Sketch the two cycles, superimposed and identified, on p-V and T-S diagrams. By referring to the diagrams, show which of the two cycles has the higher thermal efficiency.

12.14 An Otto cycle using air has a compression ratio of 8. At the start of the compression process, the temperature is 540°R and the pressure is 14.7 psia. Heat is supplied at the rate of 1000 Btu/lbm of air. Determine (a) the pressure and temperature at key points of the cycle; (b) the net work; (c) the thermal efficiency.

12.15 An air-standard Diesel cycle operating with a compression ratio of 15 to 1 receives energy at the rate of 650 Btu/lbm of air. The initial conditions are 14.7 psia and 75°F for the air used in the cycle. Calculate (a) work output per lbm of air; (b) thermal efficiency of the cycle; (c) expansion ratio.

12.16 A theoretical air-standard Diesel cycle has an initial pressure and temperature of 14 psia and 80°F. The compression ratio is 14 to 1, and the temperature at the end of heat interaction is 3100°F. The specific heat ratios ($c_p/c_v = \gamma$)

for the compression, heat supply, and expansion processes are 1.37, 1.34, and 1.31, respectively.

(a) What is the thermal efficiency of the cycle?

(b) What is the specific work for the cycle?

(c) What is the entropy change for the heat supply process? Sketch p-V and T-S diagrams.

12.17 A gas turbine operates between a low and a high temperature limit. The low temperature is dictated by the temperature of the surrounding air; the high temperature is dictated by the maximum temperature the turbine material can withstand.

(a) Determine an expression for the work output in terms of T_{min}, r_p, c_p, and γ

(b) Prove that the maximum work output corresponds to a pressure ratio given by

$$r_p = \left(\frac{T_{max}}{T_{min}}\right)^{\gamma/[2(\gamma-1)]}.$$

12.18 A closed regenerative gas-turbine cycle operating with air as a fluid. Data for the proposed cycle are

$p_1 = 20$ psia	$T_1 = 560°R$
$p_2/p_1 = 5$	$T_{max} = 1900°R$
Effectiveness ratio of regenerator $= 0.6$	
Net output $= 4000$ hp	

Assuming the compressor and turbine to be isentropic, calculate (a) thermal efficiency; (b) flow rate lbm air/min.

12.19 Find the efficiency and the work per pound mass of fluid for a Brayton air cycle working between pressures of 15 psia and 75 psia. The maximum temperature in the cycle is 1200°F and the minimum temperature is 70°F.

(a) Solve the problem by (1) gas laws; (2) air tables. State the reasons for differences in answers, if any, by the two methods. (c_p for air $= 0.24$ Btu/lbm °F.)

(b) What would the efficiency and the work per lbm of air be if regenerative heating is used? The regenerator effectiveness is 70 per cent. What is the temperature of the air leaving the regenerator to the atmosphere?

12.20 An air standard gas-turbine cycle accepts air at 14.7 and 90°F; compresses it to 80 psia in a compressor which is 60 per cent efficient. After compression, the air is preheated in a heat exchanger which has an effectiveness of 80 per cent. If the maximum permissable temperature is 1500°F and the turbine unit is ideal, what is the thermal efficiency of this cycle?

12.21 A jet-propelled aircraft is to operate at a speed of 676 ft/sec relative to the surrounding air at a local pressure and temperature of 8.0 psia and 460°R (Mach number $= 0.643$). Anticipated operating features are

Pressure coefficient of diffuser	0.8
Pressure ratio of compressor	5 to 1
Isentropic efficiency of compressor	0.85
Isentropic efficiency of turbine	0.88
Isentropic efficiency of nozzle	0.94
Maximum allowable gas temperature at turbine entry	1900°R

Assuming that the cycle is air-standard, and that the kinetic energy of the air entering and leaving compressor and turbine is negligible, determine: (a) the states at entry and departure for compressor and turbine; (b) the propulsive force per lbm/sec of air.

12.22 Determine the thermal efficiency for a gas-turbine cycle if the turbine is 83 per cent efficient and compression is in two stages, each 83 per cent efficient: (a) if no regeneration is used; (b) if a regenerator heats the compressed air to 570°F. Assume intercooling between the compression stages to reduce the air temperature to 70°F and the intermediate pressure is 32.4 psia.

Data: Inlet air at 14 psia, 70°F.
  Pressure at compression exit is 75 psia.
  Maximum temperature in combustor is 1200°F.
  Air expands in turbine back to 14 psia.

12.23 An ammonia refrigerating cycle operates with an evaporator saturation temperature of 0°F while removing 10,000 Btu/hr from a cold room. The saturation temperature in the condenser is 76°F. Assuming that the ammonia is saturated liquid at the entrance of the expansion valve, and saturated vapor at the entrance of the compressor, find (a) the *COP* of the cycle and the ammonia circulation rate in lbm/hr; (b) the *COP* of a Carnot refrigerator operating between the condenser and evaporator temperatures.

12.24 An ice-making unit of 15-ton capacity operates with ammonia as a refrigerant. In order to cool the brine to the proper temperature, the ammonia temperature in the evaporator is maintained at 0°F. Cooling water enables the ammonia to condense at 60°F. Assuming dry saturated vapor at the compressor inlet and isentropic compression, find:
(a) The pressure in the evaporator and in the condenser
(b) The actual and ideal *COP*
(c) Actual hp required
(d) Circulation rate (lbm/min) of refrigerant.
Sketch *T-s* and *p-h* diagrams of the cycle.

12.25 The following data were obtained in a test of an ammonia refrigerating unit.

Pressures (psia): Evaporator 40, condenser, 220.
Temperatures (°F): Liquid entering expansion valve, 88.
  Vapor leaving evaporator and entering compressor, 40.
  Vapor leaving compressor and entering condenser, 240.
Rate of flow: 5.7 lbm/min of ammonia.
Compressor efficiency (based on isentropic): 75 per cent.

Compute
(a) Capacity in tons
(b) *COP*
(c) Power required to drive compressor
(d) Heat transfer per minute from compressor
(e) Heat transfer per minute from condenser.

12.26 A vapor compression refrigerator uses freon-12 as the refrigerant. The refrigerator operates between $-30°F$ and $70°F$. The vapor leaving the evaporator and the liquid leaving the condenser are saturated vapor and saturated liquid. Assuming that the compressor operates reversibly and adiabatically, find:

(a) COP

(b) Horsepower per ton of refrigeration

(c) Mass flow rate per ton of refrigeration

(d) Power that could have been developed by a reversible process instead of the throttling process per ton of refrigeration.

12.27 The following data are obtained from a test of an ammonia refrigeration system:

Pressures: Condenser $= 150$ psia
             Evaporator $= 39$ psia
Temperatures: Leaving compressor $= 209°F$
               Entering condenser $= 190°F$
               Leaving condenser $= 65°F$
               Entering expansion valve $= 70°F$
               Leaving evaporator $= 20°F$
               Entering compressor $= 30°F$
Ammonia circulated per hour $= 192$ lbm.

Calculate

(a) Capacity of the plant in tons

(b) Heat rejected by ammonia in condenser (Btu/hr)

(c) Compressor horsepower

(d) COP

(e) Heat interaction with pipeline and receiver per lbm of ammonia.

12.28 An ammonia compression refrigeration cycle operates so as to maintain a temperature of $20°F$ in a cold storage room. The condenser for this unit is set in the air which is at $80°F$. If no finite temperature difference is necessary for heat interaction and the efficiency of the compresser is 90 per cent, find:

(a) The power necessary for 25 tons of refrigeration

(b) The compressor capacity in cfm

(c) The COP.

12.29 If a $10°F$ temperature difference is necessary in both the condenser and the evaporator in Problem 12.28, to achieve heat transfer, what mass rate of flow of refrigerant is necessary for 30 tons of refrigeration?

12.30 Determine the maximum power output and the figure of merit of a thermoelectric converter which operates between $T_h = 97°C$ and $T_c = 32°C$. The average Seebeck coefficient is 2×10^{-3} volt/°C, the thermal conductance is 4.08×10^{-2} watt/°C and the resistance is 0.07 ohm. What is the ideal thermal efficiency of the converter?

NOMENCLATURE

A	Area	t	Temperature
C	Concentration	U	Internal energy
D	Thermal diffusion coefficient	X	Driving force
G	Gibbs function	x	Distance
H	Enthalpy	$\mathscr{E}$	Electrical potential
I	Electric current	ϵ	Thermoelectric power
J	Flux	η	Efficiency
K_e	Electrical conductivity	ϕ	Potential function
K_t	Thermal conductivity	π	Peltier coefficient
L_{ij}	Onsager coefficients	τ	Thomson coefficient or time
m	Mass	μ	Chemical potential
n	Number of moles	σ	Rate of entropy production per unit volume
p	Pressure		
Q	Heat		
R_e	Electrical resistance	Subscripts:	
S	Entropy or Seebeck coefficient	i, j	Refer to ith and jth components
T	Absolute temperature		

13

INTRODUCTION TO IRREVERSIBLE THERMODYNAMICS

13-1
Introduction
Classical thermodynamics and statistical mechanics treat processes as though only the end states exist. They presume that a system exists in a state of thermodynamic or statistical equilibrium. This chapter discusses nonequilibrium states and the intermediate stages that occur in processes.

Before studying nonequilibrium systems, it is first necessary to resolve an ambiguity which exists when the properties of these systems are defined. Suppose heat is flowing through a metal bar, and it is required that the temperature gradient in the bar be measured. The flow of heat may be steady so that no changes take place as a function of time; nevertheless, a nonequilibrium state still exists because there is, in the dimension of space, a thermal gradient along the bar. Since temperature is defined on the basis of thermal equilibrium, a temperature-sensing device placed at some point along the bar will give a meaningless reading. However, if a small region is first isolated and its temperature measured when thermal equilibrium is attained, the result then has meaning. Similar procedures may be applied when other thermodynamic properties are measured. But in all cases the existence of thermodynamic equilibrium is implied when any property is measured.

Classical thermodynamics provides no information about rates of irreversible flows. In studies of processes that involve the flow of mass, heat, or electrical energy, the rate of flow is an important parameter. A major objective in studying irreversible phenomena is to obtain expressions of rates of flow.

Irreversible processes may be examined by two approaches. The microscopic behavior of the particles may be analyzed, using statistical averaging methods, to predict the macroscopic behavior of the system. Alternatively, the energy flow and the mass flow may be studied macroscopically, considering the pairs of driving forces and fluxes in conjunction with appropriate transport properties of the system. This latter approach is called *irreversible thermodynamics*. Although the subject is still in the process of development, it has proven particularly useful in explaining irreversible transport phenomena. When two or more flows are simultaneously involved, irreversible thermodynamics shows how these coupled flows are related to each other.

Methods of applying irreversible thermodynamics to chemically nonreactive, nonequilibrium systems are discussed in this chapter. In addition, laws dealing with energy and mass transport phenomena are formulated.

13-2
Single Phenomenological Flows
Transport or flow phenomena can be described by means of equations that relate *cause* (driving force) with *effect* (flux of energy or mass). The *flux of flow* is defined as the amount of flow per unit area in a unit time. Flow in which only one flux, consisting of either

energy or mass, is involved is called *single flow*. When two or more fluxes exist, the flow is called *coupled flow*. When coupled flow occurs but one flux predominates, the flow can be treated as though it were a single flow. Temperature gradients in a metal bar give rise to conductive heat transfer; in addition, they generate voltage and concentration gradients in the bar. However, the flow of matter due to these gradients is negligible compared to the primary flow of heat. Fourier noted in 1811 that the heat flow in a homogeneous solid is directly proportional to the temperature gradient. For one-dimensional flow, the heat flux due to conduction, according to Fourier, is

$$J_Q = -K_t \frac{\partial T}{\partial x}. \tag{13.1}$$

Similarly, when an electrical potential is applied across a resistor, a temperature gradient develops in the resistor, but the flow of electrons caused solely by the temperature gradient is negligible. The current flux depends linearly on the potential gradient and is given with sufficient accuracy by *Ohm's law* as

$$J_I = -K_e \frac{\partial \mathscr{E}}{\partial x}. \tag{13.2}$$

A third example of single flow is the diffusion process. The diffusion of one species of matter into another is linearly dependent on the concentration gradients. The mass flux due to diffusion, as given by *Fick's law*, is

$$J_m = -D \frac{\partial c}{\partial x}. \tag{13.3}$$

This assumes that mass flow due to voltage gradients or temperature gradients is negligible.

13-3 Entropy Production

Entropy changes occur in a system due to the interaction of the system with the environment and due to irreversible processes that occur internally. These changes may be expressed as

$$dS = dS_{\text{ext}} + dS_{\text{int}}, \tag{13.4}$$

where the subscripts "ext" and "int" refer to external and internal effects, respectively. Changes in entropy that arise from external sources may be due to mass transfer or heat interaction with the environment. Such changes can be either positive or negative, depending on the process. The internal contribution of entropy dS_{int} is of particular interest since it indicates the degradation of energy resulting from internal nonequilibrium processes. According to the second law dS_{int} is either positive or zero, but can never be negative. The change of internal entropy, or the rate of production of internal entropy, serves as a gauge when comparing irreversible processes. For example, consider two systems A and B of fixed composition. Let dQ_A and dQ_B represent the heat interaction between systems A and B with the environment during an interval of time $d\tau$. During the same interval of time the heat interaction between the two systems is dQ_{AB}. As shown in Fig. 13.1, if the temperature of each system remains unchanged, the energy balance at system A is

$$dQ_{A\,net} = dQ_A - dQ_{AB},$$

while at system B the energy balance is

$$dQ_{B\,net} = dQ_{AB} - dQ_B.$$

The change of entropy of system A is

$$dS_A = \frac{dQ_A}{T_A} - \frac{dQ_{AB}}{T_A},$$

and of system B

$$dS_B = -\frac{dQ_B}{T_B} + \frac{dQ_{AB}}{T_B}.$$

The change of entropy of the combined systems is

$$dS = dS_A + dS_B = \left(\frac{dQ_A}{T_A} - \frac{dQ_B}{T_B}\right) + dQ_{AB}\left(-\frac{1}{T_A} + \frac{1}{T_B}\right).$$

The entropy change due solely to heat interaction with the environment is therefore:

$$(dS_{AB})_{ext} = \frac{dQ_A}{T_A} - \frac{dQ_B}{T_B},$$

while the entropy change due to internal effects, resulting from heat interaction between systems A and B is

$$(dS_{AB})_{int} = dQ_{AB}\left(-\frac{1}{T_A} + \frac{1}{T_B}\right) = dQ_{AB}\left(\frac{T_A - T_B}{T_A T_B}\right) > 0.$$

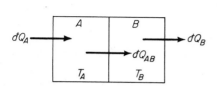

Fig. 13.1. *Heat interaction between two systems.*

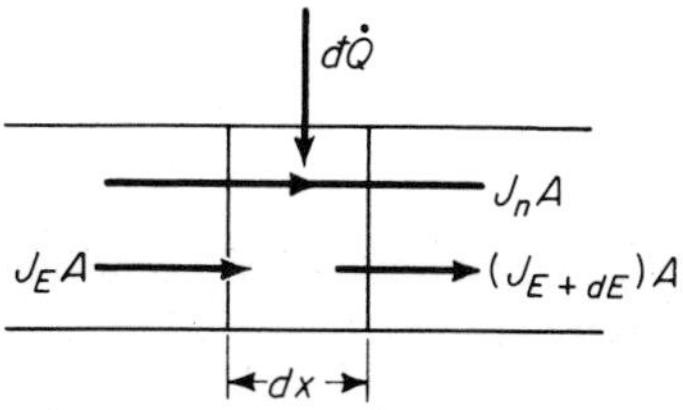

Fig. 13.2. *Isothermal flow through a semi-permeable membrane.*

This entropy production is associated with irreversible heat interaction between systems A and B. Note that if $T_A > T_B$ and $dQ_{AB} > 0$ then $(S_{AB})_{int} > 0$. On the other hand, if $T_A < T_B$ then $dQ_{AB} < 0$, and so $(dS_{AB})_{int}$ is again > 0.

The rate of production of internal entropy is

$$\frac{(dS_{AB})_{int}}{d\tau} = \frac{dQ_{AB}}{d\tau}\left(\frac{1}{T_B} - \frac{1}{T_A}\right) > 0.$$

If T_A and T_B differ by only a small amount, this equation becomes

$$\frac{dS_{int}}{d\tau} = \frac{dQ}{d\tau}\frac{dT}{T^2}.$$

From this equation, the rate of entropy production per unit volume, σ, may be obtained:

$$\sigma = \frac{dQ}{A\,dx\,d\tau}\frac{dT}{T^2} = -J_Q\frac{1}{T^2}\frac{dT}{dx} = J_Q\frac{d(1/T)}{dx} \tag{13.5}$$

where $A\,dx$ represents volume and J_Q is the heat flux. The negative sign indicates that heat flow takes place in the direction of the negative temperature gradient.

In a similar way, consider the entropy production due to flow of matter through a semipermeable membrane. As shown in Fig. 13.2, a fluid consisting of several species flows steadily and isothermally through a distance dx. A quantity of heat, dQ, must be transferred in order to maintain the isothermal flow. It is assumed that no phase changes occur in the fluid; it is also assumed that such properties as enthalpy and chemical potential vary infinitesimally across the distance dx. The change of entropy then is caused by heat transfer and by internal irreversible processes, which can be expressed as

$$dS = dS_{int} + \frac{dQ}{T}.$$

Rearranging,

$$T \, dS_{\text{int}} = T \, dS - \dbar Q. \tag{13.6}$$

But the first law may be applied to this isothermal, steady-state process, to give

$$\dbar Q + \sum_i \left[H_i - \left(H_i + \frac{\partial H_i}{\partial x} \, dx \right) \right] = 0$$

or

$$\dbar Q = \sum_i \frac{\partial H_i}{\partial x} \, dx. \tag{13.7}$$

Enthalpy can be expressed, at constant temperature, in terms of the Gibbs free energy as:

$$dH = dG + T \, dS.$$

Further, Gibbs free energy can be expressed as a function of chemical potential, according to Eq. (5.60):

$$dG = \sum_i \left(\frac{\partial \bar{\mu}_i}{\partial x} \right) dx \, dn_i,$$

where μ_i is chemical potential of the ith species. Therefore,

$$\frac{\partial H_i}{\partial x} \, dx = \sum_i \left(\frac{\partial \bar{\mu}_i}{\partial x} \right) dx \, dn_i + T \, dS.$$

The first law (Eq. 13.7) can now be expressed as

$$\dbar Q = \sum_i \left(\frac{\partial \bar{\mu}_i}{\partial x} \right) dx \, dn_i + T \, dS.$$

Hence,

$$T \, dS_{\text{int}} = T \, dS - \sum_i \left(\frac{\partial \bar{\mu}_i}{\partial x} \right) dx \, dn_i - T \, dS$$

or

$$T \, dS_{\text{int}} = -\sum_i \left(\frac{\partial \bar{\mu}_i}{\partial x} \right) dx \, dn_i.$$

The rate of internal entropy production per unit volume can therefore be expressed as

$$\sigma = \frac{dS_{\text{int}}}{A\,dx\,d\tau} = -\frac{1}{T}\sum_i \left(\frac{\partial\bar{\mu}_i}{\partial x}\right)\frac{dn_i}{A\,d\tau}.$$

Since $dn_i/A\,d\tau$ is the molal flux J_{n_i}, therefore,

$$\sigma = -\frac{1}{T}\sum_i J_{n_i}\frac{\partial\bar{\mu}_i}{\partial x} = \sum_i J_{n_i}\frac{d(-\bar{\mu}_i/T)}{dx} \geqslant 0. \qquad (13.8)$$

It is clear from these two cases that the rate of internal entropy production per unit volume is the sum of products of the flux and the conjugate driving force. This may be expressed as follows:

$$\sigma = \sum_i J_i X_i \geqslant 0, \qquad (13.9)$$

where J_i is either the energy flux or the mass flux, and X_i is a function of a potential gradient such as a temperature gradient or a chemical potential gradient.

**13-4
Relation
Between Flux
and Driving
Force**

In relatively slow processes, the flux of energy or matter, J_i is a linear function of the gradient of a potential ϕ_i. That is,

$$J_i\,\alpha\,\frac{\partial\phi_i}{\partial x},$$

where the subscript i identifies the ith irreversible process. But the gradient of the potential ϕ_i also represents the driving force, X_i so that

$$X_i = \frac{\partial\phi_i}{\partial x}. \qquad (13.10)$$

Consequently the flux, J_i, is proportional to the driving force, X_i:

$$J_i = L_i X_i, \qquad (13.11)$$

where L_i is a coefficient of proportionality which depends on the properties of the system.

When two or more flows occur in a system, questions arise about relationships between the fluxes and the driving forces. Lars Onsager in 1931 assumed that the flux of each flow bears a linear relationship not only to the conjugate force but also to the other forces to which the system is subjected. Therefore in a system consisting of n coupled flows, the ith flux is given by

$$J_i = L_{i1} X_1 + L_{i2} X_2 + L_{i3} X_3 + \cdots = \sum_{j=1}^{n} L_{ij} X_j. \qquad (13.12)$$

In coupled flows, then, the ith flux J_i depends linearly not only on the conjugate driving force X_i through its *primary* coefficient L_{ii}, but also on the other driving forces, through the *coupling* coefficients L_{ij}. The coefficients L_{ij} are called the *Onsager phenomenological coefficients*. Onsager assumed that the flux depends on the first power of the driving forces. This is not always true. However, this linear relationship occurs in phenomenological flows as long as the systems do not deviate markedly from thermodynamic equilibrium.

The coupling of thermomechanical flows can be illustrated by referring to a system in which convective heat transfer occurs. Fluid motion results from potential differences in temperature and in pressure; also, the fluid transports internal energy between source and sink. Under nonequilibrium steady-state flow conditions, all potentials are in dynamic balance, and the transfer of heat takes place at a steady rate. On the other hand, under equilibrium conditions, all thermodynamic potentials vanish. From Eq. (13.12), the mass transfer and energy transfer are:

$$J_m = L_{11} X_m + L_{12} X_E$$
$$J_E = L_{21} X_m + L_{22} X_E,$$

where J_m represents the mass flux and J_E represents the energy flux. The thermoelectric effect, which is discussed in Section 13-6, is an example of a flow in which heat and electrical energy are coupled.

An expression for the rate of entropy production per unit volume in coupled flows can be obtained by combining Eqs. (13.9) and (13.12):

$$\sigma = \sum_i \sum_j L_{ij} X_i X_j \geqslant 0. \qquad (13.13)$$

When only two flows are involved, the rate of entropy production is

$$\sigma = L_{11} X_1^2 + (L_{12} + L_{21}) X_1 X_2 + L_{22} X_2^2 \geqslant 0.$$

Since the primary coefficients L_{11} and L_{22} must be positive,* it follows that

$$L_{11} L_{22} - \left(\frac{L_{12} + L_{21}}{2} \right)^2 \geqslant 0.$$

*This may be shown by setting all coupling coefficients L_{ij} ($i \neq j$) in Eq. (13.13) to be equal to zero.

13-5
Onsager
Reciprocity
Relation
Although the linear relationship between fluxes and flows greatly simplifies the treatment of irreversible transport phenomena, the problem is still not solved. The flux equations require a large number of coefficients. To evaluate these coefficients, a large number of experiments must be performed. Furthermore, these mathematical equations cannot be solved easily. The difficulty is reduced if it can be shown that relationships exist between the various transport coefficients. Onsager postulated that the transport coefficients in coupled flows are symmetrical, so that

$$L_{ij} = L_{ji}. \tag{13.14}$$

Equation (13.14) is called the *Onsager reciprocity relation*. It applies in the absence of a magnetic field; it also applies, but in modified form, if a magnetic field is present. When Eq. (13.14) is used, the number of independent constants required to evaluate an irreversible phenomena is reduced. Coefficients which are difficult to measure are calculated through Eq. (13.14) from those which are more readily determined.

Proof of the Onsager reciprocity relation based on statistical-mechanical analysis is available in the literature.* The Onsager theorem has been very successful in describing many irreversible phenomena, especially those involving gases. By combining the Onsager reciprocity relation with linear superposition of forces and fluxes, many problems involving irreversible phenomena have been solved. However, the validity of the Onsager relation is still questioned, and further investigation is needed. Furthermore, a more general theory is needed. Like the laws of thermodynamics, the Onsager postulate can be considered as a law of nature for it shows the relationships that exist in certain physical phenomena.

13-6
Thermoelectric
Phenomena
Methods of irreversible thermodynamics are readily applicable to the analysis of thermoelectric phenomena. In this coupled-flow phenomenon the simultaneous flows are considered to be linearly superimposed and the coefficients associated with the superposition are symmetric. As shown in Section 12.19, an electrical potential gradient in a conductor causes heat flow, while at the same time, a temperature gradient in the conductor causes a flow of electrical current. These two irreversible flows are linearly coupled by the following equations:

$$J_I = -L_{11} \frac{1}{T} \frac{d\mathscr{E}}{dx} - L_{12} \frac{1}{T^2} \frac{dT}{dx} \tag{13.15}$$

*See, for example, reference 13.1.

$$J_Q = -L_{21} \frac{1}{T} \frac{d\mathscr{E}}{dx} - L_{22} \frac{1}{T^2} \frac{dT}{dx}. \tag{13.16}$$

In the absence of a temperature gradient,

$$J_I = -L_{11} \frac{1}{T} \frac{d\mathscr{E}}{dx}. \tag{13.17}$$

The coefficients, L_{ij}, of Eqs. (13.15) and (13.16) are related to the transport properties of the conducting solid. According to Ohm's law, the isothermal electrical conductivity K_e is given by

$$J_I = -K_e \frac{d\mathscr{E}}{dx}. \tag{13.18}$$

By comparing the two preceding equations, the primary coefficient L_{11} and the electrical conductivity K_e are shown to be related as follows:

$$K_e = \frac{L_{11}}{T}. \tag{13.19}$$

Similarly, in the absence of electric current flow, thermal conductivity K_t is related to heat flux through Fourier's equation:

$$J_Q = -K_t \frac{dT}{dx}. \tag{13.20}$$

When there is no current flow, J_I is zero, and Eq. (13.15) becomes

$$\left(\frac{d\mathscr{E}/dx}{dT/dx} \right)_{J_I=0} = -\frac{L_{12}}{TL_{11}}. \tag{13.21}$$

From Eq. (13.21) it is clear that an electric potential gradient develops in a body if a temperature gradient exists, even if no electric current flows. This is the Seebeck effect discussed in Chapter 12.

The ratio $-d\mathscr{E}/dT$, denoted by ϵ, is called the *thermoelectric power* of the conductor. It is a function of temperature. By combining Eqs. (13.19) and (13.21), the coupling coefficient L_{12} may be expressed as follows:

$$L_{12} = \epsilon TL_{11} = \epsilon K_e T^2. \tag{13.22}$$

When Eq. (13.21) is combined with Eq. (13.16), the heat flux can be expressed as

$$J_Q = -\frac{L_{11}L_{22} - L_{12}^2}{L_{11}T^2} \frac{dT}{dx}. \tag{13.23}$$

From the heat flux, Eqs. (13.20) and (13.23), an expression for thermal conductivity is obtained:

$$K_t = \frac{L_{11}L_{22} - L_{12}^2}{L_{11}T^2}.$$

This leads to an expression for the L_{22} coefficient as a function of conductivities and thermoelectric power:

$$L_{22} = T^2(K_t + TK_e\epsilon^2), \tag{13.24}$$

where both K_e and K_t must, necessarily, have positive values. The L_{ij} coefficients have now been expressed as functions of the current flux; heat flux may also be described in terms of the transport properties:

$$J_I = -K_e\frac{d\mathcal{E}}{dx} - \epsilon K_e\frac{dT}{dx} \tag{13.25}$$

and

$$J_Q = -\epsilon TK_e\frac{d\mathcal{E}}{dx} - (K_t + \epsilon^2 K_e T)\frac{dT}{dx}. \tag{13.26}$$

By eliminating $d\mathcal{E}/dx$ from Eqs. (13.25) and (13.26), the heat flux becomes

$$J_Q = -K_t\frac{dT}{dx} + \epsilon TJ_I. \tag{13.27}$$

Similarly, by eliminating dT/dx, the current flux becomes

$$J_I = \left(\frac{\epsilon^2 K_e T}{K_t + K_e T} - K_e\right)\frac{d\mathcal{E}}{dx} + \left(\frac{\epsilon K_e}{K_t + \epsilon K_e T}\right)J_Q. \tag{13.28}$$

In addition to the Fourier heat effect and the Seebeck effect, three other phenomena occur when an electric current flows through a junction of two dissimilar metals. These are (a) the Peltier effect; (b) the Thomson effect; and (c) Joule heat.

When an electric current flows through the junction of two dissimilar metals, the temperature of the junction will change unless heat is transferred to or from the junction. This phenomenon is illustrated in Fig. 13.3 and is known as the *Peltier effect*. If isothermal conditions are maintained, Eq. (13.25) becomes

$$J_I = -K_e\frac{d\mathcal{E}}{dx}.$$

The heat flux through each metal, according to Eq. (13.26), is

$$J_Q = -\epsilon T K_e \frac{d\mathscr{E}}{dx}.$$

The heat flux through each of the metals forming the junction can be expressed as a function of the current flux:

$$J_{Q_A} = T\epsilon_A J_I$$
$$J_{Q_B} = T\epsilon_B J_I.$$

The net heat flux due to the Peltier effect is therefore

$$J_{Q_P} = J_{Q_B} - J_{Q_A} = T(\epsilon_B - \epsilon_A)J_I = \pi_{AB}J_I. \tag{13.29}$$

The *Peltier coefficient*, π_{AB}, indicates heat per unit electric current flux and is defined by

$$\pi_{AB} = T(\epsilon_B - \epsilon_A). \tag{13.30}$$

Consider next a conductor in which a temperature gradient exists initially. When electric current flows through the conductor, heat must be transferred in order to maintain the original temperature gradient. The direction of heat flow depends on the direction of current flow and on the temperature gradient. This phenomenon is known as the *Thomson effect*. As shown in Fig. 13.4, the energy flux J_E is the sum of the heat flux and the electrical power supplied per unit area, or

$$J_E = J_Q + \mathscr{E}J_I.$$

After the heat flux from Eq. (13.27) is substituted in this equation, the energy flux becomes

$$J_E = -K_t \frac{dT}{dx} + (\epsilon T + \mathscr{E})J_I. \tag{13.31}$$

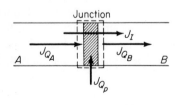

Fig. 13.3. Peltier effect.

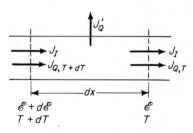

Fig. 13.4. Thomson effect.

But the gradient of the energy flux in the x direction also represents the heat transferred from the conductor:

$$J'_Q = -\frac{\partial}{\partial x}(J_E).$$

By substituting for J_E from Eq. (13.31) into this equation, the heat transferred from the conductor becomes

$$J'_Q = -\frac{\partial}{\partial x}[-K_t\frac{dT}{dx} + (\epsilon T + \mathscr{E})J_I]$$

$$= -\epsilon J_I\frac{\partial T}{\partial x} - TJ_I\frac{d\epsilon}{dx} - J_I\frac{d\mathscr{E}}{dx}.$$

Note that there is no change in temperature gradient in the x direction.

After substituting for the potential gradient $d\mathscr{E}/dx$ from Eq. (13.25), the preceding equation becomes

$$J'_Q = -TJ_I\frac{d\epsilon}{dx} + \frac{J_I^2}{K_e} = -TJ_I\frac{d\epsilon}{dT}\frac{dT}{dx} + \frac{J_I^2}{K_e}. \qquad (13.32)$$

The last term in this equation represents Joule heat due to electric current flow in the absence of a temperature gradient; the first term therefore represents Thomson heat:

$$J_{Q_T} = -TJ_I\frac{d\epsilon}{dT}\frac{dT}{dx} = -\tau J_I\frac{dT}{dx}. \qquad (13.33)$$

The *Thomson coefficient*, τ, indicates heat per unit electric current flux and per unit temperature gradient, and is defined by

$$\tau = T\frac{d\epsilon}{dT}. \qquad (13.34)$$

The total heat flux then becomes

$$J'_Q = -\tau J_I\frac{dT}{dx} + \frac{J_I^2}{K_e}. \qquad (13.35)$$

Differentiation of Eq. (13.30) with respect to temperature leads to the following expression:

$$\frac{d\pi_{AB}}{dT} = (\epsilon_B - \epsilon_A) + (\tau_B - \tau_A). \qquad (13.36)$$

Equations (13.30) and (13.36), which are called the *Kelvin relations*, were derived by Kelvin in 1854 from energy considerations alone. In Eq. (13.36), the Seebeck, Peltier, and Thomson effects are coupled with each other.

REFERENCES

13.1 Callen, H. B., *Thermodynamics*. New York: John Wiley & Sons, Inc., 1960, chap. 16, 17.

13.2 Katchalsky, A., "Non-Equilibrium Thermodynamics," *Intl. Sci. Tech.*, **22** (October, 1963), 43-49.

APPENDIX

TABLE A.1 PHYSICAL CONSTANTS

Velocity of light	$c = 2.9979 \times 10^{10}$ cm/sec
Standard gravitational acceleration	$g = 980.665$ cm/sec^2
Planck's constant	$h = 6.6254 \times 10^{-27}$ erg-sec/molecule
Avogadro's number	$N_0 = 6.0248 \times 10^{23}$ molecules/gram-mole
Universal gas constant	$\mathscr{R} = 1545.33$ ft-lbf/lb mole-°R
	$= 8.314 \times 10^7$ ergs/gm mole-°K
	$= 1.98587$ cal/gm mole-°K
	$= 0.0820544$ liter atm/gram mole-°K
Boltzmann's constant	$k = 1.38049 \times 10^{-16}$ erg/°K molecule
Electronic charge	$e = -1.60186 \times 10^{-19}$ coulomb
Electronic mass	$m_e = 9.1086 \times 10^{-28}$ gram
1 electron-volt	$ev = 1.60209 \times 10^{-12}$ erg
1 standard atmosphere	atm $= 1.01325 \times 10^6$ dyne/cm^2

TABLE A.2 Conversion factors for various units

Length	1 m = 3.280 ft = 39.37 in. 1 cm $\equiv$ 10^{-2} m = 2.540 in. = 0.0328 ft 1 mm $\equiv$ 10^{-3} m 1 micron (μ) $\equiv$ 10^{-6} m 1 Angstrom (Å) $\equiv$ 10^{-10} m
Time	1 hr $\equiv$ 3600 sec = 60 min 1 millisec $\equiv$ 10^{-3} sec 1 microsec (μ sec) $\equiv$ 10^{-6} sec
Mass	1 kg $\equiv$ 1000 g = 2.2046 lbm = 6.8521 $\times$ 10^{-2} slugs 1 slug $\equiv$ 1 lbf-sec²/ft = 32.174 lbm
Force	1 newton $\equiv$ 1 kg-m/sec² 1 dyne $\equiv$ 1 g-cm/sec² 1 lbf = 4.448 $\times$ 10^5 dynes = 4.448 newtons
Energy	1 joule $\equiv$ 1 kg-m²/sec² 1 Btu $\equiv$ 778.16 ft-lbf = 1.055 $\times$ 10^{10} ergs = 0.252 kcal 1 cal $\equiv$ 4.186 joules 1 kcal $\equiv$ 4186 joules 1 erg $\equiv$ 1 g-cm²/sec² 1 ev $\equiv$ 1.602 $\times$ 10^{-19} joules
Power	1 watt $\equiv$ 1 kg-m²/sec³ = 1 joule/sec 1 hp $\equiv$ 550 ft-lbf/sec 1 hp = 2545 Btu/hr = 746 watts 1 kw $\equiv$ 1000 watts = 3413 Btu/hr
Pressure	1 atm $\equiv$ 14.696 lbf/in.² = 760 torr 1 mm Hg = 0.01934 lbf/in.² $\equiv$ 1 torr 1 dyne/cm² = 145.04 $\times$ 10^{-7} lbf/in.² 1 bar = 14.504 lbf/in.² $\equiv$ 10^6 dynes/cm² 1 micron (μ) $\equiv$ 10^{-6} m Hg = 10^{-3} mm Hg
Volume	1 gal $\equiv$ 0.13368 ft³ 1 liter $\equiv$ 1000.028 cm³
Temperature	1°K = 1°C = 1.8°F = 1.8°R 0°C corresponds to 32°F, 273.15°K, and 491.67°R

From Reynolds, W. C., *Thermodynamics*. New York: McGraw-Hill Book Company, 1965.

TABLE A.3 CONSTANT-PRESSURE SPECIFIC HEATS AT ZERO PRESSURE*

Substance	c_p (Btu/lbm-°R)	$\bar{c}_p$ (Btu/lbm mole-°R)
Air	$c_p = 0.219 + \dfrac{0.342\,T}{10^4} - \dfrac{0.293\,T^2}{10^8}$	$\bar{c}_p = 6.36 + \dfrac{9.92\,T}{10^4} - \dfrac{8.52\,T^2}{10^8}$
Carbon monoxide, CO	$c_p = 0.338 - \dfrac{117.5}{T} + \dfrac{3.82 \times 10^4}{T^2}$	$\bar{c}_p = 9.46 - \dfrac{3290}{T} + \dfrac{107 \times 10^4}{T^2}$
Hydrogen, H_2	$c_p = 2.857 + \dfrac{2.867\,T}{10^4} + \dfrac{9.92}{\sqrt{T}}$	$\bar{c}_p = 5.76 + \dfrac{5.78\,T}{10^4} + \dfrac{20}{\sqrt{T}}$
Nitrogen, N_2	$c_p = 0.338 - \dfrac{123.8}{T} + \dfrac{4.14 \times 10^4}{T^2}$	$\bar{c}_p = 9.47 - \dfrac{3470}{T} + \dfrac{116 \times 10^4}{T^2}$
Oxygen, O_2	$c_p = 0.36 - \dfrac{5.375}{\sqrt{T}} + \dfrac{47.8}{T}$	$\bar{c}_p = 11.515 - \dfrac{173}{\sqrt{T}} + \dfrac{1530}{T}$
Carbon dioxide, CO_2	$c_p = 0.368 - \dfrac{148.4}{T} + \dfrac{3.2 \times 10^4}{T^2}$	$\bar{c}_p = 16.2 - \dfrac{6530}{T} + \dfrac{141 \times 10^4}{T^2}$
Sulfur dioxide, SO_2	$c_p = 0.1875 + \dfrac{0.0944\,T}{10^4} - \dfrac{1.336 \times 10^4}{T^2}$	$\bar{c}_p = 11.89 + \dfrac{6.05\,T}{10^4} - \dfrac{85.6 \times 10^4}{T^2}$
Water vapor, H_2O	$c_p = 1.102 - \dfrac{33.1}{\sqrt{T}} + \dfrac{416}{T}$	$\bar{c}_p = 19.86 - \dfrac{597}{\sqrt{T}} + \dfrac{7500}{T}$
Acetylene, C_2H_2	$c_p = 0.459 + \dfrac{0.937\,T}{10^4} - \dfrac{2.89 \times 10^4}{T^2}$	$\bar{c}_p = 11.94 + \dfrac{24.37\,T}{10^4} - \dfrac{75.2 \times 10^4}{T^2}$
Ethane, C_2H_6	$c_p = 0.0731 + \dfrac{7.08\,T}{10^4} - \dfrac{11.3\,T^2}{10^8}$	$\bar{c}_p = 2.195 + \dfrac{212.7\,T}{10^4} - \dfrac{340\,T^2}{10^8}$
Ethylene, C_2H_4	$c_p = 0.0965 + \dfrac{5.78\,T}{10^4} - \dfrac{9.97\,T^2}{10^8}$	$\bar{c}_p = 2.706 + \dfrac{162\,T}{10^4} - \dfrac{279.6\,T^2}{10^8}$
Isobutane, C_4H_{10}	$c_p = 0.075 + \dfrac{6.94\,T}{10^4} - \dfrac{11.77\,T^2}{10^8}$	$\bar{c}_p = 4.36 + \dfrac{403\,T}{10^4} - \dfrac{683\,T^2}{10^8}$
Methane, CH_4	$c_p = 0.211 + \dfrac{6.25\,T}{10^4} - \dfrac{8.28\,T^2}{10^8}$	$\bar{c}_p = 3.38 + \dfrac{100.2\,T}{10^4} - \dfrac{132.7\,T^2}{10^8}$
Propane, C_3H_8	$c_p = 0.0152 + \dfrac{7.27\,T}{10^4} - \dfrac{12.32\,T^2}{10^8}$	$\bar{c}_p = 2.258 + \dfrac{320\,T}{10^4} - \dfrac{543\,T^2}{10^8}$

*Values obtained by permission from Spencer, Justice, Flanagan, Chipman, and Fontana, *Jour. Am. Chem. Soc.*, Vols. 56, 57, 64, 67, and Sweigert and Beardsley, *Ga. Inst. of Tech. Eng. Exp. Sta. Bull.* No. 2.

TABLE A.4 DRY SATURATED STEAM: PRESSURE TABLE *

Abs. press., psia, p	Temp, °F, t	Sat. liquid v_f	Sat. vapor v_g	Sat. liquid h_f	Evap. h_{fg}	Sat. vapor h_g	Sat. liquid s_f	Evap. s_{fg}	Sat. vapor s_g	Sat. liquid u_f	Sat. vapor u_g	Abs. press., psia, p
1.0	101.74	0.01614	333.6	69.70	1036.3	1106.0	0.1326	1.8456	1.9782	69.70	1044.3	1.0
2.0	126.08	0.01623	173.73	93.99	1022.2	1116.2	0.1749	1.7451	1.9200	93.98	1051.9	2.0
3.0	141.48	0.01630	118.71	109.37	1013.2	1122.6	0.2008	1.6855	1.8863	109.36	1056.7	3.0
4.0	152.97	0.01636	90.63	120.86	1006.4	1127.3	0.2198	1.6427	1.8625	120.85	1060.2	4.0
5.0	162.24	0.01640	73.52	130.13	1001.0	1131.0	0.2347	1.6094	1.8441	130.12	1063.1	5.0
6.0	170.06	0.01645	61.98	137.96	996.2	1134.2	0.2472	1.5820	1.8292	137.94	1065.4	6.0
7.0	176.85	0.01649	53.64	144.76	992.1	1136.9	0.2581	1.5586	1.8167	144.74	1067.4	7.0
8.0	182.86	0.01653	47.34	150.79	988.5	1139.3	0.2674	1.5383	1.8057	150.77	1069.2	8.0
9.0	188.28	0.01656	42.40	156.22	985.2	1141.4	0.2759	1.5203	1.7962	156.19	1070.8	9.0
10	193.21	0.01659	38.42	161.17	982.1	1143.3	0.2835	1.5041	1.7876	161.14	1072.2	10
14.696	212.00	0.01672	26.80	180.07	970.3	1150.4	0.3120	1.4446	1.7566	180.02	1077.5	14.696
15	213.03	0.01672	26.29	181.11	969.7	1150.8	0.3135	1.4415	1.7549	181.06	1077.8	15
20	227.96	0.01683	20.089	196.16	960.1	1156.3	0.3356	1.3962	1.7319	196.10	1081.9	20
25	240.07	0.01692	16.303	208.42	952.1	1160.6	0.3533	1.3606	1.7139	208.34	1085.1	25
30	250.33	0.01701	13.746	218.82	945.3	1164.1	0.3680	1.3313	1.6993	218.73	1087.8	30
35	259.28	0.01708	11.898	227.91	939.2	1167.1	0.3807	1.3063	1.6870	227.80	1090.1	35
40	267.25	0.01715	10.498	236.03	933.7	1169.7	0.3919	1.2844	1.6763	235.90	1092.0	40
45	274.44	0.01721	9.401	243.36	928.6	1172.0	0.4019	1.2650	1.6669	243.22	1093.7	45
50	281.01	0.01727	8.515	250.09	924.0	1174.1	0.4110	1.2474	1.6585	249.93	1095.3	50
55	287.07	0.01732	7.787	256.30	919.6	1175.9	0.4193	1.2316	1.6509	256.12	1096.7	55

60	292.71	0.01738	7.175	262.09	915.5	1177.6	0.4270	1.2168	1.6438	261.90	1097.9	60
65	297.97	0.01743	6.655	267.50	911.6	1179.1	0.4342	1.2032	1.6374	267.29	1099.1	65
70	302.92	0.01748	6.206	272.61	907.9	1180.6	0.3309	1.1906	1.6315	272.38	1100.2	70
75	307.60	0.01753	5.816	277.43	904.5	1181.9	0.4472	1.1787	1.6259	277.19	1101.2	75
80	312.03	0.01757	5.472	282.02	901.1	1183.1	0.4531	1.1676	1.6207	281.76	1102.1	80
85	316.25	0.01761	5.168	286.39	897.8	1184.2	0.4587	1.1571	1.6158	286.11	1102.9	85
90	320.27	0.01766	4.896	290.56	894.7	1185.3	0.4641	1.1471	1.6112	290.27	1103.7	90
95	324.12	0.01770	4.652	294.56	891.7	1186.2	0.4692	1.1376	1.6068	294.25	1104.5	95
100	327.81	0.01774	4.432	298.40	888.8	1187.2	0.4740	1.1286	1.6026	298.08	1105.2	100
120	341.25	0.01789	3.728	312.44	877.9	1190.4	0.4916	1.0062	1.5878	312.05	1107.6	120
130	347.32	0.01796	3.455	318.81	872.9	1191.7	0.4995	1.0817	1.5812	318.38	1108.6	130
140	353.02	0.01802	3.220	324.82	868.2	1193.0	0.5069	1.0682	1.5751	324.35	1109.6	140
150	358.42	0.01809	3.015	330.51	863.6	1194.1	0.5138	1.0556	1.5694	330.01	1110.5	150
160	363.53	0.01815	2.834	335.93	859.2	1195.1	0.5204	1.0436	1.5640	335.39	1111.2	160
170	368.41	0.01822	2.675	341.09	854.9	1196.0	0.5266	1.0324	1.5590	340.52	1111.9	170
180	373.06	0.01827	2.532	346.03	850.8	1196.9	0.5325	1.0217	1.5542	345.42	1112.5	180
190	377.51	0.01833	2.404	350.79	846.8	1197.6	0.5381	1.0116	1.5497	350.15	1113.1	190
200	381.79	0.01839	2.288	355.36	843.0	1198.4	0.5435	1.0018	1.5453	354.68	1113.7	200
250	400.95	0.01865	1.8438	376.00	825.1	1201.1	0.5675	0.9588	1.5263	375.14	1115.8	250
300	417.33	0.01890	1.5433	393.84	809.0	1202.8	0.5879	0.9225	1.5104	392.79	1117.1	300

* Abridged from "*Thermodynamic Properties of Steam*" by Joseph H. Keenan and Frederick G. Keyes, by permission of John Wiley & Sons, Inc., New York, 1936.

TABLE A.4 DRY SATURATED STEAM: PRESSURE TABLE (cont.)

Abs. press., psia, p	Temp, °F, t	Sat. liquid v_f	Sat. vapor v_g	Sat. liquid h_f	Evap. h_{fg}	Sat. vapor h_g	Sat. liquid s_f	Evap. s_{fg}	Sat. vapor s_g	Sat. liquid u_f	Sat. vapor u_g	Abs. press., psia, p
350	431.72	0.01913	1.3260	409.69	794.2	1203.9	0.6056	0.8910	1.4966	408.45	1118.0	350
400	444.59	0.0193	1.1613	424.0	780.5	1204.5	0.6214	0.8630	1.4844	422.6	1118.5	400
450	456.28	0.0195	1.0320	437.2	767.4	1204.6	0.6356	0.8378	1.4734	435.5	1118.7	450
500	467.01	0.0197	0.9278	449.4	755.0	1204.4	0.6487	0.8147	1.4634	447.6	1118.7	500
550	476.94	0.0199	0.8424	460.8	743.1	1203.9	0.6608	0.7934	1.4542	458.8	1118.2	550
600	486.21	0.0201	0.7698	471.6	731.6	1203.2	0.6720	0.7734	1.4454	469.4	1117.7	600
650	494.90	0.0203	0.7083	481.8	720.5	1202.3	0.6826	0.7548	1.4374	479.4	1117.1	650
700	503.10	0.0205	0.6554	491.5	709.7	1201.2	0.6925	0.7371	1.4296	488.8	1116.3	700
750	510.86	0.0207	0.6092	500.8	699.2	1200.0	0.7019	0.7204	1.4223	598.0	1115.4	750
800	518.23	0.0209	0.5687	509.7	688.9	1198.6	0.7108	0.7045	1.4153	506.6	1114.4	800
850	525.26	0.0210	0.5327	518.3	678.8	1197.1	0.7194	0.6891	1.4085	515.0	1113.3	850
900	531.98	0.0212	0.5006	526.6	668.8	1195.4	0.7275	0.6744	1.4020	523.1	1112.1	900
950	538.43	0.0214	0.4717	534.6	659.1	1193.7	0.7355	0.6602	1.3957	530.9	1110.8	950
1000	544.61	0.0216	0.4456	542.4	649.4	1191.8	0.7430	0.6467	1.3897	538.4	1109.4	1000
1100	556.31	0.0220	0.4001	557.4	630.4	1187.8	0.7575	0.6205	1.3780	552.9	1106.4	1100
1200	567.22	0.0223	0.3619	571.7	611.7	1183.4	0.7711	0.5956	1.3667	566.7	1103.0	1200
1300	577.46	0.0227	0.3293	585.4	593.2	1178.6	0.7840	0.5719	1.3559	580.0	1099.4	1300
1400	587.10	0.0231	0.3012	598.7	575.7	1173.4	0.7963	0.5491	1.3454	592.7	1095.4	1400
1500	596.23	0.0235	0.2765	611.6	556.3	1167.9	0.8082	0.5269	1.3351	605.1	1091.2	1500
2000	635.82	0.0257	0.1878	671.7	463.4	1135.1	0.8619	0.4230	1.2849	662.2	1065.6	2000
2500	668.13	0.0287	0.1307	730.6	360.5	1091.1	0.9126	0.3197	1.2322	717.3	1030.6	2500
3000	695.36	0.0346	0.0858	802.5	217.8	1020.3	0.9731	0.1885	1.1615	783.4	972.7	3000
3206.2	705.40	0.0503	0.0503	902.7	0	902.7	1.0580	0	1.0580	872.9	872.9	3206.2

TABLE A.5 DRY SATURATED STEAM: TEMPERATURE TABLE *

Temp, °F, t	Abs. press., psia, p	Specific volume ft³/lbm			Enthalpy Btu/lbm			Entropy Btu/lbm-°R			Temp, °F, t
		Sat. liquid v_f	Evap. v_{fg}	Sat. vapor v_g	Sat. liquid h_f	Evap. h_{fg}	Sat. vapor h_g	Sat. liquid s_f	Evap. s_{fg}	Sat. vapor s_g	
32	0.08854	0.01602	3306	3306	0.00	1075.8	1075.8	0.0000	2.1877	2.1877	32
35	0.099995	0.01602	2947	2947	3.02	1074.1	1077.1	0.0061	2.1709	2.1770	35
40	0.12170	0.01602	2444	2444	8.05	1071.3	1079.3	0.0162	2.1435	2.1597	40
45	0.14752	0.01602	2036.4	2036.4	13.06	1068.4	1081.5	0.0262	2.1167	2.1429	45
50	0.17811	0.01603	1703.2	1703.2	18.07	1065.6	1083.7	0.0361	2.0903	2.1264	50
60	0.2563	0.01604	1206.6	1206.7	28.06	1059.9	1088.0	0.0555	2.0393	2.0948	60
70	0.3631	0.01606	867.8	867.9	38.04	1054.3	1092.3	0.0745	1.9902	2.0647	70
80	0.5069	0.01608	633.1	633.1	48.02	1048.6	1096.6	0.0932	1.9428	2.0360	80
90	0.6982	0.01610	468.0	468.0	57.99	1042.9	1100.9	0.1115	1.8972	2.0087	90
100	0.9492	0.01613	350.3	350.4	67.97	1037.2	1105.2	0.1295	1.8531	1.9826	100
110	1.2748	0.01617	265.3	265.4	77.94	1031.6	1109.5	0.1471	1.8106	1.9577	110
120	1.6924	0.01620	203.25	203.27	87.92	1025.8	1113.7	0.1645	1.7694	1.9339	120
130	2.2225	0.01625	157.32	157.34	97.90	1020.0	1117.9	0.1816	1.7296	1.9112	130
140	2.8886	0.01629	122.99	123.01	107.89	1014.1	1122.0	0.1984	1.6910	1.8894	140
150	3.718	0.01634	97.06	97.07	117.89	1008.2	1126.1	0.2149	1.6537	1.8685	150
160	4.741	0.01639	77.27	77.29	127.89	1002.3	1130.2	0.2311	1.6174	1.8485	160
170	5.992	0.01645	62.04	62.06	137.90	996.3	1134.2	0.2472	1.5822	1.8293	170
180	7.510	0.01651	50.21	50.23	147.92	990.2	1138.1	0.2630	1.5480	1.8109	180
190	9.339	0.01657	40.94	40.96	157.95	984.1	1142.0	0.2785	1.5147	1.7932	190
200	11.526	0.01663	33.62	33.64	167.99	977.9	1145.9	0.2938	1.4824	1.7762	200

* Abridged from "*Thermodynamic Properties of Steam*" by Joseph H. Keenan and Frederick G. Keyes, by permission of John Wiley & Sons, Inc., New York, 1936.

TABLE A.5 DRY SATURATED STEAM: TEMPERATURE TABLE (cont.)

Temp, °F, t	Abs. press., psia, p	Specific volume ft³/lbm			Enthalpy Btu/lbm			Entropy Btu/lbm-°R			Temp, °F, t
		Sat. liquid v_f	Evap. v_{fg}	Sat. vapor v_g	Sat. liquid h_f	Evap. h_{fg}	Sat. vapor h_g	Sat. liquid s_f	Evap. s_{fg}	Sat. vapor s_g	
210	14.123	0.01670	27.80	27.82	178.05	971.6	1149.7	0.3090	1.4508	1.7598	210
212	14.696	0.01672	26.78	26.80	180.07	970.3	1150.4	0.3120	1.4446	1.7566	212
220	17.186	0.01677	23.13	23.15	188.13	965.2	1153.4	0.3239	1.4201	1.7440	220
230	20.780	0.01684	19.365	19.382	198.23	958.8	1157.0	0.3387	1.3901	1.7288	230
240	24.969	0.01692	16.306	16.323	208.34	952.2	1160.5	0.3531	1.3609	1.7140	240
250	29.825	0.01700	13.804	13.821	216.48	945.6	1164.0	0.3675	1.3323	1.6998	250
260	35.429	0.01709	11.746	11.763	228.64	938.7	1167.3	0.3817	1.3043	1.6860	260
270	41.858	0.01717	10.044	10.061	238.84	931.8	1170.6	0.3958	1.2769	1.6727	270
280	49.203	0.01726	8.628	8.645	249.06	924.7	1173.8	0.4096	1.2501	1.6597	280
290	57.556	0.01735	7.444	7.461	259.31	917.5	1176.8	0.4234	1.2238	1.6472	290
300	67.013	0.01745	6.449	6.466	269.59	910.1	1179.7	0.4369	1.1980	1.6350	300
310	77.68	0.01755	5.609	5.626	279.92	902.6	1182.5	0.4504	1.1727	1.6231	310
320	89.66	0.01765	4.896	4.914	290.28	894.9	1185.2	0.4637	1.1478	1.6115	320
330	103.06	0.01776	4.289	4.307	300.68	887.0	1187.7	0.4769	1.1233	1.6002	330
340	118.01	0.01878	3.770	3.788	311.13	879.0	1190.1	0.4900	1.0992	1.5891	340
350	134.63	0.01799	3.324	3.342	321.63	870.7	1192.3	0.5029	1.0754	1.5783	350
360	163.04	0.01811	2.939	2.957	332.18	862.2	1194.4	0.5158	1.0519	1.5677	360
370	173.37	0.01823	2.606	2.625	342.79	853.5	1196.3	0.5286	1.0287	1.5573	370
380	195.77	0.01836	2.317	2.335	353.45	844.6	1198.1	0.5413	1.0059	1.5471	380
390	220.37	0.01850	2.0651	2.0836	364.17	835.4	1199.6	0.5539	0.9832	1.5371	390

400	247.31	0.01864	1.8447	1.8633	374.97	826.0	1201.0	0.5664	0.9608	1.5272	400
410	276.75	0.01878	1.6512	1.6700	385.83	816.3	1202.1	0.5788	0.9386	1.5174	410
420	308.83	0.01894	1.4811	1.5000	396.77	806.3	1203.1	0.5912	0.9166	1.5078	420
430	343.72	0.01910	1.3308	1.3499	407.79	796.0	1203.8	0.6035	0.6035	0.8947	430
440	381.59	0.01926	1.1979	1.2171	418.90	785.4	1204.3	0.6158	0.8730	1.4887	440
450	422.6	0.0194	1.0799	1.0993	430.1	774.5	1204.6	0.6280	0.8513	1.4793	450
460	466.9	0.0196	0.9748	0.9944	441.4	763.2	1204.6	0.6402	0.8298	1.4700	460
470	514.7	0.0198	0.8811	0.9009	452.8	751.5	1204.3	0.6523	0.8083	1.4606	470
480	566.1	0.0200	0.7972	0.8172	464.4	739.4	1203.7	0.6645	0.7868	1.4513	480
490	621.4	0.0202	0.7221	0.7423	476.0	726.8	1202.8	0.6766	0.7653	1.4419	490
500	680.8	0.0204	0.6545	0.6749	487.8	713.9	1201.7	0.6887	0.7438	1.4325	500
520	812.4	0.0209	0.5385	0.5594	511.9	686.4	1198.2	0.7130	0.7006	1.4136	520
540	962.5	0.0215	0.4434	0.4649	536.6	656.6	1193.2	0.7374	0.6568	1.3942	540
560	1133.1	0.0221	0.3647	0.3868	562.2	624.2	1186.4	0.7621	0.6121	1.3742	560
580	1325.8	0.0228	0.2980	0.3217	577.9	588.4	1177.3	0.7872	0.5659	1.3532	580
600	1342.9	0.0236	0.2432	0.2668	617.0	548.5	1165.5	0.8131	0.5176	1.3307	600
620	1786.6	0.0247	0.1955	0.2201	646.7	503.6	1150.3	0.8398	0.4664	1.3062	620
640	2059.7	0.0260	0.1538	0.1798	678.6	452.0	1130.5	0.8679	0.4110	1.2789	640
660	2365.4	0.0278	0.1165	0.1442	714.2	390.2	1104.4	0.8987	0.3485	1.2472	660
680	2708.1	0.0305	0.0819	0.1115	757.3	309.9	1067.2	0.9351	0.2719	1.2071	680
700	3093.7	0.0369	0.0392	0.0761	823.3	172.1	995.4	0.9905	0.1484	1.1389	700
705.4	3206.2	0.0503	0	0.0503	902.7	0	902.7	1.0580	0	1.0580	705.4

TABLE A.6 PROPERTIES OF SUPERHEATED STEAM *

Abs. press., psia (Sat. temp)		Temperature, degrees Fahrenheit												
		200	300	400	500	600	700	800	900	1000	1100	1200	1400	1600
1 (101.74)	v	393.6	452.3	512.0	571.6	631.2	690.8	750.4	809.9	869.9	929.1	988.7	1107.8	1227.0
	h	1150.4	1195.8	1241.7	1288.3	1335.7	1383.8	1432.8	1482.7	1533.5	1585.2	1637.7	1747.5	1857.5
	s	2.0512	2.1153	2.1720	2.2233	2.2702	2.3137	2.3542	2.3923	2.4283	2.4625	2.4952	2.5566	2.6137
5 (162.24)	v	78.16	90.25	102.26	114.22	126.16	138.10	150.03	161.95	173.87	185.79	197.71	221.6	245.4
	h	1148.8	1195.0	1241.2	1288.0	1335.4	1383.6	1432.7	1482.6	1533.4	1585.1	1637.7	1745.7	1857.4
	s	1.8718	1.9370	1.9942	2.0456	2.0927	2.1361	2.1767	2.2148	2.2509	2.2851	2.3178	2.3792	2.4363
10 (193.21)	v	38.85	45.00	51.04	57.05	63.03	69.01	74.98	80.95	86.92	92.88	98.84	110.77	122.69
	h	1146.6	1193.9	1240.7	1287.5	1335.1	1383.4	1432.5	1482.4	1533.2	1585.0	1637.6	1745.6	1857.3
	s	1.7927	1.8595	1.9172	1.9689	2.0160	2.0596	2.1002	2.1383	2.1744	2.2086	2.2413	2.3028	2.3598
14.696 (212.00)	v	.....	30.53	34.68	38.78	42.86	46.94	51.00	55.07	59.13	63.19	67.37	75.37	83.48
	h	.....	1192.8	1239.9	1287.1	1334.8	1383.2	1432.3	1482.3	1533.1	1584.8	1637.5	1747.5	1857.3
	s	.....	1.8160	1.8743	1.9261	1.9734	2.0170	2.0576	2.0958	2.1319	2.1662	2.1989	2.2603	2.3174
20 (227.96)	v	.....	22.36	25.43	28.46	31.47	34.47	37.46	40.45	43.44	46.42	49.41	55.37	61.34
	h	.....	1191.6	1239.2	1286.6	1334.4	1382.9	1432.1	1482.1	1533.0	1584.7	1637.4	1745.4	1857.2
	s	.....	1.7808	1.8396	1.8918	1.9392	1.9829	2.0235	2.0718	2.0978	2.1321	2.1648	2.2263	2.2834
40 (267.25)	v	.....	11.040	12.628	14.168	15.688	17.198	18.702	20.20	21.70	23.20	24.69	27.68	30.66
	h	.....	1186.8	1236.5	1284.8	1333.1	1381.9	1431.3	1481.4	1532.4	1584.3	1637.0	1745.1	1857.0
	s	.....	1.6994	1.7608	1.8140	1.8619	1.9058	1.9467	1.9850	2.0212	2.0555	2.0883	2.1498	2.2069
60 (292.71)	v	.....	7.259	8.357	9.403	10.427	11.441	12.449	13.452	14.454	15.453	16.451	18.446	20.44
	h	.....	1181.6	1233.6	1283.0	1331.8	1380.9	1430.5	1480.8	1531.9	1583.8	1636.6	1744.8	1856.7
	s	.....	1.6492	1.7135	1.7678	1.8162	1.8605	1.9015	1.9400	1.9762	2.0106	2.0434	2.1049	2.1621

Abs. Press., Lb./Sq. In. (Sat. Temp.)													
80 (312.03)	v..	6.220	7.020	7.797	8.562	9.322	10.077	10.830	11.582	12.332	13.830	15.325
	h..	1230.7	1281.1	1330.5	1379.9	1429.7	1480.1	1531.3	1583.4	1636.2	1744.5	1856.5
	s..	1.6791	1.7346	1.7836	1.8281	1.8694	1.9079	1.9442	1.9787	2.0115	2.0731	2.1303
100 (327.81)	v..	4.937	5.589	6.218	6.835	7.446	8.052	8.656	9.259	9.860	11.060	12.258
	h..	1227.6	1279.1	1329.1	1378.9	1428.9	1479.9	1530.8	1582.9	1635.7	1744.2	1856.2
	s..	1.6518	1.7085	1.7581	1.8029	1.8443	1.8829	1.9193	1.9538	1.9867	2.0484	2.1056
120 (341.25)	v..	4.081	4.636	5.165	5.683	6.195	6.702	7.207	7.710	8.212	9.214	10.213
	h..	1224.4	1277.2	1327.7	1377.8	1428.1	1478.8	1530.2	1582.4	1635.3	1743.9	1856.0
	s..	1.6287	1.6869	1.7370	1.7822	1.8237	1.8625	1.8990	1.9335	1.9664	2.0281	2.0854
140 (353.02)	v..	3.468	3.954	4.413	4.861	5.301	5.738	6.172	6.604	7.035	7.895	8.752
	h..	1221.1	1275.2	1326.4	1376.8	1427.3	1478.2	1529.7	1581.9	1634.9	1743.5	1855.7
	s..	1.6087	1.6683	1.7190	1.7645	1.8063	1.8451	1.8817	1.9163	1.9493	2.0110	2.0683
160 (363.53)	v..	3.008	3.443	3.849	4.244	4.631	5.015	5.396	5.775	6.152	6.906	7.656
	h..	1217.6	1273.1	1325.0	1375.7	1426.4	1477.5	1529.1	1581.4	1634.5	1743.2	1855.5
	s..	1.5908	1.6519	1.7033	1.7491	1.7911	1.8301	1.8667	1.9014	1.9341	1.9962	2.0535
180 (373.06)	v..	2.649	3.044	3.411	3.764	4.110	4.452	4.792	5.129	5.466	6.136	6.804
	h..	1214.0	1271.0	1323.5	1374.7	1425.6	1476.8	1528.6	1581.0	1634.1	1742.9	1855.2
	s..	1.5743	1.6373	1.6894	1.7355	1.7776	1.8167	1.8534	1.8882	1.9212	1.9831	2.0404
200 (381.79)	v..	2.361	2.726	3.060	3.380	3.693	4.002	4.309	4.613	4.917	5.521	6.123
	h..	1210.3	1268.9	1322.1	1373.6	1424.8	1476.2	1528.0	1580.5	1633.7	1742.6	1855.0
	s..	1.5594	1.6240	1.6767	1.7232	1.7655	1.8048	1.8415	1.8763	1.9094	1.9713	2.0287
220 (389.86)	v..	2.125	2.465	2.772	3.066	3.352	3.634	3.913	4.191	4.467	5.017	5.565
	h..	1206.5	1266.7	1320.7	1372.6	1424.0	1475.5	1527.5	1580.0	1633.3	1742.3	1854.7
	s..	1.5453	1.6117	1.6652	1.7120	1.7545	1.7939	1.8308	1.8656	1.8987	1.9607	2.0181

* Abridged from *Thermodynamic Properties of Steam* by Joseph H. Keenan and Frederick G. Keyes, by permission of John Wiley & Sons, Inc., New York, 1936.

TABLE A.6 Properties of superheated steam (cont.)

Abs. press., psia (Sat. temp)		200	300	400	500	600	700	800	900	1000	1100	1200	1400	1600
						Temperature, degrees Fahrenheit								
240 (397.37)	v	....	....	1.9276	2.247	2.533	2.804	3.068	3.327	3.584	3.839	4.093	4.597	5.100
	h	....	....	1202.5	1264.5	1319.2	1371.5	1423.2	1474.8	1526.9	1579.6	1632.9	1742.0	1854.5
	s	....	....	1.5319	1.6003	1.6546	1.7017	1.7444	1.7839	1.8209	1.8558	1.8889	1.9510	2.0084
260 (404.42)	v	....	....	....	2.063	2.330	2.582	2.827	3.067	3.305	3.541	3.776	4.242	4.707
	h	....	....	....	1262.3	1317.7	1370.4	1422.3	1474.2	1526.3	1579.1	1632.5	1741.7	1854.2
	s	....	....	....	1.5897	1.6447	1.6922	1.7352	1.7748	1.8118	1.8467	1.8799	1.9420	1.9995
280 (411.05)	v	....	....	....	1.9047	2.156	2.392	2.621	2.845	3.066	3.286	3.504	3.938	4.370
	h	....	....	....	1260.0	1316.2	1369.4	1421.5	1473.5	1525.8	1578.6	1632.1	1741.4	1854.0
	s	....	....	....	1.5796	1.6354	1.6834	1.7265	1.7662	1.8033	1.8383	1.8716	1.9337	1.9912
300 (417.33)	v	....	....	....	1.7675	2.005	2.227	2.442	2.652	2.859	3.065	3.269	3.674	4.078
	h	....	....	....	1257.6	1314.7	1368.3	1420.6	1472.8	1525.2	1578.1	1631.7	1741.0	1854.7
	s	....	....	....	1.5701	1.6268	1.6751	1.7184	1.7582	1.7954	1.8305	1.8633	1.9260	1.9835
350 (431.72)	v	....	....	....	1.4923	1.7036	1.8980	2.084	2.266	2.445	2.622	2.798	3.147	3.493
	h	....	....	....	1251.5	1310.9	1365.5	1418.5	1471.1	1523.8	1577.0	1630.7	1740.3	1853.1
	s	....	....	....	1.5481	1.6070	1.6563	1.7002	1.7403	1.7777	1.8130	1.8463	1.9086	1.9663
400 (444.59)	v	....	....	....	1.2851	1.4770	1.6508	1.8161	1.9767	2.134	2.290	2.445	2.751	3.055
	h	....	....	....	1245.1	1306.9	1362.7	1416.4	1469.4	1522.4	1575.8	1629.6	1739.5	1852.5
	s	....	....	....	1.5281	1.5894	1.6398	1.6842	1.7247	1.7623	1.7977	1.8311	1.8936	1.9513

TABLE A.6 Properties of superheated steam (cont.)

Abs press., psi (Sat. temp)		500	550	600	620	640	660	680	700	800	900	1000	1200	1400	1600
							Temperature, degrees Fahrenheit								
450 (456.28)	v	1.1231	1.2155	1.3005	1.3332	1.3652	1.3967	1.4278	1.4584	1.6074	1.7516	1.8928	2.170	2.443	2.714
	h	1238.4	1272.0	1302.8	1314.6	1326.2	1337.5	1348.8	1359.9	1414.3	1467.8	1521.0	1628.6	1738.7	1851.9
	s	1.5095	1.5437	1.5735	1.5845	1.5951	1.6054	1.6153	1.6250	1.6699	1.7108	1.7486	1.8177	1.8803	1.9381
500 (467.01)	v	0.9927	1.0800	1.1591	1.1893	1.2188	1.2478	1.2763	1.3044	1.4405	1.5715	1.6996	1.9504	2.197	2.442
	h	1231.3	1266.8	1298.6	1310.7	1322.6	1334.2	1345.7	1357.0	1412.1	1466.0	1519.6	1627.6	1737.9	1851.3
	s	1.4919	1.5280	1.5588	1.5701	1.5810	1.5915	1.6016	1.6115	1.6571	1.6982	1.7363	1.8056	1.8683	1.9262
550 (476.94)	v	0.8852	0.9686	1.0431	1.0714	1.0989	1.1259	1.1523	1.1783	1.3038	1.4241	1.5414	1.7706	1.9957	2.219
	h	1223.7	1261.2	1294.3	1306.8	1318.9	1330.8	1342.5	1354.0	1409.9	1464.3	1518.2	1626.6	1737.1	1850.6
	s	1.4751	1.5131	1.5451	1.5568	1.5680	1.5787	1.5890	1.5991	1.6452	1.6868	1.7250	1.7946	1.8575	1.9155
600 (486.21)	v	0.7947	0.8753	0.9463	0.9729	0.9988	1.0241	1.0489	1.0732	1.1899	1.3013	1.4096	1.6208	1.8279	2.033
	h	1215.7	1255.5	1289.9	1302.7	1315.2	1327.4	1339.3	1351.1	1407.7	1462.5	1516.7	1625.5	1736.3	1850.0
	s	1.4586	1.4990	1.5323	1.5443	1.5558	1.5667	1.5773	1.5875	1.6343	1.6762	1.7147	1.7846	1.8476	1.9056
700 (503.10)	v	.....	0.7277	0.7934	0.8177	0.8411	0.8639	0.8860	0.9088	1.0108	1.1082	1.2024	1.3853	1.5641	1.7405
	h	.....	1243.2	1280.6	1294.3	1307.5	1320.3	1332.8	1345.0	1403.2	1459.0	1513.9	1623.5	1734.8	1848.8
	s	.....	1.4722	1.5084	1.5212	1.5333	1.5449	1.5559	1.5665	1.6147	1.6573	1.6963	1.7666	1.8299	1.8881
800 (518.23)	v	.....	0.6154	0.6779	0.7006	0.7223	0.7433	0.7635	0.7833	0.8763	0.9633	1.0470	1.2088	1.3662	1.5214
	h	.....	1229.8	1270.7	1285.4	1299.4	1312.9	1325.9	1338.6	1398.6	1455.4	1511.0	1621.4	1733.2	1847.5
	s	.....	1.4467	1.4863	1.5000	1.5129	1.5250	1.5366	1.5476	1.5972	1.6407	1.6801	1.7510	1.8146	1.8729
900 (531.98)	v	.....	0.5264	0.5873	0.6089	0.6294	0.6491	0.6680	0.6863	0.7716	0.8506	0.9262	1.0714	1.2124	1.3409
	h	.....	1215.0	1260.1	1275.9	1290.9	1305.1	1318.8	1332.1	1393.9	1451.8	1508.1	1619.3	1731.6	1846.3
	s	.....	1.4216	1.4653	1.4800	1.4938	1.5066	1.5187	1.5303	1.5814	1.6257	1.6656	1.7371	1.8009	1.8595

TABLE A.6 PROPERTIES OF SUPERHEATED STEAM (cont.)

Temperature, degrees Fahrenheit

Abs. press., psia (Sat. temp)		500	550	600	620	640	660	680	700	800	900	1000	1200	1400	1600
1000 (544.64)	v	0.4533	......	0.5140	0.5350	0.5546	0.5733	0.5912	0.6084	0.6878	0.7604	0.9294	0.9615	1.0893	1.2146
	h	1198.3	......	1248.8	1265.9	1281.9	1297.0	1311.4	1325.3	1389.2	1448.2	1505.1	1617.3	1730.0	1845.0
	s	1.3961	......	1.4450	1.4610	1.4757	1.4893	1.5021	1.5141	1.5670	1.6121	1.6525	1.7245	1.7886	1.8474
1100 (556.31)	v	......	......	0.4532	0.4738	0.4929	0.5110	0.5281	0.5445	0.6191	0.6866	0.7503	0.8716	0.9885	1.1031
	h	......	......	1236.7	1255.3	1272.4	1288.5	1303.7	1318.3	1384.3	1444.5	1502.2	1615.2	1728.4	1843.8
	s	......	......	1.4251	1.4425	1.4583	1.4728	1.4862	1.4989	1.5535	1.5995	1.6405	1.7130	1.7775	1.8363
1200 (567.22)	v	......	......	0.4016	0.4222	0.4410	0.4586	0.4752	0.4909	0.5617	0.6250	0.6843	0.7967	0.9046	1.0101
	h	......	......	1223.5	1243.9	1262.4	1279.6	1295.7	1311.0	1379.3	1440.7	1499.2	1613.1	1726.9	1842.5
	s	......	......	1.4052	1.4243	1.4413	1.4568	1.4710	1.4843	1.5409	1.5879	1.6293	1.7025	1.7672	1.8263
1400 (587.10)	v	......	......	0.3174	0.3390	0.3580	0.3753	0.3912	0.4062	0.4714	0.5281	0.5805	0.6789	0.7727	0.8040
	h	......	......	1193.0	1218.4	1240.4	1260.3	1278.5	1295.5	1369.1	1433.1	1493.2	1608.9	1723.7	1840.0
	s	......	......	1.3639	1.3877	1.4079	1.4258	1.4419	1.4567	1.5177	1.5666	1.6093	1.6836	1.7489	1.8083
1600 (602.90)	v	......	......	......	0.2733	0.2936	0.3112	0.3271	0.3417	0.4034	0.4553	0.5027	0.5906	0.6738	0.7545
	h	......	......	......	1187.8	1215.2	1238.7	1259.6	1278.7	1358.4	1425.3	1487.0	1604.6	1720.5	1837.5
	s	......	......	......	1.3489	1.3741	1.3952	1.4137	1.4303	1.4964	1.5476	1.5914	1.6669	1.7328	1.7926
1800 (621.03)	v	......	......	......	......	0.2407	0.2597	0.2760	0.2907	0.3502	0.3986	0.4421	0.5218	0.5968	0.6693
	h	......	......	......	......	1185.1	1214.0	1238.5	1260.3	1347.2	1417.4	1480.8	1600.4	1717.3	1835.0
	s	......	......	......	......	1.3377	1.3638	1.3855	1.4044	1.4765	1.5301	1.5752	1.6520	1.7185	1.7786
2000 (635.82)	v	......	......	......	......	0.1936	0.2161	0.2337	0.2489	0.3074	0.3532	0.3935	0.4668	0.5352	0.6011
	h	......	......	......	......	1145.6	1184.9	1214.8	1240.0	1335.5	1409.2	1474.5	1596.1	1714.1	1832.5
	s	......	......	......	......	1.2945	1.3300	1.3564	1.3783	1.4576	1.5139	1.5603	1.6384	1.7055	1.7660

2500 (668.13)	v	0.1484	0.1686	0.2294	0.2710	0.3061	0.3678	0.4244	0.4784
	h	1132.3	1176.8	1303.6	1387.8	1458.4	1585.3	1706.1	1826.2
	s	1.2687	1.3073	1.4127	1.4772	1.5273	1.6088	1.6775	1.7389
3000 (695.36)	v		0.0984	0.1760	0.2159	0.2476	0.3018	0.3505	0.3966
	h		1060.7	1267.2	1365.0	1441.8	1574.3	1698.0	1819.9
	s		1.1966	1.3690	1.4439	1.4984	1.5837	1.6540	1.7163
3206.2 (705.40)	v			1.1583	0.1981	0.2288	0.2806	0.3267	0.3703
	h			1250.5	1355.2	1434.7	1569.8	1694.6	1817.2
	s			1.3508	1.4309	1.4874	1.5742	1.6452	1.7080
3500	v		0.0306	0.1364	0.1762	0.2058	0.2546	0.2977	0.3381
	h		780.5	1224.9	1340.7	1424.5	1563.3	1689.8	1813.6
	s		0.9515	1.3241	1.4127	1.4723	1.5615	1.6336	1.6968
4000	v		0.0287	0.1052	0.1462	0.1743	0.2192	0.2581	0.2943
	h		763.8	1174.8	1314.4	1406.8	1552.1	1681.7	1807.2
	s		0.9347	1.2757	1.3827	1.4482	1.5417	1.6154	1.6795
4500	v		0.0276	0.0798	0.1226	0.1500	0.1917	0.2273	0.2602
	h		753.5	1113.9	1286.5	1388.4	1540.8	1673.5	1800.9
	s		0.9235	1.2204	1.3529	1.4253	1.5235	1.5990	1.6640
5000	v		0.0268	0.0593	0.1036	0.1303	0.1696	0.2027	0.2329
	h		746.4	1047.1	1256.5	1369.5	1529.5	1665.3	1794.5
	s		0.9152	1.1622	1.3231	1.4034	1.5066	1.5839	1.6499
5500	v		0.0262	0.0463	0.0880	0.1143	0.1515	0.1825	0.2106
	h		741.3	985.0	1224.1	1349.3	1518.2	1657.0	1788.1
	s		0.9090	1.1093	1.2930	1.3821	1.4908	1.5699	1.6369

TABLE A.7 SATURATION

Specific Volume, ft³/lbm

Temp. °F	Abs. Press., lbf/in.²	Sat. Liquid	Evap.	Sat. Vapor
	p	v_f	v_{fg}	v_g
−60	5.55	0.0228	44.707	44.73
−55	6.54	0.0229	38.357	38.38
−50	7.67	0.0230	33.057	33.08
−45	8.95	0.0231	28.597	28.62
−40	10.41	0.02322	24.837	24.86
−35	12.05	0.02333	21.657	21.68
−30	13.90	0.0235	18.947	18.97
−25	15.98	0.0236	16.636	16.66
−20	18.30	0.0237	14.656	14.68
−15	20.88	0.02381	12.946	12.97
−10	23.74	0.02393	11.476	11.50
−5	26.92	0.02406	10.206	10.23
0	30.42	0.02419	9.092	9.116
5	34.27	0.02432	8.1257	8.150
10	38.51	0.02446	7.2795	7.304
15	43.14	0.02460	6.5374	6.562
20	48.21	0.02474	5.8853	5.910
25	53.73	0.02488	5.3091	5.334
30	59.74	0.02503	4.8000	4.825
35	66.26	0.02518	4.3478	4.373
40	73.32	0.02533	3.9467	3.971
45	80.96	0.02548	3.5885	3.614
50	89.19	0.02564	3.2684	3.294
55	98.06	0.02581	2.9822	3.008
60	107.6	0.02597	2.7250	2.751
65	117.8	0.02614	2.4939	2.520
70	128.8	0.02632	2.2857	2.312
75	140.5	0.02650	2.0985	2.125
80	153.0	0.02668	1.9283	1.955
85	166.4	0.02687	1.7741	1.801
90	180.6	0.02707	1.6339	1.661
95	195.8	0.02727	1.5067	1.534
100	211.9	0.02747	1.3915	1.419
105	228.9	0.02769	1.2853	1.313
110	247.0	0.02790	1.1891	1.217
115	266.2	0.02813	1.0999	1.128
120	286.4	0.02836	1.0186	1.047
125	307.8	0.02860	0.9444	0.973

*Abridged by permission, National Bureau of Standards Circular No. 142,

PROPERTIES OF AMMONIA*

Enthalpy, Btu/lbm			Entropy, Btu/lbm-°R		
Sat. Liquid h_f	Evap. h_{fg}	Sat. Vapor h_g	Sat. Liquid s_f	Evap. s_{fg}	Sat. Vapor s_g
−21.2	610.8	589.6	−0.0517	1.5286	1.4769
−15.9	607.5	591.6	−0.0386	1.5017	1.4631
−10.6	604.3	593.7	−0.0256	1.4753	1.4497
−5.3	600.9	595.6	−0.0127	1.4495	1.4368
0	597.6	597.6	0.000	1.4242	1.4242
5.3	594.2	599.5	0.0126	1.3994	1.4120
10.7	590.7	601.4	0.0250	1.3751	1.4001
16.0	587.2	603.2	0.0374	1.3512	1.3886
21.4	583.6	605.0	0.0497	1.3277	1.3774
26.7	580.0	606.7	0.0618	1.3044	1.3664
32.1	576.4	608.5	0.0738	1.2820	1.3558
37.5	572.6	610.1	0.0857	1.2597	1.3454
42.9	568.9	611.8	0.0975	1.2377	1.3352
48.3	565.0	613.3	0.1092	1.2161	1.3253
53.8	561.1	614.9	0.1208	1.1949	1.3157
59.2	557.1	616.3	0.1323	1.1739	1.3062
64.7	553.1	617.8	0.1437	1.1532	1.2969
70.2	548.9	619.1	0.1551	1.1328	1.2879
75.7	544.8	620.5	0.1663	1.1127	1.2790
81.2	540.5	621.7	0.1775	1.0929	1.2704
86.8	536.2	623.0	0.1885	1.0733	1.2618
92.3	531.8	624.1	0.1996	1.0539	1.2535
97.9	527.3	625.2	0.2105	1.0348	1.2453
103.5	522.8	626.3	0.2214	1.0159	1.2373
109.2	518.1	627.3	0.2322	0.9972	1.2294
114.8	513.4	628.2	0.2430	0.9786	1.2216
120.5	508.6	629.1	0.2537	0.9603	1.2140
126.2	503.7	629.9	0.2643	0.9422	1.2065
132.0	498.7	630.7	0.2749	0.9242	1.1991
137.8	493.6	631.4	0.2854	0.9064	1.1918
143.5	488.5	632.0	0.2958	0.8888	1.1846
149.4	483.2	632.6	0.3062	0.8713	1.1775
155.2	477.8	633.0	0.3166	0.8539	1.1705
161.1	472.3	633.4	0.3269	0.8366	1.1635
167.0	466.7	633.7	0.3372	0.8194	1.1566
173.0	460.9	633.9	0.3474	0.8023	1.1497
179.0	455.0	634.0	0.3576	0.7851	1.1427
185.1	448.9	634.0	0.3679	0.7679	1.1358

Tables of Thermodynamic Properties of Ammonia.

TABLE A.8 PROPERTIES OF SUPERHEATED AMMONIA*

Temperature, °F

Abs. press. (lb/in²) (Sat. temp.)		0	20	40	60	80	100	150	200	250	300
5 (−63.11)	v	57.55	60.12	62.69	65.24	67.79	70.33	76.68	....	....	....
	h	620.4	630.4	640.4	650.5	660.6	670.7	696.4	....	....	....
	s	1.5608	1.5821	1.6026	1.6223	1.6413	1.6598	1.7038	....	....	....
10 (−41.34)	v	28.58	29.90	31.20	32.49	33.78	35.07	38.26	41.45	....	....
	h	618.9	629.1	639.3	649.5	659.7	670.1	695.8	722.2	....	....
	s	1.4773	1.4992	1.5200	1.5400	1.5593	1.5779	1.6222	1.6637	....	....
15 (−27.29)	v	18.92	19.82	20.70	21.58	22.44	23.31	25.46	27.59	....	....
	h	617.2	627.8	638.2	648.5	658.9	669.2	695.3	721.7	....	....
	s	1.4272	1.4497	1.4709	1.4912	1.5108	1.5296	1.5742	1.6158	....	....
20 (−16.64)	v	14.09	14.78	15.45	16.12	16.78	17.43	19.05	20.66	....	....
	h	615.5	626.4	637.0	647.5	658.0	668.5	694.7	721.2	....	....
	s	1.3907	1.4138	1.4356	1.4562	1.4760	1.4950	1.5399	1.5817	....	....
25 (−7.96)	v	11.19	11.75	12.30	12.84	13.37	13.90	15.21	16.50	17.79	....
	h	613.8	625.0	635.8	646.5	657.1	667.7	694.1	720.8	748.0	....
	s	1.3616	1.3855	1.4077	1.4287	1.4487	1.4679	1.5131	1.5552	1.5948	....
30 (−0.57)	v	....	9.731	10.20	10.65	11.10	11.55	12.65	13.73	14.81	....
	h	....	623.5	634.6	645.5	656.2	666.9	693.5	720.3	747.5	....
	s	....	1.3618	1.3845	1.4059	1.4261	1.4456	1.4911	1.5334	1.5733	....
35 (5.89)	v	....	8.287	8.695	9.093	9.484	9.869	10.82	11.75	12.68	....
	h	....	622.0	633.4	644.4	655.3	666.1	692.9	719.9	747.2	....
	s	....	1.3413	1.3646	1.3863	1.4069	1.4265	1.4724	1.5148	1.5547	....
40 (11.86)	v	....	7.203	7.568	7.922	8.268	8.609	9.444	10.27	11.08	11.88
	h	....	620.4	632.1	643.4	654.4	665.3	692.3	719.4	746.8	774.6
	s	....	1.3231	1.3470	1.3692	1.3900	1.4098	1.4561	1.4987	1.5387	1.5766
50 (21.67)	v	....	....	5.988	6.280	6.564	6.843	7.521	8.185	8.840	9.489
	h	....	....	629.5	641.2	652.6	663.7	691.1	718.5	746.1	774.0
	s	....	....	1.3169	1.3399	1.3613	1.3816	1.4286	1.4716	1.5219	1.5500
60 (30.21)	v	....	....	4.933	5.184	5.428	5.665	6.239	6.798	7.348	7.892
	h	....	....	626.8	639.0	650.7	662.1	689.9	717.5	745.3	773.3
	s	....	....	1.2913	1.3152	1.3373	1.3581	1.4058	1.4493	1.4898	1.5281
70 (37.70)	v	....	....	4.177	4.401	4.615	4.822	5.323	5.807	6.287	6.750
	h	....	....	623.9	636.6	648.7	660.4	688.7	716.6	744.5	772.7
	s	....	....	1.2688	1.2937	1.3166	1.3378	1.3863	1.4302	1.4710	1.5095
80 (44.40)	v	....	....	....	3.812	4.005	4.190	4.635	5.063	5.487	5.894
	h	....	....	....	634.3	646.7	658.7	687.5	715.6	743.8	772.1
	s	....	....	....	1.2745	1.2981	1.3199	1.3692	1.4136	1.4547	1.4933

P (sat. temp)								
90 (50.47)	v	3.353	3.529	3.698	4.100	4.484	4.859	5.228
	h	631.8	644.7	657.0	686.3	714.7	743.0	771.5
	s	1.2571	1.2814	1.3038	1.3539	1.3988	1.4401	1.4789
100 (56.05)	v	2.985	3.149	3.304	3.672	4.021	4.361	4.695
	h	629.3	642.6	655.2	685.0	713.7	742.2	770.8
	s	1.2409	1.2661	1.2891	1.3401	1.3854	1.4271	1.4660
120 (66.02)	v	.....	2.576	2.712	3.029	3.326	3.614	3.895
	h	.....	638.3	651.6	682.5	711.8	740.7	769.6
	s	.....	1.2386	1.2628	1.3157	1.3620	1.4042	1.4435
140 (74.79)	v	.....	2.166	2.288	2.569	2.830	3.080	3.323
	h	.....	633.8	647.8	679.9	709.9	739.2	768.3
	s	.....	1.2140	1.2396	1.2945	1.3418	1.3846	1.4243
160 (82.64)	v	.....	.....	1.969	2.224	2.457	2.679	2.895
	h	.....	.....	643.9	677.2	707.9	737.6	767.1
	s	.....	.....	1.2186	1.2757	1.3240	1.3675	1.4076
180 (89.78)	v	.....	.....	1.720	1.995	2.167	2.367	2.561
	h	.....	.....	639.9	674.6	705.9	736.1	765.8
	s	.....	.....	1.1992	1.2586	1.3081	1.3521	1.3926
200 (96.34)	v	.....	.....	.....	1.740	1.935	2.118	2.295
	h	.....	.....	.....	671.8	703.9	734.5	764.5
	s	.....	.....	.....	1.2429	1.2935	1.3382	1.3791
220 (102.42)	v	.....	.....	.....	1.564	1.745	1.914	2.076
	h	.....	.....	.....	669.0	701.9	732.9	763.2
	s	.....	.....	.....	1.2281	1.2801	1.3255	1.3668
240 (108.09)	v	.....	.....	.....	1.416	1.587	1.745	1.895
	h	.....	.....	.....	666.1	699.8	731.3	762.0
	s	.....	.....	.....	1.2145	1.2677	1.3137	1.3554
260 (113.42)	v	.....	.....	.....	1.292	1.453	1.601	1.741
	h	.....	.....	.....	663.1	697.7	729.7	760.7
	s	.....	.....	.....	1.2014	1.2560	1.3027	1.3349
280 (118.45)	v	.....	.....	.....	1.184	1.339	1.478	1.610
	h	.....	.....	.....	660.1	695.6	728.1	759.4
	s	.....	.....	.....	1.1888	1.2449	1.2924	1.3350
300 (123.21)	v	.....	.....	.....	1.091	1.239	1.372	1.496
	h	.....	.....	.....	656.9	693.5	726.5	758.1
	s	.....	.....	.....	1.1767	1.2344	1.2827	1.3257

*Abridged by permission, National Bureau of Standards Circular No. 142, *Tables of Thermodynamic Properties of Ammonia.*

TABLE A.9 SATURATION PROPERTIES OF FREON-12*

Temp. (°F) t	Press. (lb/in²) p	Specific Vol. ft³/lbm		Enthalpy Btu/lbm			Entropy Btu/lbm-°R		
		Sat. liquid v_f	Sat. vapor v_g	Sat. liquid h_f	Evap. h_{fg}	Sat. vapor h_g	Sat. liquid s_f	Evap. s_{fg}	Sat. vapor s_g
−60	5.37	0.01036	6.516	−4.20	75.33	71.13	−0.0102	0.1681	0.1783
−50	7.13	0.01047	5.012	−2.11	74.42	72.31	−0.0050	0.1717	0.1767
−40	9.32	0.0106	3.911	0.00	73.50	73.50	0.00000	0.17517	0.17517
−30	12.02	0.0107	3.088	2.03	72.67	74.70	0.00471	0.16916	0.17387
−20	15.28	0.0108	2.474	4.07	71.80	75.87	0.00940	0.16335	0.17275
−10	19.20	0.0109	2.003	6.14	70.91	77.05	0.01403	0.15772	0.17175
0	23.87	0.0110	1.637	8.25	69.96	78.21	0.01869	0.15222	0.17091
5	26.51	0.0111	1.485	9.32	69.47	78.79	0.02097	0.14955	0.17052
10	29.35	0.0112	1.351	10.39	68.97	79.36	0.02328	0.14687	0.17015
20	35.75	0.0113	1.121	12.55	67.94	80.49	0.02783	0.14166	0.16949
30	43.16	0.0115	0.939	14.76	66.85	81.61	0.03233	0.13654	0.16887
40	51.68	0.0116	0.792	17.00	65.71	82.71	0.03680	0.13153	0.16833
50	61.39	0.0118	0.673	19.27	64.51	83.78	0.04126	0.12659	0.16785
60	72.41	0.0119	0.575	21.57	63.25	84.82	0.04568	0.12173	0.16741
70	84.82	0.0121	0.493	23.90	61.92	85.82	0.05009	0.11692	0.16701
80	98.76	0.0123	0.425	26.28	60.52	86.80	0.05446	0.11215	0.16662
86	107.9	0.0124	0.389	27.72	59.65	87.37	0.05708	0.10932	0.16640
90	114.3	0.0125	0.368	28.70	59.04	87.74	0.05882	0.10742	0.16624
100	131.6	0.0127	0.319	31.16	57.46	88.62	0.06316	0.10268	0.16584
110	150.7	0.0129	0.277	33.65	55.78	89.43	0.06749	0.09793	0.16542
120	171.8	0.0132	0.240	36.16	53.99	90.15	0.07180	0.09315	0.16495

*Abridged by permission from E. I. duPont de Nemours and Company.

TABLE A.10 PROPERTIES OF SUPERHEATED FREON-12*

Abs. press. (lb/in²) (Sat. temp.)		Temperature, °F											
		−40	−20	0	20	40	60	80	100	150	200	250	300
5 (−62.5)	v	7.363	7.726	8.088	8.450	8.812	9.173	9.533	9.893	10.79	11.69	.....	.....
	h	73.72	76.36	79.05	81.78	84.56	87.41	90.30	93.25	100.84	108.75	.....	.....
	s	0.1859	0.1920	0.1979	0.2038	0.2095	0.2150	0.2205	0.2258	0.2388	0.2513	.....	.....
10 (−37.3)	v	.....	3.821	4.006	4.189	4.371	4.556	4.740	4.923	5.379	5.831	6.281	.....
	h	.....	76.11	78.81	81.56	84.35	87.19	90.11	93.05	100.66	108.63	116.88	.....
	s	.....	0.1801	0.1861	0.1919	0.1977	0.2033	0.2087	0.2141	0.2271	0.2396	0.2517	.....
15 (−20.8)	v	.....	2.521	2.646	2.771	2.895	3.019	3.143	3.266	3.571	3.877	4.191	.....
	h	.....	75.89	78.59	81.37	84.18	87.03	89.94	92.91	100.53	108.49	116.78	.....
	s	.....	0.17307	0.17913	0.18499	0.19074	0.19635	0.20185	0.20723	0.22028	0.23282	0.24491	.....
20 (−8.2)	v	.....	.....	1.965	2.060	2.155	2.250	2.343	2.437	2.669	2.901	3.130	.....
	h	.....	.....	78.39	81.14	83.97	86.85	89.78	92.75	100.40	108.38	116.67	.....
	s	.....	.....	0.17407	0.17996	0.18573	0.19138	0.19688	0.20229	0.21537	0.22794	0.24005	.....
25 (2.2)	v	.....	.....	.....	1.712	1.793	1.873	1.952	2.031	2.227	2.422	2.615	.....
	h	.....	.....	.....	80.95	83.78	86.67	89.61	92.56	100.26	108.26	116.56	.....
	s	.....	.....	.....	0.17637	0.18216	0.18783	0.19336	0.19748	0.21190	0.22450	0.23665	.....
30 (11.1)	v	.....	.....	.....	1.364	1.430	1.495	1.560	1.624	1.784	1.943	2.099	.....
	h	.....	.....	.....	80.75	83.59	86.49	89.43	92.42	100.12	108.13	116.45	.....
	s	.....	.....	.....	0.17278	0.17859	0.18429	0.18983	0.19527	0.20843	0.22105	0.23325	.....
35 (18.9)	v	.....	.....	.....	1.109	1.237	1.295	1.352	1.409	1.550	1.689	1.827	.....
	h	.....	.....	.....	80.49	83.40	86.30	89.26	92.26	99.98	108.01	116.33	.....
	s	.....	.....	.....	0.16963	0.17591	0.18162	0.18719	0.19266	0.20584	0.21849	0.23069	.....
40 (25.9)	v	.....	.....	.....	.....	1.044	1.095	1.144	1.194	1.315	1.435	1.554	.....
	h	.....	.....	.....	.....	83.20	86.11	89.09	92.09	99.83	107.88	116.21	.....
	s	.....	.....	.....	.....	0.17322	0.17896	0.18455	0.19004	0.20325	0.21592	0.22813	.....
50 (38.3)	v	.....	.....	.....	.....	0.821	0.863	0.904	0.944	1.044	1.142	1.239	1.332
	h	.....	.....	.....	.....	82.76	85.72	88.72	91.75	99.54	107.62	116.00	124.69
	s	.....	.....	.....	.....	0.16895	0.17475	0.18040	0.18591	0.19923	0.21196	0.22419	0.23600
60 (48.7)	v	.....	.....	.....	.....	.....	0.708	0.743	0.778	0.863	0.946	1.028	1.108
	h	.....	.....	.....	.....	.....	85.33	88.35	91.41	99.24	107.36	115.54	124.29
	s	.....	.....	.....	.....	.....	0.17120	0.17689	0.18246	0.19585	0.20865	0.22094	0.23280

*Abridged by permission from E. I. duPont de Nemours and Company.

TABLE A.10 PROPERTIES OF SUPERHEATED FREON-12 (cont.)

Abs. press. (lb/in²) (Sat. temp.)		Temperature, °F											
		−40	−20	0	20	40	60	80	100	150	200	250	300
70 (57.9)	v	.....	.....	.....	.....	.....	0.553	0.642	0.673	0.750	0.824	0.896	0.967
	h	.....	.....	.....	.....	.....	84.94	87.96	91.05	98.94	107.10	115.54	124.29
	s	.....	.....	.....	.....	.....	0.16765	0.17399	0.17961	0.19310	0.20597	0.21830	0.23020
80 (66.3)	v	.....	.....	.....	.....	.....	.....	0.540	0.568	0.636	0.701	0.764	0.826
	h	.....	.....	.....	.....	.....	.....	87.56	90.68	98.64	106.84	115.30	124.08
	s	.....	.....	.....	.....	.....	.....	0.17108	0.17675	0.19035	0.20328	0.21566	0.22760
90 (73.6)	v	.....	.....	.....	.....	.....	.....	.....	0.505	0.568	0.627	0.685	0.742
	h	.....	.....	.....	.....	.....	.....	.....	90.31	98.32	106.56	115.07	123.88
	s	.....	.....	.....	.....	.....	.....	.....	0.17443	0.18813	0.20111	0.21356	0.22554
100 (80.9)	v	.....	.....	.....	.....	.....	.....	.....	0.442	0.499	0.553	0.606	0.657
	h	.....	.....	.....	.....	.....	.....	.....	89.93	97.99	106.29	114.84	123.67
	s	.....	.....	.....	.....	.....	.....	.....	0.17210	0.18590	0.19894	0.21145	0.22347
120 (93.4)	v	.....	.....	.....	.....	.....	.....	.....	0.357	0.407	0.454	0.500	0.543
	h	.....	.....	.....	.....	.....	.....	.....	89.13	97.30	105.70	114.35	123.25
	s	.....	.....	.....	.....	.....	.....	.....	0.16803	0.18207	0.19529	0.20792	0.22000
140 (104.5)	v	.....	.....	.....	.....	.....	.....	.....	.....	0.341	0.383	0.423	0.462
	h	.....	.....	.....	.....	.....	.....	.....	.....	96.65	105.14	113.85	122.85
	s	.....	.....	.....	.....	.....	.....	.....	.....	0.17868	0.19205	0.20479	0.21701
160 (114.5)	v	.....	.....	.....	.....	.....	.....	.....	.....	0.318	0.335	0.372	0.408
	h	.....	.....	.....	.....	.....	.....	.....	.....	95.82	104.50	113.33	122.39
	s	.....	.....	.....	.....	.....	.....	.....	.....	0.17561	0.18927	0.20213	0.21444
180 (123.7)	v	.....	.....	.....	.....	.....	.....	.....	.....	0.294	0.287	0.321	0.353
	h	.....	.....	.....	.....	.....	.....	.....	.....	94.99	103.85	112.81	121.92
	s	.....	.....	.....	.....	.....	.....	.....	.....	0.17254	0.18648	0.19947	0.21187
200 (132.1)	v	.....	.....	.....	.....	.....	.....	.....	.....	0.241	0.255	0.288	0.317
	h	.....	.....	.....	.....	.....	.....	.....	.....	94.16	103.12	112.20	121.42
	s	.....	.....	.....	.....	.....	.....	.....	.....	0.16970	0.18395	0.19717	0.20970
220 (139.9)	v	.....	.....	.....	.....	.....	.....	.....	.....	0.188	0.232	0.254	0.282
	h	.....	.....	.....	.....	.....	.....	.....	.....	93.32	102.39	111.59	120.91
	s	.....	.....	.....	.....	.....	.....	.....	.....	0.16685	0.18142	0.19387	0.20753

TABLE A.11 Thermodynamic Properties of Air at Low Pressure*

T, °R	t, °F	h, Btu/lbm	p_r	u, Btu/lbm	v_r	φ, Btu/lbm°F	T, °R	t, °F	h, Btu/lbm	p_r	u, Btu/lbm	v_r	φ, Btu/lbm°F
100	-360	23.7	.00384	16.9	9640	.1971	500	40	119.5	1.059	85.2	174.9	.5823
120	-340	28.5	.00726	20.3	6120	.2408	520	60	124.3	1.215	88.6	158.6	.5917
140	-320	33.3	.01244	23.7	4170	.2777	540	80	129.1	1.386	92.0	144.3	.6008
160	-300	38.1	.01982	27.1	2990	.3096	560	100	133.9	1.574	95.5	131.8	.6095
180	-280	42.9	.0299	30.6	2230	.3378	580	120	138.7	1.780	98.9	120.7	.6179
200	-260	47.7	.0432	34.0	1715	.3630	600	140	143.5	2.00	102.3	110.9	.6261
220	-240	52.5	.0603	37.4	1352	.3858	620	160	148.3	2.25	105.8	102.1	.6340
240	-220	57.2	.0816	40.8	1089	.4067	640	180	153.1	2.51	109.2	94.3	.6416
260	-200	62.0	.1080	44.2	892	.4258	660	200	157.9	2.80	112.7	87.3	.6490
280	-180	66.8	.1399	47.6	742	.4436	680	220	162.7	3.11	116.1	81.0	.6562
300	-160	71.6	.1780	51.0	624	.4601	700	240	167.6	3.45	119.6	75.2	.6632
320	-140	76.4	.2229	54.5	532	.4755	720	260	172.4	3.81	123.0	70.1	.6700
340	-120	81.2	.2754	57.9	457	.4900	740	280	177.2	4.19	126.5	65.4	.6766
360	-100	86.0	.336	61.3	397	.5037	760	300	182.1	4.61	130.0	61.1	.6831
380	-80	90.8	.406	64.7	347	.5166	780	320	186.9	5.05	133.5	57.2	.6894
400	-60	95.5	.486	68.1	305	.5289	800	340	191.8	5.53	137.0	53.6	.6956
420	-40	100.3	.576	71.5	270	.5406	820	360	196.7	6.03	140.5	50.4	.7016
440	-20	105.1	.678	74.9	241	.5517	840	380	201.6	6.67	144.0	47.3	.7075
460	0	109.9	.791	78.4	215.3	.5624	860	400	206.5	7.15	147.5	44.6	.7132
480	20	114.7	.918	81.8	193.6	.5726	880	420	211.4	7.76	151.0	42.0	.7189

* The properties given here are abridged from *Gas Tables* by J. H. Keenan and J. Kaye, by permission of John Wiley & Sons, Inc., New York, 1948.

TABLE A.11 THERMODYNAMIC PROPERTIES OF AIR AT LOW PRESSURE (cont.)

T, °R	t, °F	h, Btu/lbm	p_r	u, Btu/lbm	v_r	φ, Btu/lbm°F
900	440	216.3	8.41	154.6	39.6	.7244
920	460	221.2	9.10	158.1	37.4	.7298
940	480	226.1	9.83	161.7	35.4	.7351
960	500	231.1	10.61	165.3	33.5	.7403
980	520	236.0	11.43	168.8	31.8	.7454
1000	540	241.0	12.30	172.4	30.1	.7504
1020	560	246.0	13.22	176.0	28.6	.7554
1040	580	251.0	14.18	179.7	27.2	.7602
1060	600	256.0	15.20	183.3	25.8	.7650
1080	620	261.0	16.28	186.9	24.6	.7696
1100	640	266.0	17.41	190.6	23.4	.7743
1120	660	271.0	18.60	194.2	22.3	.7788
1140	680	287.1	19.86	197.9	21.3	.7833
1160	700	281.1	21.2	201.6	20.29	.7877
1180	720	286.2	22.6	205.3	19.38	.7920
1200	740	291.3	24.0	209.0	18.51	.7963
1220	760	296.4	25.2	212.8	17.70	.8005
1240	780	301.5	27.1	216.5	16.93	.8047
1260	800	306.6	28.8	220.3	16.20	.8088
1280	820	311.8	30.6	224.0	15.52	.8128

T, °R	t, °F	h, Btu/lbm	p_r	u, Btu/lbm	v_r	φ, Btu/lbm°F
1400	940	342.9	42.9	246.9	12.10	.8360
1420	960	348.1	45.3	250.8	11.62	.8398
1440	980	353.4	47.8	254.7	11.17	.8434
1460	1000	358.6	50.3	258.5	10.74	.8470
1480	1020	363.9	53.0	262.4	10.34	.8506
1500	1040	369.2	55.9	266.3	9.95	.8542
1520	1060	374.5	58.8	270.3	9.58	.8568
1540	1080	379.8	61.8	274.2	9.23	.8611
1560	1100	385.1	65.0	278.1	8.89	.8646
1580	1120	390.4	68.3	282.1	8.57	.8679
1600	1140	395.7	71.7	286.1	8.26	.8713
1620	1160	401.1	75.3	290.0	7.97	.8746
1640	1180	406.4	79.0	294.0	7.69	.8779
1660	1200	411.8	82.8	298.0	7.42	.8812
1680	1220	417.2	86.8	302.0	7.17	.8844
1700	1240	422.6	91.0	306.1	6.92	.8876
1720	1260	428.0	95.2	310.1	6.69	.8907
1740	1280	433.4	99.7	314.1	6.46	.8939
1760	1300	438.8	104.3	318.2	6.25	.8970
1780	1320	444.3	109.1	322.2	6.04	.9000

1300	840	316.9	32.4	227.8	14.87	.8168	1800	1340	449.7	114.0	326.3	5.85	.9031
1320	860	322.1	34.3	231.6	14.25	.8208	1820	1360	455.2	119.2	330.4	5.66	.9061
1340	880	327.3	36.3	235.4	13.67	.8246	1840	1380	460.6	124.5	334.5	5.48	.9091
1360	900	332.5	38.4	239.2	13.12	.8265	1860	1400	466.1	130.0	338.6	5.30	.9120
1380	920	337.7	40.6	243.1	12.59	.8323	1880	1420	471.6	135.6	342.7	5.13	.9150
1900	1440	477.1	141.5	346.8	4.97	.9179	2300	1840	588.8	308	431.2	2.76	.9712
1920	1460	482.6	147.6	351.0	4.82	.9208	2320	1860	594.5	319	435.5	2.69	.9737
1040	1480	488.1	153.9	355.1	4.67	.9236	2340	1880	600.2	331	439.8	2.62	.9761
1960	1500	493.6	160.4	359.3	4.53	.9264	2360	1900	605.8	343	444.1	2.55	.9785
1980	1520	499.1	167.1	363.4	4.39	.9293	2380	1920	611.5	355	448.4	2.48	.9809
2000	1540	504.7	174.0	367.6	4.26	.9320	2400	1940	617.2	368	452.7	2.42	.9833
2020	1560	510.3	181.2	371.8	4.13	.9348	2420	1960	622.9	380	457.0	2.36	.9857
2040	1580	515.8	188.5	376.0	4.01	.9376	2440	1980	628.6	394	461.4	2.30	.9880
2060	1600	521.4	196.2	380.2	3.89	.9403	2460	2000	634.3	407	465.7	2.24	.9904
2080	1620	527.0	204.0	384.4	3.78	.9430	2480	2020	640.0	421	470.0	2.18	.9927
2100	1640	532.6	212	388.6	3.67	.9456	2500	2040	645.8	436	474.4	2.12	.9950
2120	1660	538.2	220	392.8	3.56	.9483	2520	2060	651.5	450	478.8	2.07	.9972
2140	1680	543.7	229	397.0	3.46	.9509	2540	2080	657.2	466	483.1	2.02	.9995
2160	1700	549.4	238	401.3	3.36	.9535	2560	2100	663.0	481	487.5	1.971	1.0018
2180	1720	555.0	247	405.5	3.27	.9561	2580	2120	668.7	497	491.9	1.922	1.0040
2200	1740	560.6	257	409.8	3.18	.9587	2600	2140	674.5	514	496.3	1.876	1.0062
2220	1760	566.2	266	414.0	3.09	.9612	2620	2160	680.2	530	500.6	1.830	1.0084
2240	1780	571.9	276	418.3	3.00	.9638	2640	2180	686.0	548	505.0	1.786	1.0106
2260	1800	577.5	287	422.6	2.92	.9663	2660	2200	691.8	565	509.4	1.743	1.0128
2280	1820	583.2	297	426.9	2.84	.9688	2680	2220	697.6	583	513.8	1.702	1.0150

TABLE A.11 THERMODYNAMIC PROPERTIES OF AIR AT LOW PRESSURE (cont.)

T, °R	t, °F	h, Btu/lbm	p_r	u, Btu/lbm	v_r	φ, Btu/lbm°F
2700	2240	703.4	602	518.3	1.662	1.0171
2720	2260	709.1	621	522.7	1.623	1.0193
2740	2280	714.9	640	527.1	1.585	1.0214
2760	2300	720.7	660	531.5	1.548	1.0235
2780	2320	726.5	681	536.0	1.512	1.0256
2800	2340	723.3	702	540.4	1.478	1.0277
2820	2360	738.2	724	544.8	1.444	1.0297
2840	2380	744.0	746	549.3	1.411	1.0318
2860	2400	749.8	768	553.7	1.379	1.0338
2880	2420	755.6	791	558.2	1.348	1.0359
2900	2440	761.4	815	562.7	1.318	1.0379
2920	2460	767.3	839	567.1	1.289	1.0399
2940	2480	773.1	864	571.6	1.261	1.0419
2960	2500	779.0	889	576.1	1.233	1.0439
2980	2520	784.8	915	580.6	1.206	1.0458
3000	2540	790.7	941	585.0	1.180	1.0478
3020	2560	796.5	969	589.5	1.155	1.0497
3040	2580	802.4	996	594.0	1.130	1.0517
3060	2600	808.3	1025	598.5	1.106	1.0536
3080	2620	814.2	1054	603.0	1.083	1.0555
3100	2640	820.0	1083	607.5	1.060	1.0574
3120	2660	825.9	1114	612.0	1.038	1.0593
3140	2680	831.8	1145	616.6	1.016	1.0612
3160	2700	837.7	1176	621.1	.995	1.0630
3180	2720	843.6	1209	625.6	.975	1.0649
3200	2740	849.5	1242	630.1	.955	1.0668
3220	2760	855.4	1276	634.6	.935	1.0686
3240	2780	861.3	1310	639.2	.916	1.0704
3260	2800	867.2	1345	643.7	.898	1.0722
3280	2820	873.1	1381	648.3	.880	1.0740
3300	2840	879.0	1418	652.8	.862	1.0758
3320	2860	884.9	1455	657.4	.845	1.0776
3340	2880	890.9	1494	661.9	.828	1.0794
3360	2900	896.8	1533	666.5	.812	1.0812
3380	2920	902.7	1573	671.0	.796	1.0830
3400	2940	908.7	1613	675.6	.781	1.0847
3420	2960	914.6	1655	680.2	.766	1.0864
3440	2980	920.6	1697	684.8	.751	1.0882
3460	3000	926.5	1740	689.3	.736	1.0899
3480	3020	932.4	1784	693.9	.722	1.0916
3500	3040	938.4	1829	698.5	.709	1.0933
3520	3060	944.4	1875	703.1	.695	1.0950
3540	3080	950.3	1922	707.6	.682	1.0967
3560	3100	956.3	1970	712.2	.670	1.0984
3580	3120	962.2	2018	716.8	.637	1.1000
3600	3140	968.2	2068	721.4	.645	1.1017
3620	3160	974.2	2118	726.0	.633	1.1034
3640	3180	980.2	2170	730.6	.621	1.1050
3660	3200	986.1	2222	735.3	.610	1.1066
3680	3220	99.21	2276	739.9	.599	1.1083

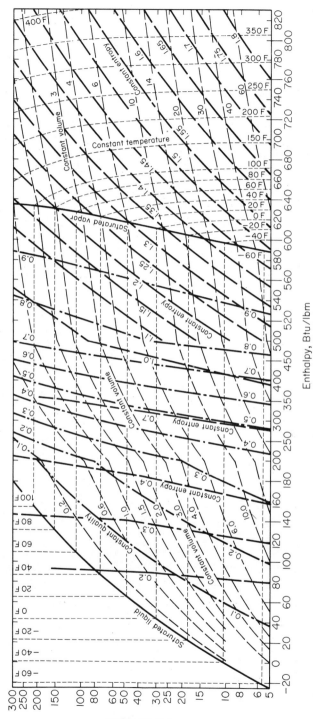

Fig. A.3 *Pressure-enthalpy diagram for ammonia.* SOURCE: "Thermodynamic Properties of Ammonia," National Bureau of Standards Circular 142.

INDEX

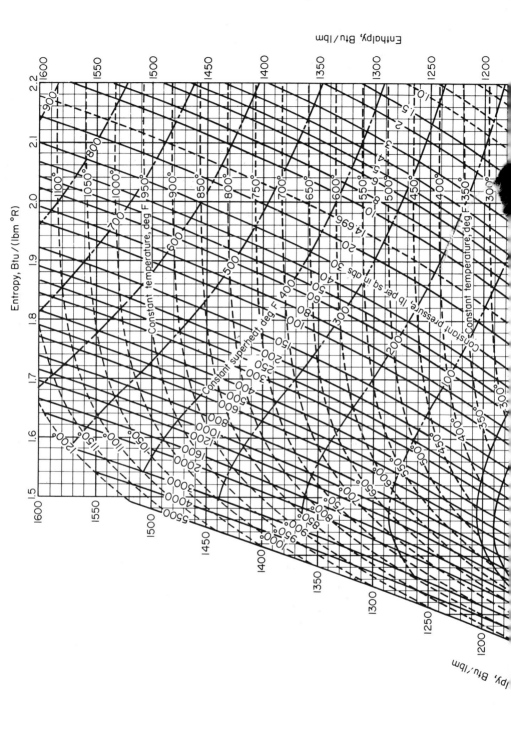

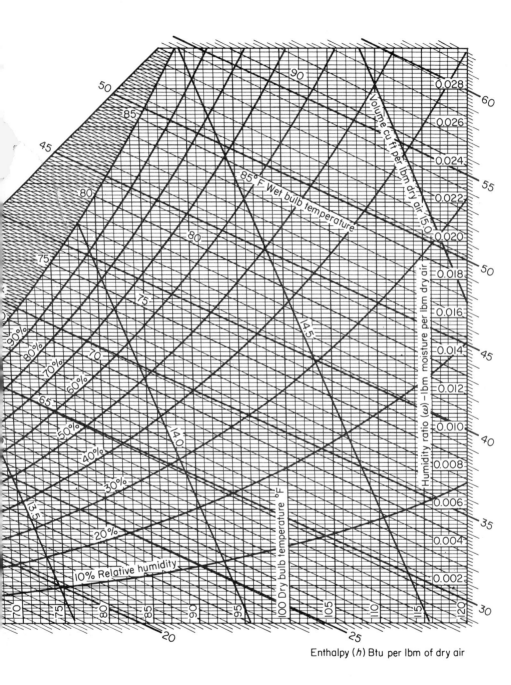

Enthalpy (h) Btu per lbm of dry air